Physiology
of
Fungi

VINCENT W. COCHRANE

Professor of Biology

Wesleyan University

Physiology

of

Fungi

NEW YORK · JOHN WILEY & SONS, INC.

LONDON · CHAPMAN & HALL, LIMITED

Preface

Although study of the physiology of the fungi has not kept pace with that of, for example, bacterial metabolism, it has in recent decades had much the same development. It seems fair to say that there have been two disparate types of study. Research on some problems—reproduction, parasitism, development—has been, with significant but not very numerous exceptions, descriptive. At the other extreme, it has been possible to develop basic biochemical knowledge on the implicit assumption that the microbial cell is a small bag of enzymes which only require to be extracted and enumerated. Our need now is to extend the valuable results of the abstract analytical study to the type of problem that has remained in the descriptive, natural history, stage.

This, however, is for the future. We work with what we have, and it is the purpose of this book to summarize and organize our knowledge of the physiology of the fungi, indicating whenever possible some of the problems that lie immediately ahead. If there is one guiding principle, it is that the fungi, however unusual or unique they may be as functioning intact organisms, can be studied at the cellular and molecular levels only by taking account of the findings of other disciplines, particularly bacterial physiology. This is the point of view of comparative biochemistry. No doubt, in a decade or two, some more useful principle of organization will emerge, but for the present an ordering of knowledge around this central principle seems valid.

To stress the fundamental biochemical similarities of all organisms is to assert in a concrete instance the general proposition of the unity of all living things, the unity of the science of biology. The separation of the various fields of biology has caused incalculable damage to all, possibly most to the botanical sciences. This is not to deny the need for specialization within biology, but when this specialization reaches the point where a student can, for example, be considered well trained in botany without having had any contact with animal sciences or with bacteriology, it seems time to reconsider. Some way must be found, both at the teaching and at the research level, to ensure that biologists of all sorts will be conversant with each other's problems and will be able to draw on each other's experience in the prosecution of their own specialties.

The literature on the physiology of fungi is very large and is growing rapidly. Much of it is of necessity repetitious and limited in scope to particular organisms or to practical applications. Some of it fails to meet criteria of accuracy or logic. I have attempted to exercise the author's prerogative of selection so as to exclude work which, in my judgment, falls into either category. However, I have preferred to err on the side of citing too much literature rather than too little. All-inclusiveness is, of course, out of the question; the references are designed to give immediately most of the work of the last three decades and to open up the entire literature for the student or research worker. In this connection, it is to be regretted that the "old-fashioned" review of the literature has been largely squeezed out of modern journal articles. No doubt it was often overdone and wasted valuable space, but the current practice of publishing the past month's work in the form of a letter to the editor has even less to recommend it.

Professor Frank Dickens once spoke in a seminar to the effect that for the purposes of biochemistry the yeasts are considered to be animals. With something of the sort in mind, I have omitted much of the physiological work on yeasts, feeling that it has been well treated elsewhere and that its importance to the filamentous fungi is of a background nature only. On the other hand, I have included the aerobic actinomycetes on the ground that ecologically and physiologically they have close affinities to the true fungi. Both groups are filamentous, both require oxygen for growth, both form exogenous spores, and both occur in similar habitats. The scope of the book is then the filamentous fungi and actinomycetes and that work on the yeasts which has a direct bearing on the physiology of the true fungi.

In the naming of organisms I have followed the usage of the original author unless confusion is thereby introduced. A few exceptions to this rule have been made, e.g., in the use of *Streptomyces* for the aerobic actinomycetes forming conidia in chains.

Two important and interesting topics have been almost entirely omitted: the genetics of fungi and the interactions of fungi with other organisms in nature. Both of these subjects deserve more space than could here be given to them, and the second—the ecology of fungi—probably requires a type of conceptual approach different from that of this book.

Individual chapters have been read in manuscript by S. H. Hutner, Frederick Kavanagh, Albert Kelner, Leonard Machlis, S. E. A. McCallan, W. C. Snyder, and C. E. Yarwood. It is a pleasure to acknowledge their advice and help. I am grateful, too, to the many authors and publishers who have allowed me to use published material, and to the staffs of the Olin Library of Wesleyan University, the Mann Library of Cornell University, and the New York Agricultural Experiment Station Library.

A considerable part of the work embodied here was done during a sabbatical leave spent as guest of the Department of Plant Pathology of the University of California at Berkeley, to the members of which I am greatly indebted. The Board of Trustees of Wesleyan University generously provided support for this period.

Jean Conn Cochrane has given invaluable assistance in all phases of preparation of the manuscript, which without her help would have been poorer in quality and later in appearance.

VINCENT W. COCHRANE

October 1958

Contents

1. Cultivation and Growth

The precise definition of growth in fungi depends on the method of measurement used. Most methods determine, directly or indirectly, the increase in mass of an inoculum after a known incubation in a complete medium. Increase in mass or in number of cells may therefore be used as an operational definition of growth.

In considering cultivation and growth we shall first concern ourselves with methods of cultivation and preservation of fungi, the dynamics of growth, dimorphism, and the measurement of growth. Then we turn to external factors—temperature, hydrogen-ion concentration, oxygen, carbon dioxide, and water—as they affect growth. The same external conditions also influence spore germination (Chapter 12); radiant energy effects are taken up in Chapter 13.

1. METHODS OF CULTIVATION

Cultures of fungi are usually maintained on conventional agar slants, and the agar petri dish has been employed in experimental work. Most quantitative studies, however, require a liquid medium which may be either surface (still) or submerged (aerated) culture.

The general technique of surface culture is too well known to require description here. It is not always realized that normal aerobic growth can be obtained only if the inoculum floats on the surface of the liquid. Many spores float naturally; for those that do not, use of a bran-cultivated inoculum (206) or inclusion of a small amount of agar,

1

gum arabic, or polyvinyl alcohol in the medium (334) may be necessary.

Two major objections attach to the use of surface culture for fungi. The cells of the developed mat are not only visibly of different types—aerial and submerged growth—but also are exposed to different environmental conditions. Aerial hyphae are remote from the nutrient supply and are bathed in the atmosphere; the lower cells, by contrast, are in close contact with nutrients and with soluble metabolic products but suffer from a partially anaerobic environment (167). Examination of submerged hyphae in such a culture shows them to be highly vacuolated. The culture as a whole is probably always deficient in oxygen. This deficiency is shown by the favorable effect on sugar utilization of an increase in surface : volume ratio (208) and by the effect, mentioned below, of aeration on growth rate of most fungi.

The commonest and most useful laboratory-scale aerated culture apparatus is the shaker, first thoroughly studied by Kluyver and Perquin (161). Flasks are mounted on a platform which is either rotated rapidly or moved horizontally with a reciprocating motion. Problems of design are considered by Shu and Johnson (270), Paladino (230), and Chain and Gualandi (54).

Representatives of all the major groups of fungi and of the genus *Streptomyces* have been grown successfully in stirred or shake culture. The growth rate is usually at least double that of the same organism in surface culture (1, 61, 162, 286, 319, 335), although some fungi do not show this effect (14, 268) and some grow so poorly that the method cannot be used for them. One of the chief advantages, apart from more rapid growth, is that shaker-grown mycelium is usually homogeneous enough to be used directly in respirometric and other metabolic studies.

In shake culture each colony is exposed to a uniform environment in all spatial directions; hence the typical colony is a globose structure. Colonial morphology varies, however, with the species—even within a genus—and with the medium (48). Sporulation is usually, although not always, suppressed—another factor of homogeneity. Microscopic characteristics of the mycelium are also affected by aeration and agitation (76, 83).

Although a shaken culture has a measurably higher content of dissolved oxygen and rate of oxygen diffusion than a still culture (283), for certain purposes a still higher rate of oxygen supply may be desirable (249, 252). This usually arises when a high concentration of a readily utilizable carbon source is employed; the peak oxygen demand under specified conditions is 16 mM oxygen per liter per hour for *Ustilago zeae* and 56 mM per liter per hour for *Aspergillus niger* (97). Rates of aeration of this magnitude require an apparatus in which a sterile medium can be agitated and aerated. Various laboratory-scale devices have been described (10, 55, 142, 168, 252), and some are commercially available. Theoretical and practical problems of design have been studied in several laboratories (9, 49, 68, 97).

Growth on solid media other than agar is useful in special problems; such materials include soil (224, 260), sawdust (6), bran (206), and cotton (25). The use of plant materials sterilized by treatment with propylene oxide is particularly valuable in the induction of sporulation (Chapter 11) and may have wider application in the study of physiology.

The inoculum used for cultures is usually a population of spores from an agar slant. A common occurrence in the fungi is the replacement of the normal type by a variant arising in culture; this development has been analyzed especially with regard to sporulation. Other examples include the loss of biochemical capacities (63), change in virulence to a host plant (202), and change in assimilatory capacity (246). The ultimate recourse is to preservation of cultures in a dormant state (p. 4). Methods of obtaining single-spore cultures of fungi are reviewed by Hildebrand (136); such cultures may be necessary in order to recover or purify the desired type. It must, however, be remembered that some spores are multinucleate (Chapter 12) and may contain genetically different nuclei.

Three physiological aspects of the inoculation process may be mentioned. First, growth is more rapid with a heavy than with a light inoculum; in addition, a heavy inoculation of a submerged culture usually results in the development of small colonies, with less danger that oxygen diffusion into the colony will limit growth or respiration. Second, the use of old spores of low viability is to be avoided; both the age and the conditions of growth of the inoculum, especially medium and temperature, should be standardized. For certain fungi the "chemostat" provides an easily standardized inoculum (221). Finally, a large inoculum may be required in order to initiate growth on an unfavorable medium (235).

When rapid growth is a desideratum, the inoculum may be pregerminated spores or mycelium (207). Mechanically macerated mycelium can be used as inoculum (233, 259). This is often the method of choice for fungi which do not sporulate (3). The treatment, to minimize injury, should be as brief as possible.

Special methods of cultivating particular fungi are too numerous to mention here. Continuous-flow apparatus may have some general interest; these include devices in which only the solution is renewed (325) and those in which both nutrients and cell population are controlled (138).

Culture media for fungi are described by Fred and Waksman (101), Levine (176), and Lilly and Barnett (180). In general, it has been too readily assumed that fungi need and tolerate high nutrient levels and high acidity; this is true of many fungi but by no means of all. For certain purposes, concentrated media are of course useful, but morphology, physiology, and reproduction are best studied in more dilute media than those often used.

2. PRESERVATION

Interest in the preservation of fungi springs from the desire to avoid excessive labor in maintaining stock cultures and, more important, the wish to maintain cultures with a minimum of genetic change. The problem is to maintain a viable inoculum in a non-growing condition.

Cultures and herbarium specimens often survive for surprisingly long periods after drying, probably by virtue of the formation of long-lived spores. Zobl (344) reviews early records of up to 21-year survival; in his own work he found that survival of dried cultures is common in ascomycetes and basidiomycetes, but the Mucorales are relatively short-lived. The sclerotia of several fungi, which may live for as long as 13 years (336), are less viable if stored dry (294). A few of the more leathery basidiomycete sporophores survive dry for a period of years; more succulent types are less durable (41, 43).

In the soil tube method (5, 121), a fungus is transferred to moist sterile soil, preferably brought to pH 6–7 with calcium carbonate, and grows and sporulates until the soil dries out. The limited data available indicate that although some fungi survive at least 5 years in soil tubes, too many do not live that long, and the method therefore is to be regarded as a special one not adapted for general use.

Preservation of cultures under sterile mineral oil is relatively simple and has the advantage that sporulation is not essential (39, 267). Limited tests indicate, however, that although many fungi survive at least 2 years, others die out earlier (146, 331, 333).

Lyophilization of spores suspended in serum, gelatin, dextran, or other colloidal materials appears to be a usable method, although again not successful with some fungi, e.g. the Entomophthorales and the dermatophytes (199, 239, 265, 337). Simple vacuum drying without freezing is suitable for many fungi (244). The structure of the fungus is important; thus, oogonia but not sporangia or mycelium, of *Pythium* spp. can be successfully lyophilized (281). Haskins and Anastasiou (126) report successful use of a modification of the lyophil technique. Too rapid rehydration of vacuum-dried uredospores is apparently injurious (265a).

For sporulating fungi, lyophilization appears to be the best single method; until more information is available, however, preservation of many fungi will have to be on an experimental basis. Lyophilization is comparatively easy and apparatus is commercially available. Preliminary studies (197) indicate that spray drying of fungus spores may also be feasible.

3. THE DYNAMICS OF GROWTH

Growth cannot be precisely defined; a provisional operational definition is increase in either mass of cells or number of cells. Mass—dry weight, usually—in the filamentous fungi may be deceptive inasmuch as it can represent in part the accumulation of polysaccharides, lipids, or wall materials without any increase in living protoplasm. Conversely, in *Neurospora crassa* protein synthesis appears to continue for a period of time after weight increase has ceased (7).

The time course of growth of filamentous fungi in liquid shaken cultures is exemplified by the data of Figure 1. Similar curves are obtained with surface cultures (2, 105, 248). Typical curves are characterized by three major phases, with transitions between them:

1. A phase of no apparent growth.
2. A phase of rapid and approximately linear growth.
3. A phase of no net growth or of autolysis and decline in dry weight.

It should not, however, be assumed that all data fit this scheme. In particular, a two-phase growth curve, in which an initial growth period is succeeded by a second, with a leveling off of growth intervening, has been reported (30). The second phase may represent polysaccharide synthesis only, without increase in other cell components, or it may depend on a mobilization of nitrogen from older hyphae and use of it for new growth. The observations of Morton and Broadbent (205) on *Scopulariopsis brevicaulis* support the second explanation; at least in a medium relatively high in carbon, it appears that nitrogen is reutilized after exhaustion of the available exogenous nitrogen.

Probably by suitable adjustment of cultural factors, especially nutrient concentrations, a variety of growth curves very different from those of Figure 1 can be obtained. Provision of calcium, for example,

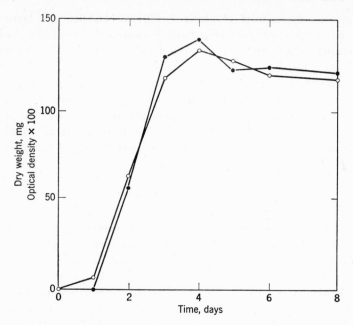

Figure 1. The growth of *Fusarium solani* in an aerated medium. Open circles, dry weight; closed circles, optical density.

to *Streptomyces fradiae* delays the onset of the autolytic phase (132).

The growth rate varies not only between species, but between different isolates or clones of the same species; this has been found to be true in both liquid and agar cultures (71, 88, 89, 130).

The first phase, that of no apparent growth, presumably has two components: a genuine lag phase before spore germination, and a phase in which growth is occurring but is undetectable by the methods used. The details of this growth period have not been studied in the fungi. In bacteria it appears that growth, as measured by protein and nucleic acid synthesis, begins immediately, with no true lag period (298).

The second phase is that of rapid growth. As Emerson (86) has shown, the cube root of the dry weight increases linearly with time over a major portion of the period (Figure 2). It should be stressed, however, that this relation holds only if no external factor, e.g., oxygen or nutrient concentration, is limiting to growth. Conversely, a curve conforming to that of Figure 2 indicates that the organism is growing unrestrictedly.

The morphological basis of mycelial development is that growth

occurs only at hyphal tips (272, 273, 280). Interior cells of the mycelium do not normally contribute to the new growth directly, although
they supply nutrients to peripheral cells, especially to aerial structures
in still culture. Growth in any one time period is therefore a function,
not of the total number of cells present, as in bacteria and yeasts, but
of the number of hyphal tips and of the rate at which these tips are
supplied nutrients.

Some of the chemical events during the phase of rapid growth are
illustrated in Figure 3; these include especially utilization of carbohydrate, nitrogen, and phosphate. Metabolic products, e.g., acids,
may or may not appear in the medium at this time. Characteristically,
respiratory activity is at a maximum (Chapter 7).

Few studies have considered critically the relation of reproduction
to growth phases; casual observation and the data of Robinson (248)
on *Sporodinia grandis* indicate that in still culture spores usually develop at the end of the phase of rapid growth; spores may, however,
appear earlier (209).

The third and last phase is, as shown in Figure 3, characterized usually by a decline in mycelial weight and in the appearance of nitrogen
and phosphate in the medium. The loss in weight varies from negligible to extreme; a common pattern is a rapid loss of weight for a

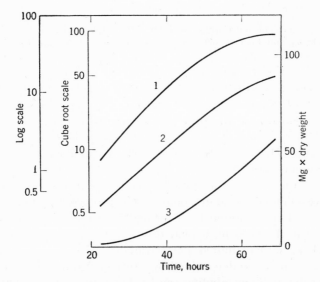

Figure 2. The growth of *Neurospora crassa* as a function of time. Curve 1, loga-
rithmic plot; curve 2, cube root plot; curve 3, linear plot. Redrawn from Emerson
(86), by permission of the Williams and Wilkins Company.

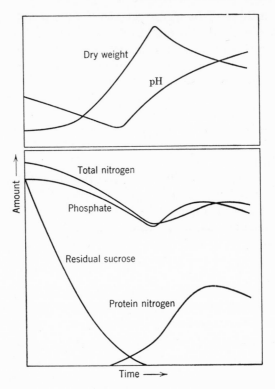

Figure 3. Growth of and changes in the medium by *Aspergillus oryzae.* Redrawn from Crewther and Lennox (62), by permission of the *Australian Journal of Biological Sciences.*

short time with no further change thereafter (151). Autolyzing mycelium of *Penicillium griseofulvum* undergoes an extensive breakdown of chitin, carbohydrates, and protein, catalyzed by enzymes of the fungus (275). Other autolytic products include ammonia (74, 80, 160), free amino acids (71, 108), organic phosphorus compounds (200), and sulfur compounds (137, 245).

Cells at the end of the growth phase appear vacuolate; younger cells have a denser and more homogeneous protoplasm (49). Such old cells, of course, are found even during the growth period in regions remote from the growing hyphal tips.

From the rather limited data available, the cessation of active growth appears to be determined by either of two factors. In concentrated media, toxic metabolites can be shown to accumulate and these materials, earlier called "staling substances," demonstrably retard growth (27, 37, 236). Probably organic acids, in high-carbohydrate media, and ammonia, in high-nitrogen media, are the compounds most frequently involved.

In better balanced and more dilute media the principal factor in cessation of growth is exhaustion of the carbohydrate supply (15, 74, 79), as shown by the data of Figure 3.

The extent of autolytic breakdown, once growth has ceased, varies, as mentioned above, with species and cultural conditions. Autolytic breakdown of *Aspergillus niger* mycelium is much more extensive in nitrate than in ammonium salt media, possibly because of the alkalinity of the nitrate medium (15). However, autolysis of a thermophilic *Streptomyces* sp. is more rapid at acid than at neutral pH (158).

So much for growth in liquid media. A fungus colony on an agar surface follows a different course. Typically, a period of little or no growth is succeeded by the establishment of a constant growth rate which is maintained unless toxic metabolites accumulate (36, 93, 308). The growth rate tube of Ryan et al. (253) may be used to show this linear relation of extension to time; the data of Figure 4 are typical. Growth on soil should follow the same course if measured by horizontal spread only; specialized rhizomorphs of *Armillaria mellea* grow several times as rapidly as unorganized mycelium (111).

Neurospora crassa and other fungi respond to certain toxicants, e.g.,

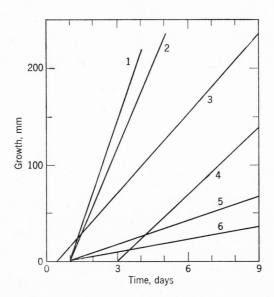

Figure 4. The linear growth of several fungi in growth rate tubes. Curve 1, *Neurospora crassa;* curve 2, *Rhizopus oryzae;* curve 3, *R. nigricans;* curve 4, *Sordaria fimicola;* curve 5, *Fusarium oxysporum lycopersici;* curve 6, *Monilinia fructicola.*

sorbose, by a more colonial and less rapid growth on agar (293). The growing hyphal tips are killed and new branches then form and grow laterally (181).

4. DIMORPHISM

Several fungi pathogenic to man are found in infected tissues in a unicellular yeastlike form, but when cultivated at room temperature grow out in a mycelial form. The term dimorphism strictly applies to these forms only, but related phenomena in the normally filamentous fungi may provisionally be considered as in the same category. A dimorphic fungus is one, therefore, in which a reversible transformation from a mycelial to a non-mycelial and unicellular growth type occurs.

Dimorphism is common in the yeasts (262), and unicellular bacteria may be caused experimentally to form filaments by, for example, magnesium deficiency (216, 326). Some normally filamentous fungi, e.g., smut fungi, grow in culture as unicellular budding cells. The fungi listed in Table 1 include both the pathogenic dimorphic fungi

Table 1.   Factors Affecting Non-mycelial Growth in Fungi

Organism	Non-mycelial Phase Favored by
Candida albicans, C. tropicalis	Cysteine, NH_4Cl, glucose carbon source (152, 211, 214, 217)
Blastomyces dermatitidis	High temperature (35–37°C) cultivation (177, 256)
Histoplasma capsulatum	Cysteine, high temperature (255)
Histoplasma farciminosum	High CO_2 (40)
Paracoccidioides brasiliensis	High temperature (37°C) cultivation (82, 256)
Sporotrichum schencki	High CO_2 (81, 254)
Trichosporon capitatum	Cysteine (217)
Ceratostomella ulmi	Aeration (75), low pH (26)
Dematium pullulans	Low aeration (11), low carbohydrate (263)
Fusarium oxysporum f. nicotianae	Aeration (339)
Mucor guillermondii	Low aeration (186)
Ophiostoma multiannulatum	High (12 mg per liter) inositol (107)
Romanoa terricola	Aeration (299)

and those filamentous fungi in which production of a unicellular growth phase can be induced reversibly. It should be stressed that in this second group the morphology of the unicellular phase may not be the same for all forms listed; i.e., the available information does not discriminate between, say, conidia and hyphal fragments. The diversity of non-mycelial growth phases is rendered more likely by the variety of stimuli which induce the phase in different fungi (Table 1).

Several theories, reviewed elsewhere (152, 262), have been proposed to explain dimorphism in the fungi pathogenic to animals. The most attractive concept is that synthesis of new protoplasm and cell division are separate processes. Filaments form when growth occurs under conditions not permitting rapid cell division. The studies of Nickerson and co-workers (152, 211, 212, 214, 215, 217) indicate that a supply of reduced organic sulfhydryl compounds is essential for rapid cell division and hence for maintenance of the unicellular condition. At least in principle, all the stimuli known to affect dimorphism in the pathogenic fungi could act through their effect on sulfhydryl content of the cells. Whether this will apply to the non-pathogenic fungi listed in Table 1 is not known.

The yeast phase of *Blastomyces dermatitidis* and *Paracoccidioides* (*Blastomyces*) *brasiliensis* is multinucleate, that of some other dimorphic fungi uninucleate (82). The yeast and mycelial forms of *Blastomyces* spp. differ in their respiratory capacities (213).

Dimorphism in yeastlike fungi suggests, of course, that the true yeasts may have arisen by a more or less permanent acquisition of the unicellular habit. It is also perhaps legitimate to ask whether the filamentous habit in the true fungi and the algae is an expression of the same metabolic idiosyncrasy as the filamentous habit of *Blastomyces* and *Histoplasma*.

5. THE MEASUREMENT OF GROWTH

As mentioned earlier, the meaning of growth is determined by the method of measurement chosen. Some methods are useful only for particular organisms or for special problems; no method is so general that it can be recommended for all.

The most widely used and within limits the most satisfactory measurement of growth is by determination of dry weight of the mycelium. The principal limitation is that weight may reflect accumulation of polysaccharides or other reserve materials rather than synthesis of new protoplasm. Oxidative assimilation (Chapter 7) is often very active in the fungi under conditions which restrict protein synthesis.

Various procedures may be used for the determination of dry weight. Often a coherent mycelium can be removed from a liquid medium, washed, and dried in a tared container. More commonly filtration is required; tared filter paper, protected from atmospheric moisture, or porous discs (ceramic or sintered glass) held in a demountable suction assembly are practical filtration devices. Gelatinous growth which filters slowly may be separated by centrifugation. The use of solvents (16) to hasten drying is practicable, of course, only if the extracted lipids are negligible. Drying is usually effected by high temperature, 70–80°C.

The dry weight of agar colonies, although of dubious significance in most contexts, has been determined by scraping or peeling off of the surface growth (91). Removal of agar with hot water results in a significant loss in dry weight (67).

Turbidimetric measurements of growth are suitable for those fungi which grow as single cells or very short dispersed hyphae. *Ustilago violacea* is of the first type, and turbidity is correlated with dry weight (22). Methods have been evolved primarily for studies on bacteria (305, 306); although most workers use a colorimeter, in principle the nephelometer is better adapted to turbidity measurements. A turbidimetric method should, of course, always be calibrated against dry weight or other standard measure; Figure 1 illustrates the correlation.

Determination of growth by measurement of the total cellular nitrogen has been used only rarely in work with fungi (222). Although the chitin nitrogen complicates interpretation, this is the best method for determination of growth defined as synthesis of protoplasm, and deserves wider use.

Linear growth on agar is the least laborious method of estimating growth and has been correspondingly popular. The radial spread of a colony in a petri dish or linear advance in a growth rate tube (93, 253) are most frequently determined. Growth is commonly expressed as the constant rate established after the initial period of slow growth.

Naturally, the impurities present in agar rule out this method for certain problems. There are, however, more fundamental objections. Chaudhuri (56) found no response of colony diameter to even a fourfold dilution of the nutrient medium. Nor does the rate of advance on agar always respond to necessary vitamins (106, 179) or essential ions (238); strain differences in growth on agar are not always reflected in dry weight measurements (133).

Chaudhuri (56) found, on the other hand, excellent correlation of radial growth on agar with dry weight and germ tube growth in temperature studies on *Verticillium albo-atrum;* more recently, Domsch (77) has confirmed the correlation in temperature response. Wood-destroying fungi usually respond to temperature in agar culture about as they do in wood blocks (317). One crucial detail is often overlooked: the depth of the medium influences growth and must be standardized (28, 36, 56).

We may conclude that the agar method is adequate for studies of some environmental factors, e.g., temperature and (probably) composition of the atmosphere, although even in these experiments the results are not always correlated with dry weight (94, 134, 145, 250). It is decidedly not adequate for nutritional studies. Whether it should be used for essentially chemical problems like the effct of pH or toxic agents is still uncertain. The burden of proof that spread on agar is a fair index of growth rests on the investigator who chooses to use the method. Its value cannot be assumed.

6. TEMPERATURE AND GROWTH

Temperature affects growth, spore germination, reproduction, and indeed all activities of the organism. Typical curves of growth as a function of temperature are shown in Figure 5. There is characteristically a linear portion in which growth increases directly with temperature, an optimum range which may be narrow or rather broad, and a descending limb as the temperature becomes too high for growth. The curve as a whole is usually skewed to the right; an empirical method for converting this skewed curve to a straight line is described by Cohen and Yarwood (58).

The temperature-growth curve tends to become more nearly symmetrical as the optimum becomes lower: fungi with optima of 22–24°C or less often have a much less skewed curve (53, 98, 143, 171, 311). Not all low-temperature fungi, however, follow this pattern (113, 164).

Fungi with high temperature optima generally have the typical skewed curve even more pronouncedly; in a few cases, the high optimum is associated with a broader range of good growth, but this is not the rule.

It should be noted that the concept of an optimum, usually taken for granted, is not in fact very clear. The response of *Phycomyces blakesleeanus* to temperature (247) illustrates the principal ambiguities in the concept of optimum temperature. First, growth is most rapid at 20–25°C, but the maximum total amount of growth at limiting levels of thiamine is greatest at 10°. Second, the effect of temperature on final dry weight can be almost wiped out if the nitrogen supply is made limiting.

Another example of the dependence of temperature characteristics on other factors has been elucidated by L. Fries (103). *Coprinus fimetarius* grows poorly at 44°C because of the failure of methionine biosynthesis to keep pace with other processes; if exogenous methionine is supplied, growth at the elevated temperature is normal. The ap-

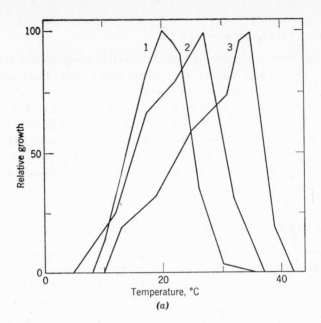

(a)

Figure 5A. Temperature and growth (dry weight) of fungi. Curve 1, *Cephalosporium costantii,* from data of Treschow (311); curve 2, *Pullularia pullulans,* from data of Rennerfelt (243); curve 3, *Coprinus* sp., from data of Johnson and Jones (154).

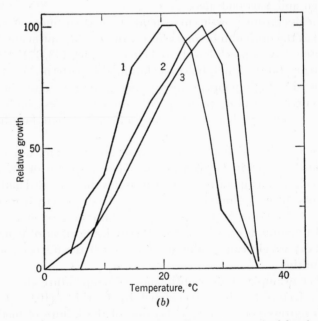

(b)

Figure 5B. Temperature and growth (colony diameter on agar) of fungi. Curve 1, *Verticillium tricorpus,* redrawn from Isaac (144) by permission of the Cambridge University Press; curve 2, *Polyporus vaporarius,* from data of Gäumann (112); curve 3, *Pythium debaryanum,* from data of Roth (250).

14

parent optimum temperature for radial growth of *Sclerotinia fructicola* is affected by pH (301).

It is clear that temperature optima and ranges reported are valid only under specified conditions of time, medium, and method of measurement. There is no single temperature optimum of growth. Nevertheless, we shall continue to employ the concept of an optimum temperature, on the grounds that it is empirically useful and that gross differences in apparent optima provide a basis for ecological studies.

A given metabolic process—respiration, antibiotic production, or vitamin synthesis—does not, of course, necessarily respond to temperature in the same way as does growth. Studies on penicillin production in particular support this generalization (49, 227), as do studies of bacterial growth and metabolism (78).

Over the range in which growth is proportional to temperature, the relation may be expressed by the value of Q_{10}, defined as the ratio of the growth rate at a given temperature to that at a temperature 10°C lower. The values found by Fawcett (92) in studies on four fungi are comparable to those reported for bacterial growth (298).

The shape of the temperature-growth curve is somewhat affected by the time of incubation. Growth at suboptimal temperatures is often so slow that it is not apparent at all at a time when cultures at more favorable temperatures are growing vigorously. Growth at supra-optimal temperature may begin rapidly but slow down or cease entirely after a period of time (34, 223, 278, 286). Both of these factors, of course, affect the curve, so that use of only one incubation period may introduce error.

Most fungi make at least some growth over a 25- or 30-degree range of temperatures, but narrower ranges are known, e.g., in *Merulius lacrymans* (53) and *Capnodium salicinum* (98). Narrow ranges are often associated with low optima, but the reverse is not true—many fungi with low optima grow over a normally wide range of temperature.

Temperature optima for plant pathogenic fungi have been collected by Togashi (307) and are depicted graphically in Figure 6. Not all of these reports can be accepted, and details of the distribution are unduly affected by popular incubator temperatures, but it can be seen that most members of this ecological group have optima in the region 20–30°C and about half have their optima between 26 and 30°C.

The relation between temperature and habitat is not yet entirely clear. Many fungi are probably world-wide in distribution, i.e., their growth is limited by factors other than temperature. Species of *Allomyces*, on the other hand, are clearly confined naturally to the tropical

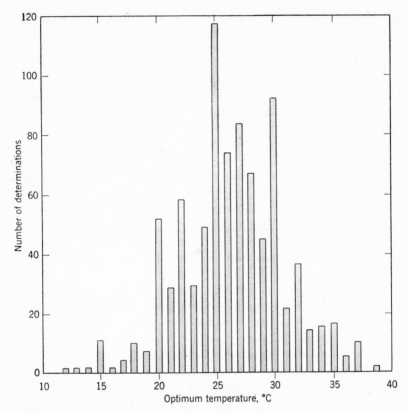

Figure 6. The optimum temperatures for growth of plant pathogenic fungi. Compiled by Dr. C. E. Yarwood from Togashi (307).

and warmer temperate regions of the earth (84). Subtropical strains of a species may have a higher temperature optimum than strains from temperate regions (38). The distribution of *Phymatotrichum omnivorum* is determined by winter soil temperature (90). The few marine fungi studied so far have temperature optima for growth that are somewhat higher than the temperature of the sea (8). The occurrence and dominance of fungi in decomposing plant materials are largely determined by temperature (150, 223).

Dermatophytic fungi grow best in culture at 25–35°C, i.e., below the host body temperature (284); fungi causing systemic mycoses grow well at 37° but optima have not been reported. It is significant that *Aspergillus fumigatus,* a thermotolerant species, can cause disease in warm-blooded animals.

Some examples of high and low temperature optima are collected in

Table 2. Low and High Temperature Optima in the Fungi

Fungus	Criterion of Growth	Optimum, °C
Botrytis cinerea (115)	Dry weight	15–18
Gnomonia spp. (135)	Linear extension	17–19
Hendersoniella sp. (98)	Linear extension	18
Herpotrichia nigra (113)	Linear extension	15
Mastigosporium album (23)	Linear extension	15
Phacidium infestans (232)	Dry weight	15
Phoma apiicola (17)	Linear extension	16–20
Phycopsis sp. (98)	Linear extension	15
Phytophthora primulae (309)	Linear extension	15–20
Actinomyces (*Streptomyces*) sp. (123)	Linear extension	35–37
Aspergillus fumigatus (243)	Dry weight	37
Aspergillus nidulans (223)	Linear extension	40
Coprinus fimetarius (104)	Dry weight	35–40
Lenzites trabea (53)	Linear extension	35
Mucor pusillus (218)	Linear extension	40–46
Rhizopus chinensis (330)	Linear extension	37.5–40.5
Sclerotium (*Rhizoctonia*) *bataticola* (224, 310)	Linear extension	31–35
Sepedonium sp. (223)	Linear extension	45

Table 2. It should be mentioned that not only may species within a genus differ widely (300, 330), but strains or geographical isolates of the same species may respond differently (83a, 143).

Surprisingly many fungi are able to grow, although usually only slowly, at 0° or slightly less. Plants under snow may be infected by the parasitic "snow molds"—*Typhula* spp., *Fusarium nivale*, and an unidentified basidiomycete (32, 65, 242). *Phacidium infestans*, cause of a disease of pines, is able to grow in culture at −3°, although its optimum temperature is about 15° (232).

A second ecological group of fungi tolerant of low temperature is commonly associated with the spoilage of refrigerated foods. Fungi of many different genera fall into this group and some, especially strains of *Cladosporium* and *Sporotrichum*, grow at temperatures well below zero, e.g., −5 to −8°. The literature on these forms is reviewed by Berry and Magoon (19) and, more briefly, by Pehrson (232). Again, although these fungi tolerate extremely low temperatures, their optima are higher (122).

Survival of spores and mycelium at temperatures too low for growth is discussed briefly in Chapter 13.

Most fungi are unable to grow at 35–40°C. There are, however, two general types of exceptions to this rule. The first group is a miscellaneous one, examples of which appear in Table 2; it includes saprophytes—especially coprophilic forms—and several wood-destroying fungi. The second group, the true thermophiles, is defined by the ability to grow at 50°C or higher and the inability to grow at temperatures below about 30°. Relatively few such fungi are known; examples include *Thermomyces lanuginosus* (*Monotospora lanuginosa*) (135a, 313), *Thermoascus aurantiacus* (201), *Penicillium duponti* (240), and *Chaetomium thermophile* (169). No study of the fundamental basis of this behavior in fungi has appeared.

Truly thermophilic forms also are found among the actinomycetes, reviewed by Bernstein and Morton (18). The obligately thermophilic *Micromonospora vulgaris* is distinguished by the high resistance of its conidia to heat damage (87). Both fungi and actinomycetes are active in decomposition of compost at 50°C (320).

Killing of fungi by high temperature is considered elsewhere (Chapter 13); spores are the usual experimental material. It need only be noted here that mycelium is easily killed by elevated temperatures and that many fungi die slowly when held in culture at a temperature just above the maximum for growth.

Fluctuations in temperature induce two types of zonation, the more common of which results from the presence of zones of reproductive structures (Chapter 11). In a second type of temperature-induced zonation the zones are entirely mycelial; this phenomenon occurs in *Cercospora beticola* (60) and in other fungi (20, 124).

The data compiled by Togashi (307) indicate that the optimum temperature for spore germination is generally very close to that for growth in culture. There are instances, however, in which spore germination is less inhibited than growth by supraoptimal temperatures (185, 330). Spore germination at temperatures too low for growth has been reported in *Rhizopus* spp. (330), and is presumably common.

The relation between a fungus-incited plant disease and temperature is rather more complex, inasmuch as at least two organisms are necessarily involved. In general, storage and transit rot diseases are most severe at the temperature which favors mycelial growth of the pathogen; examples include the decay of sweet potato by *Rhizopus* spp. (172, 330) and storage rots caused by *Rhizoctonia solani* (170, 332). Typically, however, the pathogen will grow in culture at temperatures below the minimum for infection (33).

The vascular wilts of plants caused by *Fusarium* spp. often have the same pattern, i.e., the disease optimum is close to that of the

pathogen (155, 156, 302, 322). However, it is not certain that the
relation is as simple as it appears, and in some wilt diseases temperature affects the host (100, 174) and, probably, other soil organisms
which influence the disease (264).

For a few plant diseases it has been definitely shown that differences
between temperature optima for disease and for growth of the pathogen occur and reflect the effect of temperature on the host. This has
been established particularly for the seedling blight of wheat and
corn caused by *Gibberella saubinetii* (72, 73) and a root rot of sweet
clover caused by *Plenodomus meliloti* (258), and has been suggested
for other diseases (114).

Finally, there are some plant diseases in which the observed action
of temperature appears to be exerted on the pathogen, but on spore
germination or sporulation rather than on mycelial growth (95, 155,
156). It is conceivable, of course, that pathogenicity, as distinct from
growth, is affected by temperature, but so far this has not been demonstrated.

7. pH AND GROWTH

Under given conditions, a fungus will grow maximally over a
certain range of initial pH values of the medium, and will fail to
grow at high and low extremes. However, it must be borne in mind
that pH is not a unitary factor; the mechanism of its action differs
at different concentrations of hydrogen ion. For example, one part
of the pH-growth curve may reflect the effect of a low pH on enzyme
systems, another the effect of a high pH on metal solubilities. Acidity
may also affect the entry of essential vitamins (341), surface metabolic
reactions, entry into the cell of organic acids, or the uptake of minerals (226).

It is not surprising, therefore, to find that almost any factor in
the environment may change the shape of the pH-growth curve. Such
factors include temperature (232, 327), time of harvest (175, 210),
gross changes in the medium (187, 340), growth factor supply (178),
calcium and magnesium levels (314), and nitrogen source (140).

Furthermore, pH is affected during growth by metabolic activities
—raised by absorption of anions or production of ammonia from
nitrogenous compounds, lowered by formation of organic acids or
absorption of cations. These effects of growth on pH complicate
results, particularly in the poorly buffered media commonly employed. It seems probable that many of the broad optima recorded

Table 3. pH Optima of Some Fungi and Actinomycetes*

Organism	Criterion of Growth	Optimum†
Aphanomyces euteiches (274)	Linear extension	4.5–6.5
Aspergillus flavus (28)	Linear extension	5.5–8.4
A. niger (28)	Linear extension	4.4–7.5
Boletus variegatus (198)	Dry weight	5.0
Botryosporium (?) sp. (149)	Dry weight	6.6–7.4
Cercospora kikuchii (70)	Dry weight	4.1
Chalara quercina (14)	Dry weight	4.5
Chytridium sp. (61)	Dry weight	5.2–7.5
Colletotrichum hibisci (314)	Linear extension	3.5–8.0‡
Coprinus sp. (154)	Dry weight	4.8–6.9
Fomes annosus (89)	Linear extension	4.6–4.9
F. fraxineus (203)	Linear extension	6.0–7.0
Fusarium aquaeductum (229)	Dry weight	4.0–9.0
F. aurantiacum (260)	Linear extension	6.3–7.0
Geotrichum sp. (229)	Dry weight	3.0
Marasmius graminum (182)	Dry weight	5.7–6.4
Merulius confluens (219)	Dry weight	4.0
Mycogone perniciosa (311)	Dry weight	6.7
Neurospora crassa (253)	Linear extension	4.3–6.5
Ophiobolus graminis (327)	Dry weight	4.9–7.4
Penicillium expansum (28)	Linear extension	4.4–7.5
P. glaucum (2)	Dry weight	5.0–6.5
Phlyctorhiza variabilis (251)	Dry weight	7.2–7.6
Phycomyces blakesleeanus (47)	Dry weight	3.5–4.6
Pythiogeton sp. (52)	Dry weight	6.5
Sepedonium sp. (230)	Dry weight	7.0–8.5
Septoria pepli (266)	Linear extension	4.8–6.8
Streptomyces coelicolor (57)	Dry weight	6.9–7.7
S. scabies (318)	Dry weight	6.9
Tricholoma nudum (222)	Dry weight	5.0–6.0
Trichophyton persicolor (285)	Dry weight	6.5–7.0
Trichosporon cutaneum (229)	Dry weight	4.0–9.0
Verticillium malthousii (311)	Dry weight	5.3
V. psalliotae (311)	Dry weight	6.7–7.0

* For reasons discussed in the text, these figures must be considered as approximations and as limited to the conditions of the particular experiment.

† Defined for this table as the pH range tested in which the growth was within 10 per cent of the maximum growth.

‡ With added calcium and magnesium in the medium.

in Table 3 reflect the ability of the fungus to raise or lower the pH of an initially unfavorable medium; data on *Colletotrichum lindemuthianum* (173) illustrate this phenomenon.

The values of Table 3 should, therefore, be viewed with some caution; at best they offer a rough guide to choice of media and a possible indication of ecological preferences. They are not to be regarded as absolute figures in any sense.

A double pH optimum is frequently reported, a minimum appearing between two maxima in the curve. This type of response has been exhaustively analyzed in studies on *Coprinus* spp. (102, 104). It appears that the minimum merely reflects pH-dependent unavailability of one or more inorganic elements; provision of iron, zinc, and calcium in available forms eliminates the double optimum and replaces it with a broad single optimum zone.

An organism may also be able to grow, even quite well, at a pH which does not permit the initiation of growth (189). The metabolic basis of this phenomenon is not clear; again, the artificiality of the simple pH-growth curve is emphasized.

In contrast to the bacteria and the actinomycetes, fungi are relatively more able to invade acid environments, although we should avoid the common assumption that they are restricted to such environments. In culture, the larger basidiomycetes are often unable to grow at an initial pH above 7.0; examples include most species of *Marasmius* (182), and *Tricholoma* (222). Correspondingly, limited ecological studies of these fungi indicate that they are in general restricted to acid environments (338). However, *Marasmius rotula* grows in culture and is found in nature on substrates of widely different pH (182, 338), and several other fleshy basidiomycetes, notably species of *Coprinus*, actually require alkaline conditions for best growth (104, 120, 312).

Biological types of fungi may only roughly be characterized as to pH preference. Most plant pathogens—exceptions are evident in Table 3—grow best in media with an initial pH of 5.0 to 6.5. Species of *Streptomyces* are marked by a relative intolerance of acidity; very few can grow at a pH lower than 5.0. The same intolerance of acidity appears also in other groups, e.g., the lower phycomycetes (61, 85). The dermatophytic fungi, perhaps because they are usually grown in complex media, seem rather indifferent to pH over the range 4.0 to 10.0 (284, 285).

Other biological activities of the fungi respond to pH, but not necessarily in the same way as growth. As a rule, the pH range for sporulation is narrower than that for vegetative growth (Chapter

11). The range for spore germination is similarly more narrow (185, 291); this is to be expected, inasmuch as the design of the spore germination experiment does not permit sufficient time for metabolic activities of the organism to modify the pH of the medium. Soil-borne plant diseases may or may not show the same pH curve as do the fungi which cause them (96, 260); here, of course, the effect of pH on the plant presumably exerts an important influence, and the complex effect of pH on the soil itself may be even more decisive.

In most physiological studies it is necessary that the pH be controlled, at least within limits. Periodic addition of alkali (51) and the use of solid calcium carbonate in the medium (99) are satisfactory for certain problems, but in general it is necessary to employ a buffer system. Of these, the most common and generally useful is the phosphate buffer. The usefulness of phosphate is limited, however, by the tolerance of the fungus to the ion; this may be as low as 0.003 M (61) or as high as 0.20 M (66, 151), and must be determined for each organism. Other buffer systems must be employed with caution: acetate is often toxic (64, 183, 291), and citrate may be utilized by the fungus as a source of carbon, with consequent displacement of the apparent pH optimum (64). Phthalate, borate, and citrate buffers are satisfactory for *Neurospora crassa* (253); α-hydroxybutyrate has been proposed as a non-utilizable buffer for studies on fungi (303). Equipment for automatic pH control has been described (50).

Physiological buffer systems can be devised for particular problems, e.g., acetate as carbon source and ammonium ion as nitrogen source (188), or mixtures of ammonium and nitrate ions (141). In both these systems, utilization of an anion is balanced by utilization of a cation and the pH is thereby held relatively constant.

In conclusion, the pH-growth curve has, to say the least, a limited usefulness. In designing experiments of this type, the first question to ask is whether the information to be gained is worth the effort required. Once such an experiment is decided upon, two rather elementary precautions should be observed. First, the final pH of the medium, after growth, must be reported. Second, the results will be more meaningful if buffer systems are used to control pH; in the alkaline range, addition of sodium hydroxide to control pH is followed by absorption of carbon dioxide from the air, with a consequent false impression of the upper pH limit of growth.

The internal pH of the fungus cell—and the fungus cell is usually large enough so that the concept of pH may legitimately be applied —is not known with any precision. Indicator methods, which have obvious uncertainties, yield in most hands a value of about 6.0 (4,

193, 219), close to the value for resting cells of yeast (59). Bünning (44) reports a lower internal pH, below 5.0, for *Aspergillus niger*. Whether or not the internal pH responds to changes in the acidity of the external medium is uncertain: there may be some effect (44, 228), but it is to be presumed that any large change would result in injury and death. The principal effects of external pH are probably on permeability and other surface phenomena.

8. OXYGEN AND GROWTH

Fungi are commonly thought of as strictly aerobic, and this opinion is basically correct. However, the quantitative relations of growth and oxygen supply vary considerably among different forms.

Visually observable growth of fungi occasionally occurs under nitrogen or in a liquid-filled container (61, 191, 220). This limited growth probably depends on oxygen previously dissolved in the medium. *Blastocladia pringsheimii* grows well in tank nitrogen or carbon dioxide but fails to grow if oxygen is chemically absorbed by pyrogallol; the fungus has, therefore, a very low but real oxygen demand (85).

Achlya prolifera has been reported to grow in the presence of pyrogallol (134). However, this report cannot be accepted without confirmation, in view of the overwhelming evidence that other fungi and species of *Streptomyces* fail to grow at very low or zero oxygen pressures (69, 94, 119, 127, 166, 192, 195, 204, 234, 237, 257, 292, 342, 343).

When growth on agar is the criterion, it appears that most fungi grow as well at 20–40 mm oxygen pressure as at atmospheric (160 mm) (69, 116, 118, 261, 295). However, the dry weight is usually affected at somewhat higher oxygen pressures; growth of *Ophiobolus graminis* is reduced at 105 mm oxygen (94), *Aspergillus oryzae* grows best at oxygen pressures higher than atmospheric (292). Contradictory data may be cited (12, 166), but it seems that mass increase is more sensitive to oxygen deficit than is the more diffuse and thinner growth of a colony on agar.

In keeping with the relatively low oxygen requirement for growth, fungi successfully colonize environments in which oxygen is limited, e.g., relatively stagnant aquatic milieu. It is doubtful whether invasion of woody tissues is ever prevented by lack of oxygen (295), and the same is probably true of invasion by vascular pathogens and decay fungi. The number of fungi usually falls off at lower soil depths (31, 45, 147), but this may be caused more by high carbon dioxide than by low oxygen (46). The adverse effect of flooding the soil on the growth and survival of fungi is, however, believed to reflect a deficit in oxygen (287, 288, 289).

Very high oxygen pressure may somewhat reduce growth or change the mycelial habit, but does not usually have a lethal effect (159, 328).

Many discussions of aerobiosis in the fungi have confused growth and fermentation. Numerous fungi ferment sugars anaerobically (Chapter 7); this capacity has no essential bearing on growth, and these forms should not be referred to as anaerobes. The term anaerobe, in fact, cannot be applied to any fungus; all require at least some oxygen and none has as yet been reported to grow better at low than at atmospheric oxygen pressure, although reducing substances favor growth of *Armillaria mellea* (148). The vigorous anaerobic fermentation of some aquatic phycomycetes (Chapter 7) is coupled with a low oxygen demand and this relation is presumably a causal one.

9. CARBON DIOXIDE AND GROWTH

Growth stimulation by carbon dioxide is considered later, with carbon dioxide fixation (Chapter 7). High carbon dioxide pressures generally inhibit the growth of fungi but the level at which inhibiton appears is quite variable. Thus, *Alternaria solani* is markedly inhibited by 38 mm of carbon dioxide (159) and *Coniophora cerebella* by 23 mm (345), but many other fungi are only slightly retarded in growth by carbon dioxide pressures of 150 mm or more (12, 69, 117, 295). An isolate of *Zygorhynchus vuilleminii* found only below the soil surface is retarded about 35 per cent by 152 mm of carbon dioxide, while the surface soil inhabitant *Penicillium nigricans* is completely inhibited under the same conditions (46). Finally, we may mention *Blastocladia pringsheimii*, which grows well in an atmosphere of tank carbon dioxide and which requires carbon dioxide for the formation of resistant sporangia (85).

10. WATER AND GROWTH

The association of moisture and fungal growth is well known in relation to the deterioration of natural and manufactured products. Fungi require relatively high moisture levels, but most of the higher fungi can grow in the absence of liquid water.

Two related types of study concern us here: the effect of relative humidity on growth and the effect of osmotic pressure on growth. Both presumably measure the ability of the organism to draw water from its environment. Spore germination per se is considered elsewhere (Chapter 12); but it should be noted that experimental designs used in growth studies do not fully discriminate between spore germination and mycelial development.

Relative humidity effects must, of course, be determined by growing the organism on a substrate which is in equilibrium with the atmosphere. Agar and other solid substrates—bran, wood blocks, fabrics, etc.—have been used. Unfortunately, quantitative determination of growth on such materials is difficult, and the data are rather imprecise. This imprecision makes it hard to decide whether relative humidity itself or the moisture content of the equilibrated substrate is the more important factor in fungus growth. Data can be cited for each view (21, 277). Probably the amount of water in the substrate is the more important: thus if cotton and wool are incubated at 92 per cent relative humidity only the wool, which absorbs more water at this humidity than does cotton, supports growth of fungi (21).

The influence of moisture on fungal deterioration of economically important materials has been studied intensively and reviewed often (13, 184, 271, 277). Fungi tolerant of low humidity (85 to 90 per cent) include *Stereum frustulosum* (13), *Schizophyllum commune* (131), and *Aspergillus* spp. (163, 276). A few fungi attack substrates at as low as 65 per cent relative humidity (276), but most are limited to much higher humidities, 95 per cent or more.

Tolerance to low relative humidity appears, as expected, to be associated with tolerance to high osmotic pressure (131, 157); this relation is especially clear in spore germination experiments (Chapter 12). Species in which spore germination occurs at low humidity also tolerate a low humidity during growth (321, 323), and it is reasonable to infer that spore germination is more affected by marginal water supply than is mycelial growth (329).

Studies on the role of osmotic pressure are always complicated by possible non-osmotic effects of the solute. Sodium chloride is distinctly inhibitory to some fungi (207); other complications are discussed by Brancato and Golding (29) and Stuart (290). Tolerance of high osmotic pressure is specific. Thus, a mutant of *Neurospora crassa* is inhibited at 0.17 M glucose (139); at the other extreme, species of *Aspergillus* can grow in media with an osmotic pressure of as high as 100 atmospheres (28, 282). Most fungi cease growth or are markedly inhibited when the concentration of soluble sugar exceeds about 2.0 M (109, 129, 159).

Obligate halophily—an absolute salt requirement—has been reported for several fungi (194, 225, 315, 316), although at least some marine fungi do not require salt (8). Further quantitative studies on halophily in marine fungi would be of great interest.

Protoplasm is presumably always more concentrated than the external solution, and limited data support this assumption for the fungi (35). The indications are that the internal concentration, as measured by freezing point depression or by plasmolysis methods, increases as the external concentration is raised (195, 225, 231). In *Aspergillus niger* the relative amount of bound water is greater when the organism is grown in concentrated glucose (304). Ohtsuki (225), relying on the cryoscopic method, reports an osmotic concentration in *Aspergillus glaucus* var. *tonophilus* equivalent to approximately 250 atmospheres, i.e., the freezing point of the expressed cell sap was $-21°C$.

Thatcher (296, 297), using plasmolytic methods, found that the osmotic pressure of plant pathogenic fungi exceeds that of their hosts and may be a factor in parasitism. Osmotic pressure of hyphae was found in this study to be 15.5–41.3 atmospheres, that of haustoria of rust fungi to be 18.6–21.9 atmospheres.

Fungi are more active at moderate than at high soil moisture (287); this is presumably to be ascribed to the effect of excessive soil water on aeration.

11. BIOLUMINESCENCE

The phenomenon of bioluminescence in organisms generally is reviewed by Harvey (125); Wassink (324) critically reviews its occurrence in fungi, and the biochemistry of the process is summarized by Johnson et al. (153). Bioluminescence occurs in at least 17 species of the basidiomycetes, possibly in one ascomycete, and has not been reported from phycomycetes (125, 324). Within a species, both luminescent and non-luminescent strains occur in nature (24, 42); in *Panus stipticus* luminescence is governed by a single gene (190). Luminescence occurs in sporophores, rhizomorphs, sclerotia, and vegetative hyphae (42, 125, 241). As Robert Boyle discovered almost three centuries ago, oxygen is necessary; modern work shows that the oxygen requirement for fungal luminescence is much higher than that for bacterial (128). The reaction is temperature sensitive and is reversibly

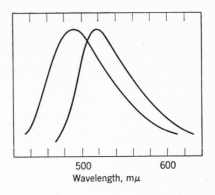

Figure 7. Emission spectra of bioluminescence in *Photobacterium fischeri* (left) and *Armillaria mellea*
(right). Redrawn from Spruit-van
der Burg (279), by permission of Elsevier Publishing Company, Amsterdam.

500   600
Wavelength, mμ

inhibited by narcotics (42). Active extracts have not as yet been prepared from fungi; by analogy with other luminescent organisms, we
may safely assume that the process is enzymatic.

Figure 7 compares the emission spectrum of the light produced by
Armillaria mellea with that of *Photobacterium fischeri.* Other fungi
which have been examined—*Agaricus melleus, Mycena* spp., *Omphalia
flavida, Pleurotus lunaillustris,* and *Polyporus hanedai*—have approximately the same maximum as *A. mellea,* 520 to 530 mμ (125).

BIBLIOGRAPHY

1. Abe, M., T. Yamano, Y. Kozu, and M. Kusumoto. 1951. *J. Agr. Chem. Soc.
   Japan* 24: 416–422.
2. Acklin, O. and W. Schneider. 1928. *Biochem. Z.* 202: 246–283.
3. Andrus, C. F. 1941. *Phytopathology* 31: 566–567.
4. Armstrong, J. I. 1929. *Protoplasma* 8: 222–260.
5. Atkinson, R. G. 1954. *Can. J. Botany* 32: 673–678.
6. Badcock, E. C. 1942. *Trans. Brit. Mycol. Soc.* 25: 200–205.
7. Ballentine, R. and D. G. Stephens. 1951. *J. Cellular Comp. Physiol.* 37: 369–
   387.
8. Barghoorn, E. S. and D. H. Linder. 1944. *Farlowia* 1: 395–467.
9. Bartholomew, W. H. et. al. 1950a. *Ind. Eng. Chem.* 42: 1801–1809.
10. Bartholomew, W. H. et al. 1950b. *Ind. Eng. Chem.* 42: 1827–1830.
11. Bauer, R. 1938. *Zentr. Bakteriol. Parasitenk. Abt. II,* 98: 133–167.
12. Bavendamm, W. 1928. *Centr. Bakteriol. Parasitenk. Abt. II,* 75: 426–452, 503–
    533.
13. Bavendamm, W. and H. Reichelt. 1938. *Arch. Mikrobiol.* 9: 486–544.
14. Beckman, C. H., J. E. Kuntz, and A. J. Riker. 1953. *Phytopathology* 43:
    441–447.
15. Behr, G. 1930. *Arch. Mikrobiol.* 1: 418–444.
16. Benham, R. 1945. *Proc. Soc. Exp. Biol. Med.* 58: 199–201.
17. Bennett, C. W. 1921. *Mich. State Univ. Agr. Exp. Sta. Tech. Bull.* 53: 1–40.
18. Bernstein, A. and H. E. Morton. 1934. *J. Bacteriol.* 27: 625–629.
19. Berry, J. A. and C. A. Magoon. 1934. *Phytopathology* 24: 780–796.

20. Bisby, G. R. 1925. *Mycologia* 17: 89–97.
21. Block, S. S. 1953. *Appl. Microbiol.* 1: 287–293.
22. Blumer, S. 1937. *Arch. Mikrobiol.* 8: 458–478.
23. Bollard, E. G. 1950. *Trans. Brit. Mycol. Soc.* 33: 250–264.
24. Bothe, F. 1935. *Arch. Protistenk.* 85: 369–383.
25. Bottcher, E. J. and H. J. Conn. 1942. *J. Bacteriol.* 44: 137.
26. Boudru, M. 1933. *Bull. inst. agron. et stas. recherches Gembloux* 2: 310–346. (*Rev. Appl. Mycol.* 13: 335. 1934.)
27. Boyle, C. 1924. *Ann. Botany* 38: 113–135.
28. Brancato, F. P. and N. S. Golding. 1953. *Mycologia* 45: 848–864.
29. Brancato, F. P. and N. S. Golding. 1954. *Mycologia* 46: 442–456.
30. Bretzloff, C. W., Jr. 1954. *Am. J. Botany* 41: 58–67.
31. Brierley, W. B., S. T. Jewson, and M. Brierley. 1928. *Proc. Intern. Congr. Soil Sci.* 3: 48–71.
32. Broadfoot, W. C. and M. W. Cormack. 1941. *Phytopathology* 31: 1058–1059.
33. Brooks, C. and J. S. Cooley. 1917. *J. Agr. Research* 8: 139–163.
34. Brooks, C. and J. S. Cooley. 1921. *J. Agr. Research* 22: 451–465.
35. Brooks, S. C. and M. M. Brooks. 1941. *The Permeability of Living Cells.* Berlin-Zehlendorf: Gebrüder Borntraeger., pp. 395.
36. Brown, W. 1923. *Ann. Botany* 37: 105–129.
37. Brown, W. 1925. *Ann. Botany* 39: 373–408.
38. Brown, W. and R. K. S. Wood, 1953. *Symposium Soc. Gen. Microbiol.,* 3: 326–339.
39. Buell, C. B. and W. H. Weston. 1947. *Am. J. Botany* 34: 555–561.
40. Bullen, J. J. 1949. *J. Pathol. Bacteriol.* 61: 117–120.
41. Buller, A. H. R. 1912. *Trans. Brit. Mycol. Soc.* 4: 106–112.
42. Buller, A. H. R. 1924. *Researches on Fungi,* Vol. 4. London: Longmans, Green and Co., pp. 611.
43. Buller, A. H. R. and A. T. Cameron. 1912. *Trans. Roy. Soc. Can.* 6, IV: 73–78.
44. Bünning, E. 1936. *Flora* 131: 87–112.
45. Burges, A. 1939. *Broteria, Sér. trimestral,* 8: 64–81.
46. Burges, A. and E. Fenton. 1953. *Trans. Brit. Mycol. Soc.* 36: 104–108.
47. Burkholder, P. R. and I. McVeigh. 1940. *Am. J. Botany* 27: 634–640.
48. Burkholder, P. R. and E. W. Sinnott. 1945. *Am. J. Botany* 32: 424–431.
49. Calam, C. I., N. Driver, and R. H. Bowers. 1951. *J. Appl. Chem. (London)* 1: 209–216.
50. Callow, D. S. and S. J. Pirt. 1956. *J. Gen. Microbiol.* 14: 661–671.
51. Cantino, E. C. 1949a. *Am. J. Botany* 36: 95–112.
52. Cantino, E. C. 1949b. *Am. J. Botany* 36: 747–756.
53. Cartwright, K. St. G. and W. P. K. Findley. 1934. *Ann. Botany* 48: 481–495.
54. Chain, E. B. and G. Gualandi. 1954. *Rend. ist. super. sanità* (English ed.) 17: 5–60.
55. Chain, E. B. et al. 1954. *Rend. ist. super. sanità* (English ed.) 17: 61–86.
56. Chaudhuri, H. 1923. *Ann. Botany* 37: 519–539.
57. Cochrane, V. W. and J. E. Conn. 1947. *J. Bacteriol.* 54: 213–218.
58. Cohen, M. and C. E. Yarwood. 1952. *Plant Physiol.* 27: 634–638.
59. Conway, E. J. and M. Downey. 1950. *Biochem. J. (London)* 47: 355–360.
60. Coons, G. H. and F. G. Larmer. 1930. *Papers Mich. Acad. Sci.* 11: 75–104.
61. Crasemann, J. M. 1954. *Am. J. Botany* 41: 302–310.
62. Crewther, W. G. and F. G. Lennox. 1953. *Australian J. Biol. Sci.* 6: 410–427.
63. Cunningham, K. G. and G. G. Freeman. 1953. *Biochem. J. (London)* 53: 328–332.
64. Dagys, J. and O. Kaikaryte. 1943. *Protoplasma* 38: 127–154.
65. Dahl, A. S. 1934. *Phytopathology* 24: 197–214.

66. Darby, R. T. and G. R. Mandels. 1954. *Mycologia* 46: 276–288.
67. Day, D. and A. Hervey. 1946. *Plant Physiol.* 21: 233–236.
68. Deindoerfer, F. and E. L. Gaden, Jr. 1955. *Appl. Microbiol.* 3: 253–257.
69. Denny, F. E. 1933. *Contribs. Boyce Thompson Inst.* 5: 95–102.
70. Deutschmann, F. 1953. *Phytopathol. Z.* 20: 297–310.
71. De Vay, J. E. 1954. *Phytopathology* 44: 583–587.
72. Dickson, J. G. 1923. *J. Agr. Research* 23: 837–870.
73. Dickson, J. G., S. H. Eckerson, and K. P. Link. 1923. *Proc. Nat. Acad. Sci. U. S.* 9: 434–439.
74. Dietzel, E., H. Behrenbruch, and M. Eucken. 1950. *Arch. Mikrobiol.* 15: 179–184.
75. Dimond, A. E., G. H. Plumb, E. M. Stoddard, and J. G. Horsfall. 1949. *Conn. (New Haven) Agr. Exp. Sta. Bull.* 531: 1–69.
76. Dion, M., A. Carilli, M. Sermonti, and E. B. Chain. 1954. *Rend. ist. super. sanità* (English ed.) 17: 187–205.
77. Domsch, K. H. 1955. *Arch. Mikrobiol.* 23: 79–87.
78. Dorn, F. L. and O. Rahn. 1939. *Arch. Mikrobiol.* 10: 6–12.
79. Dox, A. W. 1913. *J. Biol. Chem.* 16: 479–484.
80. Dox, A. W. and L. Maynard. 1912. *J. Biol. Chem.* 12: 227–231.
81. Drouhet, E. and F. Mariat. 1952. *Ann. inst. Pasteur* 83: 506–514.
82. Drouhet, E. and R. C. Zapater. 1954. *Ann. inst. Pasteur* 87: 396–402.
83. Duckworth, R. B. and G. C. M. Harris. 1949. *Trans. Brit. Mycol. Soc.* 32: 224–235.
83a. Edgington, L. V. and J. C. Walker. 1957. *Phytopathology* 47: 594–598.
84. Emerson, R. 1941. *Lloydia* 4: 77–144.
85. Emerson, R. and E. C. Cantino. 1948. *Am. J. Botany* 35: 157–171.
86. Emerson, S. 1950. *J. Bacteriol.* 60: 221–223.
87. Erikson, D. 1952. *J. Gen. Microbiol.* 6: 286–294.
88. Erwin, D. C. 1954. *Phytopathology* 44: 137–144.
89. Etheridge, D. E. 1955. *Can. J. Botany* 33: 416–428.
90. Ezekiel, W. N. 1945. *Phytopathology* 35: 296–301.
91. Farries, E. H. M. and A. F. Bell. 1930. *Ann. Botany* 44: 423–455.
92. Fawcett, H. S. 1921. *Univ. Calif. Publ. Agr. Sci.* 4: 183–232.
93. Fawcett, H. S. 1925. *Ann. Appl. Biol.* 12: 191–198.
94. Fellows, H. 1928. *J. Agr. Research* 37: 349–355.
95. Felton, M. W. and J. C. Walker. 1946. *J. Agr. Research* 72: 69–81.
96. Fikry, A. 1932. *Ann. Botany* 46: 29–70.
97. Finn, R. K. 1954. *Bacteriol. Revs.* 18: 254–274.
98. Fisher, E. E. 1939. *Ann. Botany* 3: 399–426.
99. Foster, J. W. and J. B. Davis. 1948. *J. Bacteriol.* 56: 329–338.
100. Foster, R. E. and J. C. Walker. 1947. *J. Agr. Research* 74: 165–186.
101. Fred, E. B. and S. A. Waksman. 1928. *Laboratory Manual of General Microbiology.* New York: McGraw-Hill Book Co., pp. 145.
102. Fries, L. 1945. *Arkiv Botan.* 32 (10): 1–8.
103. Fries, L. 1953. *Physiol. Plantarum* 6: 551–563.
104. Fries, L. 1956. *Svensk Botan. Tidskr.* 50: 47–96.
105. Fries, N. 1938. *Symbolae Botan. Upsalienses* 3 (2): 1–188.
106. Fries, N. 1943. *Symbolae Botan. Upsalienses* 7 (2): 5–73.
107. Fries, N. 1950. *Arkiv Botan.* Ser. 2, 1: 271–287.
108. Fromageot, C., M. Jutis, and P. Tessier. 1949. *Bull. soc. chim. biol.* 31: 689–695.
109. Fukuda, Y., S. Takami, and Y. Ikeshoji. 1954. *Japan. J. Botany* 14: 67–90.
110. Garner, H. H., et al. 1953. *Am. J. Botany* 40: 289–296.
111. Garrett, S. D. 1953. *Ann. Botany* 17: 63–79.
112. Gäumann, E. 1939. *Angew. Botan.* 21: 59–69.

113. Gäumann, E., C. Roth, and J. Anliker. 1934. *Z. Pflanzenkrankh. u. Pflanzenschutz* 44: 97–116.
114. Gäumann, E. and E. Häfliger. 1945. *Phytopathol. Z.* 16: 85–105.
115. Gäumann, E. and U. Nef. 1947. *Ber. schweiz botan. Ges.* 57: 258–271.
116. Golding, N. S. 1940a. *J. Dairy Sci.* 23: 879–889.
117. Golding, N. S. 1940b. *J. Dairy Sci.* 23: 891–898.
118. Golding, N. S. 1945. *J. Dairy Sci.* 28: 737–750.
119. Gottlieb, D. and H. W. Anderson. 1947. *Bull. Torrey Botan. Club* 74: 293–302.
120. Grainger, J. 1946. *Trans. Brit. Mycol. Soc.* 29: 52–64.
121. Greene, H. C. and E. B. Fred. 1934. *Ind. Eng. Chem.* 26: 1297–1299.
122. Haines, R. B. 1930. *J. Exp. Biol.* 8: 379–388.
123. Haines, R. B. 1931. *J. Exp. Biol.* 9: 45–60.
124. Hall, M. P. 1933. *Ann. Botany* 47: 543–578.
125. Harvey, E. N. 1952. *Bioluminescence.* New York: Academic Press, pp. 649.
126. Haskins, R. H. and J. Anastasiou. 1953. *Mycologia* 45: 523–532.
127. Haskins, R. H. and W. H. Weston, Jr. 1950. *Am. J. Botany* 37: 739–750.
128. Hastings, J. W. 1952. *J. Cellular Comp. Physiol.* 39: 1–30.
129. Hawkins, L. A. 1916. *J. Agr. Research* 7: 255–260.
130. Hawn, E. J. and T. C. Vanterpool. 1953. *Can. J. Botany* 31: 699–710.
131. Hayashi, K. 1954. *Japan. J. Botany* 14: 91–98.
132. Heim, A. H. and H. Lechevalier. 1956. *Mycologia* 48: 628–636.
133. Held, V. M. 1955. *Phytopathology* 45: 39–42.
134. Hemmi, T. and T. Abe. 1928. *Japan. J. Botany* 4: 113–123.
135. Henriksson, L. E. and J. F. Morgan-Jones. 1951. *Svensk Botan. Tidskr.* 45: 648–657.
135a. Henssen, A. 1957. *Arch. Mikrobiol.* 27: 63–81.
136. Hildebrand, E. M. 1938. *Botan. Rev.* 4: 627–664.
137. Hockenhull, D. J. D. 1946. *Biochem. J. (London)* 40: 337–343.
138. Hofsten, B. von, A. von Hofsten, and N. Fries. 1953. *Exp. Cell Research* 5: 530–535.
139. Horowitz, N. H. 1951. *Growth* 15 (Suppl.): 47–62.
140. How, J. E. 1940. *Ann. Botany* 4: 135–150.
141. Hultin, E. and L. Nordström. 1949. *Acta Chem. Scand.* 3: 1405–1417.
142. Humfeld, H. 1947. *J. Bacteriol.* 54: 689–696.
143. Humphrey, C. J. and P. V. Siggers. 1933. *J. Agr. Research* 47: 997–1008.
144. Isaac, I. 1953. *Trans. Brit. Mycol. Soc.* 36: 180–195.
145. Jaarsveld, A. 1940. *De invloed van verschillende bodemschimmels op de virulentie van* Rhizoctonia solani *Kühn.* Thesis, Univ. of Amsterdam, 101 pp.
146. Jacquiot, C. 1951. *Rev. mycol. (Paris)* 16: 27–29.
147. Jeffreys, E. G., P. W. Brian, H. G. Hemming, and D. Lowe. 1953. *J. Gen. Microbiol.* 9: 314–341.
148. Jennison, M. W., M. D. Newcomb, and R. Henderson. 1955. *Mycologia* 47: 275–304.
149. Jensen, H. L. 1930. *Proc. Linnean Soc. N. S. Wales* 55: 699–707.
150. Jensen, H. L. 1941. *Proc. Linnean Soc. N. S. Wales* 66: 276–286.
151. Jermyn, M. A. 1953. *Australian J. Biol. Sci.* 6: 48–69.
152. Jillson, O. F. and W. J. Nickerson. 1948. *Mycologia* 40: 369–385.
153. Johnson, F. H., H. Eyring, and M. J. Polissar. 1954. *The Kinetic Basis of Molecular Biology.* New York: John Wiley and Sons, pp. 874.
154. Johnson, G. T. and A. C. Jones. 1941. *Mycologia* 33: 424–433.
155. Jones, L. R. 1924. *Am. J. Botany* 11: 601–609.
156. Jones, L. R., J. Johnson, and J. G. Dickson. 1926. *Wisconsin Univ. Agr. Exp. Sta. Research Bull.* 71: 1–144.
157. Kaess, G. and W. Schwartz. 1935. *Arch. Mikrobiol.* 6: 208–214.
158. Katznelson, H. 1940. *Soil Sci.* 49: 83–93.

159. Klaus, H. 1941. *Phytopathol. Z.* 13: 126–195.
160. Klotz, L. J. 1923. *Ann. Missouri Botan. Garden* 10: 299–368.
161. Kluyver, A. J. and L. H. C. Perquin. 1933. *Biochem. Z.* 266: 66–81.
162. Koch, O. G. and G. A. Dedic. 1956. *Zentr. Bakteriol. Parasitenk. Abt. II,* 109: 17–21.
163. Koehler, B. 1938. *J. Agr. Research* 56: 291–307.
164. Koellreuter, J. 1950. *Phytopathol. Z.* 17: 129–160.
165. Koffler, H., R. L. Emerson, D. Perlman, and R. H. Burris. 1945. *J. Bacteriol.* 50: 517–548.
166. Kuhn, F. 1938. *Zentr. Bakteriol. Parasitenk. Abt. II,* 98: 430–444.
167. Kusnetzow, S. J. 1932. *Mikrobiologiya* 1: 3–18, 83.
168. Lakata, G. D. 1954. *Appl. Microbiol.* 2: 2–4.
169. La Touche, C. J. 1950. *Trans. Brit. Mycol. Soc.* 33: 94–104.
170. Lauritzen, J. I. 1929. *J. Agr. Research* 38: 93–108.
171. Lauritzen, J. I. 1932. *J. Agr. Research* 44: 861–912.
172. Lauritzen, J. I. and L. L. Harter. 1925. *J. Agr. Research* 30: 793–810.
173. Leach, J. G. 1923. *Minn. Univ. Agr. Exp. Sta. Tech. Bull.* 14: 1–41.
174. Leach, J. G. and T. M. Currence. 1938. *Minn. Univ. Agr. Exp. Sta. Tech. Bull.* 129: 1–32.
175. Lehman, S. G. 1923. *Ann. Missouri Botan. Garden* 10: 111–178.
176. Levine, M. 1930. *A Compilation of Culture Media for the Cultivation of Microorganisms.* Baltimore: The Williams and Wilkins Co., pp. 969.
177. Levine, S. and Z. J. Ordal. 1946. *J. Bacteriol.* 52: 686–694.
178. Lilly, V. G. and H. L. Barnett. 1947a. *Am. J. Botany* 34: 131–138.
179. Lilly, V. G. and H. L. Barnett. 1947b. *Mycologia* 39: 699–708.
180. Lilly, V. G. and H. L. Barnett. 1951. *Physiology of the Fungi.* New York: McGraw-Hill Book Co., pp. 464.
181. Lilly, V. G. and H. L. Barnett. 1953. *West Va. Univ. Agr. Exp. Sta. Bull.* 362T: 1–58.
182. Lindeberg, G. 1944. *Symbolae Botan. Upsalienses* 8 (2): 1–183.
183. Lindeberg, G. and M. Korjus. 1949. *Physiol. Plantarum* 2: 103–113.
184. Lindgren, R. M. 1942. *U. S. Dept. Agr. Tech. Bull.* 807: 1–35.
185. Ling, L. and J. Y. Yang. 1944. *Ann. Botany* 8: 91–104.
186. Lüers, H., R. Kühles, and H. Fink. 1930. *Biochem. Z.* 217: 253–278.
187. Luz, G. 1934. *Phytopathol. Z.* 7: 585–638.
188. Machlis, L. 1953a. *Am. J. Botany* 40: 450–460.
189. Machlis, L. 1953b. *Am. J. Botany* 40: 460–464.
190. Macrae, R. 1942. *Can. J. Research C,* 20: 411–434.
191. McVickar, D. L. 1942. *Am. J. Botany* 29: 372–380.
192. Macy, H. 1929. *Minn. Univ. Agr. Exp. Sta. Tech. Bull.* 64: 1–86.
193. Mahdihassan, S. 1930. *Biochem. Z.* 226: 203–208.
194. Malevich, O. A. 1936. *Mikrobiologiya* 5: 813–817.
195. Matsumoto, T. 1921. *Ann. Missouri Botan. Garden* 8: 1–62.
196. Mayenburg, O. H. von. 1901. *Jahrb. wiss. Botan.* 36: 381–420.
197. Mazur, P. and W. H. Weston. 1956. *J. Bacteriol.* 71: 257–266.
198. Melin, E. 1925. *Untersuchungen über die Bedeutung der Baummykorrhiza, eine ökologisch-physiologische Studie.* Jena: Gustav Fischer, pp. 152.
199. Meyer, E. 1955. *Mycologia* 47: 664–667.
200. Michel-Durand, E. 1938. *Bull. soc. chim. biol.* 20: 339–412.
201. Miehe, H. 1907. *Die Selbsterhitzung des Heus.* Jena: Gustav Fischer, pp. 127.
202. Miller, J. J. 1945. *Can. J. Research C,* 23: 16–43.
203. Montgomery, H. B. S. 1936. *Ann. Appl. Biol.* 23: 465–486.
204. Moore, E. J. 1937. *Phytopathology* 27: 918–930.
205. Morton, A. G. and D. Broadbent. 1955. *J. Gen. Microbiol.* 12: 248–258.
206. Moyer, A. J. and R. D. Coghill. 1945. *Arch. Biochem.* 7: 164–183.

207. Moyer, A. J. and R. D. Coghill. 1946. *J. Bacteriol.* 51: 57–78.
208. Moyer, A. J., O. E. May, and H. T. Herrick. 1936. *Zentr. Bakteriol. Parasitenk. Abt. II,* 95: 311–324.
209. Müller, F. W. 1941. *Ber. schweiz. botan. Ges.* 51: 165–256.
210. Neal, D. C. 1927. *Ann. Missouri Botan. Garden* 14: 359–407.
211. Nickerson, W. J. 1951. *Trans. N. Y. Acad. Sci.* II, 13: 140–145.
212. Nickerson, W. J. and C. W. Chung. 1954. *Am. J. Botany* 41: 114–120.
213. Nickerson, W. J. and G. A. Edwards. 1949. *J. Gen. Physiol.* 33: 41–55.
214. Nickerson, W. J. and Z. Mankowski. 1953a. *Am. J. Botany* 40: 584–591.
215. Nickerson, W. J. and Z. Mankowski. 1953b. *J. Infectious Diseases* 92: 20–25.
216. Nickerson, W. J. and F. G. Sherman. 1952. *J. Bacteriol.* 64: 667–678.
217. Nickerson, W. J. and N. J. W. Van Rij. 1949. *Biochim. et Biophys. Acta* 3: 461–475.
218. Noack, K. 1912. *Jahrb. wiss. Botan.* 51: 593–646.
219. Nord, F. F. 1932. *Ergeb. Enzymforsch.* 1: 77–112.
220. Nord, F. F. and L. J. Sciarini. 1946. *Arch. Biochem.* 9: 419–437.
221. Nordbring-Hertz, B. 1955. *Physiol. Plantarum* 8: 691–717.
222. Norkrans, B. 1950. *Symbolae Botan. Upsalienses* 11 (1): 5–126.
223. Norman, A. G. 1930. *Ann. Appl. Biol.* 17: 575–613.
224. Norton, D. C. 1953. *Phytopathology* 43: 633–636.
225. Ohtsuki, T. 1953. *Japan. J. Botany* 14: 147–160.
226. Overstreet, R. and L. Jacobson. 1952. *Ann. Rev. Plant Physiol.* 3: 189–206.
227. Owen, S. P. and M. J. Johnson. 1955. *Appl. Microbiol.* 3: 374–379.
228. Owens, R. G. 1955. *Contribs. Boyce Thompson Inst.* 18: 125–144.
229. Painter, H. A. 1954. *J. Gen. Microbiol.* 10: 177–190.
230. Paladino, S. 1954. *Rend. ist. super. sanità* (English ed.) 17: 145–148.
231. Pantanelli, E. 1904. *Jahrb. wiss. Botan.* 40: 303–367.
232. Pehrson, S. O. 1948. *Physiol. Plantarum* 1: 38–56.
233. Perlman, D. 1948. *Am. J. Botany* 35: 360–363.
234. Pine, L. 1954. *J. Bacteriol.* 68: 671–679.
235. Pine, L. 1955. *J. Bacteriol.* 70: 375–381.
236. Pratt, C. A. 1924. *Ann. Botany* 38: 563–595, 599–615.
237. Preston, A. and E. I. McLennan. 1948. *Ann. Botany* 12: 53–64.
238. Purdy, L. H., Jr. and R. G. Grogan. 1954. *Phytopathology* 44: 36–39.
239. Raper, K. B. and D. F. Alexander. 1945. *Mycologia* 37: 499–525.
240. Raper, K. B. and C. Thom. 1949. *A Manual of the Penicillia.* Baltimore: The Williams and Wilkins Co., pp. 875.
241. Reitsma, J. 1932. *Phytopathol. Z.* 4: 461–522.
242. Remsberg, R. E. 1940. *Mycologia* 32: 52–96.
243. Rennerfelt, E. 1941. *Arch. Mikrobiol.* 12: 19–40.
244. Rhodes, M. 1950. *Trans. Brit. Mycol. Soc.* 33: 35–39.
245. Rippel, A. and G. Behr. 1936. *Arch. Mikrobiol.* 7: 584–589.
246. Robbins, W. J. 1947. *Ann. N. Y. Acad. Sci.* 49: 75–86.
247. Robbins, W. J. and F. Kavanagh. 1944. *Bull. Torrey Botan. Club* 71: 1–10.
248. Robinson, R. 1926. *Trans. Brit. Mycol. Soc.* 10: 307–314.
249. Rolinson, G. N. 1952. *J. Gen. Microbiol.* 6: 336–343.
250. Roth, C. 1935. *Phytopathol. Z.* 8: 1–110.
251. Rothwell, F. M. 1956. *Am. J. Botany* 43: 28–32.
252. Roxburgh, J. M., J. F. T. Spencer, and H. R. Sallans. 1954. *J. Agr. Food Chem.* 2: 1121–1124.
253. Ryan, F. J., G. W. Beadle, and E. L. Tatum. 1943. *Am. J. Botany* 30: 784–799.
254. Salvin, S. B. 1947. *J. Invest. Dermatol.* 9: 315–320.
255. Salvin, S. B. 1949a. *J. Infectious Diseases* 84: 275–283.
256. Salvin, S. B. 1949b. *Mycologia* 41: 311–319.
257. Sanford, G. B. 1926. *Phytopathology* 16: 525–547.

258. Sanford, G. B. 1933. *Can. J. Research C,* 8: 337–348.
259. Savage, G. M. and M. J. Vander Brook. 1946. *J. Bacteriol.* 52: 385–391.
260. Schaffnit, E. and K. Meyer-Hermann. 1930. *Phytopathol. Z.* 2:99–166.
261. Scheffer, T. C. and B. E. Livingston. 1937. *Am. J. Botany* 24: 109–119.
262. Scherr, G. H. and R. H. Weaver. 1953. *Bacteriol. Revs.* 17: 51–92.
263. Schostakowitsch, W. 1895. *Flora* 81: 362–393.
264. Schroeder, W. T. and J. C. Walker. 1942. *J. Agr. Research* 65: 221–248.
265. Sharp, E. L. and F. G. Smith. 1952. *Phytopathology* 42: 263–264.
265a. Sharp, E. L. and F. G. Smith. 1957. *Phytopathology* 47: 423–429.
266. Shaw, D. E. 1951. *Proc. Linnean Soc. N. S. Wales* 76: 7–25.
267. Sherf, A. F. 1943. *Phytopathology* 33: 330–332.
268. Shirakawa, H. S. 1955. *Am. J. Botany* 42: 379–384.
269. Shu, P. 1953. *J. Agr. Food Chem.* 1: 1119–1123.
270. Shu, P. and M. J. Johnson. 1948. *Ind. Eng. Chem.* 40: 1202–1205.
271. Siu, R. G. H. 1951. *Microbiological Decomposition of Cellulose.* New York: Reinhold Publ. Corp., pp. 531.
272. Smith, J. H. 1923. *Ann. Botany* 37: 341–343.
273. Smith, J. H. 1924. *New Phytologist* 23: 65–78.
274. Smith, P. G. and J. C. Walker. 1941. *J. Agr. Research* 63: 1–20.
275. Smithies, W. R. 1953. *Biochem. J. (London)* 55: 346–350.
276. Snow, D. 1945. *Ann. Appl. Biol.* 32: 40–44.
277. Snow, D., M. H. G. Crichton, and N. C. Wright. 1944. *Ann. Appl. Biol.* 31: 102–110.
278. Sost, H. 1955. *Arch. Protistenk.* 100: 541–564.
279. Spruit-van der Burg, A. 1950. *Biochim. et Biophys. Acta* 5: 175–178.
280. Stadler, D. R. 1952. *J. Cellular Comp. Physiol.* 39: 449–474.
281. Staffeldt, E. E. and E. L. Sharp. 1954. *Phytopathology* 44: 213–215.
282. Stare, A. 1942. *Arch. Mikrobiol.* 13: 74–92.
283. Starks, O. B. and H. Koffler. 1949. *Science* 109: 495–496.
284. Stockdale, P. M. 1953a. *Biol. Revs. Cambridge Phil. Soc.* 28: 84–104.
285. Stockdale, P. M. 1953b. *J. Gen. Microbiol.* 8: 434–441.
286. Stoll, C. 1954. *Phytopathol. Z.* 22: 233–274.
287. Stover, R. H. 1953. *Can. J. Botany* 31: 693–697.
288. Stover, R. H. 1955. *Soil Sci.* 80: 397–412.
289. Stover, R. H., N. C. Thornton, and V. C. Dunlap. 1953. *Soil Sci.* 76: 225–238.
290. Stuart, L. S. 1940. *J. Agr. Research* 61: 259–266.
291. Tamiya, H. 1927. *Acta Phytochim. (Japan)* 3: 51–173.
292. Tamiya, H. 1929. *Acta Phytochim. (Japan)* 4: 227-295.
293. Tatum, E. L., R. W. Barratt, and V. M. Cutter, Jr. 1949. *Science* 109: 509–511.
294. Taubenhaus, J. J. and W. N. Ezekiel. 1935. *Am. J. Botany* 23: 10–12.
295. Thacker, D. G. and H. M. Good. 1952. *Can. J. Botany* 30: 475–485.
296. Thatcher, F. S. 1939. *Am. J. Botany* 26: 449–458.
297. Thatcher, F. S. 1942. *Can. J. Research C,* 20: 283– 311.
298. Thimann, K. V. 1955. *The Life of Bacteria.* New York: The Macmillan Co., pp. 775.
299. Thirumalachar, M. J. 1954. *Rend. ist. super. sanità* (English ed.) 17: 206–212.
300. Thom, C. and K. B. Raper. 1941. *U. S. Dept. Agr. Misc. Publ.* 426: 1–46.
301. Tilford, P. E. 1936. *Ohio Agr. Exp. Sta. Bull.* 567: 1–27.
302. Tisdale, W. B. 1923. *J. Agr. Research* 24: 55–86.
303. Tobie, W. C. and G. B. Ayres. 1945. *J. Bacteriol.* 50: 333–335.
304. Todd, G. W. and J. Levitt. 1951. *Plant Physiol.* 26: 331–336.
305. Toennies, G. and D. L. Gallant. 1948. *J. Biol. Chem.* 174: 451–463.
306. Toennies, G. and D. L. Gallant. 1949. *Growth* 13: 7–20.
307. Togashi, K. 1949. *Biological Characters of Plant Pathogens. Temperature Relations.* Tokyo: Meibundo, pp. 478.

308. Tomkins, R. G. 1932. *Trans. Brit. Mycol. Soc.* 17: 150–153.
309. Tomlinson, J. A. 1952. *Trans. Brit. Mycol. Soc.* 35: 221–235.
310. Tompkins, C. M. and M. W. Gardner. 1935. *Hilgardia* 9: 219–230.
311. Treschow, C. 1941. *Dansk Botan. Arkiv* 11 (1): 1–31.
312. Treschow, C. 1944. *Dansk Botan. Arkiv* 11 (6): 1–180.
313. Tsilinsky, P. 1899. *Ann. inst. Pasteur* 13: 500–505.
314. Venning, F. D. and B. S. Crandall. 1954. *Phytopathology* 44: 465–468.
315. Vishniac, H. S. 1955a. *J. Gen. Microbiol.* 12: 455–463.
316. Vishniac, H. S. 1955b. *Mycologia* 47: 633–645.
317. Wagener, W. W. and R. W. Davidson. 1954. *Botan. Rev.* 20: 61–134.
318. Waksman, S. A. 1922. *Soil Sci.* 14: 61–79.
319. Waksman, S. A., A. Schatz, and H. C. Reilly. 1946. *J. Bacteriol.* 51: 753–759.
320. Waksman, S. A., W. W. Umbreit, and T. C. Cordon. 1939. *Soil Sci.* 47: 37–54.
321. Walderdorff, M. G. 1924. *Botan. Arch.* 6: 84–110.
322. Walker, M. N. 1941. *Florida Univ. Agr. Exp. Sta.* (Gainesville) *Bull.* 363: 3–29.
323. Walter, H. 1924. *Z. Botan.* 16: 353–417.
324. Wassink, E. C. 1948. *Rec. trav. botan. Néerl.* 41: 150–211.
325. Wean, R. E. and J. E. Young. 1939. *Phytopathology* 29: 895–898.
326. Webb, M. 1948. *J. Gen. Microbiol.* 2: 275–287.
327. Webb, R. W. and H. Fellows. 1926. *J. Agr. Research* 33: 845–872.
328. Webley, D. M. 1954. *J. Gen. Microbiol.* 11: 114–121.
329. Wehmer, C. 1914. *Mycol. Centr.* 4: 241–252, 287–299.
330. Weimer, J. L. and L. L. Harter. 1923. *J. Agr. Research* 24: 1–40.
331. Weiss, F. and B. A. Oteifa. 1953. *Phytopathology* 43: 407.
332. Wellman, F. L. 1932. *J. Agr. Research* 45: 461–469.
333. Wernham, C. C. 1946. *Mycologia* 38: 691–692.
334. Wetter, C. 1954. *Arch. Mikrobiol.* 20: 261–272.
335. White, I. G. 1955. *Am. J. Botany* 42: 759–764.
336. Wilhelm, S. 1955. *Phytopathology* 45: 180–181.
337. Wilkin, G. D. and A. Rhodes. 1955. *J. Gen. Microbiol.* 12: 259–264.
338. Wilkins, W. H., J. L. Harley, and G. C. Kent. 1938. *Ann. Appl. Biol.* 25: 472–489.
339. Wolf, F. T. 1955. *Bull. Torrey Botan. Club* 82: 343–354.
340. Wolpert, F. S. 1924. *Ann. Missouri Botan. Garden* 11: 43–97.
341. Wyss, O., V. G. Lilly, and L. H. Leonian. 1944. *Science* 99: 18–19.
342. Yoshii, H. 1935. *Bull. Sci. Fakultato Terkultura, Kjuŝu Imp. Univ.* (Japan) 6: 312–330.
343. Yoshii, H. 1936. *Ann. Phytopathol. Soc. Japan* 6: 199–204.
344. Zobl, K. H. 1943. *Arch. Mikrobiol.* 13: 191–206.
345. Zycha, H. 1937. *Zentr. Bakteriol. Parasitenk. Abt. II*, 97: 222–244.

2. The Composition of Fungus Cells

U nder this head are considered those constituents which as a class if not individually are common to most or all fungi. Materials which are found only in some species are discussed, if significant, in the section on metabolism; thus, sugar alcohols and carotenoids do not occur in the mycelium of all fungi and so are not included here, but are considered in, respectively, Chapters 5 and 6. Known vitamins produced by fungi are reviewed in Chapter 10.

The theoretical significance of chemical composition is somewhat limited. It will be seen that, within bounds set by the metabolic capacities of the species, the composition varies widely with the environment. The quantities of fat, carbohydrate, ash, wall material, and total nitrogen are all more or less responsive to the culture medium.

In composition, the principal difference between fungi and bacteria is in the high chitin content of most fungi. Chitin is present in the bacteria (176); the green algae do not have chitin walls. Absence of chitin in the Oomycetes, discussed below, in turn suggests a polyphyletic origin of the true fungi. A second difference between fungi and bacteria is also quantitative rather than absolute: lipid accumulation is more common and attains higher levels in the fungi than in most bacteria. *Mycobacterium* and related forms, however, are exceptions to this rule and may have a rather high lipid content (130).

1. THE MAJOR CONSTITUENTS OF THE CELL

Growing fungus cells are, of course, largely water; early measurements indicate that 85–90 per cent of the fresh weight of mycelium and fleshy sporophores is water. Presumably the more leathery sporophores and sclerotia have less water (25, 197). The conidia of most fungi appear to have a relatively low water content, e.g., 17.4 per cent in *Aspergillus oryzae* (171), 25 per cent in *Monilinia fructicola*, and 6 per cent in *Penicillium digitatum* (195). It is probable, as suggested by Yarwood (195), that most of the water in these spores is hygroscopic. Their water content is largely, therefore, a function of the environmental humidity; this may explain some of the rather high values reported in the early literature.

Species of *Erysiphe* are unusual in that the conidia have a high water content (195, 196). With this is associated the ability to germinate at low relative humidity (Chapter 12).

The bound water of *Aspergillus niger* mycelium, defined as water which is removed by heat but not by *in vacuo* drying over a desiccant at moderate temperatures, amounts to 7.1–8.4 per cent of the dry weight when the fungus is cultivated on 5 per cent glucose; at higher glucose concentrations the bound water rises to as much as 30 per cent of the dry matter (182).

The elementary composition of fungi has been studied chiefly with respect to carbon and nitrogen. The carbon content of a number of fungi studied by Heck (78) was 40–44 per cent of the dry weight; Pinck and Allison (128) report a somewhat wider range—43 to 53 per cent. *Aspergillus oryzae* mycelium is about 49 per cent carbon (173), and *A. niger* mycelium about 46 per cent (129), but other species of *Aspergillus* may be as high as 55 per cent (194). Most fungi are 40–50 per cent carbon, and the value is relatively little affected by cultural conditions (173, 194) or age (126).

Bacteria and viruses in general have carbon contents of the same order as fungi (130). The mycelium of *Streptomyces griseus* has slightly less carbon—about 38 per cent of the dry weight (58).

In contrast to the relative uniformity of carbon content, the total nitrogen of fungal mycelium is quite variable; both the kind and the concentration of the nitrogen source influence the composition.

The major constituents of the mycelium of several fungi are listed in Table 1. These data cannot be considered typical of all fungi, since it is known that at least four of the fractions—carbohydrate, protein, lipid, and ash—are strongly affected by cultural conditions

Table 1. Major Constituents of Cultivated Fungi and Actinomycetes*

Organism	Carbo-hydrate	Chitin	Protein	Lipid	Ash
Aspergillus oryzae (spores) (171)	9.00	—	22.75†	2.20	5.33
Gliocladium roseum (157)	34.4	8.4	21.2‡	22.4	—
Rhizopus japonicus (99)	—	—	38.8†	9.72	5.52
Penicillium chrysogenum (157)	60.0	10.6	16.4‡	1.4	—
Penicillium griseofulvum (165)	45.0	5.5	12.0§	34.5	—
Phymatotrichum omnivorum (42)	32.42	—	23.94†	4.49	6.24

* As per cent of dry weight.
† Estimated from total nitrogen only.
‡ Estimated from total nitrogen after subtraction of chitin nitrogen.
§ Determined in a chitin-free fraction.

and differ in amount from one species to another. As discussed below, those protein values of Table 1 which are based only on the total nitrogen are almost certainly high.

2. MINERAL CONSTITUENTS OF THE CELL

The ash content of fungi varies with the medium used and, presumably, with species. Some figures reported for total ash as per cent of dry weight are: *Rhizopus japonicus,* 5.52 (99); *Aspergillus niger,* 2.39 (129); *A. oryzae,* 7.19 (78); *Coprinus radians,* 4.97 (78); *Penicillium notatum,* 28.3–34.0 (50). Fruiting bodies collected in the field may be as low as 1.08 or as high as 29.8 per cent ash; most have 5–10 per cent (197).

The composition of the ash of a few fungi is summarized in Table 2. Although no figures should be considered typical, it is clear that the most abundant minerals are phosphorus and potassium. Probably none of the analyses of Table 2 is complete, and inspection raises some obvious problems, e.g., the accumulation of silicon in *Rhizopus japonicus* and aluminum in *Penicillium notatum.*

The total ash content and the concentration of individual elements are influenced by the environment and by the stage of development. In *Aspergillus niger* the total ash of conidia is about three times that of mycelium; the increase is confined, however, to a few of the elements, particularly phosphorus, potassium, and magnesium (5, 139). Autolysis is accompanied by loss of phosphorus (61) and by a decline in total ash (100). Among the environmental effects, the simplest is the increase in the internal concentration of an element in the mycelium as its external concentration is raised (62, 139, 144, 164). The total ash and the concentration of individual elements are also influ-

Table 2. The Mineral Constituents of Fungi*

Mineral	Rhizopus japonicus (99)	Penicillium notatum (50)	Trametes suaveolens (198)	Morchella esculenta (94)
K	27.3	4.52	31.52	63.07
Na	12.9	7.89	0.46	0.38
Ca	—	26.72	22.57	1.75
Mg	1.42	8.56	6.07	1.77
P	28.7	25.01	4.64	26.13
S	0.28	2.17	19.06	1.78
Si	21.2			0.63
Cl	—	0.5	0.52	1.37
Al	—	20.62	0.26	—
Fe	1.84	4.52	—	2.00
Zn	0.18	—	—	—

* As per cent of total ash.

enced, probably indirectly through effects on growth or pH, by the type of nitrogen source (64, 143, 194) and by the concentration of nitrogen (78). A low nitrogen supply may be expected to act directly on phosphorus content by restriction of the synthesis of nucleic acids (63).

It is assumed that only phosphorus, sulfur, and chlorine occur in fungi in organic combination; an attempt to isolate organic compounds of magnesium failed (143). Phosphorus is, of course, present in several types of organic molecules: sugar phosphates and adenosine phosphates (22, 92, 113), phosphoproteins (107), nucleic acids (63), and phospholipids (p. 47). None of these has been investigated thoroughly in the fungi.

The inorganic phosphate of fungal mycelium includes orthophosphate and inorganic condensed phosphates (151). Pyrophosphate occurs in *Aspergillus niger* (106), but most attention has been directed to the metaphosphates, polymers of the general formula $(NaPO_3)_n$. Volutin, a common visible intracellular inclusion, is probably metaphosphate (85). Metaphosphates have been found in cells of *Aspergillus niger* (96) and, possibly, *Neurospora crassa* (83). The metaphosphate of *A. niger* has a molecular weight of 6000–7000 (86). Fungal enzymes which hydrolyze these condensed inorganic phosphates are considered briefly in Chapter 9. Utilization of the bond energy of these compounds to drive synthetic reactions, although not impossible in principle, has not as yet been demonstrated.

3. THE CELL WALL

The most serious defect in our knowledge of cell wall composition in the filamentous fungi is the fact that no "pure" wall material is yet available. The major sources of error are the inclusion of extraneous substances in the preparation, and the loss of wall material during purification. We do not have, therefore, for any fungus even a qualitative picture of the chemical components of the wall. This section, consequently, can only review work in which one or the other major constituent has been studied. When we speak of a chitin wall, we mean a wall with detectable chitin, not necessarily or even probably a wall which is exclusively chitin. Morphologically, in fact, the wall may be a multiple structure with layers of different composition (15, 46).

In most fungi the basic material of the cell wall is chitin, a polymer of N-acetylglucosamine, identical chemically with the chitin of arthropods. The history of the study of chitin in fungi is reviewed by Schmidt (152) and by Frey (56). Much confusion exists, however, because of the use of methods which are not critical. The most acceptable method of qualitative identification of chitin is determination of the X-ray diffraction pattern (56, 66, 79, 87, 91). However, if chitin is present only in small amounts, the X-ray method may not reveal it. Other methods—microchemical tests, isolation of derivatives from a hydrolyzate, and determination of the nitrogen in a purified preparation—are usually in agreement with X-ray results, but are not sufficiently discriminating to stand by themselves. Microchemical methods for chitin and cellulose are particularly unsatisfactory (56).

The quantitative determination of chitin requires purification, usually by the method of Scholl (153), and determination of the nitrogen of the product. In a survey of 25 fungi, chitin contents from 2.6 to 26.2 per cent of the dry weight have been reported (18); other quantitative data are found in Table 1 above, and in the paper of Schmidt (152). The possibility that some protein nitrogen, from resistant proteins, is included in these analyses cannot be ignored.

On the basis of microchemical tests for chitin, von Wettstein (186) proposed that large taxonomic groups of the fungi differ in the constitution of the cell wall. Specifically, he found chitin in the Zygomycetes and in the higher fungi—ascomycetes and basidiomycetes; representative Myxomycetes, Oomycetes and Monoblepharidales were found not to form chitin. This supports a polyphyletic origin of the phycomycetes.

Table 3. Cell Wall Materials of Fungi*

Organism	Classification	Chitin	Cellulose
Pythium debaryanum	Oomycetes	Absent	Present
Phytophthora spp.	Oomycetes	Absent	Present
Saprolegnia lapponica	Oomycetes	Absent	Present
Achlya caroliniana	Oomycetes	Absent	Present
Lagenidium giganteum	Oomycetes	Absent	Present
Allomyces arbuscula	Blastocladiales	Present	Absent
Blastocladiella variabilis	Blastocladiales	Present	Absent
Phycomyces blakesleeanus	Zygomycetes	Present	Absent
Mucor spp.	Zygomycetes	Present	Absent
Rhizopus bovinus	Zygomycetes	Present	Absent
Absidia glauca	Zygomycetes	Present	Absent
Basidiobolus ranarum	Zygomycetes	Present	Absent
Eremascus fertilis	Endomycetaceae †	Present	Absent
Endomyces decipiens	Endomycetaceae †	Present	Absent
Endomycopsis fibuliger	Endomycetaceae †	Present	Absent
Saccharomyces spp.	Saccharomycetaceae †	Absent	Absent
Schizosaccharomyces spp.	Saccharomycetaceae †	Absent	Absent
Zygosaccharomyces vini	Saccharomycetaceae †	Absent	Absent
Pichia membranaefaciens	Saccharomycetaceae †	Absent	Absent
Ashbya gossypii	Spermophthoraceae †	Absent	Absent
Eremothecium ashbyii	Spermophthoraceae †	Absent	Absent
Torula spp.	Pseudosaccharomycetaceae †	Absent	Absent
Rhodotorula rubra	Pseudosaccharomycetaceae †	Absent	Absent
Mycoderma vini	Pseudosaccharomycetaceae †	Absent	Absent
Aspergillus oryzae	Ascomycetes ‡	Present	Absent
Nectria cinnabarina	Ascomycetes	Present	Absent
Sclerotinia fructicola	Ascomycetes	Present	Absent
Ctenomyces farinulentis	Ascomycetes	Present	Absent
Boletus edulis	Basidiomycetes	Present	Absent
Cantharellus cibarius	Basidiomycetes	Present	Absent
Coprinus atramentarius	Basidiomycetes	Present	Absent
Hypholoma fasciculare	Basidiomycetes	Present	Absent
Ustilago violacea (budding sporidia)	Basidiomycetes	Absent	Absent
Blastomyces dermatitidis	Fungi Imperfecti	Present	Absent
Epidermophyton floccosum	Fungi Imperfecti	Present	Absent
Histoplasma capsulatum	Fungi Imperfecti	Present	Absent
Paracoccidioides brasiliensis	Fungi Imperfecti	Present	Absent
Sabouraudites audouini	Fungi Imperfecti	Present	Absent
Sporobolomyces roseus	Fungi Imperfecti	Present	Absent
Sporotrichum schenckii	Fungi Imperfecti	Present	Absent
Trichoderma viride	Fungi Imperfecti	Present	Absent
Trichophyton ferrugineum	Fungi Imperfecti	Present	Absent

* Limited to data from X-ray diffraction studies of Blank (16, 17), Frey (56), and Gonell (66).

† Classification of Gäumann (60).

‡ Assuming a perfect stage in the ascomycetes.

Although several reports since 1921 have challenged von Wettstein's generalizations, more recent work with the X-ray diffraction method has confirmed them. These results are summarized in Table 3. From this compilation it can be seen that chitin is found in most of the true fungi, except for the Oomycetes, which are characterized by cellulose. The Chytridiales have not been studied by modern methods; individual species have been claimed to form chitin (111, 186).

Two points need to be made in connection with the yeasts. The X-ray diffraction data of Table 3 indicate that they divide on family lines, only the mycelial yeasts having chitin. The principal cell wall material of the unicellular yeasts appears to be a polyglucose distinct from cellulose (8) with a second membrane containing a mannan-protein complex (45, 119). However, microchemical tests suggest that there is a small amount of chitin in unicellular yeasts; glucosamine can be isolated (45, 145). The amount present in these yeasts is probably so small as to escape detection by the X-ray diffraction method.

The amount of chitin produced is lower in a medium with nitrate than in one with ammonium ion as the nitrogen source (7, 152); this may be a pH effect. Autolytic loss of chitin is said to occur in nitrate but not in ammonium media (7).

Although it is probable that other materials are more or less closely associated with chitin in the cell wall, unambiguous evidence of such association is lacking. Pectic materials, protein, lipids, cellulose, callose, and minerals have all been suggested (47, 103, 104, 178–181). The cellulose problem is considered by Castle (23) and by Farr (46). In *Herpomyces stylopygae,* parasitic on insects, histochemical studies indicate the presence in the basal shield of a chitin-protein layer, and a process of sclerotization similar to that in the development of insect cuticle may take place (141).

Chitin appears not to occur in the actinomycetes (57a); staining reactions of *Streptomyces* spp. are the basis of a suggestion that a lipid layer is associated, perhaps loosely, with the spore wall (43).

The sheath surrounding the stalk of *Dictyostelium discoideum* is composed of cellulose, laid down extracellularly (137).

Callose, described by Mangin (105) and by Thomas (179), appears to be an acidic polyglucose; its relation to the cell wall itself is uncertain and cannot at present be accepted.

A material identified as lignin occurs in relatively large amounts in several fungi (128, 177). The identification rests on solubility characteristics alone, and it seems very doubtful that the substance is chemically the same as the lignin of higher plants (69, 155, 165).

4. CELLULAR CARBOHYDRATES

In this section are included polysaccharides and related compounds exclusive of chitin, just discussed. Some of these may be found later to be associated with the cell wall, and others appear in the medium as well as the mycelium. Characteristically, cells grown on high-carbohydrate media are rich in polysaccharides; for example, the mycelium of *Aspergillus niger* may be 25 per cent polysaccharide (148).

The first fungal polysaccharide to be studied was that of *Penicillium glaucum* spores, named "spore starch" by Cramer (29). In the period from 1894 to about 1925 several polysaccharides were described, but with few exceptions the criteria of identification were inadequate and the nature of the materials remains in doubt. These early studies have been reviewed by Dox and Neidig (36) and by Schmidt (149). It need only be pointed out here that none of the presumed identifications with the starch of higher plants is based on sufficient evidence.

Fungal polysaccharides of known or partially known constitution are listed in Table 4. Most are formed by species of *Penicillium* and *Aspergillus,* but this may only mirror the more intensive study which has been devoted to these genera. The most common sugar component is glucose, the next most common galactose.

Galactocarolose is distinguished by two unusual features: galactose is in the furanose form, and the galactose units are joined by a 1,5-glycosidic bond (76). It has been speculated that the galactofuranose structure may be metabolically related to the tetronic acid derivatives also formed by *Penicillium charlesii* (Chapter 6).

The glycogen of fungi is chemically identical with or very similar to that of animals (40) and occurs also in yeast (118). The fraction appearing as glycogen in routine analyses usually comprises about 5 per cent of the mycelial or spore dry weight (140, 171), but in the sclerotia of *Phymatotrichum omnivorum* the glycogen content is 36.7 per cent (40).

Polysaccharides of which the constitution is not fully known include especially the hemicelluloses, defined by their solubility and ease of hydrolysis. The crude hemicellulose fraction of *Aspergillus niger* constitutes 12 to 31 per cent of the dry matter of the mycelium, and is, like several other constituents of the mycelium, profoundly affected by the supply of metals in the medium (129, 156). Pentosans have been isolated as about 1 per cent of the dry matter of fungi (35, 150), but the possibility that these materials are in fact hemicelluloses can-

Table 4. Polysaccharides of Fungi and Actinomycetes*

Polysaccharide	Hydrolysis Product(s)	Organism
Glycogen	Glucose	*Aspergillus niger* (171), *Phymatotrichum omnivorum* (40, 41, 42)
Sclerotiose	Glucose	*Penicillium sclerotiorum* (2)
Compactose	Glucose	*Penicillium brevi-compactum* (65)
Nigeran (mycodextran)	Glucose	*Aspergillus niger* (6, 34), *Penicillium* spp. ‡ (36, 185)
Polyglucose	Glucose	*Aspergillus fischeri* (116, 117)
Polyglucose	Glucose	*Pencillium charlesii* (14)
Acidic polyglucose	Glucose	*Penicillium luteum* (55)
Capsular polyglucose	Glucose	*Torulopsis* spp. (101, 102)
Luteic acid	Beta-glucose, malonic acid	*Penicillium luteum* (3)
Varianose	Glucose, galactose†	*Penicillium varians* (75)
Capreolinose	Glucose, mannose, galactose, malonic acid	*Penicillium capreolinum* (26)
Polyuronide (?)	Glucose, galacturonic acid†	*Coccidioides immitis* (72)
Levan	Fructose	*Aspergillus sydowi* (95)
Polyfructose	Fructose	*Streptomyces* sp. (183)
Polygalactose	Galactose	*Penicillium charlesii* (27)
Rugulose	Galactose	*Penicillium rugulosus* (26)
Mycogalactan	Galactose	*Aspergillus niger* (37)
Neutral polygalactose	Galactose	*Penicillium luteum* (55)
Galactocarolose	Galactose	*Penicillium charlesii* (76)
Mannocarolose	Mannose	*Penicillium charlesii* (73–75)
Capsular polysaccharide	Xylose, mannose, glucuronic acid	*Cryptococcus* (*Torulopsis*) *neoformans* (38, 44)
Capsular pentosan	Xylose	*Torulopsis* spp. (101, 102)

* Including only those polysaccharides for which some information on structure is available.
† All hydrolysis products not identified.
‡ Identification uncertain.

not be excluded.   Mannans are common in yeasts but not in fungi (59).

5. NITROGENOUS CONSTITUENTS

The total amount of nitrogen in mycelium is usually determined by the Kjehldahl method, which is only approximately complete.   Heck

(78) found the total nitrogen of cultivated fungi to range from 2.27 per cent of the dry weight in *Coprinus radians* to 5.13 per cent in *Trichoderma lignorum;* sporophores from nature had as little as 1.56 per cent nitrogen. These data are fairly typical, although fungi grown in culture may be as high as 7.6 per cent nitrogen (115, 132). Different species of *Tricholoma* vary from 3.1 to 7.7 per cent nitrogen (114).

Measurements of total nitrogen are, however, not highly significant, by reason of the susceptibility of the value to environmental influences and its variation with developmental status. Characteristically, young mycelium is higher in nitrogen than old (7); during autolysis both proteins and other nitrogen compounds are liberated into the medium (Chapter 1). In *Aspergillus niger,* the onset of sporulation is coincident with a decline in mycelial protein (168).

The most important single influence on the total nitrogen content is the concentration of nitrogen in the medium; an increase in the amount of available nitrogen is accompanied by a significant—as much as threefold—increase in cell nitrogen (78, 81, 166, 173).

The nitrogen source used also exerts an influence on the total nitrogen of the mycelium; in general, the nitrogen content is higher when ammonium salts are used than when nitrates provide the nitrogen (93, 170, 173, 194). The cause of this effect is uncertain; either the low pH incident upon utilization of ammonium ion reduces autolytic loss of nitrogen, or the nitrate is simply less available to the cell for synthesis.

Fractionation of the total nitrogen of the cell reveals that only about 60–70 percent is in proteins (67, 165); still lower values have been reported (99). Determination of cellular protein by calculation from total nitrogen is therefore inadmissible in principle, although most protein determinations have been made in this way.

A few specific proteins have been described (20, 28, 112, 125), but no general or systematic study of fungal proteins has been undertaken. Michel-Durand (107) found indications of phosphoproteins in *Aspergillus niger.* Qualitatively, the amino acids of fungal proteins are much the same as those of other proteins; surveys of the amino acids in hydrolyzates of *Aspergillus flavus* (127), *Penicillium chrysogenum* (135), *Ustilago zeae* (32), and *Venturia inaequalis* (124) have been made by chromatography of the acid hydrolysate, and indicate a general similarity among these diverse fungi, with minor qualitative differences.

Quantitative analyses of the amino acids in hydrolysates of cellular material of fungi and actinomycetes (168, 191) similarly do not reveal any striking differences between these and higher organisms when all proteins are hydrolysed together.

The biological utilization of fungal proteins has been studied in two contexts. Mycelium added to the soil is decomposed by the microflora about as rapidly as are other organic materials (78). Norman (115) could find no evidence of a decay-resistant nitrogenous fraction in mycelium (89). In animal nutrition, the utilizability of fungus proteins is generally low, i.e., they do not support growth of the rat (49–52, 162, 163, 189). The nutritional value of fungal proteins is reviewed by Thatcher (175); the mycelium of some fungi is toxic to laboratory animals, but the underlying mechanism—whether an amino acid deficiency or a toxic substance—is not known.

The non-protein nitrogen of the fungus cell consists of chitin, already discussed, nucleic acids, free amino acids, and miscellaneous nitrogen compounds of low molecular weight. The nucleic acid of *Penicillium* spp. accounts for 4 per cent of the total nitrogen and about 1 per cent of the dry weight (1, 165). These findings cast some doubt on earlier claims, reviewed by Akasi (1), of high nucleic acid concentrations in fungi. Spores of *Penicillium* spp. contain 158–592 μg ribonucleic acid per billion (33). The conidia of *Aspergillus nidulans* contain measurable deoxyribonucleic acid and the amount is, as in other organisms, twice as high in diploid as in haploid cells (77).

Free amino acids occur in fungus mycelium (31, 68, 109, 120, 127, 158, 190) and are also found in the culture medium (32, 109, 135).

The other nitrogenous constituents known in fungi include many different and unrelated compounds, several of which are discussed in Chapter 8. Nitrogen bases and amines have been found (90, 171, 197) possibly arising by degradation of larger molecules during analysis. Cyclic choline sulfate has been isolated from fungi (31, 167, 192). Urea appears to be a frequent constituent of the higher basidiomycetes (88), and constitutes 3.9 per cent of the total nitrogen of *Aspergillus fischeri* mycelium (67). Allantoic acid has been reported in appreciable amounts in the sporophores of Agaricales (54) and may be one precursor of urea (Chapter 8).

6. CELL LIPIDS

The total lipid content of fungus mycelium, usually expressed as a percentage of the dry weight, is so strongly affected by cultural conditions and age that any set of figures is misleading. The effect of these conditions is brought out especially well in a survey by Walker and co-workers (110, 160, 188); some of the known environmental factors determining fat content are discussed in Chapter 6. High fat values—20 per cent or more of the dry weight—are found among species and strains of *Aspergillus, Endomyces, Fusarium, Mucor, Oospora, Penicillium,* and *Torula* (10, 48, 110, 131, 132, 160, 161, 185, 188), and in individual species of other genera (147, 157, 188). The highest fat contents reported are about 50 per cent of the dry weight (10, 110). Conidia of common saprophytic fungi do not have unusually high fat contents, but the sclerotia of *Claviceps purpurea* contain 43 per cent lipids (154) and uredospores of *Puccinia graminis tritici* are high in fat (Chapter 12).

Some variation in apparent lipid content arises from the use of different methods of extraction; these are discussed with reference to the fungi by Peck (122) and by Bernhauer and others (11).

In Table 5 are collected a few partial analyses of fungal lipids. The

Table 5. Lipids of Fungi

Organism	Iodine Number	Acid Number	Phospha-tides*	Unsapon-ifiable Matter*	Sterols*
Aspergillus niger (13)	95.1	71.2	—	12.0	1.4†
Aspergillus sydowi (169)	114.4	43.4	Present	8.2	5.4
Blastomyces dermatitidis (123)	106.1	45.3	24.3	8.0	—
Fusarium graminearum (108)	84.7	—	—	2.1	—
Penicillium javanicum (184)	84.0	10.6	—	2.0	—
Phycomyces blakesleeanus (9)	—	—	9.9	5.3	4.0†

* As per cent of total lipid.
† Ergosterol.

most striking feature is the usually very high proportion of free fatty acids; up to 88 per cent of the readily extractible lipids may be free acids (138). However, it should be noted that the content of free acid is markedly affected by cultural conditions. In *Penicillium javanicum* the acid number rises from 10.6 to 50.7 as the glucose level of the medium is increased from 20 to 40 per cent (185). In general, any factor which increases fat formation also increases the relative amount of free fatty acids (138). It should also be noted that *Aspergillus nidulans* lipids are very low in free acid (161), as are sclerotia of *Claviceps purpurea* (197). It seems possible that lipase action during preparation of the mycelium may contribute to the high apparent acid value of fungal lipids.

The fatty acid composition of some fungal lipids is summarized in Table 6. These and other data (10, 53, 97) show that the 16- and 18-carbon acids are the most abundant, and that with few exceptions the unsaturated acids—especially oleic and linoleic—predominate. The low Reichert-Meissl number of fungal lipids reflects the relative absence of the lower fatty acids (10).

The antibiotic activity of a strain of *Penicillium crustosum* has been traced to the presence of linoleic acid in its mycelium (142).

A number of fatty acids which are not known to be constituents of fats have been isolated from fungi. Three of these—agaric, spiculisporic, and mineoluteic acids—are long chain hydroxy-tricarboxy acids similar to some of the lichen acids (136). *Actinomyces* (*Streptomyces*) *flavus* forms a wax, the dodecyl ester of 5-keto-octadecanoic acid (82), and 6-keto-octadecanoic acid has been isolated from sporophores of *Lactarius* spp. (21). The ustilic acids, identified as di- and trihydroxy-hexadecanoic acids, occur as constituents of the glucolipid ustilagic acid, a metabolic product of *Ustilago zeae* (98).

The phosphatides, determined by their solubility, are usually less than 10 per cent of the total lipid, but in *Blastomyces dermatitidis* may amount to as much as one-third of the lipid fraction (122). In *Aspergillus* spp. the phosphatides constitute at least 0.15 to 0.7 per cent of the dry weight (138, 193).

Excluding earlier studies, reviewed by Czapek (30), which employed inadequate methods, well-characterized phosphatides are a lecithin and a cephalin from *Aspergillus sydowi* (193) and a lecithin and a cephalin, not identical with these, from *Blastomyces dermatitidis* (122). These have been characterized by their physical properties and their hydrolysis products; structures have not been determined. In addition, a cephalin fraction from *Neurospora crassa* has been described and evidently comprises more than one compound, since both serine and ethanolamine are present (39). The phospholipid fraction of *Penicillium chrysogenum* yields inositol phosphate (84), and an inositol phospholipid occurs in *Neurospora crassa* (57). Similarly the positive Molisch reaction of the acetone-insoluble lipids of several fungi indicates that a carbohydrate-containing phospholipid may be present (122).

The mycelium of *Aspergillus sydowi* contains at least 0.1–0.4 per cent of a cerebrin (19); this partially characterized nitrogenous lipid is probably identical with that isolated earlier from yeast, *Claviceps purpurea,* and from the sporophores of several basidiomycetes. The

Table 6. The Fatty Acid Composition of Fungal Lipids*

Acid	Aspergillus nidulans (161)	A. sydowi (169)	Penicillium javanicum (184)	Penicillium sp. (80)	Phycomyces blakesleeanus (9)	Penicillium lilacinum (159)
Myristic (dodecanoic)	0.7	—	—	3.5	—	0.1
Palmitic (tetradecanoic)	20.9	10.9	23.4	40.5	23.7	32.3
Stearic (octadecanoic)	15.9	13.6	9.4	7.9	4.7	9.4
Arachidic (eicosanoic)	} 1.4 {	—	—	1.1	—	1.4
Behenic (docosanoic)		—	—	—	1.7	—
Lignoceric (tetracosanoic)	—	1.1	0.8	—	2.1	—
Hexacosanoic	—	—	—	—	1.3	3.4
Hexadecenoic	1.2	—	—	7.9 (?)	—	—
Oleic (octadecenoic)	40.3	36.7	34.6	19.0	29.6	38.6
Linoleic (octadecadienoic)	17.0	20.0	31.8	20.1	25.8	13.4
Linolenic (octadecatrienoic)	0.2	—	—	—	3.4	—
Tetracosenoic	—	—	—	—	2.9	—
Hexacosenoic†	—	—	—	—	4.9	—

* As per cent of the total fatty acids after saponification.

† Unidentified as to structure.

occurrence and the chemistry of the cerebrins are reviewed by Celmer and Carter (24).

Virtually all fungi appear to form sterols. The amount in mycelium is usually about 1 per cent or less of the dry weight. Comprehensive surveys have been made by Pruess and others (132–134): the sterol content was found to be affected by the growth medium, the highest level attained being 1.70 per cent of the dry weight, in *Paecilomyces varioti*. Different isolates assigned to *Aspergillus niger* vary in sterol content from 0.23 to 1.16 per cent (12). A more recent survey (4) finds that the sterol content of fungi ranges from zero, in *Colletotrichum graminicolum*, to 2.2 per cent of the dry weight, in *Penicillium westlingii*.

The principal sterol of fungi is ergosterol; a dihydro derivative, fungisterol, occurs in ergot (174). Ergosterol occurs as the palmitate in *Penicillium* spp. (121) and *Aspergillus fumigatus* (187). Other sterols have been only tentatively identified (70, 71, 146).

The metabolism of exogenous steroids and the composition of the carotenoid pigments are considered elsewhere (Chapter 6).

BIBLIOGRAPHY

1. Akasi, S. 1939. *J. Biochem.* (*Tokyo*) 29: 21–29.
2. Albericci, V. J., T. P. Curtin, and D. Reilly. 1943. *Biochem. J.* (*London*) 37: 243–246.
3. Anderson, C. G., W. N. Haworth, H. Raistrick, and M. Stacey. 1939. *Biochem. J.* (*London*) 33: 272–279.
4. Appleton, G. S., R. J. Kieber, and W. J. Payne. 1955. *Appl. Microbiol.* 3: 249–251.
5. Bajaj, V., S. P. Damle, and P. S. Krishnan. 1954. *Arch. Biochem. Biophys.* 50: 451–460.
6. Barker, S. A., E. J. Bourne, and M. Stacey. 1953. *J. Chem. Soc.* (*London*) 1953: 3084–3090.
7. Behr, G. 1930. *Arch. Mikrobiol.* 1: 418–444.
8. Bell, D. J. and D. H. Northcote. 1950. *J. Chem. Soc.* (*London*) 1950: 1944–1947.
9. Bernhard, K. and H. Albrecht. 1948. *Helv. Chim. Acta* 31: 977–988.
10. Bernhauer, K. 1943. *Ergeb. Enzymforsch.* 9: 297–360.
11. Bernhauer, K., P. Müller, and E. Theile. 1950. *Biochem. Z.* 320: 294–298.
12. Bernhauer, K. and G. Patzelt. 1935. *Biochem. Z.* 280: 388–393.
13. Bernhauer, K. and G. Posselt. 1937. *Biochem. Z.* 294: 215–220.
14. Birkinshaw, J. H., J. H. V. Charles, and H. Raistrick. 1931. *Phil. Trans. Roy. Soc. London, Ser. B* 220: 355–362.
15. Blackwell, E. 1940. *Trans. Brit. Mycol. Soc.* 24: 68–86.
16. Blank, F. 1953. *Biochim. et Biophys. Acta* 10: 110–113.
17. Blank, F. 1954. *Can. J. Microbiol.* 1: 1–5.
18. Blumenthal, H. J. and S. Roseman. 1957. *J. Bacteriol.* 74: 222–224.
19. Bohonos, N. and W. H. Peterson. 1943. *J. Biol. Chem.* 149: 295–300.

20. Bohonos, N., D. W. Woolley, and W. H. Peterson. 1942. *Arch. Biochem.* 1: 319–324.
21. Bougalt, J. and C. Charoux. 1911. *Compt. rend. (Paris)* 153: 572–573.
22. Buston, H. W. and A. H. Khan. 1956. *J. Gen. Microbiol.* 14: 655–660.
23. Castle, E. S. 1945. *Am. J. Botany* 32: 148–151.
24. Celmer, W. D. and H. E. Carter. 1952. *Physiol. Revs.* 32: 167–196.
25. Chatfield, C. and G. Adams. 1940. *U. S. Dept. Agr. Circ.* 549: 1–91.
26. Clutterbuck, P. W. 1936. *J. Soc. Chem. Ind. (London)* 55: 55T–61T.
27. Clutterbuck, P. W., W. N. Haworth, H. Raistrick, G. Smith, and M. Stacey. 1934. *Biochem. J. (London)* 28: 94–110.
28. Clutterbuck, P. W., R. Lovell, and H. Raistrick. 1932. *Biochem. J. (London)* 26: 1907–1918.
29. Cramer, E. 1894. *Arch. Hyg.* 20: 197–210.
29a. Cummins, C. S. and H. Harris. 1958. *J. Gen. Microbiol.* 18: 173–189.
30. Czapek, F. 1922. *Biochemie der Pflanzen*, 3d ed., Vol. 1. Jena: Gustav Fischer, pp. 828.
31. DeFlines, J. 1955. *J. Am. Chem. Soc.* 77: 1676–1677.
32. DeVay, J. E. 1954. *Phytopathology* 44: 583–587.
33. Dirkx, J. 1952. *Biochim. et Biophys. Acta* 8: 194–201.
34. Dox, A. W. 1915. *J. Biol. Chem.* 20: 83–85.
35. Dox, A. W. and R. E. Neidig. 1911. *J. Biol. Chem.* 9: 267–269.
36. Dox, A. W. and R. E. Neidig. 1914a. *J. Biol. Chem.* 18: 167–175.
37. Dox, A. W. and R. E. Neidig. 1914b. *J. Biol. Chem.* 19: 235–237.
38. Drouhet, E., G. Segretain, and J.-P. Aubert. 1950. *Ann. inst. Pasteur* 79: 891–900.
39. Ellman, G. L. and H. K. Mitchell. 1954. *J. Am. Chem. Soc.* 76: 4028–4030.
40. Ergle, D. R. 1947. *J. Am. Chem. Soc.* 69: 2061–2062.
41. Ergle, D. R. 1948. *Phytopathology* 28: 142–151.
42. Ergle, D. R. and L. M. Blank. 1947. *Phytopathology* 37: 153–161.
43. Erikson, D. 1947. *J. Gen. Microbiol.* 1: 39–44.
44. Evans, E. E. and R. J. Theriault. 1953. *J. Bacteriol.* 65: 571–577.
45. Falcone, G. and W. J. Nickerson. 1956. *Science* 124: 272–273.
46. Farr, W. K. 1954. *Trans. N. Y. Acad. Sci. II,* 16: 209–214.
47. Farr, W. K. and S. H. Eckerson. 1934. *Contribs. Boyce Thompson Inst.* 6: 189–203.
48. Fink, H., H. Haehn, and W. Hoerburger. 1937. *Chemiker-Ztg.* 61: 689–693, 723–726, 744–747.
49. Fink, H. and A. Hock. 1947. *Z. Naturforsch.* 2 (b): 187–203.
50. Fink, H., I. Schlie, and U. Ruge. 1953a. *Z. physiol. Chem. Hoppe-Seyler's.* 292: 251–263.
51. Fink, H., I. Schlie, and U. Ruge. 1953b. *Z. physiol. Chem. Hoppe-Seyler's.* 293: 264–267.
52. Fink, H., I. Schlie, and U. Ruge. 1953c. *Z. physiol. Chem. Hoppe-Seyler's.* 294: 123–128.
53. Fiore, J. V. 1948. *Arch. Biochem.* 16: 161–168.
54. Fosse, R. and A. Brunel. 1933. *Compt. rend. (Paris)* 197: 288–290.
55. Freeman, G. G. and C. S. Macpherson. 1949. *Biochem. J. (London)* 45: 179–185.
56. Frey, R. 1950. *Ber. schweiz. botan. Ges.* 60: 199–230.
57. Fuller, R. C. and E. L. Tatum. 1956. *Am. J. Botany* 43: 361–365.
58. Garner, H. H. et al. 1953. *Am. J. Botany* 40: 289–296.
59. Garzuly-Janke, R. 1940. *Zentr. Bakteriol. Parasitenk. Abt. II,* 102: 361–365.
60. Gäumann, E. 1949. *Die Pilze.* Basel: Verlag Birkhäuser, pp. 382.
61. Gayet, J. 1948a. *Bull. soc. chim. biol.* 30: 488–496.
62. Gayet, J. 1948b. *Bull. soc. chim. biol.* 30: 542–547.

63. Gayet, J. 1949a. *Bull. soc. chim. biol.* 31: 796–800.
64. Gayet, J. 1949b. *Bull. soc. chim. biol.* 31: 1046–1051.
65. Godin, P. 1953. *Biochim. et Biophys. Acta* 12: 528–532.
66. Gonell, H. W. 1926. *Z. physiol. Chem. Hoppe-Seyler's.* 152: 18–30.
67. Gorcica, H. J., W. H. Peterson, and H. Steenbock, 1934. *Biochem. J. (London)* 28: 504–511.
68. Gordon, M., P. Numerof, and S. C. Pan. 1954. *J. Am. Chem. Soc.* 76: 4037–4038.
69. Gottlieb, S. and M. J. Pelczar, Jr. 1951. *Bacteriol. Revs.* 15: 55–77.
70. Gruber, W. and G. Proske. 1951. *Monatsh. Chem.* 82: 255–258.
71. Guider, J. M., T. G. Halsall, and E. R. H. Jones. 1954. *J. Chem. Soc. (London)* 1954: 4471–4475.
72. Hassid, W. A., E. E. Baker, and R. M. McCready. 1943. *J. Biol. Chem.* 149: 303-311.
73. Haworth, W. N., E. L. Hirst, F. Isherwood, and J. K. N. Jones. 1939. *J. Chem. Soc. (London)* 1939: 1878–1880.
74. Haworth, W. N., H. Raistrick, and M. Stacey. 1935a. *Biochem. J. (London)* 29: 612–621.
75. Haworth, W. N., H. Raistrick, and M. Stacey. 1935b. *Biochem. J. (London)* 29: 2668–2678.
76. Haworth, W. N., H. Raistrick, and M. Stacey. 1937. *Biochem. J. (London)* 31: 640–644.
77. Heagy, F. C. and J. A. Roper. 1952. *Nature (London)* 170: 713–714.
78. Heck, A. F. 1929. *Soil Sci.* 27: 1–46.
79. Heyn, A. N. J. 1936. *Protoplasma* 25: 372–396.
80. Hilditch, T. P. et al. 1944. *J. Soc. Chem. Ind. (London)* 63: 112–114.
81. Hilpert, R. S., G. Friesen, and W. Rossée. 1937. *Biochem. Z.* 289: 193–197.
82. Hirata, Y. and K. Nakanishi. 1949. *Bull. Chem. Soc. Japan* 22: 121–127.
83. Houlahan, M. B. and H. K. Mitchell. 1948. *Arch. Biochem.* 19: 257–264.
84. Imai, Y. 1950. *J. Japan. Biochem. Soc.* 22: 192–196. (*Chem. Abstr.* 45: 9121, 1951.)
85. Ingelman, B. 1950. In J. B. Sumner and K. Myrbäck (eds.), *The Enzymes*, Vol. 1 (1), p. 511–516. New York: Academic Press.
86. Ingelman, B. and H. Malmgren. 1950. *Acta Chem. Scand.* 4: 478–486.
87. Iterson, G. van, Jr., K. H. Meyer, and W. Lotmar. 1936. *Rec. trav. chim.* 55: 61–63.
88. Iwanoff, N. N. 1927. *Z. physiol. Chem. Hoppe-Seyler's.* 170: 274–288.
89. Jensen, H. L. 1932. *J. Agr. Sci.* 22: 1–25.
90. Keil, W. and H. Bartmann. 1935. *Biochem. Z.* 280: 58–60.
91. Khouvine, Y. 1932. *Compt. rend. (Paris)* 195: 396–397.
92. Kita, D. A. and W. H. Peterson. 1953. *J. Biol. Chem.* 203: 861–868.
93. Klotz, L. J. 1923. *Ann. Missouri Botan. Garden* 10: 299–368.
94. König, J. 1920. *Chemie der Nahrungs- und Genussmittel sowie der Gerbrauchsgegenstände*, Vol. 2. Berlin: Julius Springer, pp. 932.
95. Kopeloff, N., L. Kopeloff, and C. J. Welcome. 1920. *J. Biol. Chem.* 43: 171–187.
96. Krishnan, P. S. and V. Bajaj. 1953. *Arch. Biochem. Biophys.* 47: 39–55.
97. Kroeker, E. H., F. M. Strong, and W. H. Peterson. 1935. *J. Am. Chem. Soc.* 57: 354–356.
98. Lemieux, R. U. 1953. *Can. J. Chem.* 31: 396–417.
99. Lim, H. 1935. *J. Fac. Agr. Hokkaido Imp. Univ. (Sapporo, Japan)* 37: 165–209.
100. Luz, G. 1934. *Phytopathol. Z.* 7: 585–638.
101. Mager, J. 1947. *Biochem. J. (London)* 41: 603–609.
102. Mager, J. and M. Aschner. 1947. *J. Bacteriol.* 53: 283–295.

103. Mangin, L. 1890. *Compt. rend. (Paris)* 110: 644–647.
104. Mangin, L. 1899. *J. de Botan.* 13: 209–216, 276–287, 307–316, 339–348, 371–378.
105. Mangin, L. 1910. *Compt. rend. (Paris)* 151: 279–283.
106. Mann, T. 1944. *Biochem. J. (London)* 38: 345–351.
107. Michel-Durand, E. 1938. *Bull. soc. chim. biol.* 20: 399–412.
108. Mull, R. P. and F. F. Nord. 1944. *Arch. Biochem.* 5: 283–290.
109. Murray, H. C. and F. P. Zscheile. 1956. *Phytopathology* 46: 363–366.
110. Murray, S., M. Woodbine, and T. K. Walker. 1953. *J. Exp. Botany* 4: 251–256.
111. Nabel, K. 1939. *Arch. Mikrobiol.* 10: 515–541.
112. Nelson, C. I. 1933. *J. Agr. Research* 46: 183–186.
113. Nord, F. F., H. Hofstetter, and E. Dammann. 1937. *Biochem. Z.* 293: 231–255.
114. Norkrans, B. 1950. *Symbolae Botan. Upsalienses* 11 (1): 5–126.
115. Norman, A. G. 1933. *Ann. Appl. Biol.* 20: 146–164.
116. Norman, A. G. and W. H. Peterson. 1932. *Biochem. J. (London)* 26: 1946–1953.
117. Norman, A. G., W. H. Peterson, and R. C. Houtz. 1932. *Biochem. J. (London)* 26: 1934–1945.
118. Northcote, D. H. 1953. *Biochem. J. (London)* 53: 348–352.
119. Northcote, D. H. and R. W. Horne. 1952. *Biochem. J. (London)* 51: 231–236.
120. Okazaki, K., S. Koyama, and O. Tamemasa. 1955. *J. Pharm. Soc. Japan* 75: 1090–1093.
121. Oxford, A. E. and H. Raistrick. 1933. *Biochem. J. (London)* 27: 1176–1180.
122. Peck, R. L. 1947. In W. J. Nickerson (ed.), *Biology of Pathogenic Fungi*, p. 167–188. Waltham, Mass.: Chronica Botanica Co.
123. Peck, R. L. and C. R. Hauser. 1938. *J. Am. Chem. Soc.* 60: 2599–2603.
124. Pelletier, R. L. and G. W. Keitt. 1954. *Am. J. Botany* 41: 362–371.
125. Petermann, M. L., M. G. Hamilton, and H. C. Reilly. 1952. *Arch. Biochem. Biophys.* 37: 117–130.
126. Peterson, W. H., E. B. Fred, and E. G. Schmidt. 1922. *J. Biol. Chem.* 54: 19–34.
127. Pillai, N. C. and K. S. Srinivasan. 1956. *J. Gen. Microbiol.* 14: 248–255.
128. Pinck, L. A. and F. E. Allison. 1944. *Soil Sci.* 57: 155–161.
129. Porges, N. 1932. *Botan. Gaz.* 94: 197–205.
130. Porter, J. R. 1946. *Bacterial Chemistry and Physiology.* New York: John Wiley and Sons, pp. 1073.
131. Prill, E. A., P. R. Wenck, and W. H. Peterson. 1935. *Biochem. J. (London)* 29: 21–33.
132. Pruess, L. M., E. C. Eichinger, and W. H. Peterson. 1934. *Zentr. Bakteriol. Parasitenk. Abt. II,* 89: 370–377.
133. Pruess, L. M., H. J. Gorcica, H. C. Greene, and W. H. Peterson. 1932. *Biochem. Z.* 246: 401–413.
134. Pruess, L. M., W. H. Peterson, H. Steenbock, and E. B. Fred. 1931. *J. Biol. Chem.* 90: 369–384.
135. Pyle, A. J. H. 1954. *J. Gen. Microbiol.* 11: 191–194.
136. Raistrick, H. 1950. *Proc. Roy. Soc. (London)* B 136: 481–508.
137. Raper, K. B. and D. I. Fennell. 1952. *Bull. Torrey Botan. Club* 79: 25–51.
138. Raveux, R. 1948. *Bull. soc. chim. biol.* 30: 357–366.
139. Rennerfelt, E. 1934. *Planta* 22: 221–239.
140. Reuter, C. 1912. *Z. physiol. Chem. Hoppe-Seyler's.* 78: 167–245.
141. Richards, A. G. 1954. *Science* 120: 761–762.
142. Riley, R. F. and D. K. Miller. 1948. *Arch. Biochem.* 18: 13–26.
143. Rippel, A. and G. Behr. 1930. *Arch. Mikrobiol.* 1: 271–276.
144. Rippel, A. and G. Behr. 1934. *Arch. Mikrobiol.* 5: 561–577.

145. Rolelofsen, P. A. and I. Hoette. 1951. *Antonie van Leeuwenhoek J. Microbiol. Serol.* 17: 297–313.
146. Saito, A. 1953. *J. Fermentation Technol.* (*Japan*) 31: 140–141, 141–145, 328–333. (*Chem. Abstr.* 48: 5275–5276. 1954.)
147. Satina, S. and A. F. Blakeslee. 1928. *Proc. Nat. Acad. Sci. U. S.* 14: 308–316.
148. Schmidt, C. F., Jr. 1935. *J. Biol. Chem.* 110: 511–520.
149. Schmidt, D. 1925. *Biochem. Z.* 158: 223–252.
150. Schmidt, E. G., W. H. Peterson, and E. B. Fred. 1923. *Soil Sci.* 15: 479–488.
151. Schmidt, G. 1951. In W. D. McElroy and B. Glass (eds.), *Phosphorus Metabolism*, Vol. 1, p. 443–475. Baltimore: Johns Hopkins Press.
152. Schmidt, M. 1936. *Arch. Mikrobiol.* 7: 241–260.
153. Scholl, E. 1908. *Monatsh. Chem.* 29: 1023–1037.
154. Schönborn, W. 1955. *Arch. Mikrobiol.* 22: 408–431.
155. Schubert, W. J. and F. F. Nord. 1950. *J. Am. Chem. Soc.* 72: 5337–5338.
156. Schulz, G. 1937. *Planta* 27: 196–218.
157. Shu, P. and J. A. Thorn. 1952. *Can. J. Botany* 30: 252–265.
158. Simonart, P. and K. Y. Chow. 1954. *Antonie van Leeuwenhoek J. Microbiol. Serol.* 20: 174–180, 210–216.
159. Singh, J., S. Shah, and T. K. Walker. 1956. *Biochem. J.* (*London*) 62: 222–224.
160. Singh, J. and T. K. Walker. 1956. *Biochem. J.* (*London*) 62: 286–289.
161. Singh, J., T. K. Walker, and M. L. Meara. 1955. *Biochem. J.* (*London*) 61: 85–88.
162. Skinner, C. E. 1934. *J. Bacteriol.* 28: 95–106.
163. Skinner, J. T., W. H. Peterson, and H. Steenbock. 1933. *Biochem. Z.* 267: 169–178.
164. Smith, A. M. 1936. *J. Soc. Chem. Ind.* (*London*) 55: 217T–221T.
165. Smithies, W. R. 1952. *Biochem. J.* (*London*) 51: 259–264.
166. Steinberg, R. A. and J. D. Bowling. 1939. *J. Agr. Research* 58: 717–732.
167. Stevens, C. M. and P. Vohra. 1955. *J. Am. Chem. Soc.* 77: 4935–4936.
168. Stokes, J. L. and M. Gunness. 1946. *J. Bacteriol.* 52: 195–207.
169. Strong, F. M. and W. H. Peterson. 1934. *J. Am. Chem. Soc.* 56: 952–955.
170. Subramaniam, C. V. and K. V. Srinivasa Pai. 1953. *Proc. Indian Acad. Sci.* 37B: 149–157.
171. Sumi, M. 1928. *Biochem. Z.* 195: 161–174.
172. Takata, F. 1929. *J. Soc. Chem. Ind. Japan* 32: 497–510, 544–547. (*Chem. Abstr.* 23: 4748. 1929.)
173. Tamiya, H. 1942. *Advances in Enzymol.* 2: 183–238.
174. Tanret, C. 1908. *Compt. rend.* (*Paris*) 147: 75–77.
175. Thatcher, F. S. 1954. *Ann. Rev. Microbiol.* 8: 449–472.
176. Thimann, K. V. 1955. *The Life of Bacteria.* New York: The Macmillan Company, pp. 775.
177. Thom, C. and M. Phillips. 1932. *J. Wash. Acad. Sci.* 22: 237–239.
178. Thomas, R. C. 1928. *Am. J. Botany* 15: 537–547.
179. Thomas, R. C. 1930. *Am. J. Botany* 17: 779–788.
180. Thomas, R. C. 1942. *Ohio J. Sci.* 42: 60–62.
181. Thomas, R. C. 1943. *Ohio J. Sci.* 43: 135–138.
182. Todd, G. W. and J. Levitt. 1951. *Plant Physiol.* 26: 331–336.
183. Veibel, S. 1938. *Biochem. J.* (*London*) 32: 1949–1953.
184. Ward, G. E. and G. S. Jamieson. 1934. *J. Am. Chem. Soc.* 56: 973–975.
185. Ward, G. E., L. B. Lockwood, O. E. May, and H. T. Herrick. 1935. *Ind. Eng. Chem.* 27: 318–322.
186. Wettstein, F. von. 1921. *Sitzber. Akad. Wiss. Wien, Math.-naturw. Kl. Abt. I,* 130: 3–20.
187. Wieland, P. and V. Prelog. 1947. *Helv. Chim. Acta* 30: 1028–1030.

54   THE COMPOSITION OF FUNGUS CELLS

188. Woodbine, M., M. E. Gregory, and T. K. Walker. 1951. *J. Exp. Botany* 2: 204–211.
189. Woodman, H. E. and R. E. Evans. 1947. *J. Agr. Sci.* 37: 81–93.
190. Woolley, D. W. and W. H. Peterson, 1936. *J. Biol. Chem.* 114: 85–90.
191. Woolley, D. W. and W. H. Peterson. 1937a. *J. Biol. Chem.* 121: 507–520.
192. Wolley, D. W. and W. H. Peterson. 1937b. *J. Biol. Chem.* 122: 213–218.
193. Woolley, D. W., F. M. Strong, W. H. Peterson, and E. A. Prill. 1935. *J. Am. Chem. Soc.* 57: 2589–2591.
194. Yamagata, S. 1934. *Acta Phytochim. (Japan)* 8: 107–116.
195. Yarwood, C. E. 1950. *Am. J. Botany* 37: 636–639.
196. Yarwood, C. E. 1952. *Mycologia* 44: 506–522.
197. Zellner, J. 1907. *Chemie der höheren Pilze.* Leipzig: W. Engelmann, pp. 257.
198. Zellner, J. 1908. *Monatsh. Chem.* 29: 45–54.

3. Carbon Nutrition

1. PROBLEMS OF METHOD

Carbon compounds serve two essential functions in the metabolism of fungi, as of all heterotrophic organisms. They supply in the first place the carbon needed for the synthesis of the compounds which go to make up the living cell—proteins, nucleic acids, cell wall materials, reserve foods, and so on; in a typical fungus about 50 per cent of the dry weight is carbon (Chapter 2). Second, the sole source of appreciable amounts of energy is the oxidation of carbon compounds, which may account for half or more of the carbon supplied to a culture.

Knowledge of carbon nutrition, therefore, is fundamental to an understanding of the physiology of the fungi. Much valuable work has been done in this area, but it will be apparent that the data required for confident generalization are usually still lacking, and that much of our knowledge is based on experiments which are open to criticism on the ground of method.

The study of the carbon nutrition of fungi, or of other microorganisms, involves general problems of two sorts: conceptual and methodological.

The concept of utilization may have more than one operational meaning. The commonest usage describes an experiment in which a small inoculum is placed in a medium containing one major source of carbon and all other materials necessary for growth; the organism must initiate and maintain growth at the expense of the test compound. A second, more narrow, meaning of utilization is the ability of viable active mycelium to make further growth at the expense of a test compound. Here, the design usually involves providing a small amount of a utilizable carbon source and measuring the additional growth, if any, obtained from a second compound. It is often found that materials which are not by themselves satisfactory carbon sources are used in this kind of experiment; examples in particular fungi include lactose (135), sugar alcohols (150), and cellobiose (142). As discussed later, a compound which is used only in association with another carbon source is probably dependent for its metabolism on the induced synthesis of an adaptive enzyme system or upon the occurrence of mutants possessing the enzyme system.

So long as these two experimental designs are not confused, each has its place. Confusion, however, does arise if an author proposes to use the first design—one compound as the sole source of carbon—but includes other carbon sources in the medium, either as complex extracts or as amino acids. Unless the additional carbon is negligible, and this must be shown by control experiments without carbohydrate, there is the possibility that the experiment measures utilization in its second meaning rather than the one intended. Fortunately, most fungi can be grown in a synthetic medium with an inorganic nitrogen source and with pure growth factors at levels which do not contribute significant amounts of carbon.

There are several methodological errors which are common enough to deserve comment. A cluster of such errors is associated with acidity. The initial pH should be determined after sterilization, to guard against the possibility that compounds in the medium are broken down by autoclaving. Some compounds, particularly organic acids, may not enter the cell at the pH chosen, in which case it is necessary to determine whether or not the organism can tolerate a pH at which penetration is more likely. Finally, the organism itself may produce organic acids which in a poorly buffered medium lower the pH so far as to restrict growth. Media may be buffered with phosphate for most organisms; for those fungi which cannot tolerate the level of phosphate required for effective buffer action (45), the pH may be controlled by addition of sterile solid calcium carbonate after autoclaving or by inclusion of an indicator and periodic adjustment of the pH with sterile alkali (58). The only way in which these problems can be detected in a particular instance is to determine the culture pH at frequent intervals and to exercise judgment in the interpretation of growth results which may be affected by pH changes.

It is possible that metabolites other than acids may accumulate in inhibitory concentrations; for example, the accumulation of ethanol has been suggested (181) as the explanation of thiamine toxicity to *Rhizopus suinus*.

Another set of problems is associated with contamination of supposedly pure chemicals with growth-active substances. There is evident in the literature an unjustified confidence in the label placed on a chemical by the manufacturer. Even compounds rated as "reagent" quality or the equivalent may be contaminated with biologically significant amounts of other substances, particularly inorganic ions and organic growth factors. Such contamination is particularly likely in a compound derived from natural sources, and most of the important carbon and organic nitrogen sources are so derived. In a highly purified medium one source of carbon may appear superior to another merely because it is contaminated with a required inorganic element in which the basal medium is partially deficient. More commonly, the fungus has an unrecognized vitamin requirement which is met by the less pure of a series of carbon compounds; thus, the early and anomalous finding that *Diplodia macrospora* grows with starch, maltose, or sucrose but not with glucose or fructose is now known to reflect contamination of the first group of compounds with biotin, required by the fungus as a growth factor (199, 241). Growth factors for fungi have been found in many carbon compounds, e.g., soluble starch (172), glucose (121), galactose (44), and saponin (19).

Growth inhibition by contaminants is less commonly encountered but has been reported from the ions present in crude natural materials (153) and from an unidentified alcohol-soluble contaminant of glucose and galactose (44).

It should not be necessary to point out that such materials as cellulose and chitin as they occur in nature may be contaminated with organic materials in sufficient amount to provide the carbon source for visible growth of fungi. It is not, for example, justified to claim that an organism can utilize chitin merely on the evidence that it grows on the exoskeleton of an insect, particularly since insect cuticle is less than 50 per cent chitin (239).

Breakdown of sugars during autoclaving constitutes another serious and often unrecognized source of error in studies of carbon nutrition. Growth inhibition from sugar breakdown products occurs in both bacteria and fungi (9, 116, 193). Breakdown is more extensive if the sugar is in contact during autoclaving with phosphate (59) or with amino acids (86, 125). Ketohexoses, e.g., fructose and sorbose, break down (to 5-hydroxymethylfurfural) more rapidly than do the aldohexoses (138), and furfural formation from autoclaved xylose is sufficient to inhibit bacterial growth (120). Autoclaving of carbohydrate in the medium has been reported also to cause the formation of growth-promoting substances for bacteria (36) and fungi (114).

Oligosaccharides may be partially hydrolyzed during autoclaving, especially at low pH (7, 22), and probably many claims of slight growth on oligosaccharides reflect merely the partial hydrolysis of a non-utilizable sugar to a utilizable monosaccharide.

It follows that sugars and other carbon sources should never be autoclaved in a medium. As a general rule, they may be autoclaved separately and then added aseptically to the cooled basal medium. The expedient of intermittent sterilization is no better than autoclaving (136). The ultimate recourse is to filter sterilization, and questionable results with a possibly labile sugar should always be checked with this method.

It is usual in carbon nutrition experiments to harvest all cultures after a predetermined, often arbitrarily chosen, incubation period. No objection can be made to this procedure if the only purpose of the experiment is to find a practicable growth medium for a specific purpose. If, however, it is intended to yield meaningful information on the intrinsic utilizability of compounds, some error may be introduced. One compound may be used with a very long lag, probably adaptive in nature (p. 86); the classification of this compound as utilizable or non-utilizable will depend on the length of the incubation period chosen. On the other hand, if time is allowed for slow utilization of compounds, growth on rapidly utilized substrates may have been completed and followed by extensive autolysis before the cultures are harvested. Ideally, both these difficulties may be met by planning periodic harvests; comparison of compounds can then be made on the basis of two criteria, maximum growth and the time required to reach maximum growth. The data of Lilly and Barnett (116) show for many fungi the gain in understanding which flows from the use of more than one incubation period.

Some additional information, and considerably greater confidence in interpretation, may be gained by analysis of the medium at the time of harvest for residual carbon source. This procedure affords an additional check upon growth evidence, especially if growth is limited.

Differences in results between different laboratories are often casually explained as an expression of strain differences or as the result of variation. There is, of course, no doubt that strains of a given species may differ in their nutritional requirements, and there are authenticated cases of metabolic changes resulting from spontaneous genetic change. Nevertheless, in the absence of adequate evidence, these phenomena should not be accepted as sufficient explanation of the failure of one laboratory to confirm the work of another. It is clear that extensive recourse to such "explanation" would mean that no study could be confirmed or contradicted by later evidence.

From this review of methodological problems, a number of recommendations may be formulated. Although not of equal importance and not necessarily applicable to all cases, they should be considered carefully in designing experiments on the carbon nutrition of fungi.

1. Complex natural products which supply carbon should if possible not be included in the basal medium.

2. A control series with only the basal medium should be included in every experiment. Failure to include such a control makes it almost impossible to detect limited utilization of the test carbon compound, since it is not known to what extent impurities in the basal medium support growth.

3. Adequate replication of cultures is necessary, the number to be determined by the variance found in pilot experiments. Probably for most fungi a minimum of four replicates for each harvest is required.

4. The carbon source should always be autoclaved separately from the basal medium and added aseptically to it. If it is found to be labile to heat, it should be sterilized by filtration.

5. The pH of the medium should be determined electrometrically after all ingredients are added, and periodically during growth.

6. The inoculum should be of minimum size, to avoid carry-over of materials from the parent culture. In doubtful cases, serial subculture on the same medium may be necessary. All cultures should be inoculated with the same amount (mass or number) of cells.

7. The measurement of growth must be objective and quantitative, e.g., by dry weight, total nitrogen, or turbidity (Chapter 1).

8. For fungi which have rapid rates of growth and autolysis or which grow adaptively on some substrates it may be necessary to construct a growth curve for each carbon source or at least to make more than one harvest.

9. Analysis of the spent medium for residual carbon source is highly desirable, although not always practicable.

10. Possible interactions between carbon and nitrogen sources should be considered; in some cases it may be necessary to study all putative carbon sources in media with different nitrogen sources.

11. When applicable, the distinction between initiation of growth

and maintenance of preformed growth should be a factor in the interpretation of results.

12. Reasonable precautions should be taken against complications arising from (a) contamination of the carbon source with impurities which affect growth, or (b) the formation of toxic metabolites during growth. Hydrogen ion is the most common toxic metabolite, and consequently the most important precaution in this connection is the periodic determination of the pH of the culture during the growth period.

The most frequent, and perhaps the least excusable, deficiency in experiments on carbon nutrition is failure to meet the criterion of objective and quantitative measurement of growth. As a rule, it is wise to disregard results which are reported in qualitative terms only, although the complete absence of growth in such experiments may on occasion be significant. This stricture applies with almost equal force to the evaluation of growth on the basis of linear extension of a colony on agar; this type of growth measurement has its uses (Chapter 1) but is not sufficiently accurate to assess the relative utilizability of different carbon sources.

2. MONOSACCHARIDES AND THEIR DERIVATIVES

Hexoses. Of the 6-carbon sugars, the hexoses, D-glucose is biologically the most important and is utilized for growth by virtually all cultivable fungi. A few forms have been reported not to grow with glucose; the only convincing evidence so far presented is the qualitative observation of Schade (175) that *Leptomitus lacteus* uses none of the common hexoses but grows with acetate or other fatty acids as the sole source of carbon. This pattern resembles that of the "acetate flagellates," e.g., *Polytomella caeca,* in which it has been suggested (122) that enzymes necessary for the phosphorylation of glucose are lacking. A similar deficiency in *Pseudomonas putrefaciens* has the same effect (106).

For the great majority of fungi and actinomycetes D-fructose and D-mannose are equivalent to glucose for growth. Occasionally, as in *Stachybotrys atra* (99), one of these may appear superior to glucose for unknown reasons. Particularly among the lower fungi there appear to be numerous exceptions to the general rule that fructose and mannose are equivalent to glucose. In conventional experiments of limited duration it is found that either or both of these sugars fail to support the growth of several members of the Chytridiales (2, 45) and

Blastocladiales (94, 123). Less exhaustive studies suggest that the same is true of some species of the Saprolegniales (17, 234). Of several reports of failure of higher fungi to utilize fructose, that of Shirakawa (184) is the most convincing, although the fructose was autoclaved in the medium. Several isolates of *Streptomyces* fail to grow in an agar medium with fructose as carbon source (14).

Considerable light has recently been thrown on the non-utilization of mannose and fructose through the work of Sistrom and Machlis (185) on *Allomyces macrogynus,* one of the species of the Blastocladiales previously found not to grow appreciably on these sugars in experiments of conventional duration. It is now clear that *A. macrogynus* can grow on both mannose and fructose with a very long period of incubation; the final growth is comparable to that on glucose. In addition, provision of a small amount of glucose to a medium in which the main carbon source is mannose or fructose allows normal growth with no delay. Both of these observations are consistent with the hypothesis that this fungus—and by implication perhaps others—utilizes fructose and mannose only under conditions which permit or encourage the formation of an "adaptive" or induced enzyme, although other observations remain to be reconciled with this hypothesis. It would seem, therefore, that utilization of these monosaccharides is dependent on an enzyme system which is constitutive in some organisms and inducible in others; strains of a given species may fall into different groups in this regard.

Data from a comprehensive study of 57 fungal species, mostly of the Fungi Imperfecti (116), show that relatively few—about one-fifth of the sample—are completely unable to grow with D-galactose as carbon source in a medium containing asparagine and salts. Many, especially in the genus *Fusarium,* grow with galactose as well as with glucose. Other fungi, e.g., *Helminthosporium sativum,* reach the same final dry weight as with glucose but reach it slowly, suggesting that here too an "adaptive" mechanism is at work and that the inclusion of asparagine in the medium may have biased the results by providing a substrate able to support the formation of induced enzymes. Finally, for many fungi galactose is clearly utilized but does not even in a long time period support the same level of growth as does glucose. We may conclude from this and other work that galactose is used by most fungi but is not usually so good a source of carbon as glucose. A substantial number of fungi are unable to utilize it, and it may even be toxic to a few (90, 194). The ability or inability to utilize galactose bears no apparent relation to taxonomic position.

On comparative grounds, it seems probable that the ability of an organism to use fructose, mannose, or galactose depends upon its ability to convert the sugar in question into a phosphorylated derivative of glucose able to enter the main respiratory pathways. The metabolic relationships of these four sugars in yeast and animal cells are shown in the diagram (67):

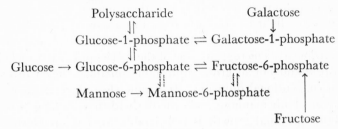

From this diagram it may be suggested that in adaptive growth on fructose, mannose, or galactose, the enzyme actually lacking in the cell and induced by the environment is the specific kinase responsible for the phosphorylation of the free sugar. However, no data are available and other possibilities and other pathways are of course conceivable. The occurrence of mannose-1-phosphate in the mycelium of *Penicillium chrysogenum* (105), for example, suggests a pathway of mannose utilization similar to that of galactose in the scheme outlined above.

Studies on the economic coefficient (p. 89) and similar indices of growth indicate that poorly utilizable monosaccharides are such because they are not attacked or do not penetrate the cell, rather than because once attacked they do not provide energy or usable metabolic products. This is especially clear from experiments with *Aspergillus niger,* for which the small amount of a poor carbon source which disappears from the medium is as efficient in supplying carbon for growth as an equivalent amount of glucose (208, 209). The sugars which do not support growth adequately remain, that is, in the medium. Whether this is the result of specific enzymatic deficiencies as suggested above or whether it is to be attributed to slow penetration of the sugar remains to be determined. The two possibilities are not necessarily mutually exclusive if penetration of sugars depends, as it may, on a surface enzymatic reaction. It is perhaps significant that the yeast cell is impermeable to sorbose, galactose, and arabinose (171), all of which are generally poor sources of carbon for microorganisms.

L-Sorbose, a ketohexose differing from fructose in the configuration of carbon atom 5, supports normal growth of a few fungi and actinomycetes (14, 116, 146). Although unequivocal data are not available, it appears not to be utilizable by most forms and it is definitely toxic to some. The toxicity is evidenced by death of the hyphal tips, followed by branching of the mycelium below the killed portion (116). Fungi, e.g., *Neurospora crassa*, which normally spread widely on an agar plate grow as small colonies in a medium with sorbose (204). The fundamental basis of sorbose toxicity is not yet known; although often more pronounced in a maltose medium, toxicity to some fungi is equally well expressed in glucose media, so that interference with maltose utilization cannot be the explanation. Sorbose inhibition occurs only at relatively high concentrations and is strongly affected by temperature (116). A possible line of approach to the problem of its mode of action may be found in the hypothesis that sorbose interferes with a respiratory pathway; organisms dependent on this pathway would then be inhibited completely, fungi which have alternate pathways would be less or not at all affected.

Heptoses. The naturally occurring 7-carbon sugars have not been tested as carbon sources for fungi, except for the report (195) that *Aspergillus niger* does not grow with D-mannoheptulose.

Pentoses. D-Xylose is the most generally utilizable of the pentoses, and has even been reported to be superior to glucose for some organisms (12, 150, 216). Some fungi and actinomycetes grow poorly or not at all with xylose, and species within the same genus may differ markedly (195, 201). It must be remembered that xylose is known to be broken down to furfural during autoclaving, for which reason all reports of its non-utilizability should be regarded with some reserve until confirmed with filter-sterilized xylose. *Phymatotrichum omnivorum* makes better growth with alcohol-sterilized than with autoclaved xylose (18), but the poor growth of *Venturia inaequalis* strains on agar with xylose is not improved by filter sterilization of the sugar (113).

Both isomers of arabinose occur in nature and are commercially available. Probably, in those publications in which the isomer used is not specified the L-isomer, which is more easily available, was used. *Penicillium urticae* utilizes D-arabinose much less well than it does L-arabinose (57). In most studies, L-arabinose is inferior to xylose and glucose as a carbon source (116a). In a medium containing a second carbon source, however, several fungi, e.g., *Endoconidiophora adiposa*, utilize L-arabinose with a long incubation period, apparently adaptively (116).

Relatively few studies on rhamnose, a methyl pentose, have been made, but the indications are that it is used by only a few organisms, including *Stachybotrys atra* (99) and *Streptomyces coelicolor* (39).

Although *Penicillium urticae* grows with D-ribose as carbon source (57), it and the other naturally occurring pentoses and methyl pentoses have not been investigated thoroughly. Early studies, not all satisfactory in their methods, on pentose utilization by fungi are reviewed by Hawkins (80) and by Peterson et al. (155).

It seems, in conclusion, that xylose is often a good source of carbon for fungi and that contrary findings should be examined closely. The pathway of utilization of xylose is not known; it seems likely that it enters the phosphogluconate oxidation pathway (Chapter 7) as pentose phosphate. L-Arabinose is used by several fungi, probably not by most. The other pentoses and methyl pentoses have been investigated rather infrequently, but they appear in general to be poor sources of carbon or not utilizable at all.

Other Monosaccharides. A single study of a 4-carbon sugar (195) indicates that D-threose is not utilized by *Aspergillus niger*.

The L-isomers of the naturally occurring aldohexoses and of xylose do not support growth of fungi, nor do those monosaccharides which do not occur in nature (99, 195, 201). Acetylation or methylation of the ring carbons of glucose yields derivatives which are not utilized by representative fungi (187), although *Aspergillus niger* has been reported to make a limited growth, after adaptation, with pentaacetyl-glucose (8). *Aspergillus niger* also grows with 2-deoxyglucose as carbon source (8).

Polyhydric Alcohols. Reduction of the sugars yields sugar alcohols, e.g., D-sorbitol arises by reduction of D-glucose, D-mannitol by reduction of D-fructose or D-mannose. In addition to the hexitols, derived from the hexose sugars, tetritols, pentitols, and heptitols, related respectively to 4-, 5-, and 7-carbon sugars, occur in nature. Glycerol may be considered as a reduction product of a 3-carbon sugar.

Mannitol is the most generally utilizable of the hexitols, and is equivalent to glucose for many fungi and actinomycetes (39, 100, 144, 180). However, many fungi with generally wide substrate ranges grow only poorly or not at all with mannitol as sole carbon source (65, 129, 152). In the lower phycomycetes, a few forms grow poorly with mannitol (17, 32); most do not utilize it at all.

Sorbitol and dulcitol are unavailable to most fungi and actinomycetes. From the limited data, it appears that sorbitol, the reduction product of glucose, is more generally used than is dulcitol, which is related chemically to galactose. It may be significant that many organisms able to utilize dulcitol are also able to grow more or less well with galactose (17, 180, 201). Erythritol is apparently only rarely utilizable, although the data again are extremely limited.

Glycerol is often the best carbon source of all for actinomycetes (40, 43, 221). In the fungi the ability to utilize glycerol appears to be specific; thus, among fairly omnivorous saprophytes, *Aspergillus oryzae* and *A. niger* make only poor growth (195, 201), but *Memnoniella echinata* grows well with glycerol as sole carbon source (150).

Although the data are insufficient for generalization, it may tentatively be concluded that the only polyhydric alcohols available to many fungi are glycerol and mannitol. These may be expected on oxidation to yield, respectively, fructose and glyceraldehyde or dihydroxyacetone, all of which can after phosphorylation enter known respiratory pathways.

Sugar Acids. Oxidation of the aldehyde carbon of an aldohexose yields an acid; D-gluconic acid, from D-glucose, is the only one to have been investigated as a source of carbon for fungi. As might be expected from the fact that many strains of *Aspergillus niger* form and then consume gluconic acid during sugar metabolism (Chapter 6), it is a good source of carbon for *A. niger* (46) and *A. oryzae* (201), although the strain of *A. niger* studied by Steinberg (195) could not grow with gluconate as sole carbon source. Several other organisms grow on gluconate (40, 99, 121), but others, e.g., *Chalara quercina*, do not utilize it (12). Growth with gluconate is probably often limited by an unfavorably high pH resulting from utilization of the neutralized acid.

Utilization of 2-ketogluconic acid by fungi is, like that of gluconic acid, highly specific (50) and is probably a function of the respiratory systems available.

A single report (87) indicates, without quantitative data, that *Aspergillus niger* grows with D-glucuronic or D-galacturonic acids as sole carbon source.

D-Saccharic acid, the dibasic acid resulting from the oxidation of carbon atoms 1 and 6 of D-glucose, has been reported a good source of carbon for *Aspergillus niger* (46), but a relatively poor source for *A. oryzae* (201).

Glycosides. Limited studies of the methylglucosides indicate, as would be expected from the relative ubiquity of β-glucosidases (Chapter 5), that β-methylglucoside is much more easily utilizable than the α-isomer (54, 180). Amygdalin, which is hydrolyzed to gentiobiose and mandelonitrile, is utilized by several members of the Saprolegniaceae (17); in general it may be expected that the ability of an organism to use a given β-glycoside will depend on its ability to use the sugar which is split off from it. The cyanogenetic glycosides, however, may not be utilizable by reason of the toxicity of the cyanide liberated on hydrolysis (174).

3. OLIGOSACCHARIDES

Chemically, the oligosaccharides are glycosides composed of two or more monosaccharides and are characterized by the nature of the component sugars, the number of units, and the type of glycosidic bond. Those which are important in the nutrition of fungi include five disaccharides—maltose, cellobiose, trehalose, sucrose, and lactose—and one trisaccharide, raffinose, which is made up of galactose, glucose, and fructose units. In addition to data on specific sugars, two general problems are relevant at this point: (1) the enzymatic basis of disaccharide utilization, and (2) adaptive growth with oligosaccharides.

Maltose occurs in nature as a product of starch hydrolysis and is utilized by virtually all fungi which have been tested, even those which have a limited substrate range. A few fungi are known, on the basis of quantitative studies, to grow poorly or not at all with maltose: *Chytridium* sp. (45), *Polychytrium aggregatum* (2), *Entomophthora* (*Empusa*) sp. (242), and *Penicillium digitatum* (65, 244). Surprisingly, the two chytrids mentioned make at least some growth with starch; the other fungi use neither starch nor maltose. Maltose is more easily hydrolyzed by autoclaving than are sucrose or lactose (136), but even with this possible source of error it seems that it is very generally available to fungi.

Cellobiose, like maltose, is composed of two glucose residues but the linkage is of the β-configuration. The data are more limited than those for maltose, but indicate that it is almost as widely utilizable as maltose. Indeed, two of the fungi mentioned above which do not grow with maltose do with cellobiose. *Tricholoma flavobrunneum* is among the small group of tested fungi which fail to utilize cellobiose, but other species of the same genus grow well with it as sole carbon source (142). The utilizability of cellobiose reflects the general occurrence of β-glucosidases in fungi (Chapter 5).

Trehalose, a glucose-containing disaccharide produced by fungi and a few higher plants (Chapter 5), appears from the few studies which have been made to be generally available, even to rather fastidious fungi (40, 99, 201, 242).

Sucrose, the characteristic sugar of higher plants, is generally a good source of carbon for fungi but is not so nearly universally available as maltose. Thus, of 57 fungi studied by Lilly and Barnett (116) only 4 were completely unable to utilize sucrose, but several grew slowly with it. Among the major groups of fungi, failure to utilize sucrose appears to be particularly common in the Chytridiales (Table 1) and the Mucorales (174), less common in other groups. Actinomycetes rarely, if ever, utilize sucrose (13, 221).

Lactose, the β-galactosido-glucose of mammalian milk, is used by far fewer fungi than any of the disaccharides so far mentioned, and may be characterized as a poor carbon source (61, 116). At least some actinomycetes grow with lactose (40, 51, 215). Adaptation to lactose occurs among fungi (p. 87), and whether or not an organism is reported as able to utilize the sugar often, therefore, depends on the length of the incubation period chosen.

Melibiose, an α-glycoside, has not been investigated often; the few data available (Table 1) indicate that it is not utilizable by many fungi. Data for gentiobiose are similarly too limited to allow generalization. Growth on amygdalin, the β-glycoside of gentiobiose, by aquatic fungi (17) presumably indicates gentiobiose utilization.

Raffinose attacked at one linkage yields galactose and sucrose, attacked at the other yields fructose and melibiose. From the limited data of Table 1 and the more extensive studies of Lilly and Barnett (116), it would appear that the majority of fungi utilize raffinose, but that non-utilization is common. Some doubt is raised with regard to raffinose utilization by the finding (18) that raffinose supports growth of *Phymatotrichum omnivorum* if autoclaved but not if sterilized by alcohol treatment; a reinvestigation of this problem by comparing filter-sterilized to heat-sterilized raffinose may show that raffinose is broken down by autoclaving at least to the extent that some simple sugars are available to initiate growth and to permit, therefore, the formation of adaptive enzymes which then hydrolyze the unchanged raffinose.

The utilization of an oligosaccharide is believed to be preceded by and dependent on its conversion to hexoses or, possibly, hexose phosphates. The evidence for this generalization may be summarized:

1. Fungi that can use a disaccharide possess enzymes which hydrolyze it (17, 79). An organism which grows on sucrose, for example, proves on examination to form sucrase. Formation of the enzyme is not, however, a sufficient condition for utilization—a mutant of *Neurospora crassa* produces lactase (β-galactosidase) but does not grow with lactose as sole carbon source (112).

Table 1. Carbon Nutrition of Some Fungi and Actinomycetes*

Carbon Source	Chytridium sp. (45)	Macrochytrium botrydioides (45)	Polychytrium aggregatum (2)	Allomyces javanicus (94)
None	4	1	0	0
Glucose	100	100	100	100
Fructose	101	1	0	0
Mannose	101	120		109
Galactose	99	23	0	0
Sorbose	8	1		
Xylose	7	108	0	0
L-Arabinose	4	1	0	
D-Arabinose				
Ribose				
Rhamnose	4	1		
Mannitol			0	
Sorbitol				
Dulcitol	4	2		
Adonitol				
Erythritol				
Glycerol	17	9		0
Maltose	10	116	0	103
Sucrose	9	4	0	0
Cellobiose	100	137	0	
Lactose	3	4	0	0
Trehalose				
Melibiose	5	2		
Raffinose	5	2	0	0
Glycogen	94	194		
Starch	50	106	+	+
Dextrin				
Inulin	3	3		
Cellulose	3	+	0	
Formate				
Acetate	0	<3		0
Propionate				
Oxalate				
Lactate				0
Succinate	0	<3		0
Fumarate				0
Malate				
Tartrate	0	<3		
Citrate	0	<3		
Gluconate				

* All data adjusted by taking growth on glucose as 100. Organisms arranged in order: phycomycetes, ascomycetes, basidiomycetes, Fungi Imperfecti, actinomycetes. Tr = trace of growth; + = visible growth, not measured.

Table 1 (*continued*)

Carbon Source	Allomyces javanicus macrogynus (123)	Blastocladia pringsheimii (32)	Brevilegnia gracilis (17)	Saprolegnia delica (17)
None	0	5	0	0
Glucose	100	100	100	100
Fructose	0	88	81	102
Mannose	0	97	94	0
Galactose	0	7	86	0
Sorbose	0	7		
Xylose	0	6	0	0
L-Arabinose	0	7	0	0
D-Arabinose				
Ribose				
Rhamnose			0	0
Mannitol			52	0
Sorbitol			89	29
Dulcitol			0	0
Adonitol				
Erythritol			0	0
Glycerol		39	86	14
Maltose	107	101	88	107
Sucrose	0	99	83	14
Cellobiose	0			
Lactose	0	6	61	0
Trehalose				
Melibiose	0			
Raffinose			76	0
Glycogen	50		76	93
Starch	54	95	76	100
Dextrin	98	87	86	86
Inulin	0		40	0
Cellulose		6		
Formate		5		
Acetate	37	5		
Propionate				
Oxalate				
Lactate				
Succinate	0	9		
Fumarate				
Malate		5		
Tartrate		5		
Citrate	0	6		
Gluconate				

Table 1 (*continued*)

Carbon Source	*Pytophthora* *cactorum* (129)	*Pythiogeton* sp. (33)	*Chalara* *quercina* (12)	*Coprinus* sp. (100)
None	0	3	2	34
Glucose	100	100	100	100
Fructose	50	104	119	107
Mannose	38		96	127
Galactose	63	10	115	76
Sorbose				
Xylose	42	64	215	52
L-Arabinose	55	7	46	56
D-Arabinose				
Ribose				
Rhamnose	58		13	
Mannitol	63	±10	13	111
Sorbitol	92			
Dulcitol	55		2	
Adonitol				
Erythritol	52		2	
Glycerol	102	5	15	
Maltose	125	99	133	105
Sucrose	133	101	94	84
Cellobiose		101	119	
Lactose	83	36	4	72
Trehalose				
Melibiose		5	27	
Raffinose	63		100	96
Glycogen				
Starch	125	98	6	112
Dextrin	63		217	120
Inulin	83		33	77
Cellulose		+	23	
Formate		0		
Acetate		0		
Propionate				
Oxalate		0		
Lactate		0		
Succinate		0	15	
Fumarate				
Malate		0		
Tartrate		0		
Citrate		0		
Gluconate		0	2	

Table 1 (*continued*)

Carbon Source	*Psalliota bispora* (216)	*Stereum gausapatum* (82)	*Ustilago violacea* (19)	*Fusarium oxysporum f. nicotianae* (243)
None		12	5	
Glucose	100	100	100	100
Fructose	95	104	99	104
Mannose		104		109
Galactose	73	89	63	78
Sorbose				59
Xylose	132	123	3	135
L-Arabinose	109	43	5	68
D-Arabinose				14
Ribose				74
Rhamnose		41	7	39
Mannitol	20		93	41
Sorbitol			90	24
Dulcitol				27
Adonitol				
Erythritol				7
Glycerol		24	24	48
Maltose	73	160	95	138
Sucrose	68	158	88	113
Cellobiose			78	108
Lactose			11	19
Trehalose				111
Melibiose				23
Raffinose		126	8	120
Glycogen		112		
Starch	20	160	10	59
Dextrin			25	105
Inulin	23	70	9	
Cellulose				
Formate				
Acetate	11			
Propionate				
Oxalate	100			
Lactate				
Succinate				
Fumarate				
Malate	116			
Tartrate	32			
Citrate				
Gluconate				

Table 1 (*continued*)

Carbon Source	*Memnoniella* *echinata* (150)	*Penicillium* *digitatum* (65)	*Sclerotium* *delphinii* (151)
None			
Glucose	100	100	100
Fructose	110	108	113
Mannose	90	108	
Galactose	105	99	
Sorbose			
Xylose	145	102	76
L-Arabinose	105	95	98
D-Arabinose			
Ribose			
Rhamnose		65	
Mannitol	90		
Sorbitol	50		
Dulcitol			
Adonitol			
Erythritol			46
Glycerol	85		104
Maltose	105	21	152
Sucrose	105	92	147
Cellobiose	105	101	
Lactose	120	64	
Trehalose	45		
Melibiose			
Raffinose	100		
Glycogen			
Starch	170	2	195
Dextrin	140		
Inulin		1	191
Cellulose			
Formate	45		
Acetate	35		43
Propionate	40		
Oxalate	25		
Lactate			
Succinate		2	
Fumarate		1	
Malate		21	
Tartrate	10		
Citrate		28	
Gluconate			

Table 1 (*continued*)

Carbon Source	*Stachybotrys atra* (99)	*Streptomyces coelicolor* (40)
None		17
Glucose	100	100
Fructose	241	79
Mannose	66	100
Galactose	128	84
Sorbose	0	26
Xylose	94	143
L-Arabinose	25	65
D-Arabinose	22	
Ribose	9	
Rhamnose	91	
Mannitol	100	82
Sorbitol	0	27
Dulcitol	28	20
Adonitol	25	
Erythritol	0	
Glycerol	166	135
Maltose	131	62
Sucrose	78	34
Cellobiose	72	81
Lactose	84	
Trehalose	59	90
Melibiose		
Raffinose	56	
Glycogen		
Starch	66	107
Dextrin	53	32
Inulin	113	
Cellulose	+	
Formate	0	
Acetate	22	33
Propionate	tr.	
Oxalate	tr.	
Lactate	tr.	60
Succinate	tr.	47
Fumarate		69
Malate	3	60
Tartrate	0	20
Citrate	tr.	24
Gluconate	9	82

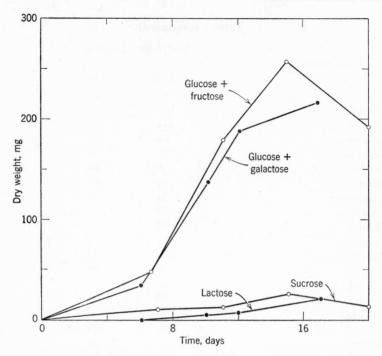

Figure 1. The growth of *Schizothecium longicolle* on disaccharides and on equivalent mixtures of their constituent hexoses. From tabular data of Lilly and Barnett (116).

2. The rate of growth of a lactase-rich mycelium on lactose is demonstrably higher than that of a lactase-poor mycelium (112).

3. Fungi which cannot use a disaccharide have been shown to use its constituent monosaccharides (Figure 1). That is, the only bar to utilization appears to be inability to convert the compound sugar to hexoses.

It is often held that direct utilization of oligosaccharides, without prior splitting of the glycosidic bond, occurs in fungi. Data cited in support of this claim include (1) quantitative superiority of a disaccharide to its constituent monosaccharides (78, 82), (2) differences in metabolic processes during disaccharide and monosaccharide utilization (52, 145), and (3) utilization of a disaccharide by intact cells at a pH at which the corresponding hydrolytic enzyme is inactive *in vitro* (141). All of these phenomena, however, can be explained without recourse to the hypothesis of direct utilization; some of the problems as they have been studied in yeast are reviewed by Hestrin (83, 84).

Direct utilization may, of course, occur in the fungi as it does in bacteria (53), but the evidence is not yet at hand.

The second general problem in oligosaccharide utilization is that of adaptive growth. Operationally, nutrition experiments often show that a given organism grows on a disaccharide only after a long incubation period, but that once growth is initiated the final crop is as heavy as that produced with glucose or other easily utilizable carbohydrates. The study of Lilly and Barnett (116) contains many examples of this phenomenon, which, as discussed later, is probably to be ascribed to the formation of an induced enzyme system.

4. POLYSACCHARIDES

Polysaccharides, as the name implies, are polymers of sugars or sugar derivatives. Although the number of units may be as small as 10, the natural polysaccharides have as a rule very high molecular weights and contain up to several thousand saccharide units. They can be divided into two broad classes: reserve or nutrient polysaccharides (e.g., starch, glycogen, and inulin) and structural polysaccharides (e.g., cellulose, pectic materials, and chitin). The structural polysaccharides, found in cell walls and other extraprotoplasmic structures, are generally insoluble linear polymers; the reserve polysaccharides contain a large percentage of branched chain structures and are usually more soluble (235). Many polysaccharides are too poorly known to be fitted into either category.

Starches and Related Polysaccharides. Starch, the principal reserve polysaccharide of plants (actually, the starches of different plants are somewhat different) is an excellent carbon source for most fungi and actinomycetes, even for rather fastidious forms. A few fungi are known on acceptable evidence not to grow with starch as the sole carbon source. They include representatives of widely different taxonomic and ecological groups: *Ustilago violacea* (180), *Rhizophlyctis rosea* (160), *Psalliota bispora* (*P. campestris*) (216), *Tricholoma imbricatum* (142), *Entomophthora* (*Empusa*) spp. (242), *Penicillium digitatum* (65), and *Chalara quercina* (12). The failure of *Penicillium digitatum* to grow with starch finds its explanation in an inability to form amylase (88).

As would be expected from the fact that starch is hydrolyzed primarily to maltose, really good growth on starch is accompanied by the ability to grow well on maltose (142), although a *Chytridium* sp. unable to utilize maltose makes limited growth on starch (45).

Most investigators have used "soluble starch," a partially depolymerized derivative prepared by acid treatment, rather than native starch. Raw starch, unless the granule structure is destroyed by autoclaving, will not support the growth of *Phymatotrichum omnivorum* (18) and, indeed, is not hydrolyzed by purified amylase. This raises, of course, the question of the utilization of plant starches in nature by plant pathogens, and by saprophytes acting on unmodified plant materials.

Starch is often a better substrate for growth than glucose; although no such case has been studied in detail, this effect presumably results either from contamination of the starch with growth factors or from the fact that utilization of a slowly hydrolyzable compound is accompanied by less accumulation of acids than utilization of glucose.

Dextrins, which are chemically or enzymatically modified starches of uncertain structure, are generally satisfactory sources of carbon for fungi. Quantitative differences between starch and dextrins as carbon sources are frequently reported but cannot easily be interpreted until the chemistry of these polysaccharides is better known. *Chalara quercina*, unable to utilize starch, grows very well on dextrin (12).

Inulin, a polymer of D-fructose possibly containing a small amount of D-glucose, is found in several of the Compositae, e.g., *Dahlia*. It is not hydrolyzed by enzymes which act on starch or on sucrose. Limited data suggest that it is a good carbon source for many but not all fungi. It should, however, be noted, that inulin, like all fructans, is susceptible to hydrolysis by heat, and in careful work it is necessary to use filter sterilization (18).

Unidentified bacterial fructans are probably utilized by *Streptomyces coelicolor* and related species (127).

Glycogens, the reserve polysaccharides of animals and some thallophytes, are glucose polysaccharides quite similar to starch, or, more precisely, to the amylopectin fraction of starch. Glycogens have not been tested extensively in the nutrition of fungi, but the data suggest that they are quite generally available to fungi of widely different ecological groups (17, 45, 82, 201). Those fungi unable to use starch can be expected not to use the glycogens, since, so far as is known, the same enzymes attack both polysaccharides.

Hemicelluloses. The hemicelluloses comprise a group of insoluble polysaccharides of plant cell walls. The group as a whole is not well defined, and there is much confusion in the literature. The hemicellulose fraction as usually isolated includes pentosans, hexosans, and polyuronides; the main constituent is probably a pentosan or mannan (235). Fungi are active in the breakdown of hemicelluloses in wood (85, 169) and in other plant materials (143, 179); the extensive early literature on hemicellulose breakdown in soil is reviewed by Waksman and Diehm (225).

Purified pentosans are attacked by most fungi and actinomycetes which have been tested (80, 99, 124, 216, 225).

Cellulose. Cellulose, the principal structural polysaccharide of plants, is by far the largest reservoir of biologically utilizable carbon on the surface of the earth, and its decomposition, in which fungi probably play a major role, is of great ecological importance. Structurally, it is a linear polymer of D-glucose, the configuration being that of a 1,4-β-glucoside. The number of units in the polymer is high; probably individual linear chains are connected by cross-linkages. Complete hydrolysis yields glucose, partial hydrolysis the disaccharide cellobiose.

The literature on the utilization of cellulose by fungi is very large, beginning with the observations of the pioneer plant pathologists of the nineteenth century. Unfortunately, frequent reliance on inadequate criteria makes it difficult to evaluate this work, and much of it must be considered of doubtful validity. The early literature is reviewed by McBeth and Scales (123), Otto (147), and Waksman (223). The monograph of Siu (186), especially concerned with fabric deterioration, offers the most complete survey available of more recent work.

Several methods have been used in attempts to assay the ability of fungi to grow on or destroy cellulose. Some of these, e.g., observation of the erosion of cotton fibers (56, 147) and measurement of the loss in breaking strength of rotted cotton fabric (73, 214), are adequate for their purpose but do not measure growth directly. Similarly, measurement of gas exchange during growth on cellulose (55, 107) determines an activity which is not necessarily a function of growth.

Visual estimate of growth on filter paper or other cellulosic materials is by itself of no value as an index of growth or cellulolytic capacity (126). Growth on reprecipitated cellulose in agar (123) is equally unreliable, probably because of chemical changes occurring in the preparation of the cellulose (143).

The quantitative methods which seem most promising are the following:

1. Measurement of growth on or hydrolysis of carboxymethylcellulose, a soluble cellulose derivative (96). However, the correlation of this property with cellulolytic capacity is uncertain (163).

2. Chemical determination of the disappearance of cellulose from complex natural materials. This has been applied extensively, to

wood (10, 31, 178), straw (143, 222), litter (117), and other materials (68, 198). It is the appropriate method for the practical problem involved in the decomposition of cellulose in nature, but suffers of course from the inherent difficulty of all growth measurements in complex materials, that the cellulose may not be the primary growth substrate.

3. Determination of the loss in weight of cellulosic materials exposed to the test organism (162, 233). The principal complication is that the mycelial weight is included with the residual cellulose; alkali treatment (191) can reduce but not eliminate this error.

4. Determination of total or protein nitrogen in the insoluble material left after growth of a test organism on cellulose in a medium with a soluble nitrogen source (142). This is without doubt the most accurate and reliable method for the measurement of real growth of a fungus on an insoluble non-nitrogenous substrate such as cellulose. Unfortunately, the method has been little used and cannot as yet be compared to others in detail.

The methods which have been used do not always agree; thus, *Aspergillus versicolor* strains appear to utilize the cellulose of straw (143) but apparently do not cause measurable deterioration of cotton fabric (126). A complete list of the fungi reported, by various methods, as able to attack cellulose has been compiled (186). It is apparent that certain genera of the Fungi Imperfecti and the ascomycetes are particularly rich in species able to decompose cellulose. In the basidiomycetes, the wood-rotting and litter-decomposing fungi are generally, although not universally, able to decompose cellulose; genera particularly involved include *Armillaria, Clitocybe, Collybia, Corticium, Fomes, Marasmius, Mycena, Polyporus, Polystictus, Schizophyllum,* and *Stereum* (31, 118, 164). It must be noted, however, that the species within a given genus are not all necessarily alike in their response to cellulose. This has been especially well established in *Aspergillus* (238) and *Tricholoma* (142). In some species, strain differences in the utilization of carboxymethylcellulose have been reported (96).

Among the phycomycetes, many members of the Chytridiales utilize cellulose (45, 233). Limited data indicate that none of the Blastocladiales is cellulolytic (34). In the Saprolegniales, members of several genera apparently produce an enzyme hydrolyzing filter paper cellulose (16, 173), as do species of Phytophthora in the Peronosporales (128); this may be taken as prima-facie evidence for their ability to grow on cellulose. None of the Mucorales so far studied is cellulolytic (126, 147, 164, 236).

Although early work, reviewed by Waksman (224), suggested that most species of the Actinomycetales are able to attack cellulose, the evidence must be considered inadequate. It is certain that some species of *Streptomyces* and at least one of *Micromonospora* decompose cellulose (56, 93, 143, 162, 222), but whether this is true of most species and whether the actinomycetes as a group play an important role in the decomposition of cellulose in nature remain to be determined.

Generalizations on the distribution of cellulolytic capacity among the different taxonomic groups are, it should be remembered, based on limited data, not only in the sense that often only a few isolates of a taxon have been tested, but also in the sense that the conditions of test may not be favorable for all potentially cellulose-utilizing forms. The utilization of cellulose is affected by such factors as the available nitrogen (108), the temperature (126), the acidity (162), and the presence of other carbon compounds (85, 142). It seems likely, therefore, that cellulose is used by more fungi than present information would indicate.

The widespread occurrence of cellulolytic fungi in soil and the fact that addition of cellulosic materials to soil results in an increase in the number of fungi isolated have led most workers to believe that, at least under aerobic conditions and at moderate temperatures, the fungi play a more important part in the initial decomposition of cellulose in soil than do the cellulolytic bacteria. The procedures of soil microbiology are, however, so inexact, and the total soil microflora is so poorly known, that this supposition, attractive as it is, is not adequately supported by the evidence.

The fact of occurrence in nature on a cellulosic substrate, even very frequent occurrence, is distinctly not acceptable evidence of ability to utilize cellulose. Thus, *Pullularia pullulans* is one of the organisms most frequently isolated from exposed cotton cloth, but it is not cellulolytic (186).

Chitin. Chitin, the structural polysaccharide of higher invertebrates, is also a constituent of many fungi (Chapter 2). Chemically, it is a linear polymer of N-acetyl-D-glucosamine, the units being linked by β-1,4-glycosidic bonds. Like cellulose, it is stable and difficult to purify without alteration of structure.

Fungi are often found growing on the exoskeletons of living or dead Arthropoda. Although it is often assumed, perhaps correctly, that these fungi attack chitin, this evidence by itself cannot establish the point. Visible growth on or erosion of chitin has been reported in studies on soil fungi and actinomycetes (189) and on aquatic fungi

(2, 45). It must, however, be concluded that there is no quantitative and entirely satisfactory evidence for the utilization of chitin or of N-acetylglucosamine. The work just mentioned suggests that an investigation of this problem in the fungi would be rewarding. Chitin-splitting enzymes must be present in those fungi which autolyze extensively, and an exocellular chitinase is formed by *Streptomyces* sp. and some fungi (Chapter 5).

Pectic Substances. The pectic substances are polysaccharides of plant cell walls, usually isolated as a mixture of which the major constituent is a polymer of methylated galacturonic acids (235). Very little attention has been devoted to these materials as carbon sources, although pectin has been reported to provide carbon for the growth of *Sclerotinia cinerea* (240) and of *Psalliota bispora* (216). From the frequent occurrence in fungi of enzymes acting upon the pectic substances (Chapter 5) and from the employment of pectin as the carbon source in experiments on enzyme production, it is probably safe to assume that they are utilized in nature by many fungi, both parasitic and saprophytic.

5. ORGANIC ACIDS

Organic acids are generally poorer sources of carbon for fungi than are the carbohydrates. Apart from what might be called intrinsic utilizability, however, three factors interfere with the utilization of the organic acids in particular cases. First, cells are often impermeable to organic acids at physiological pH levels. Impermeability is more often invoked than demonstrated, but there is no doubt that it is a factor in the utilization of acids. Second, the utilization of neutralized organic acids causes a rise of the culture pH which may interfere with growth. This phenomenon explains the repeated observation that growth with organic acids is better if nitrogen is supplied as an ammonium salt (115, 165, 207). Utilization of the ammonium cation tends to drive the pH down, partially or wholly counteracting the alkalinizing effect of acid utilization. In addition, it appears that the utilization of ammonium ion is more rapid if the medium is neutral or-alkaline (134). It has been argued (24) that a more direct reaction exists between organic acids and ammonium ion, but this appears unlikely and is not necessary in order to explain the observed phenomena.

A third, and probably only occasionally important, factor is the chelation of inorganic ions by certain of the organic acids, e.g., citrate and tartrate. This may, however, either promote growth by keeping essential ions in solution or limit growth by removing ions (183); which of these two opposite effects will occur is determined by the solubilities of the chelate complexes and the metallic salts at the culture pH chosen.

The non-fatty organic acids which are most often utilized by fungi are those, e.g., citrate, succinate, and malate, which are products of glucose metabolism. Most of the data are from studies on common saprophytes and it appears that utilization is highly specific. Thus *Penicillium janczewskii* grows well on succinate (23); succinate is a relatively poor carbon source for *P. javanicum* (121) and is not utilized at all by *P. digitatum* (65). Because of the likelihood that cells may be impermeable to acids, especially hydroxy acids, nutritional data have no necessary relevance to the acid metabolism of the cell.

Tartaric acid, the utilization of which by a fungus is so important in the history of both crystallography and microbiology (148), is in general not a good carbon source for fungi, although it is utilized as well as glucose by *Memnoniella echinata* (150). The growth of some common fungi with tartrate has been surveyed by Stadtman et al. (190); an adaptive tartrate-decomposing system of *Aspergillus versicolor* has been described (10). The dextrorotatory isomer is used preferentially (70).

Oxalic acid is used by few microorganisms, among which are *Proactinomyces* sp. and a strain of *Aspergillus oryzae* (137), *Psalliota bispora* (216), and a few bacteria (104). Possibly, the insolubility of calcium and magnesium oxalates results in a removal of these ions from solution and a consequent limitation of growth in oxalic acid media.

Malonic acid is used, although it is not a favorable carbon source, by a few fungi and actinomycetes (23, 92, 99).

Inclusive studies of polyfunctional organic acids in nutrition have been reported by Camp (30), Tamiya (201), and Steinberg (195).

The lower fatty acids—formic, acetic, propionic, etc.—are as a rule poorly utilizable or even toxic. Propionic acid, in fact, is employed as a fungistatic agent. Some fungi, however, do make at least some growth with these acids, particularly with acetate; on a carbon basis acetate is equivalent to glucose for *Allomyces javanicus* (124). Qualitative data (175) indicate that *Leptomitus lacteus* can grow with any of the lower organic acids, including some that are almost uniformly toxic to the higher fungi. Probably, it will be found that the lower fungi utilize fatty acids better than the more extensively investigated higher forms. The utilization of acetate by *Penicillium chrysogenum* is strongly pH dependent (95).

Formic acid has been used as substrate in metabolic studies and apparently supports at least limited growth (6, 15, 38, 76) but is never a good source of carbon. Its low nutritional value, however, does not exclude it or its derivates from an active role in metabolism.

6. THE LIPIDS

Perhaps because of the technical difficulty in the use of water-insoluble substrates, the lipids have been little studied. However, it seems clear that many fungi are able to grow on crude or purified natural fats and oils (62, 89, 162a). Similar observations, incidental to metabolic studies, indicate that some of but not all the higher fatty acids support the growth of *Mucor mucedo* (197) and *Penicillium glaucum* (212, 213). The quantitative data of Tausson (205) are reproduced in Table 2; although the absence of controls somewhat reduces their sig-

Table 2.　The Utilization of Fats by *Aspergillus flavus**

Experiment	Carbon Source	Dry Weight, mg	Utilization, per cent
1	Cocoa butter	508.0	30.8
	Coconut oil	459.2	—
2	Oleic acid	338.8	—
	Stearic acid	577.8	34.0
	Palmitic acid	510.2	25.0
	Tristearin	266.8	16.5
	Tripalmitin	258.4	41.4

* From Tausson (205), by permission of the *Biochemische Zeitschrift*.

nificance, it is clear that both fats and fatty acids are utilized and support growth in a medium containing no other source of carbon.

It has been observed that cholesterol and other steroids support the growth of *Proactinomyces* spp. (217, 218), and that some fungi make visible growth with ergosterol as carbon source (177). Earlier work on crude steroids suffers from the probability of contamination with other carbon compounds.

Numerous fungi and actinomycetes grow on crude or purified hydrocarbons. The evidence, reviewed by ZoBell (246, 247) is largely observational only. *Proactinomyces opacus* grows on and oxidizes dodecane and tetradecane (231). Actinomycetes as a group appear to be more active than fungi in attack on paraffins, other hydrocarbons, and steroids (60, 98, 219).

7. OTHER CARBON SOURCES

Pure Compounds. The lower monohydric aliphatic alcohols—methanol, ethanol, etc.—are not generally utilized, although *Aspergillus niger* makes a limited growth with both methanol (6) and ethanol (201). The most extensive study of the alcohols is that of Stahl and Pessen (192), who found that *Aspergillus versicolor* grows poorly with ethanol and not at all with the other primary alcohols from methyl through undecyl (C_1 through C_{11}). Alcohols with 12 to 18 carbon atoms support some growth of *A. versicolor,* and there appears to be an optimum chain length of 13 to 15.

Amino acids, of course, provide carbon as well as nitrogen and many can serve as sole sources of carbon (139, 203). In general, if enough amino acid carbon is supplied for growth the accumulation of ammonia raises the pH to an unfavorably high level, so that the amino acids alone cannot compare with the carbohydrates in the amount of growth supported.

Enrichment culture methods have been used successfully in the isolation of an actinomycete able to use urethane as sole source of carbon (176). *Proactinomyces* spp. make visible growth with several aromatic compounds, e.g., phenol, aniline, and nitrobenzene, as sole sources of carbon (133).

Natural Products. Lignin is a complex amorphous polymer of high molecular weight, the units of which are aromatic in nature, but neither the chemical nor the physical structure is known precisely. It is a plant product and is particularly abundant in wood.

There is good evidence, based on the analysis of plant materials before and after decomposition by pure cultures, that some fungi are able to decompose lignin *in situ,* i.e., in association with other substances of the plant. Evidence on the fungi is limited, however, to the litter-decomposing and the wood-destroying basidiomycetes. The lignin of litter is decomposed actively by species of *Marasmius, Collybia, Mycena, Clavaria,* and other soil-inhabiting Hymenomycetes (118). Most of the species studied use both the lignin and the cellulose of litter, but a few appear to utilize only the lignin (75, 118).

The wood-rotting basidiomycetes have long been differentiated into two groups (63, 64): the brown rot fungi, e.g., *Merulius domesticus,* attacking primarily the cellulose of wood, and the white rot fungi, e.g., *Polyporus annosus,* which attack the lignin more rapidly. Bavendamm (11) differentiated these two groups by their reaction on a tannic acid medium, the white rot fungi forming a colored zone (the "oxidase reaction"). Numerous studies on this reaction, summarized by Gottlieb and Pelczar (72), indicate that the enzyme responsible is a polyphenol oxidase (Chapter 6), generally present in but not limited to the lignin-utilizing fungi. The separation into brown and white rots, although useful, is not absolute—most white rot fungi use cellulose at one stage or another of the decomposition process (31, 81). The brown rot fungi, however, do not attack lignin appreciably (35) except perhaps in the advanced stages of wood decomposition (169).

In considering the utilization of lignin as the sole source of carbon, i.e., apart from other plant materials, we are reminded of the dependence of nutritional studies on adequate knowledge of the chemistry of the substrate. Most of the early work, reviewed by Waksman and Hutchings (226), is of doubtful validity, since it appears that the lignin used was contaminated with carbohydrates and protein degradation products (21, 72). A more recent method of preparation, employing mild procedures, is believed to yield an uncontaminated lignin (20). Studies on this material indicate that white rot fungi can utilize it (149, 220); other wood-destroying fungi may require a period of "training," i.e., a long incubation period in contact with the substrate, before they can utilize it (49, 71).

Although lignosulfonic acid disappears from media in which fungi are growing (1), it seems from other studies that lignosulfonate forms a complex with the mycelium and that the utilization, therefore, is only apparent (48).

Keratin, the insoluble protein of wool, hair, and feathers, has been implicated as a possible substrate for fungus growth since the observations of Ward (229) on *Onygena equina*. Jensen (97) reported growth and ammonia liberation by *Streptomyces* spp. in sand culture with keratin as the sole source of carbon and nitrogen. In a survey of keratin utilization (237), it was found that untreated wool is not attacked by common saprophytic fungi; actively keratinolytic forms are all dermatophytes, especially species of *Trichophyton* and *Microsporum*. The action of *Microsporum gypseum* on keratin and collagen is analyzed by Stahl et al. (191).

The success of keratin-containing materials as bait for chytrids (101, 102) and the ability of *Polychytrium aggregatum* to make visible growth on keratin (2) suggest that these fungi, which are not isolated by conventional procedures of soil and fabric microbiology, are worth study as possible agents of keratin destruction in nature.

Purified rubber is attacked by both fungi and actinomycetes (247);

as in decomposition of pure hydrocarbons, the actinomycetes appear
to be the more active.

Tannins are utilized by several common saprophytes (47, 109, 168),
presumably after elaboration of an adaptive tannase (Chapter 6). The
crude resins of *Guayule* are attacked by several fungi (3).

8. THE CONCENTRATION FACTOR IN CARBON NUTRITION

As the concentration of carbohydrate in a medium is increased the
economic coefficient declines; although more sugar may be utilized, the
dry weight does not increase proportionately. Carbohydrate is evidently being converted to metabolic products—carbon dioxide, organic
acids, soluble polysaccharides, etc. There also occurs at supraoptimal
glucose concentrations a simple failure to utilize the sugar present
(119), in which case the economic coefficient is not affected. These
two related phenomena are surely to be ascribed to the fact that other
constituents of the medium, especially nitrogen, become limiting at
the higher carbohydrate concentrations. That is, within limits, growth
is increased by higher carbohydrate provided that adequate nitrogen
is supplied (27). The role of zinc and other metals may be more
complicated than that of nitrogen supply (66), but the simple fact that
more cellular synthesis will increase the demand for all nutrients
should not be neglected in considering the effect of metals on growth
and metabolism.

For many fungi, increase in carbohydrate beyond an optimum
point results in an absolute as well as a relative decrease in growth.
The data of Figure 2 exemplify this type of response, which is com-

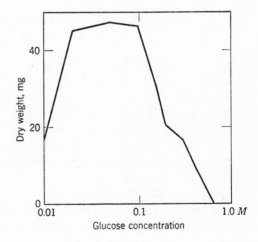

Figure 2. The effect of glucose concentration on the
growth of *Psalliota bispora.*
Drawn from tabular data of
Treschow (216).

mon in the fungi (160, 166, 227). Although most of such cases have
not been analyzed, the factor involved is almost certainly the formation of toxic metabolic products. In *Entomophthora* spp. the effect
of high concentrations of glucose is clearly to increase the acidity of
the medium (242), and the lowered pH resulting from organic acid
accumulation is probably the most general cause of poor growth at
high sugar concentrations.

The carbohydrate concentration at which growth-depressant effects
become evident is of course affected by other constituents of the
medium, especially buffers and the nitrogen source, but there are also
specific effects. Thus, growth of *Ustilago violacea* falls off above 0.2
per cent glucose (180), that of *Penicillium javanicum* only above 21.3
per cent (227). It appears probable, although there are very few
data, that in those fungi which grow well at high sugar concentrations
(above 10 per cent) the factor which ultimately limits growth is osmotic
pressure (Chapter 1).

Probably because so much of the early work on fungi concerned the
acid-tolerant species of *Aspergillus* and *Penicillium,* the media in common use for fungi are too high in available carbohydrate, giving a
distorted picture of growth and metabolism. Ideally, the level of
carbohydrate to be used should be determined by experiment for each
organism; perhaps as a rough rule of thumb, 2 per cent of available
carbohydrate in a liquid medium may be suggested as an upper limit,
considering the amounts of nitrogen usually recommended in media.
Westerdijk (232) suggests that agar stock culture media for fungi contain not more than 3 per cent carbohydrate.

9. ENZYME INDUCTION: ADAPTIVE GROWTH
AND THE UTILIZATION OF MIXED CARBON SOURCES

In this chapter we have had occasion to note that "adaptive" utilization of substrates occurs in the fungi. Operationally, adaptive growth
is usually detected in an experiment in which a relatively large population of spores in a given medium grows only after prolonged incubation. The organism is said to adapt itself to the carbon source. It
must be understood that in this type of experiment it is possible—and
in some instances very probable—that the results can be explained by
selection of a mutant pre-existing in the inoculum or arising during
the long incubation period.

In a related type of experiment, it is found that a fungus produces
much more of a given enzyme if cultivated on the substrate of the
enzyme. The literature on this phenomenon is very large, and has

been reviewed several times in the past 40 years (4, 37, 110, 245). Amylase, inulase, maltase, sucrase, lipase, pectin-polygalacturonase, and tannase are among the more frequently investigated enzymes. The results with pectin-polygalacturonase are typical, in that substances chemically related to the substrate may also increase enzyme formation (156), and in that the response to substrate occurs with some fungi and not with others (25). Here again, it must be stressed that a genetic mechanism—selection of variant cells or of variant nuclei in a heterocaryon—is as probable in many instances as a physiological mechanism.

Enzyme induction has been defined (42) as a relative increase in the rate of synthesis of a specific apoenzyme occurring in response to a specific chemical substance, the inducer. Earlier, attention was focused on the specific substrate as inducer, and the term "adaptive enzyme" was employed to denote an enzyme formed only or in increased amounts in the presence of substrate; constitutive enzymes are defined as those which are formed in quantity in a favorable medium lacking substrate or inducer (103). The inducer is most often also the substrate, but it may be a chemically related or an unrelated compound. In a classical experiment (196), resting cells of *Escherichia coli* form the enzyme formic dehydrogenase if incubated in the presence of formate, not otherwise.

It has been shown by Landman (111) that the lactase (β-galactosidase) of *Neurospora crassa* is induced under conditions which satisfy the requirements above, particularly in that lactase is formed by resting cells exposed to an inducer (Figure 3). The data show also that sugars other than lactose act as inducers. Resting cells respond somewhat differently from growing cells, and the mechanisms may not be identical. The time required for lactase induction in *N. crassa* is much longer than that required for induction of the same enzyme in yeast or in *Escherichia coli*.

The foregoing demonstration is the only one to date in the fungi. It seems reasonable, however, to postulate, in agreement with Monod (132), that at least some of the reports of adaptive growth and of stimulation of enzyme formation by substrate which have been mentioned do in fact involve enzyme induction, even though genetic change is not rigorously excluded.

Earlier in this chapter, particularly in reference to the growth of fungi with fructose and mannose, it was suggested that results with mixed carbon sources may be explained in part by the induction of new enzymes. Specifically, the effect of a small amount of glucose in permitting rapid growth on fructose or mannose, sugars which by

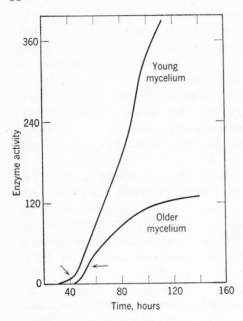

Figure 3. The formation of β-galactosidase (lactase) by resting mycelium of *Neurospora crassa.* Arrows indicate time of exposure to the inducing sugar. Redrawn from O. E. Landman, *Archives of Biochemistry and Biophysics* Vol. 52, p. 93–100 (1954), by permission of Academic Press, Inc.

themselves support growth only after a long lag, may be explained by postulating that the glucose allows sufficient growth so that an enzyme essential to fructose or mannose utilization can be synthesized. Naturally, some energy must be available for the enzyme synthesis; for resting cells endogenous reserves may be adequate, but with a spore inoculum an exogenous energy source may be necessary.

Extensive data on the utilization of mixed carbon sources have been reported by Lilly and Barnett (116). Several fungi, e.g., *Sordaria fimicola* and *Thielaviopsis basicola,* behave in accordance with the foregoing postulate—they grow on a disaccharide, melibiose for example, only if a utilizable monosaccharide is available. However, results with *Gliomastix convoluta* are not entirely explicable on this basis, unless we postulate, without proof, that the sugar which supplies energy for enzyme synthesis must be present in relatively high concentration. These experiments are complicated by the inclusion of asparagine, which supplies some carbon, in the basal medium.

The results of Steinberg (194) on the utilization of mixed carbon sources by *Aspergillus niger* are not satisfactorily explained by the hypothesis of enzyme induction. Here a mixture of two unutilizable compounds supports good growth. It is clear, from these results and from those mentioned in the preceding paragraph, that the interaction of different carbon sources requires further study.

In relation to utilization of mixed carbon sources, it should be noted that preferential utilization of one compound is common, e.g., the utilization of acetate before glucose (154) and the utilization of soluble sugars before more complex carbon compounds (62, 109, 188).

Fungi in nature live as a rule in a dilute solution with more than one carbon source available or potentially available. These conditions do not very closely resemble a single-substrate pure culture. Lignin and cellulose, for example, may be much more rapidly decomposed by the action of induced enzymes than they are when given to an organism in culture as the sole source of carbon. The ecological importance of the ability of fungi to synthesize new enzymes—if this ability proves to be general—justifies much more study of the problem. It is to be hoped, however, that such studies will be guided, more than they have been in the past, by the wealth of experience accumulated in the investigation of induced enzymes in other microorganisms.

10. EFFICIENCY OF GROWTH

Several indices of the over-all efficiency of growth in fungi have been proposed. Of these, the economic coefficient has been most frequently determined. It may best be represented as:

$$\frac{\text{Mycelial dry weight, gm}}{\text{Carbohydrate consumed, gm}} \times 100$$

Some authors have used the ratio or its reciprocal without multiplication by 100.

As an approximate index of the efficiency of carbon utilization, the economic coefficient is satisfactory. More elaborate indices, which take account of energy quantities more directly, have been devised (202, 206, 208, 210).

The economic coefficient can be seen by inspection to be maximal when respiratory carbon dioxide and soluble metabolic products are minimal in quantity. Since both of these are affected by cultural conditions, no one value or even range of values can be set down as characteristic of the fungi as a whole. Fungi grown on dilute media for no longer a time than is necessary to utilize the carbohydrate usually have an economic coefficient in the range 20 to 35; a few higher values have been reported (119, 161, 205, 209). Very low values (77, 228, 230) reflect probably the production of significant amounts of soluble carbon compounds in high-carbohydrate media.

The economic coefficient, although unaffected by temperature (209), is strongly influenced by substrate (205), metal deficiencies (29, 158, 167, 182), and nitrogen nutrition (157, 211). The influence of age is variable (28, 155). As one would expect, increasing the glucose supplied decreases the economic coefficient (119, 159, 195).

All of the factors just listed as influencing the economic coefficient almost certainly act by changing the amount of soluble metabolic products formed; it is a possibility not so far explored that the loss of carbon as CO_2 is affected, but this seems doubtful. A low economic coefficient should suggest in the first instance a search for soluble carbon compounds in the medium.

11. CONCLUSION

The most important single facet of carbon nutrition is the high degree of specificity; differences between species and strains are the rule in the fungi. Nevertheless, a search for some general principle has been and should be pursued. One such is to relate carbon nutrition to phylogeny.

It has often been pointed out, e.g., by Garrett (69), that the major groups of fungi differ with respect to cellulose and lignin utilization. The Zygomycetes do not use either of these materials; in the ascomycetes and the Fungi Imperfecti, cellulose utilization is common; the basidiomycetes contain most of the known lignin-utilizing fungi in addition to many species able to grow on cellulose. This progression toward utilization of more complex materials would be more impressive if the capacity to break down cellulose were not widespread in the Chytridiales and perhaps in the Oomycetes.

The phycomycetes, usually conceded to be the most primitive major group of fungi, have certain nutritional and metabolic characteristics which, taken together, separate them rather clearly from the higher fungi:

1. The fungi which produce large amounts of lactic acid from carbohydrate are all phycomycetes (Chapter 6).

2. The fungi able to grow at low oxygen tensions are usually phycomycetes (Chapter 1). This ability may, of course, be related to the ability to form lactic acid.

3. Requirements for organic sulfur among fungi occurring in nature are known only in the phycomycetes (Chapter 9).

4. The ability to use the lower fatty acids appears to be more common in the phycomycetes than in other groups (p. 81), although the data are still rather limited.

It may be that the appropriate theoretical framework for carbon nutrition is more the ecology than the phylogeny of fungi. The characteristics of the phycomycetes outlined above can be understood as related to the aquatic habit of most of the forms so far studied just as easily as they can be interpreted in terms of taxonomy or phylogeny. The carbon nutrition of the mycorrhizal basidiomycetes is another example. The evidence is incomplete and not entirely satisfactory, but it appears that this group is restricted in its carbon nutrition to simple sugars, starch, and the pectic substances (74, 91, 130, 131, 170). These fungi stand, therefore, in contrast to the litter-decomposing and wood-rotting basidiomycetes, which use cellulose, lignin, or both. At least one mycorrhizal basidiomycete, however, does form an adaptive cellulase (142).

The order Mucorales is cited often as a group of "sugar fungi" unable to utilize cellulose (26). This characterization appears to be sound, although relatively few of the Mucorales have been adequately investigated. Ecologically, however, the "sugar fungi" include a number of the Fungi Imperfecti, especially species of *Aspergillus* and *Penicillium*, found in soils high in fresh organic matter and in carbohydrate-containing materials. The line between "sugar fungi" and cellulose-utilizing fungi cuts therefore across taxonomic boundaries, since different species of *Aspergillus*, for example, are found in one or the other group.

In Table 1 are collected some data on the carbon nutrition of different fungi, although it cannot be said that the organisms chosen are in any way typical. The organisms of wide substrate range include a large group of soil saprophytes and plant parasites—*Aspergillus oryzae, Brevilegnia gracilis, Fusarium oxysporum f. nicotianae, Memnoniella echinata, Penicillium digitatum, Phytophthora cactorum, Psalliota bispora, Stachybotrys atra,* and *Streptomyces coelicolor.* In comparison, the aquatic phycomycetes in the list appear more fastidious; the contrast between the soil-inhabiting *Brevilegnia gracilis* and the closely related aquatic *Saprolegnia delica* is particularly instructive. On the other hand, the plant parasite *Chalara quercina* has a much narrower nutritional range than the aquatic *Pythiogeton* sp. The most restricted of all in the group are *Entomophthora coronata,* parasitic on insects, and the aquatic *Polychytrium aggregatum.*

The fungi parasitic on animals might be expected, by analogy to bacterial parasites, to be nutritionally specialized. The available data indicate that these fungi are not in fact particularly fastidious with respect to carbon sources (140, 200).

One incidental problem may be mentioned here. Throughout this chapter, it has been assumed that carbon sources are utilized by pathways involving hexoses or hexose phosphates as intermediates. However, the data of Table 1 afford several instances in which glucose is inferior to some other carbon compound, xylose, gluconic acid, disaccharides, or polysaccharides. None of these cases has been studied. The superiority of xylose or gluconate could mean that the phosphogluconate oxidation pathway (Chapter 7) is more active than others. Or, a compound may be superior to glucose for accidental reasons— pH relations, accumulation of intermediates, contamination with metals or growth factors, etc. This second explanation has been suggested earlier for the superiority of particular disaccharides and polysaccharides. It must be admitted, however, that the question is still open.

Looking at the whole field of carbon nutrition of fungi, one is struck with the gaps in our knowledge. Certain groups—the Mucorales and the Peronosporales are examples—have been more or less neglected. Comparative studies of species within a genus, particularly species of different habitat, might prove most valuable. The biochemical basis of nutritional capabilities is largely a matter of inference at present; failure to utilize fructose or mannitol, for example, probably has a simple enzymatic basis. As just discussed above, induced enzyme synthesis in the fungi is still largely a matter for speculation. Some of the data reported in this chapter, and more which have been omitted, are difficult to accept, and important points of this nature should be reinvestigated. Finally, the understanding of nutrition in nature, with numerous substrates present in low concentration, is a long-range goal progress toward which will require radically new techniques of investigation.

BIBLIOGRAPHY

1. Adams, G. A. and G. A. Ledingham. 1942. *Can. J. Research C*, 20: 101–107.
2. Ajello, L. 1948. *Am. J. Botany* 35: 135–140.
3. Allen, P. J., J. Naghski, and S. R. Hoover. 1944. *J. Bacteriol.* 47: 559–568.
4. Ammann, A. 1951. *Phytopathol. Z.* 18: 416–446.
5. Aschan, K. and B. Norkrans. 1953. *Physiol. Plantarum* 6: 564–583.
6. Baba, S. 1941. *Bull. Agr. Chem. Soc. Japan* 17: 109–110.
7. Ball, E. 1953. *Bull. Torrey Botan. Club* 80: 409–411.
8. Barnard, D. and F. Challenger. 1949. *J. Chem. Soc. (London)* 1949: 110–117.
9. Barner, H. D. and E. C. Cantino. 1952. *Am. J. Botany* 39: 746–751.
10. Barton, R. R. 1953. *Mycologia* 45: 533–547.
11. Bavendamm, W. 1927. *Ber. deut. botan. Ges.* 45: 357–367.
12. Beckman, C. H., J. E. Kuntz, and A. J. Riker. 1953. *Phytopathology* 43: 441–447.

13. Benedict, R. G., L. A. Lindenfelser, F. H. Stodola, and D. H. Traufler. 1951. *J. Bacteriol.* 62: 487–497.
14. Benedict, R. G., T. G. Pridham, L. A. Lindenfelser, and R. W. Jackson. 1955. *Appl. Microbiol.* 3: 1–6.
15. Bernhauer, K. and F. Slanina. 1933. *Biochem. Z.* 264: 109–112.
16. Bhargava, K. S. 1943. *J. Indian Botan. Soc.* 22: 85–99.
17. Bhargava, K. S. 1945. *Lloydia* 8: 60–68.
18. Blank, L. M. and P. J. Talley. 1941. *Am. J. Botany* 28: 564–569.
19. Blumer, S. 1937. *Arch. Mikrobiol.* 8: 458–478.
20. Brauns, F. E. 1939. *J. Am. Chem. Soc.* 61: 2120–2127.
21. Brauns, F. E. 1952. *The Chemistry of Lignin.* New York: Academic Press, pp. 808.
22. Bretzloff, C. W., Jr. 1954. *Am. J. Botany* 41: 58–67.
23. Brian, P. W., P. J. Curtis, and H. G. Hemming. 1946. *Trans. Brit. Mycol. Soc.* 29: 173–187.
24. Brian, P. W., P. J. Curtis, and H. G. Hemming. 1947. *Proc. Roy. Soc. (London) B* 135: 106–132.
25. Brown, W. and R. K. S. Wood. 1953. *Symposium Soc. Gen. Microbiol.* 3: 326–339.
26. Burges, A. 1939. *Broteria, Sér. trimestral,* 8: 64–81.
27. Burkholder, P. R. and I. McVeigh. 1940. *Am. J. Botany* 27: 634–640.
28. Butkewitsch, W. 1922. *Biochem. Z.* 131: 338–350.
29. Butkewitsch, W. and W. G. Orlow. 1922. *Biochem. Z.* 132: 556–565.
30. Camp, A. F. 1923. *Ann. Missouri Botan. Garden* 10: 213–298.
31. Campbell, W. G. 1932. *Biochem. J. (London)* 26: 1829–1838.
32. Cantino, E. C. 1949a. *Am. J. Botany* 36: 95–112.
33. Cantino, E. C. 1949b. *Am. J. Botany* 36: 747–756.
34. Cantino, E. C. 1950. *Quart. Rev. Biol.* 25: 269–277.
35. Cartwright, K. St. G. and W. P. K. Findlay. 1946. *Decay of Timber and Its Prevention.* London: H. M. Stationery Office, pp. 294.
36. Cheldelin, V. H. and T. E. King. 1953. *Ann. Rev. Microbiol.* 7: 113–142.
37. Christensen, J. J. and J. M. Daly. 1951. *Ann. Rev. Microbiol.* 5: 57–70.
38. Chrzaszcz, T. and M. Zakomorny. 1935. *Biochem. Z.* 279: 64–75.
39. Cochrane, V. W. 1952. *J. Bacteriol.* 63: 459–471.
40. Cochrane, V. W. and J. E. Conn. 1947. *J. Bacteriol.* 54: 213–218.
41. Cochrane, V. W., H. D. Peck, Jr., and A. Harrison. 1953. *J. Bacteriol.* 66: 17–23.
42. Cohn, M., J. Monod, M. R. Pollock, S. Spiegelman, and R. Y. Stanier. 1953. *Nature (London)* 172: 1096.
43. Conn, H. J. 1921. *N. Y. State Agr. Exp. Sta. (Geneva, N. Y.) Bull.* 83: 1–26.
44. Corum, C. J. 1942. *Botan. Gaz.* 103: 740–750.
45. Crasemann, J. M. 1954. *Am. J. Botany* 41: 302–310.
46. Czapek, F. 1903. *Beitr. Chem. Physiol. Path.* 3: 47–66.
47. Davis, D., P. E. Waggoner, and A. E. Dimond. 1953. *Nature (London)* 172: 959.
48. Day, W. C., S. Gottlieb, and M. J. Pelczar, Jr. 1953. *Appl. Microbiol.* 1: 78–81.
49. Day, W. C., M. J. Pelczar, Jr., and S. Gottlieb. 1949. *Arch. Biochem. Biophys.* 23: 360–369.
50. DeLey, J. and J. Vandamme. 1955. *J. Gen. Microbiol.* 12: 162–171.
51. Dietzel, E., H. Behrenbruch, and M. Eucken. 1950. *Arch. Mikrobiol.* 15: 179–184.
52. Dimond, A. E. and G. L. Peltier. 1945. *Am. J. Botany* 32: 46–50.
53. Doudoroff, M. 1951. In W. D. McElroy, and B. Glass (eds.), *Phosphorus Metabolism,* Vol. 1, p. 42–48. Baltimore: Johns Hopkins Press.

54. Dox, A. W. and R. E. Neidig. 1912. *Biochem. Z.* 46: 397–402.
55. Dubos, R. J. 1928a. *Ecology* 9: 12–27.
56. Dubos, R. J. 1928b. *J. Bacteriol.* 15: 223–234.
57. Ehrensvärd, G. 1955. *Exp. Cell Research Suppl.* 3: 102–109.
58. Emerson, R. and E. C. Cantino. 1948. *Am. J. Botany* 35: 157–171.
59. Englis, D. T. and D. J. Hanahan. 1945. *J. Am. Chem. Soc.* 67: 51–54.
60. Erikson, D. 1941. *J. Bacteriol.* 41: 277–300.
61. Estienne, V., E. Castagne, and E. Bertrand. 1947. *Bull. soc. chim. biol.* 29: 620–627.
62. Eyre, J. C. 1932. *Ann. Appl. Biol.* 19: 351–369.
63. Falck, R. 1926. *Ber. deut. botan. Ges.* 44: 652–664.
64. Falck, R. and W. Haag. 1927. *Ber. deut. chem. Ges.* 60: 225–232.
65. Fergus, C. L. 1952. *Mycologia* 44: 183–189.
66. Foster, J. W. 1949. *Chemical Activities of Fungi.* New York: Academic Press, pp. 648.
67. Fruton, J. S. and S. Simmonds. 1953. *General Biochemistry.* New York: John Wiley and Sons, pp. 940.
68. Fuller, W. H. and A. G. Norman. 1945. *J. Bacteriol.* 50: 667–671.
69. Garrett, S. D. 1951. *New Phytologist* 50: 149–166.
70. Górski, F. 1937. *Bull. intern. acad. polon. sci. Classe sci. math. nat., Sér. B,* 1, 1937: 89–105.
71. Gottlieb, S., W. C. Day, and M. J. Pelczar, Jr. 1950. *Phytopathology* 40: 926–935.
72. Gottlieb, S. and M. J. Pelczar, Jr. 1951. *Bacteriol. Revs.* 15: 55–76.
73. Greathouse, G. A., D. E. Klemme, and H. D. Barker. 1942. *Ind. Eng. Chem. Anal. Ed.* 14: 611–620.
74. Harley, J. L. 1952. *Ann. Rev. Microbiol.* 6: 367–386.
75. Harris, G. C. M. 1945. *Ann. Appl. Biol.* 32: 38–39.
76. Harrold, C. E. and M. Fling. 1952. *J. Biol. Chem.* 194: 399–406.
77. Harter, L. L. and J. L. Weimer. 1921. *J. Agr. Research* 21: 211–226.
78. Haskins, R. H. and W. H. Weston, Jr. 1950. *Am. J. Botany* 37: 739–750.
79. Hawker, L. E. and S. D. Chaudhuri. 1946. *Ann. Botany* 10: 185–194.
80. Hawkins, L. A. 1915. *Am. J. Botany* 2: 375–388.
81. Hawley, L. F., L. C. Fleck, and C. A. Richards. 1928. *Ind. Eng. Chem.* 20: 504–507.
82. Herrick, J. A. 1940. *Ohio J. Sci.* 40: 123–129.
83. Hestrin, S. 1948. *Wallerstein Lab. Commun.* 11: 193–207.
84. Hestrin, S. 1949. *Wallerstein Lab. Commun.* 12: 45–54.
85. Heuser, E., B. F. Shema, W. Shockley, J. W. Appling, and J. F. McCoy. 1949. *Arch. Biochem.* 21: 343–350.
86. Hill, E. G. and A. R. Patton. 1947. *Science* 105: 481–482.
87. Hofmann, E. 1931. *Biochem. Z.* 243: 423–428.
88. Holden, M. 1950. *Biochem. J. (London)* 47: 426–431.
89. Horowitz-Wlassowa, L. M. and M. J. Livschitz. 1935. *Zentr. Bakteriol. Parasitenk. Abt. II,* 92: 424–435.
90. Horr, W. H. 1936. *Plant Physiol.* 11: 81–99.
91. How, J. E. 1940. *Ann. Botany* 4: 135–150.
92. Hubbard, C. V. and H. H. Thornberry. 1950. *Trans. Illinois State Acad. Sci.* 43: 61–74.
93. Hungate, R. E. 1946. *J. Bacteriol.* 51: 51–56.
94. Ingraham, J. L. and R. Emerson. 1954. *Am. J. Botany* 41: 146–152.
95. Jarvis, F. G. and M. J. Johnson. 1947. *J. Am. Chem. Soc.* 69: 3010–3017.
96. Jeffreys, E. G., P. W. Brian, H. G. Hemming, and D. Lowe. 1953. *J. Gen. Microbiol.* 9: 314–341.
97. Jensen, H. L. 1930. *J. Agr. Sci.* 20: 390–398.

98. Jensen, H. L. 1931. *Proc. Linnean Soc. N. S. Wales* 56: 345–370.
99. Jermyn, M. A. 1953. *Australian J. Biol. Sci.* 6: 48–69.
100. Johnson, G. T. and A. C. Jones. 1941. *Mycologia* 33: 424–433.
101. Karling, J. S. 1946. *Am. J. Botany* 33: 751–757.
102. Karling, J. S. 1947. *Am. J. Botany* 34: 27–32.
103. Karström, H. 1938. *Ergeb. Enzymforsch.* 7: 350–376.
104. Khambata, S. R. and J. V. Bhat. 1953. *J. Bacteriol.* 66: 505–507.
105. Kita, D. A. and W. H. Peterson. 1953. *J. Biol. Chem.* 203: 861–868.
106. Klein, H. P. and M. Doudoroff. 1950. *J. Bacteriol.* 59: 739–750.
107. Klemme, D. E. 1942. *J. Bacteriol.* 43: 171–180.
108. Klemme, D. E., G. A. Greathouse, K. Bollenbacher, and S. Pope. 1945. *U. S. Dept. Agr. Circ. No.* 737: 1–11.
109. Knudson, L. 1913. *J. Biol. Chem.* 14: 159–184, 185–202.
110. Kylin, R. 1914. *Jahrb. wiss. Botan.* 53: 465–501.
111. Landman, O. E. 1954. *Arch. Biochem. Biophys.* 52: 93–109.
112. Landman, O. E. and D. M. Bonner. 1952. *Arch. Biochem. Biophys.* 41: 253–265.
113. Leben, C. and G. W. Keitt. 1948. *Am. J. Botany* 35: 337–343.
114. Lein, J., D. C. Appleby, and P. S. Lein. 1951. *Arch. Biochem. Biophys.* 34: 72–80.
115. Leonian, L. H. and V. G. Lilly. 1940. *Am. J. Botany* 27: 18–26.
116. Lilly, V. G. and H. L. Barnett. 1953. *West Va. Univ. Agr. Exp. Sta. Bull.* 362T: 5–58.
116a. Lilly, V. G. and H. L. Barnett. 1956. *Am. J. Botany* 43: 709–714.
117. Lindeberg, G. 1944. *Symbolae Botan. Upsalienses* 8 (2): 1–183.
118. Lindeberg, G. 1946. *Arkiv Botan.* 33A (10): 1–16.
119. Lockwood, L. B. and G. E. N. Nelson. 1946a. *Arch. Biochem.* 10: 365–374.
120. Lockwood, L. B. and G. E. N. Nelson. 1946b. *J. Bacteriol.* 52: 581–586.
121. Lockwood, L. B., G. E. Ward, O. E. May, H. T. Herrick, and H. T. O'Neill. 1934. *Zentr. Bakteriol. Parasitenk. Abt. II*, 90: 411–425.
122. Lwoff, A., H. Ionescu, and A. Gutmann. 1949. *Compt. rend. (Paris)* 228: 342–344.
123. McBeth, I. G. and F. M. Scales. 1913. *U. S. Dept. Agr. Bur. Plant Ind. Bull.* 266: 1–52.
124. Machlis, L. 1953. *Am. J. Botany* 40: 460–464.
125. McKeen, W. E. 1956. *Science* 123: 509.
126. Marsh, P. B., K. Bollenbacher, M. L. Butler, and K. B. Raper. 1949. *Textile Research J.* 19: 462–484.
127. Martin, J. P. 1945. *J. Bacteriol.* 50: 349–360.
128. Mehrotra, B. S. 1949. *J. Indian Botan. Soc.* 28: 108–124.
129. Mehrotra, B. S. 1951. *Lloydia* 14: 122–128.
130. Melin, E. 1925. *Untersuchungen über die Bedeutung der Baum-Mykorrhiza.* Jena: Gustav Fischer, pp. 152.
131. Melin, E. 1948. *Trans. Brit. Mycol. Soc.* 30: 92–99.
132. Monod, J. 1947. *Growth* 11: 223–289.
133. Moore, W. F. 1949. *J. Gen. Microbiol.* 3: 143–147.
134. Morton, A. G. and A. Macmillan. 1954. *J. Exp. Botany* 5: 232–252.
135. Moyer, A. J. and R. D. Coghill. 1946. *J. Bacteriol.* 51: 57–78.
136. Mudge, C. S. 1917. *J. Bacteriol.* 2: 403–415.
137. Müller, H. 1950. *Arch. Mikrobiol.* 15: 137–148.
138. Newth, F. H. 1951. *Advances in Carbohydrate Chem.* 6: 83–106.
139. Nickerson, W. J. and R. R. Mohan. 1953. *Intern. Congr. Microbiol., 6th Congr. Rome,* 5: 137–146.
140. Nickerson, W. J. and J. W. Williams. 1947. In W. J. Nickerson (ed.), *Biology of Pathogenic Fungi.* p. 130–156. Waltham, Mass.: The Chronica Botanica Co.

141. Nord, F. F. and E. W. Engel. 1938. *Biochem. Z.* 296: 153–170.
142. Norkrans, B. 1950. *Symbolae Botan. Upsalienses* 11 (1): 5–126.
143. Norman, A. G. 1931. *Ann. Appl. Biol.* 18: 244–259.
144. Obaton, F. 1932. *Compt. rend. (Paris)* 194: 302–304.
145. O'Connor, R. C. 1940. *Biochem. J. (London)* 34: 1008–1011.
146. Oddoux, L. 1952. *Compt. rend. (Paris)* 234: 654–657.
147. Otto, H. 1916. *Beitr. Allgem. Botan.* 1: 190–260.
148. Pasteur, L. 1860. *Compt. rend. (Paris)* 51: 298–299.
149. Pelczar, M. J., Jr., S. Gottlieb, and W. C. Day. 1950. *Arch. Biochem.* 25: 449–451.
150. Perlman, D. 1948a. *Am. J. Botany* 35: 36–41.
151. Perlman, D. 1948b. *Am. J. Botany* 35: 360–363.
152. Perlman, D. 1950. *Bull. Torrey Botan. Club* 77: 103–109.
153. Perlman, D., D. A. Kita, and W. H. Peterson. 1946. *Arch. Biochem.* 11: 123–129.
154. Peterson, W. H. 1946–1947. *Harvey Lectures, Ser. 42:* 276–302.
155. Peterson, W. H., E. B. Fred, and E. G. Schmidt. 1922. *J. Biol. Chem.* 54: 19–34.
156. Phaff, H. J. 1947. *Arch. Biochem.* 13: 67–81.
157. Pinck, L. A. and F. E. Allison. 1944. *Soil Sci.* 57: 155–161.
158. Porges, N. 1932. *Botan. Gaz.* 94: 197–205.
159. Prill, E. A., P. R. Wenck, and W. H. Peterson. 1935. *Biochem. J. (London)* 29: 21–33.
160. Quantz, L. 1943. *Jahrb. wiss. Botan.* 91: 120–168.
161. Raaf, H. 1941. *Arch. Microbiol.* 12: 131–182.
162. Reese, E. T. 1947. *J. Bacteriol.* 53: 389–400.
162a. Reese, E. T., H. Cravetz, and G. R. Mandels. 1955. *Farlowia* 4: 409–421.
163. Reese, E. T. and M. H. Downing. 1951. *Mycologia* 43: 16–28.
164. Reese, E. T. and H. S. Levinson. 1952. *Physiol. Plantarum* 5: 345–366.
165. Reischer, H. 1951. *Mycologia* 43: 319–328.
166. Reitsma, J. 1932. *Phytopathol. Z.* 4: 461–522.
167. Rippel, A. and G. Behr. 1934. *Arch. Mikrobiol.* 5: 561–577.
168. Rippel, A. and J. Keseling. 1930. *Arch. Mikrobiol.* 1: 60–77.
169. Robak, H. 1942. *Med. Vestl. Forst. Forsøksstation* 7(3): 1–248.
170. Romell, L.-G. 1938. *Svensk Botan. Tidskr.* 32: 89–99.
171. Rothstein, A. 1954. *Symposia Soc. Exp. Biol.* 8: 165–201.
172. Ryan, F. J., G. W. Beadle, and E. L. Tatum. 1943. *Am. J. Botany* 30: 784–799.
173. Saksena, R. K. and S. K. Bose. 1944. *J. Indian Botan. Soc.* 23: 108–112.
174. Satina, S. and A. F. Blakeslee. 1928. *Proc. Natl. Acad. Sci. U. S.* 14: 229–235.
175. Schade, A. L. 1940. *Am. J. Botany* 27: 376–384.
176. Schatz, A., H. D. Isenberg, A. A. Angrist, and V. Schatz. 1954. *J. Bacteriol.* 68: 1–4.
177. Schatz, A., K. Savard, and I. J. Pintner. 1949. *J. Bacteriol.* 58: 117–125.
178. Scheffer, T. C. 1936. *U. S. Dept. Agr. Tech. Bull. No. 527:* 1–45.
179. Schmidt, E. G., W. H. Peterson, and E. B. Fred. 1923. *Soil Sci.* 15: 479–488.
180. Schopfer, W. H. and S. Blumer. 1938. *Arch. Mikrobiol.* 9: 305–367.
181. Schopfer, W. H. and M. Guilloud. 1945. *Z. Vitaminforsch.* 16: 181–296.
182. Schulz, G. 1937. *Planta* 27: 196–218.
183. Schutter, J. and P. W. Wilson. 1955. *J. Gen. Microbiol.* 12: 446–454.
184. Shirakawa, H. S. 1955. *Am. J. Botany* 42: 379–384.
185. Sistrom, D. E. and L. Machlis. 1955. *J. Bacteriol.* 70: 50–55.
186. Siu, R. G. H. 1951. *Microbial Decomposition of Cellulose.* New York: Reinhold Publ. Corp., pp. 531.

187. Siu, R. G. H., R. T. Darby, P. R. Burkholder, and E. S. Barghoorn. 1949. *Textile Research J.* 19: 484–488.
188. Siu, R. G. H. and J. W. Sinden. 1951. *Am. J. Botany* 38: 284–290.
189. Skinner, C. E. and F. Dravis. 1937. *Ecology* 18: 391–397.
190. Stadtman, T. C., R. H. Vaughn, and G. L. Marsh. 1945. *J. Bacteriol.* 50: 691–700.
191. Stahl, W. H., B. McQue, G. R. Mandels, and R. G. H. Siu. 1950. *Textile Research J.* 20: 570–579.
192. Stahl, W. H. and H. Pessen. 1953. *Appl. Microbiol.* 1: 30–35.
193. Stanier, R. Y. 1942. *Bacteriol. Revs.* 6: 143–196.
194. Steinberg, R. A. 1939. *J. Agr. Research* 59: 749–764.
195. Steinberg, R. A. 1942. *J. Agr. Research* 64: 615–633.
196. Stephenson, M. and L. H. Stickland. 1933. *Biochem. J. (London)* 27: 1528–1532.
197. Stern, A. M., Z. J. Ordal, and H. O. Halvorson. 1954. *J. Bacteriol.* 68: 24–27.
198. de Stevens, G. and F. F. Nord. 1952. *J. Am. Chem. Soc.* 74: 3326–3328.
199. Stevens, N. E. and R. A. Chapman. 1942. *Phytopathology* 32: 184.
200. Stockdale, P. 1953. *Biol. Revs. Cambridge Phil. Soc.* 28: 84–104.
201. Tamiya, H. 1932. *Acta Phytochim. (Japan)* 6: 1–129.
202. Tamiya, H. 1942. *Advances in Enzymol.* 2: 183–238.
203. Tamiya, H. and S. Usami. 1940. *Acta Phytochim. (Japan)* 11: 261–298.
204. Tatum, E. L., R. W. Barratt, and V. M. Cutter, Jr. 1949. *Science* 109: 509–511.
205. Tausson, W. O. 1928. *Biochem. Z.* 193: 85–93.
206. Tausson, W. O. 1935. *Mikrobiologiya* 4: 166–175.
207. Tempel, E. 1931. *Arch. Mikrobiol.* 2: 40–71.
208. Terroine, E. F. and R. Bonnet. 1930. *Bull. soc. chim. biol.* 12: 10–19.
209. Terroine, E. F. and R. Wurmser. 1922a. *Bull. soc. chim. biol.* 4: 519–567.
210. Terroine, E. F. and R. Wurmser. 1922b. *Compt. rend. (Paris)* 174: 1435–1437.
211. Terroine, E. F. and R. Wurmser. 1922c. *Compt. rend. (Paris)* 175: 228–230.
212. Thaler, H. and W. Eisenlohr. 1941. *Biochem. Z.* 308: 88–102.
213. Thaler, H. and G. Geist. 1939. *Biochem. Z.* 302: 121–136.
214. Thom, C., H. Humfeld, and H. P. Holmes. 1938. *Am. Dyestuff Reptr.* 23: 581–586.
215. Thorne, C. B. and W. H. Peterson. 1948. *J. Biol. Chem.* 176: 413–429.
216. Treschow, C. 1944. *Dansk botan. Arkiv* 11(6): 1–180.
217. Turfitt, G. E. 1944. *J. Bacteriol.* 47: 487–493.
218. Turfitt, G. E. 1947. *J. Bacteriol.* 54: 557–562.
219. Umbreit, W. W. 1939. *J. Bacteriol.* 38: 73–89.
220. Van Vliet, W. F. 1954. *Biochim. et Biophys. Acta* 15: 211–216.
221. Waksman, S. A. 1919. *Soil Sci.* 8: 71–215.
222. Waksman, S. A. 1931. *Arch. Mikrobiol.* 2: 136–154.
223. Waksman, S. A. 1932. *Principles of Soil Microbiology,* 2d ed. Baltimore: Williams and Wilkins Co., pp. 894.
224. Waksman, S. A. 1940. *Botan. Rev.* 6: 637–665.
225. Waksman, S. A. and R. A. Diehm. 1931. *Soil Sci.* 32: 73–95, 97–117.
226. Waksman, S. A. and I. J. Hutchings. 1936. *Soil Sci.* 42: 119–130.
227. Ward, G. E., L. B. Lockwood, O. E. May, and H. T. Herrick. 1935. *Ind. Eng. Chem.* 27: 318–322.
228. Ward, G. E., L. B. Lockwood, O. E. May, and H. T. Herrick. 1936. *J. Am. Chem. Soc.* 58: 1286–1288.
229. Ward, H. M. 1899. *Phil. Trans. Roy. Soc. London Ser. B,* 191: 269–291.
230. Wassiljew, G. M. 1935. *Biochem. Z.* 278: 226–234.
231. Webley, D. M. and P. C. DeKock. 1952. *Biochem. J. (London)* 51: 371–375.

98 CARBON NUTRITION

232. Westerdijk, J. 1947. *Antonie van Leeuwenhoek J. Microbiol. Serol.* 12: 223–231.
233. Whiffen, A. J. 1941. *J. Elisha Mitchell Sci. Soc.* 57: 321–330.
234. Whiffen, A. J. 1945. *J. Elisha Mitchell Sci. Soc.* 61: 114–123.
235. Whistler, R. L. and C. L. Smart. 1953. *Polysaccharide Chemistry.* New York: Academic Press, pp. 493.
236. White, W. L., R. T. Darby, G. M. Stechert, and K. Sanderson. 1948. *Mycologia* 40: 34–84.
237. White, W. L., G. R. Mandels, and R. G. H. Siu. 1950. *Mycologia* 42: 199–223.
238. White, W. L., R. G. H. Siu, and E. T. Reese. 1948. *Bull. Torrey Botan. Club* 75: 604–632.
239. Wigglesworth, V. B. 1948. *Biol. Revs. Cambridge Phil. Soc.* 23: 408–451.
240. Willaman, J. J. 1920. *Botan. Gaz.* 70: 221–229.
241. Wilson, W. E. 1942. *Phytopathology* 32: 130–140.
242. Wolf, F. T. 1951. *Bull. Torrey Botan. Club* 78: 211–220.
243. Wolf, F. T. 1955. *Bull. Torrey Botan. Club* 82: 343–354.
244. Wooster, R. C. and V. H. Cheldelin. 1945. *Arch. Biochem.* 8: 311–320.
245. Young, V. H. 1918. *Plant World* 21: 75–87, 114–133.
246. ZoBell, C. E. 1946. *Bacteriol. Revs.* 10: 1–50.
247. ZoBell, C. E. 1950. *Advances in Enzymol.* 10: 443–486.

4. Carbon Metabolism

Part I

Introduction

The sheer bulk of the reported investigative work on carbon metabolism dictates some subdivision of the topic for the sake of convenience. In this and the two succeeding chapters we are concerned with the principal transformations of carbon compounds brought about by fungi, excluding those primarily important in the metabolism of nitrogenous compounds (Chapter 8) and a few which are better considered in conjunction with respiration (Chapter 7).

Broadly considered, the physiological problems of carbon metabolism are two: the conditions under which a compound is utilized, and the conditions under which a compound is manufactured by the cell. These lead to two corresponding biochemical problems, the pathway of breakdown and the pathway of biosynthesis. The natural occurrence of compounds and processes is also of interest. For any class of compounds the information is usually incomplete; thus, the physiology of acid formation is better known than are the biosynthetic pathways involved, and very little solid information on the breakdown of the acids is available. Many interesting compounds are known so far largely as curiosities, since neither their physiological significance nor their biosynthesis has been explored; it seems warranted, however, to include at least some examples of these in a discussion of fungus physiology.

Because so much work has been done on the metabolites which accumulate in large amounts, it is salutary to recall that probably most fungi in culture form cell material and carbon dioxide exclusively. Thus, of 40 basidiomycetes investigated by Whitaker (21), only 3 produced significant amounts of soluble carbon compounds. The classical studies of Birkinshaw, Raistrick, and others were carried out on common saprophytes growing in a medium relatively high in carbohydrates; even under these conditions numerous species of *Penicillium, Aspergillus* and other genera were found to form only carbon dioxide and cell substance. It is safe also to assume that fungi growing in soil do not accumulate the same products which they do in pure culture.

Carbon balance studies provide essential information as to the type of metabolism involved. The methods of Birkinshaw and Raistrick (6) are still valuable, and others have been developed more recently (18). Table 1 illustrates a typical carbon and oxidation-reduction balance. Determinations of carbon balances include many on members of the Fungi Imperfecti (2, 4, 5, 12, 15, 20), and a few on the lower phycomycetes (8, 13) and on the higher fungi (3, 18, 21).

Table 1.   Carbon and Oxidation-Reduction Balances in
Aspergillus Niger (18)

	mM	Carbon, mM	Oxidation- Reduction Value per Mole*	Over-all Oxidation- Reduction Value
Substrate utilized				
Glucose	38.0	228.0	0.0	0.0
Ammonium chloride	1.96		0.0	0.0
Oxygen	109.36		2.0	218.6
Total		228.0		218.6
Products formed				
Carbon dioxide	88.20	88.20	2.0	176.4
Citric acid	16.13	96.78	3.0	48.4
Extracellular polysac-				
charide (as glucose)	2.51	15.06	0.0	0.0
Cell				
Carbohydrates (as				
glucose)	2.93	17.58	0.0	0.0
Chitin	0.114	3.65	−6.0	−0.68
Protein nitrogen	0.765	5.92	−1.78†	−2.72
Lipids	Trace			
Total		227.2		221.4

Carbon recovery = 227.2/228.0 = 99.7%
Oxidation-reduction balance = 221.4/218.6 = 1.01
* See original paper for calculation.
† Per atom nitrogen.

It is not always appreciated that a carbon balance implies an oxidation-reduction balance, and that some error must have been made if the oxidized products cannot be accounted for by the reduced products.

The use of resting cells in metabolism studies is another valuable technique, but its limitations are not always recognized. The essential feature of the method is that cells are grown in a complete medium, washed, and put in contact with, usually, a single compound. This compound may be a putative precursor of a fungal metabolite which is of interest, or one may be concerned with the dissimilation of the compound itself. In a short space it is impossible to describe all the pitfalls of this method, but some of the more important may be summarized:

1. The previous history of the cells may influence the results obtained, at least quantitatively (1, 14, 19).

2. The thick, inhomogeneous mat of a surface culture is probably always less desirable than the more nearly homogeneous mycelium from a shaken or aerated culture.

3. The purpose of the method is defeated if a source of nitrogen is included; generally the cells contain and liberate some nitrogenous compounds.

4. The endogenous metabolism must be taken into account or even, if possible, manipulated, e.g., by starvation. Thus, it is possible that an added compound may simply protect an endogenously formed metabolite from utilization (7) and appear, therefore, to be a precursor of it.

5. Probably the technique is of more value in the study of the dissimilation of a compound than it is in the study of synthetic pathways. A compound, e.g., acetate, has so many metabolic channels open to it that its effect on a synthesis is difficult to interpret. Similar problems arise in studies of dissimilation, but in general the interpretation is clearer, provided the products account for the bulk of the compound disappearing. It has been observed (16) that the weight of "resting cells" may increase during incubation with sucrose; presumably this is a manifestation of oxidative assimilation (Chapter 7).

The use of the resting cell technique is discussed by Foster (11), who offers the particularly valuable suggestion that in precursor studies a known low level of carbohydrate—just sufficient to allow minimal synthesis of the product—should be supplied.

The details of particular enzymatic methods are beyond our scope here; a compendium of such methods has recently appeared (9). Two common problems which arise repeatedly in the fungi may, however, be mentioned. First, it is not always taken into account that the typical preparation contains many enzymes in addition to the one under study. Thus, the appearance of isomaltose during the hydrolysis of starch by amylase was once taken as evidence for the structure of the starch molecule; it is now known that it merely denotes the presence of a contaminating transglycosidase (17).

A second common difficulty in enzymatic work is the tendency to read too much into experiments with intact cells. Thus, the appearance of unsaturated fatty acids in the medium during the metabolism of saturated fats by intact cells is certainly prima-facie evidence for the existence inside the cells of a fatty acid dehydrogenase; it is not, however, a demonstration of the enzyme and should not be described as such. *Ex hypothesi,* an intracellular enzyme can be demonstrated unequivocally only in a cell-free preparation, although properly designed experiments with whole cells may establish a high probability that the enzyme is present.

The variability of fungi is a real problem which arises in connection with virtually all phases of metabolism. However, the amount of variation should not be exaggerated and should not be used as a crutch for a failing hypothesis. Complete loss of metabolic capacities is, of course, well known to be inducible by mutagenic agents and presumably, therefore, may occur as a result of spontaneous mutation. Most such mutants, however, are non-viable except under carefully adjusted conditions of culture. It appears that quantitative changes are more common than qualitative; an organism may change in the amount of a given substance formed but still form some. Exceptions will occur and must be taken into account, but the progress of a cumulative science requires that the material foundation be assumed constant unless the evidence clearly proves that it is not.

Variability may result from changes in the growth rate, such as those described among geographical isolates and cultural variants of *Fomes annosus* (10), rather than from a loss of metabolic capacities. If two strains have the same metabolism but different growth rates, analysis at one arbitrary time for a metabolite may give an exaggerated picture of the differences between them. Thus, if a given compound is first formed and then utilized after exhaustion of the principal carbon source, a rapidly growing strain may complete the process of reutilization at a time when a more slowly growing strain is still in the phase of rapid formation of the compound; it would appear from analysis at this single time that the rapidly growing strain was deficient in the synthesis. To circumvent this difficulty it is necessary to study cultures at the same physiological age—judged by the amount of growth or disappearance of substrate—rather than at the same chronological age.

The physiologist often, perhaps inevitably, overlooks problems of taxonomy and morphology. Particularly in rather difficult genera like *Penicillium* and *Aspergillus,* the careful description of cultures with at least some indication that the species has been correctly named is of definite value to the next student of the problem. The question of morphology arises in a different context in the fungi, in that conditions of growth or special treatments employed in preparing cells may drastically alter the ratio of different kinds of cells, e.g., the ratio of spores to mycelium or, even more important, the ratio of living to dead cells. It should not be necessary to labor this point.

BIBLIOGRAPHY

1. Bernhauer, K. 1928. *Biochem. Z.* 197: 287–308.
2. Birkinshaw, J. H., J. H. V. Charles, A. C. Hetherington, and H. Raistrick. 1931a. *Phil. Trans. Roy. Soc. London Ser. B* 220: 55–92.
3. Birkinshaw, J. H., J. H. V. Charles, A. C. Hetherington, and H. Raistrick. 1931b. *Phil. Trans. Roy. Soc. London Ser. B* 220: 99–125.
4. Birkinshaw, J. H., J. H. V. Charles, H. Raistrick, and J. A. R. Stoyle. 1931a. *Phil. Trans. Roy. Soc. London Ser. B* 220: 27–54.
5. Birkinshaw, J. H., J. H. V. Charles, H. Raistrick, and J. A. R. Stoyle. 1931b. *Phil. Trans. Roy. Soc. London Ser. B* 220: 93–98.
6. Birkinshaw, J. H. and H. Raistrick. 1931. *Phil. Trans. Roy. Soc. London Ser. B* 220: 11–26.
7. Butkewitsch, W. (Butkevich, V. S.), E. V. Menzhinskaia, and E. I. Troffimova. 1934. *Mikrobiologiya* 3: 319–342.
8. Cantino, E. C. 1949. *Am. J. Botany* 36: 95–112.
9. Colowick, S. P. and N. O. Kaplan (eds.). 1955. *Methods in Enzymology,* Vol. 1. New York: Academic Press, pp. 835.
10. Etheridge, D. E. 1955. *Can. J. Botany* 33: 416–428.
11. Foster, J. W. 1949. *Chemical Activities of Fungi.* New York: Academic Press, pp. 648.
12. Hockenhull, D. J. D. 1950. *J. Exp. Botany* 1: 194–200.
13. Ingraham, J. L. and R. Emerson. 1954. *Am. J. Botany* 41: 146–152.
14. Kluyver, A. J. and L. H. C. Perquin. 1933. *Biochem. Z.* 266: 82–95.
15. Lockwood, L. B., J. J. Stubbs, and C. E. Senseman. 1938. *Zentr. Bakteriol. Parasitenk. Abt. II,* 98: 167–171.
16. Lvoff, S. and G. M. Toupizina. 1938. *Compt. rend. acad. sci. U.R.S.S.* 21: 307–311.
17. Pan, S. C., L. W. Nicholson, and P. Kolachov. 1953. *Arch. Biochem. Biophys.* 42: 421–434.
18. Shu, P. and J. A. Thorn. 1952. *Can. J. Botany* 30: 252–265.
19. Thies, W. 1930. *Zentr. Bakteriol. Parasitenk. Abt. II,* 82: 321–347.
20. Wells, P. A., A. J. Moyer, and O. E. May. 1936. *J. Am. Chem. Soc.* 58: 555–558.
21. Whitaker, D. R. 1951. *Can. J. Botany* 29: 159–175.

5. Carbon Metabolism

Part II

The Metabolism of Carbohydrates
and Related Compounds

The principal topic of this chapter on carbon metabolism is the metabolism of oligosaccharides and polysaccharides, anticipated to some degree by the discussion of their role in carbon nutrition (Chapter 3). The related compounds included are the amino sugars and the polyhydric alcohols; discussion of the monosaccharides is limited to a few synthetic reactions.

1. THE METABOLISM OF MONOSACCHARIDES

The breakdown of monosaccharides by fungi has been considered separately, as respiration, in Chapter 7. A second aspect of monosaccharide metabolism is the synthetic one, in which the sugar or a derivative of it is incorporated into larger molecules. As an example, glucose in the glucolipid ustilagic acid is found by isotope studies to be in part incorporated as such and in part resynthesized from triose before incorporation (30). In this case and in the formation of glucose polysaccharides no modification of the basic glucose molecule need be assumed. However, the organism may synthesize a complex molecule containing sugar moieties which were not provided in the culture medium; examples include galactose in polysaccharides (Chapter 2) and amino sugars in certain antibiotics (p. 122). In these processes it is reasonable to assume that the new sugar or a derivative of it, e.g., a phosphate ester, is made and then incorporated into the larger molecule, but there is no evidence directly on this point in the fungi and actinomycetes.

Free sugars appear in the mycelium (130, 227) and in the culture medium (84, 85), but their significance is not known.

The phosphate esters of the monosaccharides are hydrolyzed by phosphatases (phosphomonoesterases). The phosphatases active on glycerophosphoric acid may be presumed to act also on hexose phosphates. No direct study of these reactions in fungi has been made, but there is no doubt that at least the common saprophytic fungi and actinomycetes can hydrolyze hexose and pentose phosphates; commercial enzyme preparations made from fungi contain acid phosphatases (179) and have been used in many laboratories for the dephosphorylation of sugar phosphates. Phosphatases are considered in more detail in Chapter 9.

2. THE METABOLISM OF OLIGOSACCHARIDES

The literature on the enzymatic breakdown of disaccharides and trisaccharides by fungi is extensive but, as in so much of fungus physiology, relatively few types have been studied. Most of our information comes from work on the Fungi Imperfecti, the wood-destroying basidiomycetes, and the Saprolegniaceae. Many other groups of fungi have not been investigated and must, therefore, be excluded from any generalization.

The most significant recent advance in our approach to the breakdown of oligosaccharides is the concept of transglycosidation. Until the formulation of this concept the breakdown of sucrose, for example, was visualized as a simple hydrolysis:

$$C_{12}H_{22}O_{11} + H_2O \rightarrow C_6H_{12}O_6 + C_6H_{12}O_6 \qquad (1)$$

$$\text{Sucrose} \qquad\qquad\qquad \text{Glucose} \qquad \text{Fructose}$$

Since sucrose is made up of glucose and fructose units linked by a glycosidic bond, this hydrolytic reaction may be schematized:

$$\text{Fr—Gl} \rightarrow \text{Fr} + \text{Gl} \qquad (2)$$

It now appears that at least some and possibly all of the so-called hydrolytic enzymes are in fact group transferases, capable of transferring a sugar residue to any suitable acceptor. The acceptor may be water, in which case Equation 2 describes the reaction, but other sugars or alcohols can also serve as acceptors. In a particular case, the action of yeast invertase, the fructose residue of sucrose is believed to be transferred as follows (72):

$$Fr—Gl + Enzyme (E) \leftrightarrows Fr—E + Gl \qquad (3)$$

$$Fr—E + Fr—Gl \leftrightarrows Fr—Fr—Gl + E \qquad (4)$$

$$Fr—E + H_2O \rightarrow Fr + E \qquad (5)$$

The fructose-enzyme complex is, of course, hypothetical but it is necessary to explain the observed reactions. Because of the irreversibility
of the fifth reaction and the great excess of water present, in a long-
term experiment virtually all of the fructose residues are transferred
to water and the result is described grossly by Equation 2. The
technique of paper chromatography applied in short-term experiments
has been essential to the elucidation of this type of group transfer.
The characteristic of transglycosidase action on disaccharides is the
transient appearance of new oligosaccharides.

Disaccharides. Most of the work on this topic has been concerned
with the breakdown of sugars, especially the common disaccharides
such as sucrose, maltose, and lactose. Synthesis of disaccharides occurs
in the fungi, the best known case being trehalose (p. 108). Sucrose
is attacked by an enzyme variously known as invertase, saccharase,
glucosaccharase, and sucrase; the name sucrase is preferred. The first
indication of its presence in fungi came from the work of Béchamp
(18, 19). As might be expected from the frequent utilizability of
sucrose as a carbon source (Chapter 3), the enzyme is widely distributed
in the fungi. Sucrase is somewhat rare in the Mucorales—again in
agreement with nutritional data—but does occur in some species (93,
203). Sucrase is found in some isolates of *Streptomyces* (101, 110),
not in any of five species of dermatophytes (229).

Fungus sucrase may be entirely intracellular (148) but is usually
found also in the medium, at least after the onset of autolysis (58).
It occurs in spores (71, 141); in *Myrothecium verrucaria* and *Aspergillus luchuensis* there is evidence that it or a sucrose phosphorylase is
located at or near the spore boundary (142). This boundary location
is thought to be characteristic of sucrase in the yeast cell (62, 155).

It has long been argued that the predominant sucrase of fungi is a
"glucosaccharase" differing from the "fructosaccharase" of yeast (121);
the history of this controversy is reviewed by Neuberg and Mandl
(156). The question has now been re-examined in the light of the
finding that both yeast and fungus sucrases are probably transfructosi-
dases. It appears that the two sucrases differ, but not in the way
formerly thought, and that it is not necessary to postulate a glucosaccharase (15, 66).

Transfructosidase activity has been demonstrated in several fungi,

Table 1. Transglycosidase Activity in Fungi

Enzyme Activity	Substrate	Fungi
Transfructosidase	Sucrose	*Aspergillus* spp. (9, 10, 16, 66, 169, 170)
	Raffinose	*Aspergillus* spp., *Penicillium spinulosum* (15)
Transglucosidase	Maltose	*Aspergillus* spp. (47a, 169, 173, 174), *Penicillium chrysogenum* (202)
	Isomaltose	*Aspergillus oryzae* (171, 172)
	Cellobiose	*Aspergillus niger* (11, 12), *Chaetomium globosum* (48), *Myrothecium verrucaria* (119)
	p-Nitrophenyl-	*Aspergillus* spp. (113, 226)
	β-glucoside	*Penicillium chrysogenum* (226)
Transgalactosidase	Lactose	*Aspergillus oryzae* (244, 245)

acting on sucrose or raffinose (Table 1).   A fructose-enzyme complex is postulated, as in Equations 3, 4, and 5 above.   In *Penicillium spinulosum* there is no evidence for any sucrase other than the transfructosidase, but in *Aspergillus oryzae* there is probably a second enzyme acting on sucrose (16).   Paper chromatography of the enzymes of *A. oryzae* similarly suggests that more than one sucrase is present (112).

Sucrase, acting as it does on β-fructofuranosides, is instrumental in the metabolism of raffinose and stachyose.

Mandels (143) presents indirect evidence for the non-hydrolytic metabolism of sucrose by spores of *Myrothecium verrucaria,* possibly to be credited to a sucrose phosphorylase of the type known in bacteria.

Maltose is used as a source of carbon by almost all fungi (Chapter 3).   Correspondingly, beginning with the work of Bourquelot (33), we find that the enzyme maltase is found in almost every fungus and actinomycete investigated, although quantitative differences between strains are common (127).   It has been claimed that *Polyporus betulinus* lacks maltase (138), and the chytrids which are unable to grow on maltose (Chapter 3) may be found to lack the enzyme.

Maltase is an α-glucosidase and is found in bacteria, animals, and higher plants.   The earlier separation of fungus from yeast maltase as a "glucomaltase" is probably not valid, but the two maltases are not identical (89).   As with sucrase, recent investigations have established in fungi the existence of a transglycosidase acting on maltose to form a series of transient oligosaccharides (Table 1).   The existence of a specific hydrolase for maltose may be doubted, but it is not yet known whether the transglucosidase of *Aspergillus niger* and *A. oryzae,* the only fungi so far studied, is of general occurrence as a single enzymatic entity. Transglucosidases which act on maltose to form polysaccharides are known in bacteria but have not yet been reported from fungi.

The disaccharide lactose is split to its constituent hexoses by the enzyme lactase, a β-galactosidase. The enzyme has been reported in several fungi and actinomycetes, but is apparently not of such general occurrence as either sucrase or maltase. Some of the early work on lactase in commercial enzyme preparations and in basidiomycete sporophores may be open to question because of the possibility of bacterial contamination.

The adaptive formation of lactase in *Neurospora crassa* has been proved (Chapter 3). A purified enzyme from *Aspergillus oryzae* acts as a transgalactosidase; galactose residues are transferred to alcohols, to lactose itself to form a trisaccharide, or to water to yield free galactose (Table 1). Whether all action of lactase can be credited to this enzyme is not yet known.

Cellobiose is formed during the hydrolysis of cellulose. Although it is common to refer to the enzyme splitting it as cellobiase, there is no reason to think that this enzyme differs in any way from β-glucosidases acting on other β-glucosides. Specific assays with cellobiose as substrate have been made infrequently, but it seems that most fungi can split it to its constituent glucose residues (191). Resting and growing cells of *Aspergillus niger* form new oligosaccharides from cellobiose (11, 12), and additional evidence for transglycosidase action on cellobiose has been obtained with other fungi (Table 1). Cellobiose is synthesized by *Ustilago zeae* as a component of ustilagic acid (128).

Trehalose, an α-glucosido-glucose, is not attacked by the usual α-glucosidases but rather by a special enzyme, trehalase, found in animals, plants and fungi (89). Early work on trehalase in fungi is reviewed by Czapek (59); this and more recent data indicate the enzyme is common (203, 256). The spores of *Aspergillus luchuensis* contain measurable amounts of the enzyme (139). In *Lycogala* sp., a myxomycete, trehalase of the fruit body disappears during ripening (108).

Trehalose is the only disaccharide to be formed free in appreciable amounts by fungi. The discovery of the sugar in ergot (*Claviceps purpurea*) by Wiggers (254) and early reports of its occurrence in other fungi are reviewed by Zellner (264) and Obaton (164). Trehalose is especially common in the basidiomycetes but is found also in many other fungi (34, 36). Usually it constitutes 2 to 3 per cent of the mycelial dry matter (108, 193, 227).

In all probability, trehalose in fungi has the role of a translocatable reserve carbohydrate, formed early in metabolism and used up later (43); under some conditions reutilization may not occur during the life of the fungus (164). An adequate picture of the course of trehalose synthesis and breakdown is not yet available. In yeast, trehalose is synthesized as its phosphate from glucose and a glucose phosphate, with uridine diphosphate glucose as coenzyme (68, 125); whether the same mechanism is operative in the filamentous fungi remains to be seen.

Melibiose, an α-galactosido-glucose occurring naturally as a constituent of raffinose, is split by an α-galactosidase (melibiase) known in yeast and higher plants and reported from *Aspergillus* spp. (100, 230).

Trisaccharides and Tetrasaccharides. Raffinose, composed of galactose, glucose, and fructose, is split by enzymes from most fungi which have been tested. This is to be expected, in view of the fact that sucrase splits raffinose to melibiose and fructose. The complete hydrolysis of raffinose requires both sucrose and melibiase; melibiase alone yields sucrase and galactose. In all likelihood, hydrolysis of raffinose by unspecified fungal enzymes should usually be attributed to sucrase (2, 15).

Melezitose is hydrolyzed, at least partially, by several fungi (15, 122). Detailed studies of the reaction are lacking; complete hydrolysis requires an enzyme able to attack the disaccharide turanose.

Gentianose is completely hydrolyzed to glucose and fructose by an enzyme preparation from *Aspergillus niger* (40, 41); the effective preparation has been shown (42) to contain a β-glucosidase acting on the gentiobiose moiety of gentianose.

Stachyose, a tetrasaccharide composed of galactose, glucose and fructose in the ratio 2:1:1, is split by enzymes from *Penicillium spinulosum* and *Aspergillus* spp. completely to its constituent sugars (15, 228). Presumably sucrase and an α-galactosidase are required.

3. THE METABOLISM OF OTHER GLYCOSIDES

The oligosaccharides, just considered, are one class of glycoside, in which the glycosidic bond connects two monosaccharide residues. The same bond can be formed between a sugar and certain other molecules; the non-carbohydrate moiety of the resulting compound is then termed an aglycon. Information on the metabolism of glycosides of this type by fungi is restricted to a few compounds, in all of which glucose or mannose is the sugar involved.

The β-glucosides have received more attention than any others in this general category. The enzyme β-glucosidase (formerly termed emulsin) occurs in almost all of the fungi and actinomycetes which have been examined for it (31, 38, 39, 101, 147, 201, 229), although it is not always found in the medium (191) and may not be so nearly universal as, for example, maltase or amylase. *Fusarium oxysporum* var. *lycopersici* forms detectable amounts of the enzyme within the living infected plant (60).

Although it is common practice to speak of a single β-glucosidase hydrolyzing all β-glucosides—including the β-linked disaccharides cellobiose and gentiobiose—it seems more likely that a group of related enzymes is involved (238) or that at least there are distinct components of the enzyme (111, 112). The β-glucosidases of *Aspergillus niger* and *A. oryzae,* for example, act at different rates on different synthetic β-glucosides (151). The enzyme of *A. niger* has been purified about 10,000-fold (160, 161).

During the action of β-glucosidase on synthetic β-glucosides, the glucose residue can be transferred to alcohols, indicating trans-glucosidase activity similar to that with cellobiose as substrate (Table 1).

Alpha-glucosides, in principle at least, should be attacked by maltase, an α-glucosidase. However, maltases from different sources have different behavior toward, e.g., methyl-α-glucoside, and the maltase of fungi seems to be of minimum activity toward this substrate (89). A crude preparation from *Aspergillus niger* hydrolyzes methyl-α-glucoside slowly (65), and in some fungi there is an α-glucosidase distinct from maltose (15), but the problem has been too little studied for any definite conclusion to emerge. *Aspergillus niger* cultivated with methyl-α-galactoside forms the corresponding α-galactosidase (182).

An enzyme of *Streptomyces griseus* converts mannosidostreptomycin to streptomycin (175). The enzyme has been found to split synthetic methyl-α-mannoside (99) and may therefore be termed an α-manno-sidase. The same action, with methyl-α-mannoside as substrate, is known in *Aspergillus niger* (98).

4. THE METABOLISM OF POLYSACCHARIDES

The Breakdown of Starch and Glycogen. These two related polysac-charides are hydrolyzed by amylases (diastases), of which there are in nature two general types (154):

1. Alpha-amylase (endoamylase, dextrinizing amylase, liquefying amylase), found in animals and microorganisms. Attack on starch, at

least in its early phases, results in the formation of dextrins, reducing sugars appearing only later.

2. Beta-amylase (exoamylase, saccharifying amylase) of resting seeds. Attack on starch liberates maltose immediately.

It has been repeatedly found, with highly purified or crystalline preparations, that the amylase of *Aspergillus oryzae* is of the α-amylase group (49, 73, 235). So also, apparently, is the amylase of *Streptomyces* spp. (213). The crude amylase of *A. oryzae* contains more than one component, as judged by electrophoretic data (82).

The enzyme of *Rhizopus delemar,* termed gluc amylase (177, 178), can be separated from α-amylase and resembles β-amylase in certain respects. There seems, however, no reason to believe that a typical β-amylase occurs in the fungi (127, 129, 146).

Table 2 summarizes some of the properties of the purified amylase of *Aspergillus oryzae* and its differences from other α-amylases.

Amylase activity, defined as the ability of cell-free materials to hydrolyze starch or glycogen, is virtually universal in the fungi and actinomycetes. *Penicillium digitatum* does not form detectable amylase in culture (103), and in view of its inability to grow on starch (Chapter 3) is presumably deficient for the enzyme. Early studies on fungal amylase are summarized by Thaysen and Galloway (230), and the industrial technology of the enzyme is reviewed by Langlykke et al. (123).

Table 2. Properties of Alpha-amylases (74)

Source of Crystalline Alpha-amylase

	Malt	Aspergillus oryzae	Bacillus subtilis	Pig Pancreas	Human Saliva, Pancreas
Activity per mg N	2350	2400	3600	4000	6200
Activity per mg protein	315	310	500	630	980
Nitrogen, per cent	13.4	12.9	15.8	15.8	15.8
Optimum pH for activity	4.7–5.4	5.5–5.9	5.3–6.8	6.9	6.9
Optimum pH for stability	4.9–9.1	5.5–8.5	4.8–8.5	7.0–8.5	4.8–11
Isoelectric point	5.6	circ. 4.2	?	5.3	5.3
Absorption maximum (mμ)	280	280	280	280	280
Saccharogenic/dextrinogenic ratio	9.8	9.8	9.8	9.8	9.6
Activation by Ca	+	−	−	−	−
Activation by Cl	−	−	+	+	+
Energy of activation	7050	10650	13350	13500	13350
			0 to 15°		

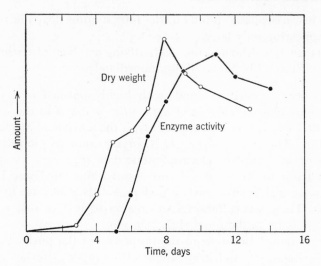

Figure 1. Amylase liberation by *Aspergillus oryzae*. Redrawn from Crewther and Lennox (58), by permission of the *Australian Journal of Biological Sciences*.

Amylase is, with some exceptions (64), found in the culture medium as well as in the cells. The amount of enzyme is usually increased by inclusion of starch in the growth medium (92, 210) and is affected by the nitrogen source (210) and by small amounts of salts (69). Figure 1 illustrates the time course of appearance of extracellular amylase in *Aspergillus oryzae;* it is to be noted that the peak of amylase activity in the culture filtrate is reached only after the onset of autolysis.

It has been reported (28) that the culture filtrate of *Streptomyces microflavus* forms gentiobiose during the hydrolysis of starch.

The Breakdown of Cellulose. Since many fungi utilize cellulose as a carbon source (Chapter 3), it is to be expected that an enzyme or enzymes are released from the cell and hydrolyze cellulose to soluble sugars. Cellulose-hydrolyzing preparations free of living cells have indubitably been made from several fungi (83, 191, 214), and distinguished from enzymes acting on lichenin and hemicelluloses (90). However, two important limitations apply to most of the reported work on cellulase: (1) native cellulose is relatively resistant to attack, and most assays of "cellulase" have therefore utilized various types of modified cellulose; (2) most data derive from studies with crude cellulase preparations contaminated with other carbohydrases and with interfering proteins (232). It is difficult, therefore, to assign more than a descriptive value to much of the work so far reported.

Crude cellulase preparations from several fungi are alike in that their optimum pH is in the acid range, 4.5 to 5.5 (90, 163, 204); the optimum for the enzyme of *Stachybotrys atra* is, however, higher, pH 6.5–8.0 (230a). Studies on *Tricholoma fumosum* indicate that the enzyme is formed only by cells in contact with cellulose or lichenin, and that the enzyme in a culture is predominantly extracellular (163). Cellulose is apparently attacked at several points along the chain of glucose residues, inasmuch as in the early stages of attack on cellulose there is a decline in optical density without a corresponding liberation of sugars (162, 163a). Other characteristics of fungal cellulases are summarized by Siu (214).

For the present, a general statement on the nature of cellulase is not possible. The classical view (183) postulates at least two enzymes, a "cellulase" splitting the long polymeric chain to cellobiose residues, and a cellobiase (β-glucosidase) splitting the disaccharide to glucose. Although substantial evidence exists for the appearance of cellobiose as an intermediate (119, 159a, 250), the process is probably more complex. Two theories, both based on work with *Myrothecium verrucaria*, have been proposed recently. The first of these postulates a minimum of three enzymes as required for cellulose hydrolysis (83, 91a, 150, 190, 191), with only one of them characteristic of the cellulolytic organisms and the others occurring also in non-cellulolytic fungi. In sharp distinction to this view, other studies on the same organism (251, 253) have resulted in the isolation of an apparently single enzyme, purified to electrophoretic homogeneity, with a molecular weight of 63,000. This single enzyme hydrolyzes cellulose to glucose without the obligatory participation of cellobiose as an intermediate, although cellobiose may be formed during the process. The enzyme acts, at different rates, on cellobiose, cellotriose, and higher oligosaccharides of this group (252), and is inhibited by sulfhydryl reagents (14). It is obvious that further work on the enzyme will be necessary before any general theory can be formulated.

The Breakdwn of Hemicelluloses and Pentosans. The hemicelluloses are poorly defined plant constituents, particularly of wood and gums. The principal components of the hemicelluloses are polysaccharides and polyuronides. The literature reports essentially two types of work, that on hemicellulose fractions of unknown composition, and that on more or less purified polysaccharides derived from hemicellulose.

Crude hemicellulose fractions from wood are attacked by enzymes of *Aspergillus oryzae,* yielding free sugars and a soluble polysaccharide

(166, 167). As might be expected, the wood-destroying basidiomycetes are especially active in the hydrolysis of hemicelluloses (31, 189); the gross utilization of hemicelluloses has been mentioned earlier (Chapter 3). The only other fungi which have been studied are some members of the Saprolegniaceae (21, 201), and of the genus *Phytophthora* (147), all of which form reducing sugars from the crude hemicellulose of date endosperm.

The most abundant of the pentosans are xylans; the rarer arabans are found in association with pectic substances. The limited literature on fungus metabolism of xylans is reviewed by Voss and Butter (240). Enzymes (xylanases) attacking xylan have been found in *Aspergillus oryzae* (90) and *Glomerella cingulata* (96). The xylanase of *Chaetomium globosum* is formed in appreciable amounts only if the organism is grown on xylan, and consists of an exocellular component converting xylan to xylobiose and an intracellular enzyme hydrolyzing the xylobiose (217, 218).

Arabans—pentosans made up largely of L-arabinose—are hydrolyzed by a crude enzyme preparation from *Aspergillus oryzae* (67).

Simpson (212) surveyed the action of 112 isolates of 24 genera on a purified pentosan of unspecified composition. An active hydrolysis was brought about by the culture filtrate of about half of the isolates tested; the most active filtrates were from cultures of strains of *Aspergillus, Fusarium, Tricothecium,* and *Trichoderma.* Of the 54 active strains, only 6 formed the enzyme during growth on glucose; in the rest, growth on the pentosan—replaceable in some instances by free pentoses—appeared to be necessary for enzyme synthesis. In the genus *Streptomyces,* 5 of the 19 isolates tested formed an extracellular enzyme active on the pentosan.

A purified arabogalactan from *Larix* is split by an enzyme from *Aspergillus niger* (189). Mannans are hydrolyzed by an enzyme of *Chaetomium globosum* which is apparently distinct from the enzyme acting on xylans (217).

The chemistry of the substrates is poorly known and the nature of the enzymes involved in their hydrolysis is uncertain. In particular, it is not possible from the data available to decide on the possible identity or non-identity of enzymes which have been studied by different workers. It is generally accepted that the enzymes attacking the pentosans and the crude hemicelluloses are distinct from cellulose-hydrolyzing enzymes and from lichenase (180), but beyond this point specificity is not known.

The Breakdown of Pectic Substances. Perhaps nowhere in the field of carbon metabolism is the confusion so great as it is in the study of the pectic materials. Historically, interest in the pectic enzymes was first stimulated by the discovery (13, 247) that crude enzyme preparations from plant pathogenic fungi macerate plant tissues by destruction of the middle lamella, the cementing material between cells. First thought to be a cellulase, the tissue-macerating enzyme has also been termed cytase. Other early studies are reviewed by Brown (46).

The insoluble pectic materials as they are found in plants are now called protopectin (116). Neither the structure nor the composition of protopectin is known. The corresponding enzyme protopectinase (pectosinase) is defined in principle as the enzyme converting protopectin to water-soluble pectinic acids (255). Operationally, the enzyme is defined by its ability to macerate blocks of living plant tissue. It is found in pathogenic and non-pathogenic fungi belonging to all of the major taxonomic groups (Table 3).

Table 3. Occurrence of the Pectic Enzymes in the Fungi*

Enzyme	Occurrence
"Protopectinase"	*Aspergillus* spp. (61, 222), *Botrytis* spp. (46, 237), *Byssochlamys fulva* (17, 105), *Chaetomium globosum* (222), *Daedalea flavida* (32), *Fomes fraxineus* (152), *Fusarium* spp. (51, 149, 211), *Gloeosporium fructigenum* (*Glomerella cingulata*) (149), *Lenzites sepiaria* (263), *Macrophomina phaseoli* (185), *Metarrhizium* sp. (222), *Monilia fructigena* (237), *Mucor racemosus* (93), *Phytophthora erythroseptica* (149), *Polyporus* spp., *Polystictus* spp. (32), *Pythium debaryanum* (4, 97), *Rhizoctonia* sp. (258), *Rhizopus* spp. (94, 95), *Stereum purpureum* (145), *Trametes* spp. (32).
Pectin-methylesterase	*Aspergillus* spp. (81, 114), *Botrytis cinerea* (80), *Fusarium* spp. (87, 241), *Penicillium* spp. (114, 176), *Sclerotinia cinerea* (61), *Sclerotium bataticola,*† *Thielaviopsis basicola*† (231).
Pectin-polygalacturonase	*Aspergillus* spp. (6, 64, 81, 114, 208), *Botrytis cinerea* (81, 114, 257), *Byssochlamys fulva* (102, 192), *Colletotrichum phomoides* (185a), *Fusarium* spp. (47, 185a, 211, 241, 243), *Mucor* spp. (185a), *Neurospora* spp. (64, 197), *Penicillium* spp. (64, 176, 185a, 243), *Rhizopus nigricans* (185a), *Stachybotrys atra*, *Syncephalastrum racemosum*, *Thamnidium elegans*, *Trichoderma* spp. (64, 185a), *Verticillium albo-atrum* (205).

* Including only the three major enzymes; for other enzyme activities, see text.

† Assayed by hydrolysis of half-calcium salt of methyl-D-tartaric acid (157).

The indefinite nature of the substrate, the crudity of the enzyme assay, and the fact that other enzymes may solubilize the pectic materials of plants (116) are compelling reasons to doubt the real existence of protopectinase. This doubt is reinforced by the finding (102) that a partially purified pectin-polygalacturonase from *Byssochlamys fulva* causes disintegration of tobacco tissue. Although it is possible, of course, that the preparation was contaminated with a protopectinase, it seems more probable that pectin-polygalacturonase has the ability, usually ascribed to protopectinase, to macerate tissue. It is significant in this connection that all protopectinase preparations examined contain pectin-polygalacturonase (115).

The present nomenclature of the pectic enzymes was first clearly formulated in 1927 (61) and fully worked out only in 1944 (117). Consequently the earlier work on these enzymes employs different and often highly individual nomenclature. In particular, the "pectinase" of the older literature is usually synonymous with what is now called protopectinase, i.e., the tissue-macerating enzyme. Pectinase as now understood is a synonym for pectin-polygalacturonase. The nomenclature used here is that of Kertesz (116).

The pectinic acids are colloidal macromolecules composed of α-D-anhydrogalacturonic acid units linked together through 1,4-α-glycosidic bonds. The carboxyl groups of some of the galacturonic acid residues are esterified with methyl alcohol. Certain pectinic acids of specific properties are designated pectins. Pectinic acids are obtained from the crude plant pectic materials by partial hydrolysis.

Excluding protopectinase from consideration, the known and postulated pectic enzymes of fungi are of three types, depending on their action on pectinic acids. They are:

1. Pectin-methylesterase, catalyzing the hydrolysis of the methyl ester groups of pectinic acids, and converting pectinic acids to pectic acids (polygalacturonic acids).

2. Pectin-polygalacturonase, hydrolyzing the pectic acids to free D-galacturonic acid.

3. Pectin-depolymerase, a less well-known enzyme thought to cause a partial hydrolysis of pectic acids to smaller units without the appearance of free galacturonic acid.

Pectin-methylesterase (pectase, pectinesterase, pectinmethoxylase) was originally defined (61) as an enzyme converting soluble pectin (pectinic acid) into insoluble calcium pectate. Its action may be schematized as:

$$(R—CO—O—CH_3)_n + (n)H_2O \rightarrow (R—COOH)_n + (n)CH_3OH \quad (6)$$

The enzyme occurs in commercial enzyme preparations of pectin-polygalacturonase (75) and in the fungi listed in Table 3. The enzyme of *Fusarium oxysporum* var. *lycopersici* appears to differ from that of commercial preparations from other fungi (241), and the latter in turn differs from the pectin-methylesterase of higher plants (145).

Production of extracellular pectin-methylesterase by *Botrytis cinerea* and *Aspergillus niger* occurs if pectin is the growth medium but only to a negligible degree with glucose as the carbon source (3, 80, 81). The extracellular enzyme of *Penicillium chrysogenum* is formed only if pectin, pectic acid, or chemically related substances are in the growth medium (176). Recently, the role of pectin-methylesterase in the pathogenicity of fungi to plants has received attention.

The third major category of the pectic substances is that of the pectic acids, derived from pectinic acids by de-esterification. They are colloidal polygalacturonic acids with molecular weights ranging from 25,000 to 100,000. The molecule consists of D-galacturonic acid units and may be visualized as follows:

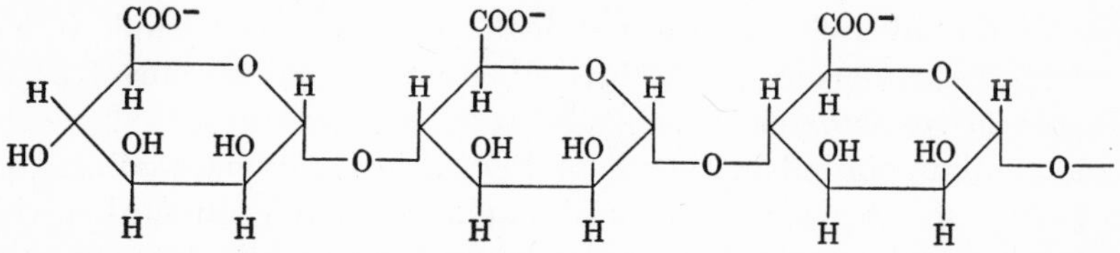

The enzyme hydrolyzing the pectic acids has been named variously pectinase, pectolase, and polygalacturonase. The most unambiguous name appears to be pectin-polygalacturonase (116). It acts on the de-esterified portions of pectinic acids or on the pectic acids resulting from complete de-esterification of pectinic acids. It is often contaminated with pectin-methylesterase, and the mixture of the two enzymes will, of course, act on pectinic acids both by de-esterification and by hydrolysis. The product of pectin-polygalacturonase activity on a polygalacturonide is, eventually, free D-galacturonic acid. The properties of the enzyme have been studied extensively by Matus (144).

Table 3 lists the fungi which have been shown to form the enzyme, as assayed on pectinic acid or polygalacturonic acids, i.e., excluding assays of tissue-macerating enzyme. Two comments are apposite to the problem of the occurrence of the enzyme in fungi. First, it is probable that the fungi producing protopectinase always form pectin-polygalacturonase or that the two enzymes are identical. If either of these hypotheses is true, then the sources of protopectinase given in Table 3 must be included, adding numerous phycomycetes and basidiomycetes to a list which is predominantly composed of ascomycetes and imperfect fungi. Second, the fact that many fungi form pectin-polygalacturonase only if pectinic acids or related materials are present in the medium means that a complete survey of representative fungi should use such a medium; in addition, in any such survey the pH of the medium should be kept below 6.0 by reason of the rapid inactivation of the enzyme at higher pH values (116). From the data available and in the light of these considerations, it seems likely that most fungi are able, at least under favorable conditions, to elaborate pectin-polygalacturonase.

The pectin-polygalacturonase of fungi differs in its properties from the corresponding enzymes of yeast and higher plants (118, 133). The enzyme is highly specific to pectic acids, failing to hydrolyze other galacturonides or other uronides (131). Separation from pectin-methylesterase has been accomplished (131, 136). It is not yet possible to assert that pectin-polygalacturonase is a single enzymatic entity. One view (114) is that it is a single enzyme acting by random scission of the pectic acid molecule to form shorter galacturonic acid chains and eventually free galacturonic acid. On the other hand, it has recently been suggested that three different enzymes are involved in *Aspergillus foetidus* (6, 63).

The pectin-polygalacturonase of *Penicillium chrysogenum* and of *Fusarium* spp. appears to be elaborated adaptively, in media with pectin as carbon source but not in glucose media (47, 176), but the same enzyme in other fungi is formed in glucose media (64, 80, 81). All these experiments were carried out by growing cells from a spore inoculum in media with or without the presumed inducing substrate; hence, a possible effect of mutation or selection was not rigorously excluded.

Other enzymes, depolymerases, acting on pectins have been described in plant parasitic and saprophytic fungi (17, 19a, 88, 195, 209). These enzymes share in common the characteristic that only certain of the glycosidic linkages of the substrate are attacked, resulting in the liberation of short-chain polyuronides. The existence of such enzymes in fungi has been challenged (192, 197), but the evidence, especially that from work on *Neurospora crassa* (195) is strong.

Assay methods for the pectic enzymes are reviewed by Kertesz (116); cup plate assays have been devised (53) and may be particularly useful in survey studies. There is some doubt (116) that assay of pectin-methylesterase by hydrolysis of the half calcium salt of methyl-D-tartaric acid (157) is valid.

It seems that the immediate problem in the study of the pectic enzymes, as in that of so many other enzymes, is to determine the action of single enzymes on substrates of definite and known composition. Once such information is available, there will be some hope of successfully analyzing the more complex situation in nature.

The Breakdown of Other Polysaccharides. It is generally considered that a special enzyme, inulase, catalyzes the breakdown of the plant fructosan inulin. The enzyme was discovered in *Aspergillus niger* by Bourquelot (37) and has since been found in many other fungi (25, 59, 79). It has often been reported that cultivation on inulin as carbon source increases the amount of enzyme (25, 184, 261), but some inulase is always formed whatever the carbon source. No systematic study of the enzyme or its occurrence has been made; some properties of fungal inulase have been determined by Pigman (179), and it is possible that two different enzymes are responsible for the activity (153). On the other hand, there is some evidence that inulase is a transfructosidase active also on sucrose (155a).

A bacterial dextran, composed of anhydroglucose units linked by 1,6-α-glucosidic bonds, is hydrolyzed by a dextranase present in the mycelium and culture fluid of several fungi, e.g., *Penicillium funiculosum, Verticillium coccorum,* and *Spicaria violacea* (106, 234). The enzyme is formed only if dextran is present in the medium.

Limit dextrin, the polysaccharide fraction remaining after starch hydrolysis by α-amylase, is hydrolyzed by a limit dextrinase from *Aspergillus oryzae;* the enzyme has been crystallized (235).

A commercial enzyme preparation, probably made from an *Aspergillus* sp., hydrolyzes a galactogen of snail eggs, yielding D- and L-galactose (248).

Lichenin, the polysaccharide of Irish moss (*Chondrus crispus*) resembles cellulose except for its high proportion of 1,3-glycosidic bonds. It is hydrolyzed by an enzyme found in animal and plant material (180) and in *Aspergillus oryzae* (200) and *Merulius lacrymans* (181). Lichenase is probably distinct from cellulase and xylanase (78, 90).

The mucopolysaccharides are complex polysaccharides yielding amino sugars on hydrolysis (76); examples include hyaluronic acid, chitin, agar, and unidentified cell wall materials. Among the enzymes attacking these materials the bacterial hyaluronidase and lysozyme are fairly well known, but the mucopolysaccharases of fungi are not. Chitinases are known among actinomycetes and both higher and lower fungi (49a, 233); the enzyme or enzymes responsible for chitin hydrolysis in *Streptomyces* sp. are adaptive (194). The lytic enzymes of actinomycetes, e.g., the enzyme system of *Streptomyces albus* (134, 135), act on cell wall polysaccharides and can therefore tentatively be classed with the mucopolysaccharases. The enzymes of this type have been reported frequently from actinomycetes (114a, 249) and must be present in those fungi in which the chitin breaks down during autolysis (216).

Certain marine actinomycetes liquefy agar (107, 219). The enzyme responsible has been called gelase; it is evidently either rare or absent in terrestrial fungi and actinomycetes, since agar is used so generally in culture media that gelase-producing organisms would have long since been detected if they were common.

The Synthesis of Polysaccharides. The known fungal polysaccharides are reviewed elsewhere (Chapter 2); it will be recalled that they include chitin, polyhexoses, and more complex polysaccharides. The most common hexose component is glucose, the next most common galactose; since all of the galactans are formed in media with glucose or sucrose as carbon source, it seems probable that a galactowaldenase is present, as in yeast, catalyzing the conversion of glucose to galactose (124).

The metabolic origin of the polysaccharides of fungi has been little investigated, but may be expected to follow the pathways known in other organisms. The two best known mechanisms of polysaccharide synthesis in bacteria are, in outline:

$$(n)C_{12}H_{22}O_{11} \leftrightharpoons (C_6H_{10}O_5)_n + (n)C_6H_{12}O_6 \tag{7}$$

Disaccharide   Polysaccharide   Monosaccharide

$$(n)\text{Glucose-1-phosphate} \leftrightharpoons \text{Polysaccharide} + \text{phosphate} \tag{8}$$

The first of these is a transglycosidation, of which the action of levansucrase is an example; the second is catalyzed by a phosphorylase and is exemplified by glycogen formation in the animal. Levan synthesis in *Aspergillus sydowi* spores may be a transglycosidation; it can be effectuated by a broken-cell preparation, and the levan is formed during growth on sucrose but not during growth on monosaccharides (120). The polyglucose of *Torulopsis rotundata,* on the other hand, is probably synthesized by a phosphorylase (139). Evidence on polysaccharide biogenesis in the fungi is so far limited to these two cases.

The polysaccharides of some fungi are formed more abundantly in acid than in neutral media (27, 140, 207), but the reverse is true of sclerotiose formation (1). In yeast, inhibition of polysaccharide formation by alkalinity is believed to result from an inhibition of phosphorylase (224). Presumably, other environmental factors are influential; on a priori grounds it is to be expected that the concentration of available carbohydrate and the carbon:nitrogen ratio of the medium are important. Oxygen is required for the synthesis of polysaccharide by *Aspergillus niger* (206).

The function of fungal polysaccharides is almost certainly as a reserve food, and the data of Ergle (70) on glycogen utilization during the germination of sclerotia bear out this contention. This view of polysaccharides as one form in which fungi can store energy was first clearly stated by Chrząszcz and Tiukow (53) in opposition to an earlier view of polysaccharide formation as a symptom of a deranged metabolism. It should be noted that under some cultural conditions the polysaccharide formed may never in fact be utilized, cell death and autolysis intervening before the carbohydrate supply becomes limiting and before the reserves are attacked.

Several fungi pathogenic to man form polysaccharides, often associated with a capsule and often immunologically active. Those of *Coccidioides immitis* and *Cryptococcus* (*Torulopsis*) spp. are listed in Chapter 2; others are reviewed by Nickerson (158).

5. THE METABOLISM OF AMINO SUGARS

The only amino sugar which has been studied extensively is D-glucosamine (2-amino-D-glucose), interest in which arises primarily from the fact that its N-acetyl derivative is the basic unit of chitin, the cell wall material of most fungi (Chapter 2).

Conceivably, the conversion of glucose to glucosamine could proceed with glucosone, $CH_2OH—(CHOH)_3—CO—CHO$, as intermediate and glucosone is formed by *Aspergillus parasiticus,* at least under some conditions (29). However, in *Neurospora crassa* extracts glucosamine is formed by transamidation from glutamine (126) as follows:

Hexose-6-phosphate + glutamine → glucosamine-6-phosphate +

glutamic acid (9)

It appears from other work that the hexose phosphate involved directly in the reaction is fructose-6-phosphate (26).

Glucosamine appears in chitin and in animal mucopolysaccharides as the N-acetyl derivative. Introduction of the acetyl group involves acetyl-coenzyme A in both animals and *Neurospora crassa* (52, 126); in *N. crassa* it is not certain whether free glucosamine or its phosphate is the compound acetylated.

Amino sugars are frequently found as constituents of antibiotics, including cordycepin of *Cordyceps militaris* (20) and many of the actinomycete antibiotics (22, 56). Whether they are related to toxicity is uncertain, but the possibility is at least suggested by the number of instances uncovered.

6. THE METABOLISM OF POLYHYDRIC ALCOHOLS

The compounds of this class that have been studied in connection with the carbon metabolism of fungi include the sugar alcohols, glycerol, and a few glycols. Mannitol and glycerol are the most important.

Sugar Alcohols. Mannitol was first discovered in fungi by Braconnot (44, 45), and subsequent work during the nineteenth century revealed its general occurrence in the sporophores of basidiomycetes and ascomycetes (36, 59, 264). Other analyses of cellular material show that mannitol occurs in mycelium, e.g., of *Aspergillus elegans* (91) and *Rhizopus japonicus* (130), in sclerotia (70), and in spores (223, 242, 265). Mannitol may also appear in the medium, and very high yields—from 20 to 50 per cent of the glucose consumed—are found in the culture medium of *Aspergillus* sp. (23) and *Byssochlamys fulva* (186).

Mannitol appears to function physiologically as a reserve food (164, 165); its general utilizability as a carbon source (Chapter 3) is consistent with this function. It is formed in culture from pentoses, hexoses, and glycerol (57, 260). The biosynthesis has not been studied, but it is a reasonable hypothesis that mannitol is formed by the reduction of fructose or a fructose phosphate. Extracts of *Stachybotrys atra* carry out the reversible reaction (54):

$$\text{Fructose} + \text{DPNH} + \text{H}^+ \rightleftharpoons \text{Mannitol} + \text{DPN}^+ \qquad (10)$$

Provided that a hydrogen donor is available, this reaction could synthesize mannitol. Consistent with a reductive origin of mannitol, mannitol formation is increased by restriction of the oxygen supply (23).

D-Sorbitol has been reported formed by *Boletus bovinus* (132), and preformed mats of several basidiomycetes dehydrogenate sorbitol to L-sorbose (239). Other sugar alcohols which are formed by fungi include: D-volemitol (35), D-arabitol (77, 182a, 259), *i*-erythritol (168, 220, 262, 265). Some of the sugar alcohols account for an appreciable fraction of the carbon metabolized; thus, D-threitol (*l*-erythritol) constitutes 13 per cent of the dry weight of the mycelium of *Armillaria mellea* (24). Intact cells of *Fusarium lini* oxidize erythritol to erythrulose (86), and it is likely that similar reactions occur in those fungi which themselves accumulate sugar alcohols.

Glycerol. The formation of glycerol by fungi is mentioned in Chapter 7 as an indication of the functioning of the Embden-Meyerhof respiratory pathway. The available data (86, 187, 188) are consistent with the metabolism of glycerol via this pathway, i.e.:

$$\text{Glycerol} \rightarrow \text{triose phosphate} \rightarrow \text{pyruvic acid} \qquad (11)$$

No enzymatic studies have, however, been made, and the role of phosphorylated intermediates is only conjectural.

Glycerol phosphates are hydrolyzed by phosphomonoesterases (phosphatases), which also attack other organic phosphates (196). Hydrolysis of organic phosphates at acid pH is brought about by mycelial extracts of *Actinomyces israeli* (104), and of fungi (5, 55, 58, 198, 199). In *Trichophyton rubrum* cytochemical tests suggest the presence of another phosphomonoesterase active at alkaline pH values (159), and enzymes of this type (alkaline phosphatases) have been reported in other fungi (50, 236). These and other phosphatases are considered elsewhere (Chapter 9).

Baba (7, 8) isolated an unusual metabolite, monoallyl phosphoric acid, $CH_2\!=\!CH\!-\!CH_2\!-\!OPO_3H_2$, from cultures of *Aspergillus niger* metabolizing glycerol, and showed in addition the presence of an enzyme, a phosphatase, able to dephosphorylate the compound.

Glycols. Exogenously supplied glycols are oxidized by some fungi, e.g., *Fusarium lini* converts ethylene glycol to glycolaldehyde (86), and *Aspergillus niger* dehydrogenates 1,2-butanediol to hydroxymethylethylketone (246). The dehydrogenation of ethylene glycol may be effected by alcohol dehydrogenase, known to catalyze this reaction in other systems.

Fusarium lini also oxidizes 2,3-butylene glycol to acetoin ($CH_3\!-\!CO\!-\!CHOH\!-\!CH_3$) (86). Acetoin occurs as a metabolite of sugar or pyruvic acid in fungi and actinomycetes (109, 221, 225), but its importance and the pathway of formation in the fungi are not known. In yeast, but not in bacteria, it seems that ketols of this type are formed with the participation of acetyl-coenzyme A and the free aldehyde (215).

124   CARBON METABOLISM II

BIBLIOGRAPHY

1. Albericci, V. J., T. P. Curtin, and D. Reilly. 1943. *Biochem. J. (London)* 37: 243–246.
2. Amelung, H. 1930. *Z. physiol. Chem. Hoppe-Seyler's.* 187: 171–172.
3. Asai, T. and H. Saito. 1952. *J. Agr. Chem. Soc. Japan* 26: 381–387.
4. Ashour, W. E. 1954. *Trans. Brit. Mycol. Soc.* 37: 343–352.
5. Auhagen, E. and S. Grzycki. 1933. *Biochem. Z.* 265: 217–222.
6. Ayres, A., et al. 1952. *Nature (London)* 170: 834–836.
7. Baba, S. 1942. *J. Agr. Chem. Soc. Japan* 18: 818. (*Chem. Abstr.* 45: 3025. 1951.)
8. Baba, S. 1943. *Proc. Imp. Acad. (Tokyo)* 19: 70–76.
9. Bacon, J. S. D. and D. J. Bell. 1953. *J. Chem. Soc. (London)* 1953: 2528–2530.
10. Barker, S. A., E. J. Bourne, and T. R. Carrington. 1954. *J. Chem. Soc. (London)* 1954: 2125–2129.
11. Barker, S. A., E. J. Bourne, G. C. Hewitt, and M. Stacey. 1955. *J. Chem. Soc. (London)* 1955: 3734–3740.
12. Barker, S. A., E. J. Bourne, and M. Stacey. 1953. *Chem. & Ind.* 1953: 1287.
13. de Bary, A. 1886. *Botan. Ztg.* 44: 393–404.
14. Basu, S. N. and D. R. Whitaker. 1953. *Arch. Biochem. Biophys.* 42: 12–24.
15. Bealing, F. J. 1953. *Biochem. J. (London)* 55: 93–101.
16. Bealing, F. J. and J. S. D. Bacon. 1953. *Biochem. J. (London)* 53: 277–285.
17. Beaven, G. H. and F. Brown. 1949. *Biochem. J. (London)* 45: 221–224.
18. Béchamp, A. 1858. *Compt. rend. (Paris)* 46: 44–47.
19. Béchamp, A. 1864. *Compt. rend. (Paris)* 59: 496–500.
19a. Beckman, C. H. 1956. *Phytopathology* 46: 605–609.
20. Bentley, H. R., K. G. Cunningham, and F. S. Spring. 1951. *J. Chem Soc. (London)* 1951: 2301–2305.
21. Bhargava, K. S. 1943. *J. Indian Botan. Soc.* 22: 85–99.
22. Binkley, S. B. 1955. *Ann. Rev. Biochem.* 24: 596–626.
23. Birkinshaw, J. H., J. H. V. Charles, A. C. Hetherington, and H. Raistrick. 1931. *Phil Trans. Roy. Soc. London Ser. B* 220: 153–171.
24. Birkinshaw, J. H., C. E. Stickings, and P. Tessier. 1948. *Biochem. J. (London)* 42: 329–332.
25. Blank, L. M. and P. J. Talley. 1941. *Am. J. Botany* 28: 564–569.
26. Blumenthal, H. J., S. T. Horowitz, A. Hemerline, and S. Roseman. 1955. *Bacteriol. Proc. (Soc. Am. Bacteriologists)* 1955: 137.
27. Boas, F. 1917. *Biochem. Z.* 78: 308–312.
28. Bois, E. and J. Savary. 1945. *Can. J. Research B* 23: 208–213.
29. Bond, C. R., E. C. Knight, and T. K. Walker. 1937. *Biochem. J. (London)* 31: 1033–1040.
30. Boothroyd, B., J. A. Thorn, and R. H. Haskins. 1955. *Can. J. Biochem. and Physiol.* 33: 289–296.
31. Bose, S. R. 1939. *Ergeb. Enzymforsch.* 8: 266–276.
32. Bose, S. R. and S. N. Sarkar. 1937. *Proc. Roy. Soc. (London) B* 123: 193–213.
33. Bourquelot, E. 1883. *Compt. rend. (Paris)* 97: 1322–1324.
34. Bourquelot, E. 1889. *Bull. soc. mycol. France* 5: 132–163.
35. Bourquelot, E. 1890. *Bull. soc. mycol. France* 6: vii–viii.
36. Bourquelot, E. 1893a. *Bull. soc. mycol. France* 9: 51–66.
37. Bourquelot, E. 1893b. *Compt. rend. (Paris)* 116: 1143–1145.
38. Bourquelot, E. 1893c. *Compt. rend (Paris)* 117: 383–386.
39. Bourquelot, E. 1894. *Bull. soc. mycol. France* 10: 49–54.

BIBLIOGRAPHY   125

40. Bourquelot, E. 1898. *Compt. rend.* (*Paris*) 126: 1045–1047.
41. Bourquelot, E. and H. Hérissey. 1901. *Compt. rend. Sci.* (*Paris*) 132: 571–574.
42. Bourquelot, E. and H. Hérissey. 1902. *Compt. rend.* (*Paris*) 135: 399–401.
43. Bourquelot, E. and H. Hérissey. 1905. *Bull. soc. mycol. France* 21: 50–57.
44. Braconnot, H. 1811a. *Ann. chim.* 79: 265–304.
45. Braconnot, H. 1811b. *Ann. chim.* 80: 272–292.
46. Brown, W. 1915. *Ann. Botany* 29: 313–348.
47. Brown, W. and R. S. K. Wood. 1953. *Symposium Soc. Gen. Microbiol., 3*: 326–339.
47a. Burger, M. and K. Beran. 1956. *Ceskoslov. Mikrobiol.* 1: 26–31.
48. Buston, H. W. and A. Jabbar. 1954. *Biochim. et Biophys. Acta* 15: 543–548.
49. Caldwell, M. L., R. M. Chester, A. H. Doebbeling, and G. Volz. 1945. *J. Biol. Chem.* 161: 361–365.
49a. Cantino, E. C., J. Lovett, and E. A. Horenstein. 1957. *Am. J. Botany* 44: 498–505.
50. Chattaway, F. W., C. C. Thompson, and A. J. E. Barlow. 1954. *Biochim. et Biophys. Acta* 14: 583–584.
51. Chona, B. L. 1932. *Ann. Botany* 46: 1033–1050.
52. Chou, T. C. and M. Soodak. *J. Biol. Chem.* 196: 105–109.
53. Chrząszcz, T. and D. Tiukow. 1929. *Biochem. Z.* 207: 39–52.
54. Cochrane, V. W. and M. Albrecht. Unpublished data.
55. Contardi, A. and A. Ercoli. 1933. *Biochem. Z.* 261: 275–302.
56. Corbaz, R. et al. 1955. *Helv. Chim. Acta* 38: 935–942.
57. Coyne, F. P. and H. Raistrick. 1931. *Biochem. J.* (*London*) 25: 1513–1521.
58. Crewther, W. G. and F. G. Lennox. 1953. *Australian J. Biol. Sci.* 6: 410–427.
59. Czapek, F. 1922. *Biochemie der Pflanzen*, 3rd ed., Vol 1. Jena: Gustav Fischer, pp. 828.
60. Davis, D., P. E. Waggoner, and A. E. Dimond. 1953. *Nature* (*London*) 172: 959.
61. Davison, F. R. and J. J. Willaman. 1927. *Botan. Gaz.* 83: 329–361.
62. Demis, D. J., A. Rothstein, and R. Meier. 1954. *Arch. Biochem. Biophys.* 48: 55–62.
63. Dingle, J., W. W. Reid, and G. L. Solomons. 1953. *J. Sci. Food Agr.* 4: 149–155.
64. Dingle, J. and G. L. Solomons. 1952. *J. Appl. Chem.* (*London*) 2: 395–399.
65. Dox, A. W. and R. E. Neidig. 1912. *Biochem. Z.* 46: 397–402.
66. Edelman, J. 1954. *Biochem. J.* (*London*) 57: 22–33.
67. Ehrlich, F. and A. Kosmahly. 1929. *Biochem. Z.* 212: 162–239.
68. Elander, M. and K. Myrbäck. 1949. *Arch. Biochem.* 21: 249–255.
69. Erb, N. M., R. T. Wisthoff, and W. L. Jacobs. 1948. *J. Bacteriol.* 55: 813–821.
70. Ergle, D. R. 1948. *Phytopathology* 38: 142–151.
71. Euler, H. von. 1921. *Fermentforschung* 4: 242–257.
72. Fischer, E. H., L. Kohtès, and J. Fellig. 1951. *Helv. Chim. Acta* 34: 1132–1138.
73. Fischer, E. H. and R. de Montmillon. 1951a. *Helv. Chim. Acta* 34: 1987–1994.
74. Fischer, E. H. and R. de Montmillon. 1951b. *Helv. Chim. Acta* 34: 1994–1999.
75. Fish, V. B. and R. B. Dustman. 1945. *J. Am. Chem. Soc.* 67: 1155–1157.
76. Fishman, W. H. 1951. In J. B. Sumner and K. Myrbäck (eds.), *The Enzymes*, Vol. 1 (2), p. 769–792. New York: Academic Press.
77. Frèrejacque, M. 1939. *Compt. rend.* (*Paris*) 208: 1123–1124.
78. Freudenberg, K. and T. Ploetz. 1939. *Z. physiol. Chem. Hoppe-Seyler's.* 259: 19–27.
79. Garren, K. H. 1938. *Phytopathology* 28: 839–845.
80. Gäumann, E. and E. Böhni. 1947a. *Helv. Chim. Acta* 30: 24–38.
81. Gäumann, E. and E. Böhni. 1947b. *Helv. Chim. Acta* 30: 1592–1595.

82. Gillespie, J. M. and E. F. Woods. 1953. *Australian J. Biol. Sci.* 6: 447–462.
83. Gilligan, W. and E. T. Reese. 1955. *Can. J. Microbiol.* 1: 90–107.
84. Godin, P. 1953a. *Biochim. et Biophys. Acta* 11: 114–118.
85. Godin, P. 1953b. *Biochim. et Biophys. Acta* 11: 119–121.
86. Goepfert, G. J. and F. F. Nord. 1942. *Arch. Biochem.* 1: 289–301.
87. Gothoskar, S. S., R. P. Scheffer, J. C. Walker, and M. A. Stahmann. 1953. *Phytopathology* 43: 535–536.
88. Gothoskar, S. S., R. P. Scheffer, J. C. Walker, and M. A. Stahmann. 1955. *Phytopathology* 45: 381–387.
89. Gottschalk, A. 1950. In J. B. Sumner and K. Myrbäck (eds.), *The Enzymes,* Vol. 1 (1), p. 551–582. New York: Academic Press.
90. Grassmann, W., R. Stadler, and R. Bender. 1933. *Ann. Chem. Liebigs* 502: 20–40.
91. Grégoire, P. 1949. *Bull. soc. chim. biol.* 31: 801–803.
91a. Halliwell, G. 1957. *J. Gen. Microbiol.* 17: 166–183.
92. Harter, L. L. 1921. *J. Agr. Research* 20: 761–786.
93. Harter, L. L. 1925. *J. Agr. Research* 30: 961–969.
94. Harter, L. L. and J. L. Weimer. 1921a. *J. Agr. Research* 21: 609-625.
95. Harter, L. L. and J. L. Weimer. 1921b. *J Agr. Research* 22: 371–377.
96. Hawkins, L. A. 1915. *Am. J. Botany* 2: 375–388.
97. Hawkins, L. A. and R. B. Harvey. 1919. *J. Agr. Research* 18: 275–297.
98. Hérissey, H. 1921. *Compt. rend. (Paris)* 172: 766–768.
99. Hockenhull, D. J. D., G. C. Ashton, K. H. Fantes, and B. K. Whithead. 1954. *Biochem. J. (London)* 57: 93–98.
100. Hofmann, E. 1934. *Biochem. Z.* 273: 198–206.
101. Hofmann, E. and E. Latzko. 1950. *Biochem. Z.* 320: 269–272.
102. Holden, M. 1950a. *Biochem. J. (London)* 47: 415–420.
103. Holden, M. 1950b. *Biochem. J. (London)* 47: 426–431.
104. Howell, A., Jr. and R. J. Fitzgerald. 1953. *J. Bacteriol.* 66: 437–112.
105. Hull, R. 1939. *Ann. Appl. Biol.* 26: 800–822.
106. Hultin, E. and L. Nordström. 1949. *Acta Chem. Scand.* 3: 1405-1417.
107. Humm, H. J. and K. S. Shepard. 1946. *Duke Univ. Marine Sta. Bull.* 3: 76–80.
108. Iwanoff, N. N. 1925. *Biochem. Z.* 162: 455–458.
109. Jagannathan, V. and K. Singh. 1953. *Enzymologia* 16: 150–160.
110. Jensen, H. L. 1930. *Soil Sci.* 30: 59–77.
111. Jermyn, M. A. 1952. *Australian J. Sci. Research Ser. B,* 5: 433-443.
112. Jermyn, M. A. 1953. *Australian J. Biol. Sci.* 6: 77–97.
113. Jermyn, M. A. and R. Thomas. 1953. *Australian J. Biol. Sci.* 6: 70–76.
114. Jermyn, M. A. and R. G. Tomkins. 1950. *Biochem. J. (London)* 47: 437–442.
114a. Jeuniaux, C. 1955. *Compt. rend. soc. biol.* 149: 1307–1308.
115. Kertesz, Z. I. 1936. *Ergeb. Enzymforsch.* 5: 233–258.
116. Kertesz, Z. I. 1951. In J. B. Sumner and K. Myrbäck (eds.), *The Enzymes,* Vol. 1 (2), p. 745–768. New York: Academic Press.
117. Kertesz, Z. I. et al. 1944. *Chem. Eng. News* 22: 105–106.
118. Kertesz, Z. I. and R. J. McColloch. 1950. *Advances in Carbohydrate Chem.* 5: 79–102.
119. Kooiman, P., P. A. Roelofsen, and S. Sweeris. 1954. *Enzymologia* 16: 237–246.
120. Kopeloff, N., L. Kopeloff, and C. J. Welcome. 1920. *J. Biol. Chem.* 43: 171–187.
121. Kuhn, R. 1923. *Z. physiol. Chem. Hoppe-Seyler's.* 129: 57–63.
122. Kuhn, R. and G. E. von Grundherr. 1926. *Ber. deut. chem Ges.* B59: 1655–1664.
123. Langlykke, A. F., C. V. Smythe, and D. Perlman. 1952. In J B. Sumner and

K. Myrbäck (eds.), *The Enzymes*, Vol. 2 (2), p. 1180–1338. New York: Academic Press.

124. Leloir, L. F. 1953. *Advances in Enzymol.* 14: 193–218.
125. Leloir, L. F. and E. Cabib. 1953. *J. Am. Chem. Soc.* 75: 5445–5446.
126. Leloir, L. F. and C. E. Cardini. 1953. *Biochim. et Biophys. Acta* 12: 15–22.
127. LeMense, E. H., J. Corman, J. M. Van Lanen, and A. F. Langlykke. 1947. *J. Bacteriol.* 54: 149–159.
128. Lemieux, R. U., J. A. Thorn, and H. F. Bauer. 1953. *Can. J. Chem.* 31: 1054–1059.
129. Leopold, H. and M. P. Starbanow. 1943. *Biochem. Z.* 314: 232–249.
130. Lim, H. 1935. *J. Fac. Agr. Hokkaido Imp. Univ. (Sapporo, Japan)* 37: 165–209.
131. Lineweaver, H., R. Jang, and E. F. Jansen. 1949. *Arch. Biochem.* 20: 137–152.
132. Lippmann, E. von. 1912. *Ber. deut. chem. Ges.* 45: 3431–3434.
133. Luh, B. S. and H. J. Phaff. 1951. *Arch. Biochem. Biophys.* 33: 212–227.
134. McCarty, M. 1952a. *J. Exp. Med.* 96: 555–568.
135. McCarty, M. 1952b. *J. Exp. Med.* 96: 569–580.
136. McColloch, R. J. and Z. I. Kertesz. 1945. *J. Biol. Chem.* 160: 149–154.
137. McColloch, R. J. and Z. I. Kertesz. 1947. *Arch. Biochem.* 13: 217–229.
138. Macdonald, J. A. 1937. *Ann. Appl. Biol.* 24: 289–310.
139. Mager, J. 1947. *Biochem. J. (London)* 41: 603–609.
140. Mager, J. and M. Aschner. 1947. *J. Bacteriol.* 53: 283–295.
141. Mandels, G. R. 1951. *Am. J. Botany* 38: 213–221.
142. Mandels, G. R. 1953. *Exp. Cell Research* 5: 48–55.
143. Mandels, G. R. 1954. *Plant Physiol.* 29: 18–26.
144. Matus, J. 1948. *Ber. schweiz. botan. Ges.* 58: 319–380.
145. Mayo, J. K. 1925. *New Phytologist* 25: 162–171.
146. Meeuse, B. J. D. 1952. *J. Exp. Botany* 3: 52–58.
147. Mehrotra, B. S. 1949. *J. Indian Botan. Soc.* 28: 108–124.
148. Mehrotra, B. S. 1952. *Lloydia* 15: 185–187.
149. Menon, K. P. V. 1934. *Ann. Botany* 48: 187–210.
150. Miller, G. L. and R. Blum. 1956. *J. Biol. Chem.* 218: 131–137.
151. Miwa, T., C-T. Cheng, M. Fujisaki, and A. Toishi. 1937. *Acta Phytochim. (Japan)* 10: 155–170.
152. Montgomery, H. B. S. 1936. *Ann. Appl. Biol.* 23: 465–486.
153. Murakami, S. 1950. *Misc. Repts. Research Inst. Nat. Resources (Tokyo)*, No. 17–18: 87–95. *(Chem. Abstr.* 47: 657. 1953.)
154. Myrbäck, K. and G. Neumüller. 1950. In J. B. Sumner and K. Myrbäck (eds.), *The Enzymes*, Vol. 1 (1), p. 653–724. New York: Academic Press.
155. Myrbäck, K. and E. Vasseur. 1943. *Z. physiol. Chem. Hoppe-Seyler's.* 277: 171–180.
155a. Nakatsu, S. 1956. *J. Biochem. (Tokyo)* 43: 119–127.
156. Neuberg, C. and I. Mandl. 1950. In J. B. Sumner and K. Myrbäck (eds.), *The Enzymes*, Vol 1 (1), p. 527–550. New York: Academic Press.
157. Neuberg, C. and C. Ostendorf. 1930. *Biochem. Z.* 229: 464–466.
158. Nickerson, W. J. 1947. In W. J. Nickerson (ed.), *Biology of the Pathogenic Fungi*, p. 157–166. Waltham, Mass. Chronica Botanica Co.
159. Nickerson, W. J. 1951. *Trans. N. Y. Acad. Sci.* II, 13: 140–145.
159a. Nisizawa, K. 1955. *J. Biochem. (Tokyo)* 42: 825–835.
160. Niwa, K. 1950. *J. Biochem. (Tokyo)* 37: 301–308.
161. Niwa, K. 1951. *J. Biochem. (Tokyo)* 38. 109–114.
162. Norkrans, B. 1950a. *Physiol. Plantarum* 3: 75–87.
163. Norkrans, B. 1950b. *Symbolae Botan. Upsalienses* 11 (1): 5–126.
163a. Norkrans, B. and B. G. Rånby. 1956. *Physiol. Plantarum* 9: 198–211.

164. Obaton, F. 1929. *Rev. gén. botan.* 41: 282–292, 365–387, 424–440, 498–512, 622–633.
165. Obaton, F. 1932. *Compt. rend. (Paris)* 194: 302–304.
166. O'Dwyer, M. H. 1939. *Biochem. J. (London)* 33: 713–717.
167. O'Dwyer, M. H. 1940. *Biochem. J. (London)* 34: 149–152.
168. Oxford, A. E. and H. Raistrick. 1935. *Biochem. J. (London)* 29: 1599–1601.
169. Pan, S. C., L. W. Nicholson, and P. Kolachov. 1953. *Arch. Biochem. Biophys.* 42: 406–420, 421–434.
170. Pazur, J. H. 1952. *J. Biol. Chem.* 199: 217–226.
171. Pazur, J. H. 1954. *Biochim. et Biophys. Acta* 13: 158–159.
172. Pazur, J. H. 1955. *J. Biol. Chem.* 216: 531–538.
173. Pazur, J. H. and D. French. 1951. *J. Am. Chem. Soc.* 73: 3536.
174. Pazur, J. H. and D. French. 1952 *J. Biol. Chem.* 196: 265–272.
175. Perlman, D. and A. F. Langlykke. 1948. *J. Am. Chem. Soc.* 70: 3968.
176. Phaff, H. J. 1947. *Arch. Biochem.* 13: 67–81.
177. Phillips, L. L. and M. L. Caldwell. 1951a. *J. Am. Chem. Soc.* 73: 3559–3563.
178. Phillips, L. L. and M. L. Caldwell. 1951b. *J. Am. Chem. Soc.* 73: 3563–3568.
179. Pigman, W. W. 1943. *J. Research Natl. Bur. Standards* 30: 159–175.
180. Pigman, W. W. 1951. In J. B. Sumner and K. Myrbäck (eds.), *The Enzymes,* Vol. 1 (2), p. 725–744. New York: Academic Press.
181. Ploetz, T. 1939. *Z. physiol. Chem. Hoppe-Seyler's.* 261: 163–168.
182. Pottevin, H. 1903. *Ann. inst. Pasteur* 17: 31–51.
182a. Prentice, N. and L. S. Cuendet. 1954. *Nature (London)* 174: 1151.
183. Pringsheim, H. 1912. *Z. physiol. Chem. Hoppe-Seyler's.* 78: 266–291.
184. Pringsheim, H. and G. Kohn. 1924. *Z. physiol. Chem. Hoppe-Seyler's.* 133: 80–96.
185. Radha, K. 1953. *Proc. Indian Acad. Sci.* 38B: 231–234.
185a. Ragheb, H. S. and F. W. Fabian. 1955. *Food Research* 20: 614–625.
186. Raistrick, H. and G. Smith. 1933. *Biochem. J. (London)* 27: 1814–1819.
187. Ramachandran, K. and T. K. Walker. 1951. *Arch. Biochem. Biophys.* 31: 224–233.
188. Ramachandran, K. and T. K. Walker. 1952. *Arch. Biochem. Biophys.* 35: 195–203.
189. Ratajak, E. J. and H. S. Owens. 1942. *Botan. Gaz.* 104: 329–337.
190. Reese, E. T., W. Gilligan, and B. Norkrans. 1952. *Physiol. Plantarum* 5: 379–390.
191. Reese, E. T. and H. S. Levinson. 1952. *Physiol. Plantarum* 5: 345–366.
192. Reid, W. W. 1952. *Biochem. J. (London)* 50: 289–292.
193. Reuter, C. 1912. *Z. physiol. Chem. Hoppe-Seyler's.* 78: 167–245.
194. Reynolds, D. M. 1954. *J. Gen. Microbiol.* 11: 150–159.
195. Roboz, E., R. W. Barratt, and E. L. Tatum. 1952. *J. Biol. Chem.* 195: 459–471.
196. Roche, J. 1950. In J. B. Sumner and K. Myrbäck (eds.), *The Enzymes,* Vol. 1 (1), p. 473–510. New York: Academic Press.
197. Roelofsen, P. A. 1953. *Biochim. et Biophys. Acta* 10: 410–413.
198. Sadasivan, V. 1950. *Arch. Biochem.* 28: 100–110.
199. Sadasivan, V. 1952. *Arch. Biochem. Biophys.* 37: 172–185.
200. Saiki, T. 1906–1907. *J. Biol. Chem.* 2: 251–265.
201. Saksena, R. K. and S. K. Bose. 1944. *J. Indian Botan. Soc.* 23: 108–112.
202. Saroja, K., R. Venkataraman, and K. V. Giri. 1955. *Biochem. J. (London)* 60: 399–403.
203. Satina, S. and A. F. Blakeslee. 1928. *Proc. Natl. Acad. Sci. U. S.* 14: 229–235.
204. Saunders, P. R., R. G. H. Siu, and R. N. Genest. 1948. *J. Biol. Chem.* 174: 697–703.
205. Scheffer, R. P., S. S. Gothoskar, C. F. Pierson, and R. P. Collins. 1956. *Phytopathology* 46: 83–87.

206. Schmidt, C. F., Jr. 1935. *J. Biol. Chem.* 110: 511–520.
207. Schmidt, D. 1925. *Biochem. Z.* 158: 223–252.
208. Schubert, E. 1952. *Biochem. Z.* 323: 78–88.
209. Schubert, E. 1954. *Helv. Chim. Acta* 37: 691–700.
210. Shu, P. and A. C. Blackwood. 1951. *Can. J. Botan.* 29: 113–124.
211. Sideris, C. P. 1924. *Phytopathology* 14: 481–489.
212. Simpson, F. J. 1955. *Can. J. Microbiol.* 1: 131–139.
213. Simpson, F. J. and E. McCoy. 1953. *Appl. Microbiol.* 1: 228–236.
214. Siu, R. G. H. 1951. *Microbial Decomposition of Cellulose.* New York: Reinhold Publ. Corp., pp. 531.
215. Smith, P. F. and D. Hendlin. 1953. *J. Bacteriol.* 65: 440–445.
216. Smithies, W. R. 1953. *Biochem. J. (London)* 55: 346–350.
217. Sørensen, H. 1952. *Physiol. Plantarum* 5: 183–198.
218. Sørensen, H. 1953. *Nature (London)* 172: 305–306.
219. Stanier, R. Y. 1942. *J. Bacteriol.* 44: 555–570.
220. Stodola, F. H. 1946. *J. Biol. Chem.* 166: 79.
221. Strauss, B. S. 1955. *Arch. Biochem. Biophys.* 55: 77–94.
222. Stuart, N. W. and S. L. Emsweller. 1943. *Science* 98: 569–570.
223. Sumi, M. 1928. *Biochem. Z.* 195: 161–174.
224. Sussman, M., S. Spiegelman, and J. M. Reiner. 1947. *J. Cellular Comp. Physiol.* 29: 149–158.
225. Takahashi, T. and T. Asai. 1932. *J. Agr. Chem. Soc. Japan* 8: 652–658. (*Chem. Abstr.* 26: 5602. 1932.)
226. Takano, K. and T. Miwa. 1950. *J. Biochem. (Tokyo)* 37: 435–444.
227. Takata, R. 1929. *J. Soc. Chem. Ind. Japan* 32 (Suppl. binding): 245–247. (*Chem. Abstr.* 24: 2206. 1930.)
228. Tanret, C. 1903. *Bull. soc. chim.*, 3 sér., 29: 888–896.
229. Tate, P. 1929. *Parasitology* 21: 31–54.
230. Thaysen, A. C. and L. D. Galloway. 1930. *The Microbiology of Starch and Sugars.* London: Oxford Univ. Press, pp. 336.
230a. Thomas, R. 1956. *Australian J. Biol. Sci.* 9: 159–183.
231. Thornberry, H. H. 1938. *Phytopathology* 28: 202–205.
232. Tracey, M. V. 1953. *Biochem. Soc. Symposia (Cambridge, Engl.)* 11: 49–61.
233. Tracey, M. V. 1955. *Biochem. J. (London)* 61: 579–586.
234. Tsuchiya, H. M., A. Jeannes, H. M. Bricker, and C. Wilham. 1952. *J. Bacteriol.* 64: 513–519.
235. Underkofler, L. A. and D. K. Roy. 1951. *Cereal Chem.* 28: 18–29.
236. Varma, T. N. R. and K. S. Srinivasan. 1954. *Enzymologia* 17: 116–122.
237. Vasudeva, R. S. 1930. *Ann. Botany* 44: 469–493.
238. Veibel, S. 1950. In J. B. Sumner and K. Myrbäck (eds.), *The Enzymes,* Vol. 1 (1), p. 583–620. New York: Academic Press.
239. Vitucci, J. C., E. S. Pallares, and F. F. Nord. 1946. *Arch. Biochem.* 9: 439–449.
240. Voss, W. and G. Butter. 1938. *Ann. Chem. Liebigs* 534: 161–185.
241. Waggoner, P. E. and A. E. Dimond. 1955. *Phytopathology* 45: 79–87.
242. Wain, R. L. and E. H. Wilkinson. 1946. *Ann. Appl. Biol.* 33: 401–405.
243. Waksman, S. A. and M. C. Allen. 1933. *J. Am. Chem. Soc.* 55: 3408–3418.
244. Wallenfels, K. 1951. *Naturwiss.* 38: 306–307.
245. Wallenfels, K. and E. Bernt. 1952. *Angew. Chem.* 64: 28–29.
246. Walti, A. 1934. *J. Am. Chem. Soc.* 56: 2723–2726.
247. Ward, H. M. 1888. *Ann. Botany* 2: 319–382.
248. Weinland, H. and K. Nüchterlein. 1954. *Z. physiol. Chem. Hoppe-Seyler's.* 298: 48–54.
249. Welsch, M. 1942. *J. Bacteriol.* 44: 571–588.
250. Whistler, R. L. and C. L. Smart. 1953. *J. Am. Chem. Soc.* 75: 1916–1918.
251. Whitaker, D. R. 1953. *Arch. Biochem. Biophys.* 43: 253–268.

252. Whitaker, D. R. 1954. *Arch. Biochem. Biophys.* 53: 439–449.
253. Whitaker, D. R., J. R. Colvin, and W. H. Cook. 1954. *Arch. Biochem. Biophys.* 49: 257–262.
254. Wiggers, H. A. L. 1832. *Ann. Pharm.* 1: 129–182.
255. Willaman, J. J. 1920. *Botan. Gaz.* 70: 221–229.
256. Willstaedt, H. and M. Borggard. 1946. *Arkiv Kemi, Mineral. Geol.* 23B (3): 1–8.
257. Winstead, N. N. and J. C. Walker. 1954. *Phytopathology* 44: 153–158.
258. Wolf, F. A. 1914. *Mycol. Centr.* 4: 278–287.
259. Yabuta, T. and Y. Sumiki. 1933. *J. Agr. Chem. Soc. Japan* 9: 492–497. (*Chem. Abstr.* 27: 4236. 1933.)
260. Yamasaki, I. and M. Simomura. 1937. *Biochem. Z.* 291: 340–348.
261. Young, V. H. 1918. *Plant World* 21: 75–87, 114–133.
262. Yuill, J. L. 1948. *Nature (London)* 162: 652.
263. Zeller, S. M. 1916. *Ann. Missouri Botan. Garden* 3: 439–509.
264. Zellner, J. 1907. *Chemie der höheren Pilze.* Leipzig: W. Engelmann, pp. 257.
265. Zellner, J. 1910. *Monatsh. Chem.* 31: 617–634.

6. Carbon Metabolism

Part III

Organic Acids, Lipids,

and Other Compounds

$\mathbf{T}$he final group of carbon metabolites of the fungi has as its most important members the organic acids and the lipids. Brief consideration must also be given to other carbon compounds of various types. Many of the miscellaneous compounds included here have not been studied from a physiological point of view. Nevertheless, they are involved in metabolism and therefore in physiology; they will not remain indefinitely as biochemical curiosities. Space does not permit an exhaustive listing of the aromatic and other compounds known to be produced by fungi; many more will be found in the reviews cited later.

1. THE METABOLISM OF ALIPHATIC ORGANIC ACIDS

The fungi are perhaps best known in microbiology for their tolerance of acidity—although this is much less general than usually thought—and for the ability of some to accumulate non-volatile organic acids. This section considers the metabolism of the organic acids, exclusive of the higher fatty acids, the keto acids of the respiratory pathways, and those acids which are basically ring compounds.

Sugar Acids. Acids derived by direct oxidation of either or both terminal carbon atoms of a sugar may be grouped together as the sugar acids. Of these, the only one to be formed in quantity is gluconic acid. The reaction was discovered by Molliard (379) in *Aspergillus niger,* and subsequent work has shown that at least small amounts of gluconate are formed by a variety of fungi (Table 1). So

131

**Table 1.   The Formation of Organic Acids from Carbohydrates
by Fungi and Actinomycetes***

Acid	Organisms
Gluconic acid $HOCH_2$—$(HCOH)_4$—$COOH$	*Mucor plumbeus, Rhizopus* spp.† (465); *Ceratostomella ulmi* (166); *Coniophora cerebella*,† *Merulius lacrymans*,† *Polyporus vaporarius* (465); *Aspergillus* spp. (80, 192, 321, 379); *Dematium pullulans* (422); *Fumago vagans* (80); *Fusarium lini* (399); *Penicillium* spp. (80, 321); *Sclerotium delphinii* (414)
Mannonic acid $HOCH_2$—$(CHOH)_4$—$COOH$	*Aspergillus niger* (321); *Penicillium luteopurpurogenum* (13)
Galactonic acid $HOCH_2$—$(CHOH)$—$COOH$	*Aspergillus niger* (321)
Glucuronic acid ‡ $HOOC$—$(HCOH)_4$—CHO	*Penicillium* spp. (298, 474); *Stereum hirsutum* (356); *Ustulina vulgaris* (567)
Saccharic acid $HOOC$—$(CHOH)_4$—$COOH$	*Aspergillus niger* (126)
2-Ketogluconic acid $HOCH_2$—$(CHOH)_3$—CO—$COOH$	*Penicillium brevi-compactum* (474)
Xylonic acid ‡ $HOCH_2$—$(CHOH)_3$—$COOH$	*Fusarium lini* (265)
Arabonic acid ‡ $HOCH_2$—$(CHOH)_3$—$COOH$	*Fusarium lini* (265)
Lactic acid CH_3—$CHOH$—$COOH$	*Allomyces arbuscula* (292); *Apodachlya* sp. (23); *Blastocladia pringsheimii* (106); *Chytridium* sp., *Macrochytrium botrydioides* (152); *Monoblepharella* sp. (374); *Mucor rouxii* (132); *Mucor* spp. (502);⁵ *Pythiogeton* sp. (107); *Rhipidium* sp. (231); *Rhizopus* spp. (453, 541); *Sapromyces elongatus* (231); *Botrytis cinerea* (224); *Monilia* spp. (377, 457); *Actinomyces* spp. (184, 291); *Streptomyces* spp. (171, 424, 562)

* Exclusive of the keto acids, the higher fatty acids, and acidic ring compounds. Organisms are listed by groups: phycomycetes, ascomycetes, basidiomycetes, Fungi Imperfecti, actinomycetes, in that order.
† Identification doubtful.
‡ See text.
§ In sulfite-inhibited culture.

Table 1 (*continued*)

Acid	Organisms
Citric acid 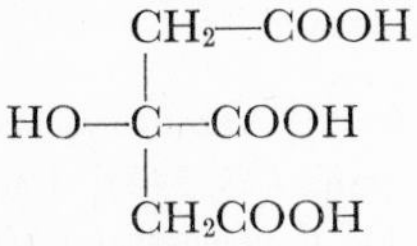	*Mucor pyriformis* (548); *Coniophora cerebella* (75); *Merulius* spp. (30); *Aspergillus* spp. (354); *Botrytis* sp. (444a, 465); *Fusarium graminearum* (159); *Monilia formosa* (458); *Penicillium* spp. (134, 136, 546, 547); *Sclerotium delphinii* (414)

$$CH_2{-}COOH$$
$$HO{-}C{-}COOH$$
$$CH_2COOH$$

Fumaric acid

$$HOOC{-}CH$$
$$\|$$
$$CH{-}COOH$$

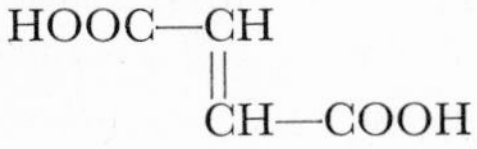

Circinella sp., *Cunninghamella* sp., *Mucor* sp. (207); *Rhizopus* spp. (177, 207); *Neurospora sitophila* (spores) (535); *Aspergillus* spp. (465, 496, 513, 549, 550); *Caldariomyces fumago* (*Fumago vagans*) (141); *Monilia formosa* (458); *Penicillium griseo-fulvum* (432); *Streptomyces coelicolor* (145)

Fumaryl-DL-alanine

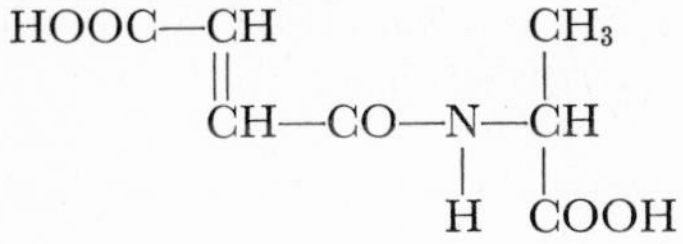

$$HOOC{-}CH \qquad CH_3$$
$$\| \qquad |$$
$$CH{-}CO{-}N{-}CH$$
$$| \quad |$$
$$H \quad COOH$$

Penicillium resticulosum (68)

Succinic acid

$$HOOC{-}CH_2{-}CH_2{-}COOH$$

Blastocladia pringsheimii (106); *Mucor* spp. (196, 502); *Rhizopus* sp. (56); *Neurospora sitophila* (spores) (535); *Fomes annosus, Merulius* spp. (400); *Aspergillus terreus* (70, 433); *Botrytis cinerea* (224); *Clasterosporium* sp., *Fumago vagans* (80); *Fusarium* spp. (351); *Monilia* spp. (377, 457); *Penicillium* spp. (81, 410); *Streptomyces coelicolor* (145)

Malic acid ‡

$$HOOC{-}CH_2{-}CHOH{-}COOH$$

Rhizopus spp. (56, 503); *Neurospora sitophila* (spores) (359); *Merulius* spp. (30); *Aspergillus* spp. (52, 70, 496, 550); *Botrytis cinerea* (224); *Fusarium graminearum* (159); *Penicillium* spp. (228, 298, 465)

Acetic acid

$$CH_3COOH$$

Mortierella spp. (416); *Mucor mucedo* (415); *Neurospora crassa* (418); *Fomes annosus, Merulius* spp. (402); *Polyporus anceps* (415); *Fusarium* spp. (225, 351); *Monilia formosa* (457); *Sclerotium delphinii* (414); *Memnoniella echinata* (419); *Actinomyces* spp. (291); *Streptomyces* spp. (416, 421)

Table 1 (*continued*)

Acid	Organisms
Ethyl acetate $CH_3COOCH_2CH_3$	*Endoconidiophora moniliformis* (241); *Penicillium digitatum* (72)
Oxalic acid HOOC—COOH	*Rhizopus nigricans* (545); *Neurospora crassa* (418); *Sclerotinia* spp. (33, 545); *Armillaria mellea* (261); *Coniophora cerebella* (75); *Corticium centrifugum* (277); *Fomes annosus* (401); *Marasmius chordalis* (478); *Merulius* spp. (401); *Polyporus tumulosus* (437); *Poria vaillantii* (402); *Aspergillus* spp. (67, 515, 545); *Botrytis cinerea* (224, 545); *Dematium pullulans* (34); *Fusarium* spp. (159, 357); *Penicillium* spp. (134, 156, 545); *Sclerotium delphinii* (414); *Trichophyton tonsurans* (533)

Itaconic acid

COOH
|
C=CH₂
|
CH₂
|
COOH

Aspergillus itaconicus (314, 315); *A. terreus* (105, 349); *Ustilago zeae* (263)

cis-Aconitic acid

CH—COOH
‖
C—COOH
|
CH₂—COOH

Aspergillus niger (455)

Itatartaric acid

COOH
|
HO—C—CH₂OH
|
CH₂
|
COOH

Aspergillus terreus mut. (492)

Tartaric acid ‡
HOOC—(CHOH)₂—COOH

Fusarium spp. (357)

Glyoxylic acid
OHC—COOH

Aspergillus niger § (87); *Botrytis cinerea* (224)

Glutaric acid ‡
HOOC—(CH₂)₃—COOH

Aspergillus niger (26)

Table 1 (*continued*)

Acid	Organisms
Glutaconic acid ‡ HOOC—CH=CH—CH₂—COOH	*Aspergillus niger* (26)
Dimethylpyruvic acid (CH₃)₂—CH—CO—COOH	*Aspergillus niger* § (272, 438, 439)
Ethylene oxide α,β-dicarboxylic acid	*Aspergillus fumigatus* (67, 368); *Monilia* *formosa*, *Penicillium viniferum* (458)

$$\text{HOOC—CH—CH—COOH}$$
$$\overset{O}{\diagup\diagdown}$$

far as is now known, the accumulation of large amounts of the acid is restricted to certain strains of *Aspergillus* spp. and *Penicillium* spp., and many fungi yield no gluconate by classical isolation procedures (321, 372, 465).

Because of the potential industrial importance of the process, the conditions of gluconate synthesis by *Aspergillus niger* have been intensively studied. It is found generally that a relatively high pH favors the formation of gluconate over that of citrate (101, 221, 513). Calcium carbonate is customarily added to the medium to control the pH; interference with metabolism by precipitated calcium gluconate can be minimized by the addition of boric acid or borax to the medium (386). As in other acid syntheses, but to a more pronounced degree, the accumulation of gluconate is favored by aeration (464, 554). It is also favored by a relatively high glucose concentration (46, 269) and a limiting amount of phosphate (269). Under appropriate conditions almost complete conversion of glucose to gluconate occurs (221).

The biochemical basis of gluconic acid formation is probably the action of enzyme glucose aerodehydrogenase (glucose oxidase) (Chapter 7), although *Dematium pullulans* is reported to form gluconate (422) and to lack the enzyme (212). The first product in the reaction is glucono-δ-lactone, which may be found in the medium with the free acid (80). Gluconate is further utilized by fungi (46, 514), but the path of metabolism is not known.

The formation by *Aspergillus niger* of other hexonic acids—mannonic acid from mannose and galactonic acid from galactose—has been reported (Table 1), but the process has not been studied further. *Penicillium chrysogenum* forms lactobionic acid from lactose (151á).

Glucuronic acid is reported to be formed in traces by fungi (Table 1), although an unequivocal identification is still lacking. Saccharic acid is found in cultures of *Aspergillus niger* (126, 539). The appearance of pentonic acids in cultures of *Fusarium lini* (265) has not been confirmed and the method of identification used leaves something to be desired.

Lactic Acid. The formation of lactic acid in fungi is restricted almost entirely to phycomycetes (Table 1), and all fungi which convert a major fraction of the carbohydrate to lactate are in this group. The early history of the problem and the cultural conditions favoring lactic acid accumulation are reviewed by Foster (200), Lockwood et al. (353), and Ward et al. (541, 542).

The optical isomer formed by fungi is usually L-lactic (dextrorotatory) (536, 541), although formation of the D- and DL-forms has been reported (453, 457, 501).

As discussed in Chapter 7, the anaerobic formation of lactate by *Rhizopus oryzae* conforms to the postulate that glucose is broken down by the Embden-Meyerhof sequence of reactions to yield lactate, ethanol, and carbon dioxide in equimolar amounts; the mechanism by which the equimolar ratio is maintained is not yet known. More lactate is formed aerobically than anaerobically, and the biosynthesis of this "extra" lactate is not understood. If it is assumed that all of the glucose used is converted to pyruvate, the aerobically produced lactate must arise from it or from ethanol, perhaps with 4-carbon acids as intermediates (109).

Some carbon dioxide enters into the lactate molecule (226). Lactic acid production in high yields is obtained from cultures which are aerated either by shaking (54) or by the rotary drum method (542). It should be noted that Sakaguchi and co-workers (460) could not confirm the stimulation of lactate formation by aerobiosis.

Lactate-forming organisms other than *Rhizopus* spp., that is, the lower phycomycetes and *Streptomyces,* do not, so far as is known, form "extra" lactate aerobically. Again in contrast to *Rhizopus,* some lower phycomycetes anaerobically convert 85 to 100 per cent of the glucose consumed to lactic acid (106, 231, 292). Evidently the biochemical basis here differs in important respects from that of *Rhizopus;* the difference recalls that between the homofermentative and the heterofermentative lactic acid bacteria.

Lactic acid is not an end product of aerobic metabolism but is consumed after exhaustion of the principal carbon source (106, 171). An aerobic lactic dehydrogenase is known in *Penicillium chrysogenum* (111), but the enzymatic basis of lactate utilization in those fungi which accumulate the acid is not known. The oxidation of lactic acid by resting cells of *P. chrysogenum* is suppressed by glucose (278).

Citric Acid. The ability of fungi to accumulate citric acid was first discovered by Wehmer (546, 547) in species of *"Citromyces"* *(Penicillium)*. Later (155) it was found that higher yields are obtained from selected strains of the black-spored Aspergilli, usually referred to as *Aspergillus niger*. Certain of these strains are presumably used for the commercial production of citric acid. Although the acid is probably a metabolic intermediate of aerobic metabolism in all fungi (Chapter 7), it appears in significant amounts only in a few forms (Table 1), primarily species—or, more correctly, certain strains of species—of *Penicillium* and *Aspergillus*. Most strains of *A. niger* have the potentiality for the accumulation of citric, gluconic, and oxalic acids; particular strains under a given set of conditions may form predominantly one acid or a mixture of two or three (48, 58). Strain differences contribute to the failure of different laboratories to agree on the details of the citric acid process, but the basic physiological events are presumably the same in all strains. Selection may increase the yield of citrate (169, 307), and, correspondingly, a strain may change its capacity as the result of mutation (218, 331). No adequate genetic analysis has been made; probably the typical strain is a heterocaryon with nuclei of different genetic types which segregate in spore formation (28).

The biosynthesis of citrate by *Aspergillus niger* was investigated extensively during the period 1920 to 1940, largely by growth and replacement culture experiments which by themselves do not discriminate among the various possible metabolic pathways. Theories based on this work, all obsolete or correct only by chance, are reviewed by Foster (200) and Walker (538).

As discussed in Chapter 7, it now seems that fungi, like other organisms, utilize the citric acid cycle in aerobic respiration; the evidence, which is admittedly still incomplete, comes from enzymatic studies and from isotope experiments with citrate formation in *Aspergillus niger*. At least one other pathway of citrate (or isocitrate) metabolism is known in fungi (405) and may be found in the future to make a significant contribution to citrate synthesis. If we postulate the ubiquity of the citric acid cycle in fungi, accumulation of citrate is best regarded as an unusual modification, under genetic and environmental control, of a process which occurs in all cells under aerobic conditions.

Figure 1 is a simplified diagram of some of the known and probable relationships of organic acids in *Aspergillus niger* and, with some exceptions, very likely in all fungi. The salient and physiologically significant implications of the scheme may be summarized:

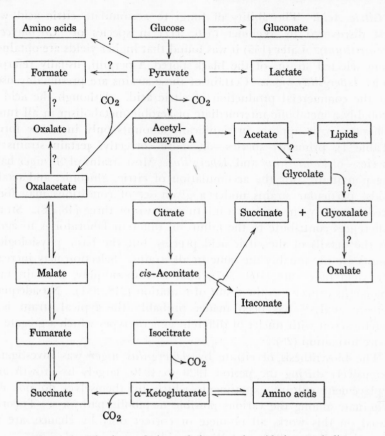

Figure 1. The interrelations of the organic acids in metabolism.

1. Citric acid is shown as arising by the condensation of oxalacetate and acetyl-coenzyme A; an origin from succinate and glyoxalate is a second possibility (405).

2. In order for citrate to accumulate, oxalacetate must therefore be provided; in Figure 1 its only indicated source is the carboxylation of pyruvic acid. Whether this mechanism is quantitatively adequate for the high yields of citrate which have been reported (553) is not finally certain, although there is no doubt that carbon dioxide does enter into the citrate molecule in substantial amount (369).

3. Citrate may be oxidized further, i.e., it is not an end product. This is borne out both by studies of the time course of citrate accumulation (47, 58a, 213) and by isotope studies (110, 337).

4. Especially during growth, the carbon of citric acid cycle intermediates is drawn upon for amino acid and lipid synthesis. The

particular reactions shown in Figure 1 may not all occur in fungi, but there is no doubt that fatty acid and amino acid skeletons are built up from intermediates of carbohydrate oxidation. It is significant that strains of *Aspergillus niger* which do not accumulate citrate have a high growth rate (185), and that highly acidogenic mutants are relatively slow growing (218).

5. Carbon may also be drawn off into gluconic or oxalic acid in *Aspergillus niger* and into still other acids in other fungi.

These biochemical relationships explain many of the known physiological requirements for citric acid accumulation. In the first place, the concentration of available carbohydrate must be high (354); usually glucose at 15 to 20 per cent is employed. Under these conditions there is an excess of carbon over that required for energy and for the synthesis of cellular material; this excess will then, we think, accumulate wherever genetic and environmental factors permit rapid formation but only slow breakdown of a metabolite. Such a metabolite may be directly on a major pathway or on a "shunt," diversionary, pathway (200).

The requirement for a high carbohydrate concentration has its counterpart in the usual finding that highest yields of citrate are obtained if other major nutrients—nitrogen, phosphorus, magnesium, sulfur—are at levels which limit growth (103, 155, 308, 443). Data which contradict this generalization are, however, often reported, and there are undoubtedly secondary physiological effects of nutrients (472, 473).

Minor elements affect citric acid production, but contradictory results have been reported. There is no doubt, on the one hand, that zinc, iron, manganese, and copper are essential to growth and acid formation (518) or, on the other, that high concentrations of metals may lower yields (420). Between these two extremes, it appears from recent work that the best yield of citric acid and other acids is obtained at concentrations of the minor elements which allow some growth but are at the same time limiting to growth (130). Increases of zinc, for example, may result in a greater total yield but the percentage of conversion of glucose to acid is lowered (129). Perhaps the clearest example is the inhibitory effect of iron on citrate accumulation; the inhibition disappears in a medium in which growth is limited by low phosphate (472).

The optimum level of any given nutrient, affected as it is by the strain used, the conditions of culture, and the other nutrients present, is a matter for individual determination. The important general

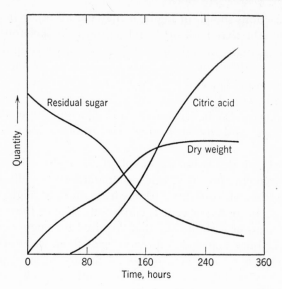

Figure 2. Growth and chemical changes in the course of citric acid synthesis by *Aspergillus niger* in shake culture. Redrawn from P. Shu and M. J. Johnson, *Industrial and Engineering Chemistry*, Vol. 40, p. 1202-1205, July 1948. Copyright 1948 by the American Chemical Society and reprinted by permission of the copyright owner.

principle that growth and acid formation are to a degree competitive should not be obscured by these secondary effects, important as they may be for other reasons.

The time course of citric acid formation in submerged aerated culture is illustrated in Figure 2, from which it is evident that there is a phase of growth with little acid production, followed by a phase of acid formation and slow growth. Maximum yields obviously require that a balance be struck between growth and acid formation; at some point there is enough cell material to convert the residual glucose with maximum efficiency into product. These considerations apply in principle to all acid syntheses, and in fact to all syntheses of non-protoplasmic materials.

Reference to Figure 1 makes it clear that many different carbon compounds, entering the metabolic pathway at different points, may be expected to provide carbon for citrate synthesis, and this proves to be true (354). There are so many possibilities here that experiments in which a carbon compound is added to a preformed mycelium in an attempt to trace biochemical pathways generally fail—almost any compound can be fed into the citric acid pool.

Oxygen is required for citrate synthesis, both in surface culture (169) and in the more recently developed submerged processes (308, 472). Too vigorous aeration may, it has been suggested (186), sweep out the carbon dioxide rapidly enough to reduce citrate formation. The probably essential role of carbon dioxide, mentioned above, is supported by experiments showing that increases in the carbon dioxide of the atmosphere increase the yield of citrate (259).

Measurements of the oxidation-reduction potential during the culture cycle suggest that there is an optimum potential for citrate formation; above the optimum, *Aspergillus niger* forms gluconic acid rather than citric, and below it ethanol is formed (332).

Virtually all studies of citric acid formation indicate that a low culture pH is essential to good yields; generally in surface culture an initial pH of about 2.0 is recommended for *Aspergillus niger,* 3.0—4.0 for *Penicillium* spp. (169, 213). In aerated cultures of *A. niger* a somewhat higher initial pH—about 4.5—appears to be optimal (472). At pH values above the optimum gluconic and oxalic acids tend to replace citric (213, 383). The mechanism of this pH effect is unknown; it has a counterpart in the effect of pH on the balance of metabolic products formed by the lactic acid and the coliform bacteria.

Metabolic poisons affect citric acid formation and have been used in attempts to elucidate the biochemistry of acid formation. The results are ambiguous, as is to be expected from the multiplicity of reactions which compete with or supply carbon to the citrate pool and from the fact that most poisons have several sites of action. The effect of slightly growth-inhibitory concentrations of the lower aliphatic alcohols on the yield of citric acid is very striking (383, 455) and may prove, on further investigation, to be specific.

Fumaric Acid and Related Acids. Four of the 4-carbon dicarboxylic acids—oxalacetic, malic, fumaric, and succinic—may be considered together inasmuch as they are readily interconvertible (see Figure 1). Oxalacetate is unstable and does not accumulate appreciably. Probably all the other acids of this group can be detected by sufficiently sensitive methods in the cells or culture fluid of fungi during aerobic metabolism. For this reason the listing of fungi which produce these acids is somewhat deceptive; it is more a history of the interest of investigators than a survey of acid formation.

Fumaric acid is formed in small amounts by many fungi (Table 1); certain of the Mucorales, especially *Rhizopus* spp., are the only fungi in which it accounts for a major fraction of the glucose consumed. *Aspergillus fumaricus* as originally isolated formed fumaric acid in large amounts (549), but the strain on examination ten years later proved to have lost the capacity to form the acid from glucose except under special circumstances (513, 550). Fumarate is also found in the sporophores of basidiomycetes (575, 576).

Penicillium resticulosum in glucose medium forms fumaryl-DL-alanine, in which the amino group of alanine is joined in a peptide linkage with one carboxyl of fumarate (68).

Succinic acid accumulation is rarely so great as that of the other acids considered thus far. Resting cells of *Blastocladia pringsheimii* accumulate succinate equivalent to about 10 per cent of the glucose metabolized (106), but the amounts formed by most organisms listed in Table 1 are much smaller. Malic acid has only rarely (56, 465) been reported to be formed in large amounts from glucose, although it is produced by a variety of saprophytic fungi (Table 1). Most of the identifications of malic acid, it should be noted, rest on color tests, the use of which is often difficult and uncertain; re-examination by enzymatic methods would be profitable.

In fumaric acid synthesis, one of the most striking physiological aspects is the effect of zinc, which increases growth and glucose consumption and decreases, by as much as 80 per cent, the formation of fumarate (208). Fumaric acid formation is thus a symptom of retarded growth in the presence of an abundance of carbohydrate. By analogy with acid formation in *Aspergillus niger,* it is likely that any metal deficiency has the same effect (129, 130), but the role of other metals is still uncertain and iron above its optimum level seems to have little influence (208).

Carbon dioxide has been shown by isotope studies to enter into the molecule of fumaric acid (204, 205) and succinic acid (144). Succinate formation by *Streptomyces coelicolor* and *Blastocladia pringsheimii* is enhanced by carbon dioxide (106, 144), but the relation of exogenous carbon dioxide to fumarate formation is uncertain (206, 207).

The 4-carbon dicarboxylic acids under discussion probably are formed by more than one biochemical mechanism. Four such mechanisms have been suggested, namely:

1. Oxidative formation in the citric acid cycle. Bulk formation by this mechanism has not been proved.

2. The reductive carboxylation of pyruvic acid, either to oxalacetate or directly, by the agency of the "malic enzyme," to malic acid. This is the best known and perhaps the major pathway; evidence for its role comes from studies on the incorporation of isotopic carbon dioxide and on the physiological effects of carbon dioxide mentioned above.

3. The direct condensation of two 2-carbon fragments in the Thun-

berg-Wieland reaction. This pathway has been proposed in fungi on the basis of both chemical and isotope data (30, 49, 102, 202, 203, 450). As noted elsewhere (Chapter 7), the evidence is not conclusive, although there is of course some mechanism for the conversion of acetate and other 2-carbon compounds to larger molecules.

4. The cleavage of isocitric acid directly to succinic and glyoxylic acids (405). This system is probably identical with one known in bacteria (477); its functions during glucose metabolism and its quantitative importance in fungi are not yet known.

Formic and Acetic Acids. These two volatile acids are more characteristically bacterial than fungal metabolites, and under normal conditions of culture neither accumulates in such large amounts as do the non-volatile acids so far considered.

Formic acid has not been reported to accumulate during carbohydrate utilization, but several fungi form it during the metabolism of lactic and pyruvic acids (133, 454). These experiments suggest the well-known transacetylase reaction:

Pyruvic acid + coenzyme A → acetyl-coenzyme A + formic acid   (1)

The entrance of formate, or a derivative, into metabolism is demonstrated by isotope results (302) and by direct utilization of formate (137, 262). It has been suggested that formate may enter through the sequence of reactions:

Glycine + formate → serine → pyruvate   (2)

Until active cell-free preparations are studied these reactions of formate must remain hypothetical in the fungi.

Acetic acid is found in traces in the medium of many fungi and actinomycetes; the list in Table 1 omits non-specific determinations of "volatile acids" (54, 73). Larger amounts of acetate are formed by *Streptomyces fradiae* (421) and by *Fusarium* spp. (351). As also shown in Table 1, two fungi form ethyl acetate from carbohydrate.

In view of the central role of acetate and acetyl-coenzyme A in metabolism we may assume their presence even if isolable amounts are not formed; this generalization is borne out by isotope dilution studies on *Penicillium chrysogenum* (368) and *Streptomyces coelicolor* (144). In particular organisms acetate may be formed from pentose (225), from ethanol by oxidation (398, 415), or, possibly, from glycine by deamination (562). Direct studies have shown that exogenous acetate is oxidized by *Merulius niveus* (30), *Penicillium chrysogenum* (278), and *Zygorhynchus moelleri* (382).

The higher fatty acids, above acetic, are considered integrally with the metabolism of lipids.

Oxalic Acid. Oxalic acid is a common metabolic product of fungi (Table 1) especially of the Agaricales. Species of *Penicillium* and *Aspergillus* accumulate the largest amounts but substantial oxalate production occurs in a few other fungi, e.g., *Sclerotium delphinii* (414). Sporophores of basidiomycetes often contain oxalate (17, 575, 576).

The physiology of oxalate formation deserves more study. The acid is formed from various carbon sources (49); the most favorable cultural conditions include a high carbohydrate concentration, adequate aeration (49, 545), a limited supply of inorganic nutrients (129, 447), and, most important, a relatively high initial pH (46, 49, 299). The enzymatic basis of the pH requirement has been elucidated by Shimazono (470): at low pH an enzyme, oxalic acid decarboxylase, is formed and converts oxalate to formate and carbon dioxide. This finding suggests, for the higher basidiomycetes at least, that oxalate is a normal metabolite and accumulates under conditions of an enzyme deficiency. Cultures of *Aspergillus niger* utilize oxalate provided that the pH is below 5.5 (27).

In *Corticium centrifugum* oxalic acid production is increased by a growth-limiting deficiency of thiamine (391). This relation is consistent with the general view that oxalic and other acids are formed maximally when available carbon cannot be used for growth.

The biochemical origin of oxalic acid has been investigated rather frequently, but none of the pathways proposed has been proved (4, 5, 403). Recent results with isotopic carbon are consistent with the origin of oxalate from oxalacetate (88, 138a, 201, 338). The possibility that glycine, which in different organisms is metabolically related to other 2-carbon compounds, is involved has not yet been explored. Progress on the problem depends on the preparation of active noncellular preparations.

Itaconic and Itatartaric Acids. Itaconic acid was discovered by Kinoshita (314, 315) to be formed by a strain which he designated *Aspergillus itaconicus* n. sp. This strain has lost its capacity to form more than small amounts of the acid, but strains of *Aspergillus terreus* have been found to produce large yields (105, 384). Other strains of the same species form no itaconate, and ultraviolet-induced mutants yield more or less acid than the parent culture (349).

The optimum conditions for itaconic acid formation are rather different from those which give best growth of the organism (348, 350,

352, 384). Distinctive features include the very low pH optimum—
about 1.9 for shaken cultures—and the pronounced effects of sodium
chloride and magnesium sulfate under certain conditions. The low
pH optimum of the processes has been shown conclusively (334) to be
determined by the fact that the enzyme system for itaconate formation
is present only during cultivation at low pH.

Itaconic acid is formed *in vitro* from *cis*-aconitic acid by the enzyme
cis-aconitic decarboxylase (41); since *cis*-aconitate is a component of the
tricarboxylic acid cycle, the formation of itaconic acid may be regarded
as an alternate metabolic pathway for glucose carbon (Figure 1).

A mutant of *Aspergillus terreus,* obtained by ultraviolet irradiation,
forms a mixture of itatartaric acid and its lactone (492). The structure (Table 1) has an obvious resemblance to that of itaconate, and
it is reasonable to suppose that the two acids are biochemically related.

Other Acids. Tartaric acid has been reported in small amounts
in cultures of *Fusarium* spp. (Table 1), but the criteria of identification
were not wholly satisfactory. Using color tests and copper reduction
as criteria, Bernhauer and Böckl (51) found that most strains of
Aspergillus niger form tartrate during incubation of preformed
mycellium with ethanol. The problem merits study with the more
sensitive methods now available for isolation and determination of
acids.

Glyoxylic acid (OHC—COOH), often accompanied by glycolic acid
(HOCH$_2$—COOH), is formed in traces during carbohydrate breakdown by some fungi (Table 1); it has also been reported as being
formed during the metabolism of acetate (55, 125, 403), ethanol (136),
and citrate (125). It should be noted that substances giving the color
reactions for glyoxylic acid are found in sterile autoclaved culture
media (157); it has not always been clear that adequate controls have
been included in experiments on the occurrence of glyoxylate.

Glyoxylate has been proposed as an intermediate in the oxidative
formation of oxalate from acetate by the following reactions (403):

$$\text{Acetate} \rightarrow \text{glycolate} \rightarrow \text{glyoxylate} \rightarrow \text{oxalate} \qquad (3)$$

It is not yet certain that these reactions occur. The fact that glyoxylic
and glycolic acids replace glycine in the nutrition of a mutant of
Neurospora crassa (566) suggests a second pathway for their utilization
and formation. Finally, the ability of fungi under some conditions
to split isocitrate to succinate and glyoxylate and to oxidize glycolate
to glyoxylate has been shown unequivocally (405). Glyoxylate is also,
it should be noted, a product of the action of allantoicase (Chapter 8).

The other acids listed in Table 1—glutaric, glutaconic, dimethyl-pyruvic, and ethylene oxide α,β-dicarboxylic acids—have as yet no established physiological or biochemical significance. The first two have been reported only once, from xylose cultures; if their formation can be confirmed, a route from pentose to α-ketoglutaric acid is a pos-sibility. Dimethylpyruvic acid accumulates in cultures poisoned with bisulfite. Suggestions on the biochemical origin of dimethyl-pyruvic acid are reviewed by Birkinshaw (63).

Ethylene oxide α,β-dicarboxylic acid (*trans*-L-epoxysuccinic acid), chemically related to tartaric acid, is formed from a variety of carbon sources by *Aspergillus fumigatus* in up to 21 per cent yield (370).

During the breakdown of citric acid by *Aspergillus niger*, two other acids, acetonedicarboxylic acid ($HOOC$—CH_2—CO—CH_2—$COOH$) and malonic acid ($HOOC$—CH_2—$COOH$) appear in the medium, and it has been suggested that they derive from a route of citrate dissimila-tion otherwise unknown (125, 495).

Conclusions. Some generalizations can be made concerning the physiology and biochemistry of those acids—gluconic, citric, fumaric, succinic, lactic, and oxalic—which are formed in large amounts and which have been studied intensively. Not all the data agree, but in general it can be said:

1. The acids occur, in small amounts at least, as normal metabolites in organisms other than the fungi. This is also true of acetate, formate, glyoxylate, and malate.

2. With few exceptions—and these are subject to confirmation—the acids which accumulate in fungus cultures are later utilized for energy and growth unless removed by a trapping agent, e.g., calcium ion, or unless their accumulation poisons the cell.

3. Most experiments agree that highest acid yields, in terms of the fraction of sugar converted to product, are obtained in media in which carbohydrate is abundant but in which some other factor, usually nu-tritional, restricts growth to a less than maximum amount.

4. Oxygen is essential for the synthesis of all but lactic acid; this requirement is, of course, obvious from the structure of the acids. Gluconate formation, catalyzed as it probably is by a flavin enzyme, is the most responsive to oxygen pressure.

5. Carbon dioxide enters by fixation into lactic, citric, fumaric, and succinic acids, and appears to be quantitatively important in providing the carbon of all of these except possibly lactate.

6. Genetic factors determine whether or not a clonal culture will accumulate acid under given external conditions.

We may visualize a metabolic pool of any given acid, with carbon flowing into it from a high level of carbohydrate and flowing out into amino acids, into respiratory carbon dioxide, and into other undetermined channels. Under conditions of minimal demand on the pool for growth, the accumulation of acid is determined by the available carbohydrate, by the relative rates of the many reactions which produce and break down the acid, and by the rate of exchange of acid between cell and environment. The scheme of Figure 1, applying specifically to citric acid, is in principle a model for all acid accumulation. An acid may be more closely related to carbohydrate, as is gluconic acid, or it may be in a metabolic "shunt" removed by one or more enzymatic steps from the main pathway of carbohydrate dissimilation.

Physiologically, a utilizable acid serves as a reserve carbon source, although the concept is more or less meaningless under the usual conditions of acid accumulation in culture. A priori, it would appear that the soluble acids, having effects on both the pH and the osmotic concentration of the medium, are less satisfactory reserve substances than the insoluble polysaccharides and fats.

The permeability of the cell membrane to organic acids deserves more study, difficult as the problem is. Obviously, a biochemical equilibrium will be reached very quickly within the cell, and very little acid will accumulate, if the formed acid cannot leave the cell. If it leaves rapidly, in fact, the concept of enzymatic equilibrium becomes almost inapplicable. Conversely, if re-entrance of external acid into the cell is slow, its utilization as a source of carbon will be limited. It is conceivable that some of the environmental factors which favor acid accumulation act primarily on the rate of exchange between cell and environment, and that differences between strains reflect membrane differences rather than enzymatic capabilities.

The genetic factor is so far a matter of observation only—acid formation is highly specific and individual strains differ from each other both quantitatively and qualitatively. These strain differences must not, however, be overemphasized; so far only one instance of complete loss of ability to form an acid has been reported, that of *Aspergillus fumaricus* (p. 141), and even the altered strain is able under some conditions to form the missing product. Quantitative changes are frequent, especially when several acids compete for carbon. The qualitative constancy is particularly remarkable in view of the fact that in many of the fungi studied for acid production the conidia used for transfer of cultures represent isolations of nuclei from a heterocaryotic mycelium.

Virtually all modern theories of acid biosynthesis assume a pre-liminary conversion of carbohydrate to pyruvic acid, except, of course, in the biosynthesis of the sugar acids. Whether this assumption represents the facts or merely the limitations of current biochemical knowledge is uncertain. The phosphogluconate pathway of glucose metabolism (Chapter 7) provides to the cell a group of compounds, including the 4- and 7-carbon sugar phosphates, previously unknown and quite possibly of direct importance in acid synthesis.

Table 1 summarizes the reported formation of acids by fungi and actinomycetes acting in culture on carbohydrates. So far as possible, duplicating reports have been omitted, and some of those included are based on questionable or at least inadequate evidence. Satisfactory proof for the identity of an acid should involve more than color tests or the chromatographic constant in a single solvent; on the other hand, the results of these presumptive tests are often correct and reports based on them cannot, therefore, be dismissed out of hand. Ideally, an acid or other metabolic product should be isolated as a crystalline derivative; if this is not possible, several independent criteria should be utilized. Enzymatic identification promises to be the most sensitive and accurate for metabolites which are found only in micro amounts.

2. THE METABOLISM OF LIPIDS

The lipids may be defined as those substances which are soluble in fat solvents; a few, like the lecithins, are somewhat water soluble, but most are insoluble in water. Lipids which are of importance to the physiology of the fungi include the true fats, the fatty acids, the compound lipids (phospholipids), the sterols, the carotenoids and triterpenes, and a few hydrocarbons. The general chemistry of the lipids is reviewed by Deuel (164). Those lipids which occur as constituents of the cell are considered in Chapter 2; here we are primarily concerned with synthesis and breakdown, although for convenience the occurrence of some lipids is included.

The Synthesis of Fats, Fatty Acids, and Phospholipids. The neutral fats are triglycerides of the higher fatty acids. These are synthesized by many fungi in amounts up to 50 per cent of the mycelial dry weight. One rather striking difference between the lipids of fungi and those of animals is the high content of free fatty acids in most fungal lipids (Chapter 2). This means that most experiments on the factors affecting gross lipid content deal indiscriminately with both neutral fats and fatty acids.

Study of the formation of fats and fatty acids by fungi has been concentrated on those fungi which form them in large amount, particularly species of Endomyces (Endomycopsis), Torula (Torulopsis), and Oospora (Geotrichum, often miscalled Oidium) among the yeast-like fungi, and Aspergillus, Fusarium, and Penicillium among the filamentous fungi. Within any given species the formation of fats varies quantitatively from one strain to another and even from one clonal culture to another (193, 428).

Fats are formed intracellularly, possibly in association with cytoplasmic particles (486). The possibility that different types of cells differ in their capacity to form fat is raised by the work of Satina and Blakeslee (461) on Absidia blakesleeana, but other explanations are possible. It is usually assumed that fats are reserve substances, and their disappearance—or, more commonly, partial disappearance—during the later phases of the culture cycle support this generalization (258, 428). It is doubtful whether starvation experiments permit accurate differentiation of essential cellular lipids from non-essential reserve lipids (39), although it seems probable that such a differentiation is valid in general, the phosphatides and lipoproteins being essential and the true fats non-essential (443).

For any given fungus which is genetically capable of forming fats, environmental conditions determine the amount actually synthesized. As would be expected from the mode of formation of fatty acids from 2-carbon fragments (p. 151), almost any utilizable carbohydrate can support fat formation (50). The specific effect of xylose on Fusarium spp. (194) is presumably attributable to the accumulation of acetate during metabolism of the pentose (225). The most important single factor in fat formation is the concentration of carbohydrate, more accurately the carbon : nitrogen ratio (442). As the carbohydrate concentration is increased, the total fat and the percentage of conversion of glucose to fat both increase (Figure 3); in some organisms, of course, high concentrations of glucose inhibit growth and thereby reduce fat synthesis (540). Spores of Fusarium roseum given carbohydrate but no nitrogen accumulate fat-staining globules (476).

Corresponding to the carbohydrate effect, a level of nitrogen which is suboptimal for growth is generally favorable for maximum fat accumulation. Thus, Aspergillus fischeri utilizes glucose most rapidly at a nitrogen level which is ten times that at which fat formation, relative to dry weight, is optimal (428). Phosphate deficiency, if not too severe, increases fat synthesis, probably by reducing the assimilation of nitrogen (358).

Other nutritional determinants include the essentiality of phosphate

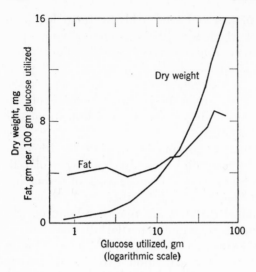

Figure 3. Glucose concentration and fat synthesis by *Aspergillus fischeri*. Plotted from data of Prill, Wenck, and Peterson (428).

(318), and effects of metals, which are definite but not susceptible of generalization (426, 466). Fat formation in most yeasts and fungi is optimal at neutral or slightly alkaline reaction (238, 428, 485, 560).

A supply of oxygen is invariably essential for fat synthesis (50). However, cultivation with shaking reduces the fat content, but not always the efficiency of conversion of glucose to fat (561). Here the effect is probably that of encouraging respiration and growth and thereby reducing the amount of carbon available for lipid synthesis.

Maximum yields of fat have been of interest because of possible industrial applications (270). Rippel (446) calculated that, considering the usual values for protein content and for the economic coefficient, the maximum synthesis by microorganisms, the "fat coefficient," is 15 gm. of fat per 100 gm. of sugar utilized. Values usually found in the yeasts and fungi are in the range 5–15 (158, 318), but cultivation of *Rhodotorula gracilis* under conditions which restrict protein formation to a minimum allows a value of 18 to be attained in aerated culture (179). Since lipids are more reduced than carbohydrate, much of the glucose carbon must be oxidized to carbon dioxide in order that the necessary hydrogen be supplied.

The composition of the fat of a given species is relatively constant, but external conditions appear to affect it in two ways. First, the ratio of unsaturated to saturated fatty acids is claimed to be greater at low than at high growth temperatures (413, 508). No such effect, however, was found in careful studies on *Aspergillus fischeri* (428). The ratio of saturated to unsaturated fats is also affected by glucose concentration and by pH (318), and in an as yet undetermined manner by cell pigments (403). Second, the content of free fatty acids is greater at high carbohydrate levels. The acid value is also stated to be affected by pH (425), but the observed effects may be attributable to other causes.

The relation of fat formation to growth is exemplified in the data of Figure 4. As discovered early by Lindner (345), two phases of metabolic activity are distinguishable in many organisms: a phase of growth and a phase of fat accumulation. This is exactly comparable to the sequence of events in citric acid accumulation (Figure 2). Separation of growth and fat synthesis is not, however, always so clear (429); Figure 5 shows parallel courses of dry weight and fat production.

In animal and bacterial systems it seems clear that fatty acids are synthesized ultimately from 2-carbon fragments, specifically acetyl-coenzyme A (114). In the fungi, precursor studies, reviewed by Foster (200), early suggested the involvement of 2-carbon compounds in fat synthesis. More conclusive evidence has been obtained with several isotope techniques. Thus, in a mutant of *Neurospora crassa* which is unable to form acetate from carbohydrate, the carbon of fatty acids is derived almost entirely from exogenous acetate (407). The importance of acetate in fatty acid synthesis appears also from studies on isotope distribution in the fatty acids of *Phycomyces blakesleeanus* (43, 45), *Fusarium lini* (146), and *Ustilago zeae* (190).

Whether the unsaturated acids are derived directly from the saturated, by dehydrogenation, is an open question. Two types of evidence—nutritional responses of a fatty acid requiring mutant

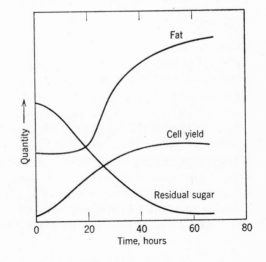

Figure 4. Growth, sugar utilization, and fat formation in cultures of *Rhodotorula gracilis.* Redrawn from Enebo, Anderson, and Lundin (179), by permission of Academic Press, Inc.

of *Neurospora crassa* (336), and direct analyses of the mycelium of *Aspergillus nidulans* (475)—indicate that the routes of formation of the two types are independent; evidence to the contrary (146) is less convincing. The only fatty acid dehydrogenase known in the fungi acts only on the short-chain acids (387). In animal tissues it seems likely that the saturated and the unsaturated fatty acids arise independently (216).

Phospholipid synthesis has been studied by Raveux (442), who found the phospholipid content of *Aspergillus niger* to be independent of the fat content and to parallel the available nitrogen of the medium. The time course of phospholipid formation has been determined in *A. niger*: lipoidal phosphorus of the mycelium rises to a peak and then declines during the later—probably autolytic—phases of culture (222).

The Breakdown of Fats and Phospholipids. Although the neutral fats are relatively poor sources of carbon, they are utilized by many fungi (Chapter 3). The first step in such utilization is the hydrolysis of the fat to glycerol and fatty acids (288); it is assumed that endogenous fats are split in the same way before utilization. The hydrolysis is catalyzed by lipase or lipases.

It is common practice to assay for lipase activity by measuring the hydrolysis of simple esters, e.g., ethyl acetate or *p*-nitrophenyl acetate. It is doubtful, however, whether the simple esterases so determined are active in hydrolysis of the true fats (7). Simple esterases occur in most fungi investigated; the esterase of *Lenzites sepiaria* fails to hydrolyze fats (574). Lipase proper, as distinct from esterases, can probably best be studied with water-soluble synthetic substrates (60, 168).

Virtually all fungi which have been studied for lipase production appear to form the enzyme (187, 317). Lipase is primarily intracellular, but both it and esterase do appear in the medium late in the culture cycle (153, 488, 570). It has been suggested (198) that *Aspergillus niger* and *Penicillium roqueforti* form two lipases, one in the mycelium and the other released into the medium.

Data on the relation of pH to activity and on the stability of fungal lipases vary widely from one organism to another (195, 198, 317, 440, 471, 512), so much so that the formation of different enzymes seems likely. The amount of extracellular lipase formed by *Mucor mucedo* is influenced by the temperature of cultivation and is increased by inclusion of a lipid in the growth medium (488). Like lipase from other sources, fungal lipase under appropriate conditions catalyzes the synthesis of esters, e.g., *n*-butyl oleate, from a fatty acid and an alcohol (440).

The phosphatides—lecithins and cephalins—are complex phospholipids in which one of the fatty acids found in the true fats is replaced by phosphoric acid linked to a nitrogen base. They are hydrolyzed, at different points in the molecule, by the phospholipases A, B, and C (498). Phospholipase A is found in *Aspergillus oryzae* (148) and *Lycoperdon giganteum* (211), phospholipase B in the mycelium of *Penicillium notatum* (191). Phospholipase C, identical with glycerophosphatase (Chapter 9), is found in a commercial enzyme preparation from *Aspergillus* sp. (3).

The Metabolism of Fatty Acids. The fatty acids occur both free and combined in mycelium (Chapter 2); information on their biosynthesis has been summarized above. In this section we are concerned with the breakdown of exogenous fatty acids, arising in natural substrates by lipase action or supplied in pure culture as such.

The breakdown of fatty acids in animal tissues is believed to occur by the so-called "β-oxidation-condensation" route: the oxidation proceeds by the removal of two carbon atoms at a time, with subsequent recombination of the 2-carbon fragments to form acetoacetic acid. Acetoacetate is formed by fungi during the oxidation of butyric acid (149, 388), but the details of its origin are not known. We are concerned, therefore, primarily with information bearing on the β-oxidation phase rather than on possible recombination processes.

Beta-oxidation in animals is essentially the conversion of a fatty acid of n carbon atoms ($R—CH_2—CH_2—COOH$) to one of $n - 2$ carbons ($R—COOH$) and acetate or a derivative of acetate. The key intermediate is a β-keto fatty acid, and the reactions may be summarized as follows:

$$R—CH_2—CH_2—COOH \rightarrow R—CO—CH_2—COOH \qquad (4)$$
Fatty acid   β-Keto acid

$$R—CO—CH_2—COOH \rightarrow R—COOH + CH_3COOH \qquad (5)$$
Acetate

Coenzyme A is required at two points: in the "activation" of the original fatty acid, forming an acyl-coenzyme A, and in the formation of acetate, which appears as acetyl-coenzyme A. Repetition of reactions 4 and 5 leads ultimately to complete conversion of the long-chain fatty acid to 2-carbon compounds. The process is reviewed in detail by Green (245) and by Chaikoff and Brown (114).

Evidence for β-oxidation in fungi derives almost entirely from studies on the breakdown of fats and fatty acids by growing or resting cells. Interest in the problem was first aroused by the finding that methyl ketones are present in certain of the fungal cheeses and in edible oils attacked by fungi (482, 494). In a number of experiments it has been shown that *Penicillium glaucum* converts a fatty acid to a methyl ketone of one less carbon atom, i.e.,

$$R—CH_2—CH_2—COOH \rightarrow R—CO—CH_3 + CO_2 \qquad (6)$$

This reaction has been demonstrated in experiments on many fatty acids (2, 509, 511), e.g.:

$$CH_3—CH_2—CH_2—COOH \rightarrow CH_3—CO—CH_3 \qquad (7)$$

Butyric acid   Acetone

$$CH_3—(CH_2)_6—COOH \rightarrow CH_3—(CH_2)_4—CO—CH_3 \qquad (8)$$

Octanoic acid   Methylamyl ketone

$$CH_3—(CH_2)_{10}—COOH \rightarrow CH_3—(CH_3)_8—CO—CH_3 \qquad (9)$$

Dodecanoic acid   Methylnonyl ketone

The same general reaction is found in *Penicillium notatum* and in *Aspergillus* spp. (149, 380, 569).

Thaler and co-workers (510) propose the following sequence of reactions in the formation of methyl ketones from fatty acids:

$$R—CH_2—CH_2—COOH \rightarrow R—CH{=}CH—COOH$$

Fatty acid   α, β–Unsaturated fatty acid

$$\rightarrow R—CHOH—CH_2—COOH$$

β–Hydroxy fatty acid

$$\rightarrow R—CO—CH_2—COOH \rightarrow R—CO—CH_3 + CO_2 \qquad (10)$$

β-Keto fatty acid   Methyl ketone

The evidence for this sequence is that methyl ketones arise during the growth of *Penicillium glaucum* on α,β-unsaturated acids and β-hydroxy acids. Thus, methylpropyl ketone is formed from hexanoic acid, 2-hexanoic acid, and β-hydroxyhexanoic acid. Further, fungi are known to form β-keto acid decarboxylases (309).

This scheme, up to the formation of the β-keto acid, agrees with our current understanding of the process in animal cells, but until enzymatic studies are made, the identity of the two systems remains hypothetical. The last step—formation of the methyl ketone—does not go on appreciably in the normal animal cell, which instead forms, as mentioned above, a 2-carbon compound and a new fatty acid. This suggests that methyl ketone formation by fungi is an abnormal or at least unusual reaction, perhaps to be attributed to toxicity of the substrate fatty acid (494). It is reasonable to suppose that complete oxidation of fatty acids in the fungi follows the animal system, with liberation of acetyl-coenzyme A or free acetate as the last step. The strongest evidence for this supposition is in the finding by Webley and others (544) that the oxidation of ω-substituted phenyl fatty acids by *Nocardia opaca,* an actinomycete, yields end products in conformity with predictions based on β-oxidation. Comparable studies on the fungi have not yet appeared.

Indirect evidence for β-oxidation in the fungi is provided by the incorporation of fatty acid carbon into the side chain of penicillin (380, 516). The most effective precursors are fatty acids which by their structure are not susceptible to complete β-oxidation.

It has been argued from simultaneous adaptation experiments that *Streptomyces aureofaciens* oxidizes octanoate by some mechanism other than β-oxidation (276). However, it is now known that the adaptation technique is unreliable in fatty acid oxidation, since the adaptive system may be that which activates the fatty acid; failure of octanoate-adapted cells to oxidize butyrate may therefore mean only that activation of the two acids is carried out by different enzymes.

Fatty acid oxidase systems probably occur in fungi and actinomycetes (387, 543). In addition, mycelial extracts of *Penicillium glaucum* and of *Aspergillus* spp. contain a lipoxidase, capable of oxidizing unsaturated fatty acids (387).

The Metabolism of Steroids and Triterpenes. Sterols occur in small amounts in the lipid fraction of most fungi; ergosterol appears to be the compound of this group most often formed by fungi, but other sterols have been tentatively identified (Chapter 2). Cultural conditions which favor sterol formation are reviewed by Bernhauer (50). It appears that sterol and fat synthesis are competitive reactions; the effect of pH on their formation (428) is perhaps the strongest evidence for this competition. Biochemical studies on yeast and on fungi indicate that ergosterol is formed in large part from 2-carbon compounds, although isovaleric acid may also be involved (146, 318, 407). The amount of sterol formed varies among strains and among single spore cultures of a given strain (556).

The breakdown of exogenously supplied steroids has been studied in two connections: (1) the utilization of steroids for energy and carbon, and (2) partial and limited transformations of the steroid molecule.

Cholesterol is oxidized in soil (521) by actinomycetes and by Gramnegative bacteria; it is not clear which organisms are responsible for steroid breakdown in natural soils (462, 523, 525). Some fungi are apparently able to grow with ergosterol as carbon source (462), and some of the products of the action of *Proactinomyces erythropolis* on steroids have been identified (522, 524, 526), but most of the pathway of steroid oxidation is unknown.

Specific microbiological transformations of steroids, i.e., reactions at single specific points on particular steroid molecules, have been studied extensively, first with bacteria and yeast (364, 532), later with actinomycetes (271, 329, 330, 555) and fungi (423). The pharmacological importance of these processes has stimulated since 1952 a very large volume of experimental work, for which the fungi and actinomycetes have been the best material. The known processes may be classified as follows (557):

1. Hydroxylations, specific introduction of the —OH group. Examples are shown in Table 2; it will be noted that among the most frequent positions of attachment are 6β, 11α, 11β, and 17α.

Table 2.   The Hydroxylation of Steroids by Fungi and Actinomycetes*

Organism	Steroid Position Hydroxylated[†]
Aspergillus spp.	6β, 11α, 17α, 21
Cephalothecium roseum	6β, 11α, 17α
Colletotrichum antirrhini	15α
Coniothyrium sp.	11β
Cunninghamella blakesleeana	11β
Curvularia spp.	7α, 8β (?), 11β, 14α
Dactylium dendroides[‡]	11α, 17α
Didymella vodakii	16α
Gibberella baccata	15α
Helicostylum piriforme	6β, 8ξ, 11α, 14α
Lenzites abietina	6β, 15β
Mucor spp.	6β, 8β (?), 14α
Neurospora crassa	8β or 9α
Ophiobolus herpotrichus	21
Penicillium spp.[§]	11α
Peziza spp.	7α
Phycomyces blakesleeanus	7ξ, 15β
Proactinomyces roseus	7ξ
Rhizopus spp.	6β, 7β, 8ξ, 11α
Streptomyces spp.	6β, 8ξ or 9ξ (?), 11β, 16α
Trichothecium roseum	6β, 17α

* Except as noted, from Wettstein (557).   A more complete list appears in the review of Eppstein et al. (182a).

† The specific compounds attacked, and often the yield of product, are given in the original papers cited by Wettstein (557).

‡ Dulaney et al. (173).

§ Dulaney et al. (172).

2. Hydrogenation of steroid aldehydes or ketones by bacteria, yeast, *Streptomyces* spp., and *Rhizopus nigricans*.

3. Hydrogenation of ring carbon atoms by *Clostridium* sp., *Streptomyces* sp., and *Rhizopus nigricans*.

4. Dehydrogenation of steroid secondary alcohols by bacteria and actinomycetes.

5. Epoxydation of steroids containing an isolated double bond, by *Curvularia lunata* and *Cunninghamella blakesleeana*.

6. Dehydrogenation in ring A, with or without degradation of the side chain, by *Fusarium solani, Calonectria decora, Cylindrocarpon radicola,* and other fungi.

7. Oxidation of the side chain only, e.g., by *Gliocladium catenulatum*.

8. Ring cleavage with lactone formation, e.g., by *Penicillium chrysogenum*.

Specific enzyme systems must, of course, be responsible for these transformations, and some knowledge of animal and bacterial enzymes is available (244, 577). The 6β-hydroxylation of progesterone by *Aspergillus ochraceus* is accelerated by zinc; it has been suggested that the metal is required for the synthesis of an induced enzyme which carries out the reaction (174).

Steroidal sapogenins, e.g., diosgenin, appear not to be hydroxylated by fungi or other microorganisms (376).

Chemical studies on several basidiomycetes have brought to light a new series of fungal metabolites, the tetracyclic triterpenes. As terpenes they are related to the carotenoids, but their structure also bears an obvious relation to that of the sterols; they are not, however, true sterols. Similar compounds are known in higher organisms, e.g., betulin in plants and squalene in animals. The structure of eburicoic acid, formed by several Hymenomycetes (151, 220, 281), may be taken as an example of the group:

Other compounds of this type include the closely related poly-porenic acids A, B, and C, isolated from *Polyporus* spp. and *Poria cocos* (91, 92, 151, 154, 257, 260). The triterpenoids are biosyntheti-cally related, as judged by the occurrence of all three polyporenic acids in one species (154) and by the fact that three strains of *Poria cocos* form polyporenic acid B and a fourth forms eburicoic acid (151). In *Polyporus eucalyptorum* eburicoic acid constitutes at least 20 per cent of the dry weight of the mycelium (220) and must therefore be con-sidered a major metabolite. The chemistry of these compounds has been reviewed by Jones and Halsall (306); triterpenoids occur also as lichen products (24).

The antibiotics cephalosporin P_1 and helvolic acid are tetracyclic compounds and may be related to the steroids, but their complete structure is not known (100).

The Metabolism of Carotenoids. The carotenoid pigments, which appear among the unsaponifiable lipids, include: (1) the true caro-tenes, e.g., β-carotene and lycopene, and (2) oxygen-containing deriva-tives, e.g., rhodoviolascin. All may be considered as built up of eight isoprene units, the carbon skeleton of which is:

$$C=\overset{\displaystyle \overset{C}{|}}{C}-C=C.$$

In addition to the colored carotenoids, colorless polyenes are found in the fungi and will be considered with the pigments.

The formula of β-carotene illustrates the essential features of the carotenoid pigments:

Carotenoids are of widespread but not universal occurrence in the fungi, including representatives of all the major taxonomic groups (232, 236, 264). Table 3 lists the carotenoids of a few fungi which

Table 3. Carotenoids of Some Fungi

Organism	Carotenoids
Allomyces javanicus	γ-carotene,* β-carotene, lycopene, phytofluene (178, 529)
Phycomyces blakesleeanus	α-carotene, β-carotene,* γ-carotene, ξ-carotene,† lycopene, neurosporene, phytofluene, phytoene (233, 310)
Neurospora crassa	β-carotene, γ-carotene,* θ-carotene, lycopene,* spiriloxanthin (rhodoviolascin),* lycoxanthin, neurosporene,* phytofluene, phytoene, unidentified compounds (264)
Dacrymyces stillatus	α-carotene, β-carotene,* γ-carotene (?), ξ-carotene,† torulene, cryptoxanthin, zeaxanthin, phytofluene, phytoene (?) (234)
Puccinia spp.	β-carotene, γ-carotene (?), lycopene (293)

* Quantitatively important.
† See Haxo (264) on fungal ξ-carotene.

have been intensively studied. In contrast to higher plants, β-carotene is not so nearly universal in the fungi, and acidic carotenoids, e.g., torularhodin, are more common (232).

The intracellular distribution of fungal carotenoids has not been systematically investigated. In certain of the higher fungi, carotenoid pigments occur both in rod-shaped structures, apparently part of the mitochondrial system, and in oil droplets in the cytoplasm (266, 267). The carotenoids of the male gametangia of *Allomyces* spp. are found in cytoplasmic oil droplets (178), those of *Rhodotorula rubra* in granules in the pericapsular region (127).

The physiological conditions of carotenogenesis are to some degree specific for individual organisms. In *Phycomyces blakesleeanus,* the time course of carotene formation (Figure 5) indicates that the bulk of the carotene is formed after growth has been completed and that carotenoid formation is independent of lipid formation. Independence of fat and carotene synthesis also appears from their divergent pH requirements (238). Carotenogenesis is affected, of course, by carbon and nitrogen nutrition, but the data do not afford a basis for generalization. Cultivation of *Phycomyces blakesleeanus* at low temperature decreases total carotene synthesis but does not affect the

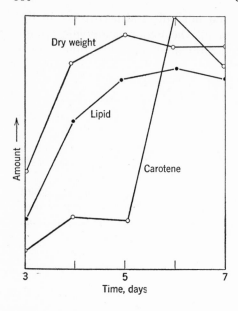

Figure 5. Growth, fat formation, and carotenogenesis in *Phycomyces blakesleeanus.* Redrawn from Goodwin and Willmer (238), by permission of the Cambridge University Press.

proportions of the different carotenoids formed (215), as it does in *Rhodotorula rubra* (392). Oxygen is required for carotene formation by *Neurospora crassa* (572), and presumably this is true of other fungi.

The mycelial carotenoids of *Neurospora crassa* do not develop in complete darkness, although the conidial carotenoids do; this problem has been studied by Zalokar (572, 573). Very brief exposure to light is sufficient to activate pigment synthesis, which is proportional to light intensity up to a saturation value. The action spectrum of light activation is consistent with, but does not, of course, prove the participation of a flavoprotein as the photoreceptor. Calculated quantum yields are so high as to make it necessary to postulate that activation is an indirect process. Carotenogenesis in other fungi is stimulated by light but does not require it (131, 219). Synthesis by green plants does not require light.

Carotenoid formation is inhibited by streptomycin, chloramphenicol, and isonicotinic hydrazide at concentrations which do not inhibit growth (235). Diphenylamine inhibits carotenogenesis in both bacteria and fungi (233, 528). Its effect is to reduce the absolute and relative amounts of the more unsaturated carotenoids, e.g., β-carotene, and to increase the relative amounts of the more saturated, e.g., phytofluene and neurosporene.

The biosynthesis of the carotenoids may be considered under three heads: (1) the origin of the isoprene skeleton, (2) the mode of condensation of isoprene units to form the 40-carbon chain of the carotenoids, and (3) the relation of the different carotenoids to one another.

On grounds of comparative biochemistry and especially from studies on higher plants (304), the most likely route of synthesis of the isoprene skeleton involves the following steps (236, 346):

1. Formation of acetoacetic acid from acetate and coenzyme A.

2. Condensation of acetoacetate with acetyl-coenzyme A to form β-hydroxy, β-methylglutaryl-coenzyme A.

3. Conversion of β-hydroxy, β-methylglutaryl-coenzyme A to β-methylcrotonyl-coenzyme A. This process involves more than one reaction and includes a decarboxylation.

The condensation of two 5-carbon units to yield a 10-carbon chain, followed by successive reactions with new 5-carbon units, could in principle yield the 40-carbon chain of the carotenoids (346).

Evidence for the foregoing scheme in the fungi is somewhat limited, but adequate to establish it as a working hypothesis. Carotenogenesis in fungi is stimulated by β-methylcrotonaldehyde (237) and by pantothenic acid and pantethine, which enter into the coenzyme A molecule (249). The labeling of the β-carotene of *Mucor hiemalis* grown on C^{14}-acetate is qualitatively consistent with the proposed mechanism (247, 248, 248a). That fungi form carotenoids during cultivation on acetate (463) cannot be urged as proof for the hypothesis, although again the fact is consistent with it.

The final set of problems is associated with the relationship of the carotenoids to one another. From genetic data on higher plants, Porter and Lincoln (427) proposed a unilinear sequence of formation of the carotenoids by successive dehydrogenations, that is, that the unsaturated hydrocarbons are derived from the saturated, as follows:

Tetrahydrophytoene → phytoene → phytofluene → ξ-carotene →
neurosporene → lycopene → γ-carotene →
β-carotene → α-carotene.

Although this scheme fits the behavior of mutants of *Chlorella vulgaris* (138), *Rhodotorula rubra* (89) and *Neurospora crassa* (264, 469), it cannot be regarded as proved. Goodwin (232, 233) has argued, largely on the basis of inhibitor studies, that the more saturated polyenes, e.g., phytofluene, are formed by one pathway, the less saturated, e.g., β-carotene, by another, both from a common precursor. The effects of added methylheptenone and β-ionone have been interpreted as supporting the second hypothesis (361). It must be concluded that the question is still open.

It is usually assumed that the oxidized carotenoids, neutral and acidic xanthophylls, arise by oxidation of the hydrocarbon polyenes (264).

Although β-ionone increases carotenogenesis in *Phycomyces blakesleeanus,* isotope evidence indicates that the molecule is not, as one might expect, incorporated as such into the β-carotene structure (182).

Two functions have been suggested for the carotenoids: a direct role as receptor for the light stimulus in phototropism, and an undefined role in sexual differentiation.

Phototropism is discussed later (Chapter 11), and it is concluded that there is no satisfactory proof of the direct involvement of carotenoids.

Although the carotenoid pigments and the colorless polyenes of *Allomyces javanicus* are restricted to the male gametangia (178, 529), an essential role in the sexual process is rendered less probable by the finding (527) that diphenylamine inhibits carotenogenesis in *A. javanicus* without appreciably affecting the sexual reaction. It seems likely that the carotenes are side products of a metabolism which is in some respects at least distinctive to the male gametangium. The (+) and (−) strains of some of the Mucorales show quantitative differences in carotenoid content; studies, as reviewed by Goodwin (232), have been confined to the fact itself, and it would appear that in *Phycomyces blakesleeanus* the difference between (+) and (−) strains is not consistent (219). Zygospore formation or merely pairing of compatible strains in some of the Mucorales is accompanied by increased formation of carotene (29, 270a).

The most serious deficiency in the study of fungal carotenoids is the failure to determine whether or not carotenes occur in association with proteins or lipoproteins. Such an association is theoretically necessary if they are to function in metabolism, e.g., in the reception of light stimuli. Carotenoproteins are well known in animals (234), and the now classical studies on rhodopsin (147, 537) provide a model for the investigation of other pigments.

The Metabolism of Hydrocarbons and Hydrocarbon Derivatives. It has been mentioned (Chapter 3) that hydrocarbons support growth of some actinomycetes and fungi. The oxidation of *n*-dodecane and other hydrocarbons by *Proactinomyces opacus* can be demonstrated manometrically (Figure 6); the organism also oxidizes long-chain saturated fatty acids, which may be intermediates in hydrocarbon oxidation. Details of the breakdown of hydrocarbons are not known;

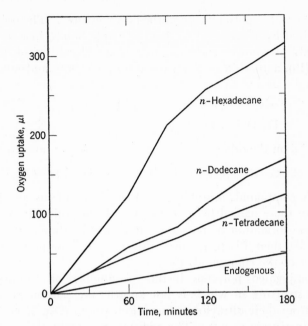

Figure 6. The oxidation of hydrocarbons by *Proactinomyces opacus.* Redrawn from Webley and DeKock (543), by permission of the Cambridge University Press.

ZoBell (577) reviews our knowledge of the process in bacteria. Intermediates appearing during the oxidation of naphthalene by *Nocardia* sp. suggest that benzenoid compounds may be formed (520).

Hydrocarbons produced by fungi fall into two groups: ethylene and its derivatives, and the substituted hydrocarbon polyenes and polyenynes.

From the biological effects of volatile products of *Penicillium digitatum* it seemed probable that the organism produces ethylene (59, 378). This has been confirmed (571); ethylene is probably produced also by *Blastomyces dermatitidis* (394) and by *Fusarium oxysporum* v. *lycopersici* (167). However, the ethylene produced by fungus-infected plant tissues is believed to be a host product, stimulated quantitatively by infection, rather than a fungus metabolite (559).

An interesting volatile hydrocarbon, 2-methylbutene-2 (trimethylethylene), is formed by uredospores of *Puccinia graminis tritici* and is perhaps responsible for self-inhibition of germination of the rust spores (199).

Several antibiotics produced by fungi and actinomycetes are in two related classes, the polyenynes and the polyenes (406). The polyenynes, characterized by a system of conjugated triple bonds, include, among compounds of known structure, diatetrynes 1 and 2 of *Clitocybe diatreta* (10), agrocybin of *Agrocybe dura* (305, 312), and mycomycin, produced by *Nocardia acidophilus* (113). Some have nitrogenous substituents, e.g., diatetryne 2:

$$HOOC—CH{=}CH—C{\equiv}C—C{\equiv}C—C{\equiv}N$$

Mycomycin, on the other hand, is an acid containing no nitrogen:

$$HC{\equiv}C—C{\equiv}C—CH{=}C{=}CH—CH{=}CH—CH{=}CH—CH_2—COOH$$

Acetylenic compounds are also known in higher plants and in other fungi than those named here (9, 11, 97). In an unidentified basidiomycete, the formation of polyacetylenes early in the culture cycle is followed by their disappearance; this may be interpreted as a reutilization of the compounds (98).

The conjugated polyenes include a number of antibiotics the complete structure of which is not known; the polyene structure is inferred from their ultraviolet absorption spectra (28a, 530, 534, 558). All are fungistatic agents. The polyenynes, except for mycomycin, have been found only among basidiomycetes; the known polyene antibiotics, on the other hand, are produced primarily by actinomycetes. Grifolin, formed by *Grifola confluens* (275), is a substituted hydrocarbon with one pair of conjugated double bonds.

Species of *Corticium* produce two yellow pigments, both containing a system of conjugated double bonds comparable to that of the carotenoid pigments (183, 246); other aspects of their structure, however, relate them to atromentin and thelephoric acid, considered later with the aromatic compounds.

The sporophore of *Lactarius* spp., and probably the ascocarp of *Peziza* sp., contain a rubberlike polymer, a *cis*-polyisoprene (491).

3. THE METABOLISM OF AROMATIC COMPOUNDS

Aromatic Compounds of Fungi. The fungi resemble the higher plants and differ from the bacteria in that many species convert carbohydrate to aromatic compounds not known to be essential metabolites. These compounds have been reviewed in detail by Birkinshaw (63), by Raistrick (430), and, in lichens, by Asahina and Shibata (24). Any classification of them must of necessity be based on their chemical structure and may unintentionally obscure physiological and biosynthetic relations. Thus, a substituted benzene and the quinone

Table 4. Representative Aromatic Compounds Produced by Fungi

Group*	Compound	Organism(s)
I	Methyl cinnamate $CH{=}CH{-}COOCH_3$	*Lentinus lepideus* (74)
	Anisaldehyde CHO OCH$_3$	*Trametes suaveolens* (64) *Daedalea juniperina* (69) *Polyporus benzoinus* (77)
	Gentisyl alcohol OH CH$_2$OH	*Penicillium* spp. (66, 93, 176, 180)
	Homoprotocatechuic acid CH$_2$COOH OH OH	*Polyporus tumulosus* (437)
	3,5-Dihydroxyphthalic acid OH COOH HO COOH	*Penicillium brevi-compactum* (142, 408)
	Gallic acid COOH HO OH OH	*Phycomyces blakesleeanus* (44)

* See text.

Table 4 (*continued*)

Group*	Compound	Organism(s)
I	Gladiolic acid (tautomeric)	*Penicillium gladioli* (253, 254)

$$CH_3 \quad OCH_3 \quad COOH$$
$$CHO$$
$$CHO$$

Cyclopolic acid   *Penicillium cyclopium* (84)

$$CH_3 \quad OCH_3 \quad COOH$$
$$HO \quad CHO \quad CH_2OH$$

Cyclopaldic acid   *Penicillium cyclopium* (84)

$$CH_3 \quad OCH_3 \quad COOH$$
$$HO \quad CHO \quad CHO$$

Chloramphenicol   *Streptomyces venezuelae* (444)

$$CO—CHCl_2$$
$$NH$$
$$NO_2—\langle\ \rangle—CHOH—CH—CH_2OH$$

Mycophenolic acid   *Penicillium* spp. (6, 65, 83, 142)

$$CH_3$$
$$HOOC—CH_2—CH_2—C{=}CH—CH_2 \quad OH \quad CO$$
$$O$$
$$CH_3O \quad CH_2$$

Sulochrin   *Oospora sulphurea-ochracea* (395, 396)

$$OCH_3 \quad\quad\quad OH$$
$$—CO—$$
$$HO \quad COOCH_3 \quad HO \quad CH_3$$

Table 4 (*continued*)

Group*	Compound	Organism(s)
II	4-Methoxy-2,5-*p*-toluquinone 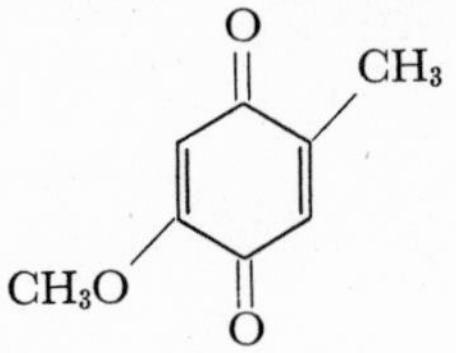	*Coprinus similis, Lentinus degener* (12)

Spinulosin

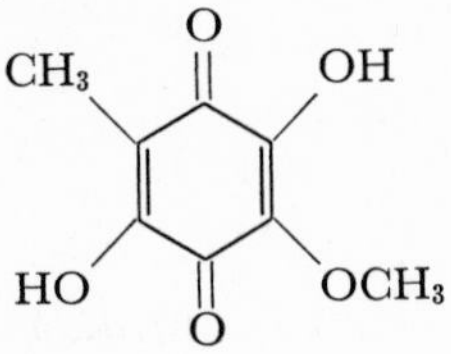

Aspergillus fumigatus, Penicillium spp. (16, 79, 94)

Oosporein

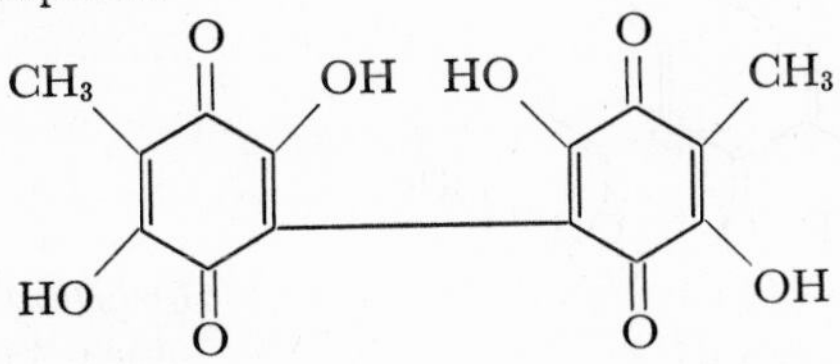

Oospora colorans (328), *Chaetomium aureum* (347)

Atromentin

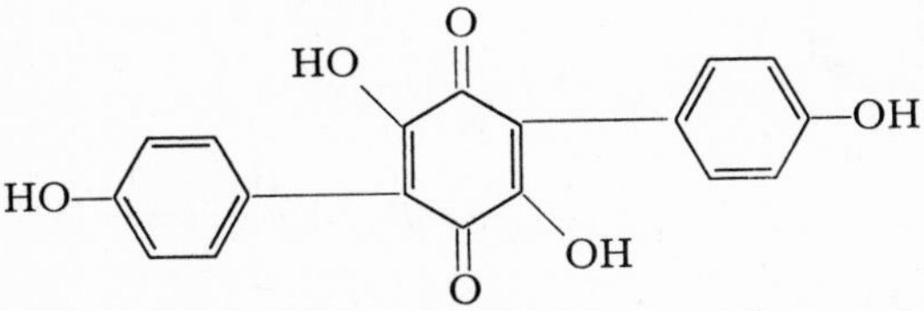

Paxillus atromentosus (325)

Thelephoric acid

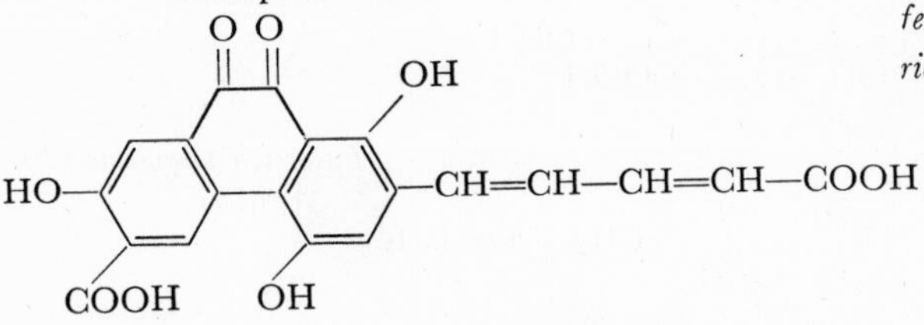

Thelephora spp., *Hydnum ferrugineum* (326), *Lobaria retigera* (lichen) (23)

Table 4 (*continued*)

Group*	Compound	Organism(s)
III	Chrysophanic acid	*Penicillium islandicum* (289)

| | Emodin | *Dermocybe sanguinea* (327) |

| | Asperthecin | *Aspergillus quadrilineatus* (290) |

| IV | Ravenelin | *Helminthosporium ravenelii* (389, 431) |

| | Pinselic acid | *Penicillium amarum* (390) |

| V | Javanicin | *Fusarium javanicum* (20. 21, 61a) |

Table 4 (*continued*)

Group*	Compound	Organism(s)
VI	Stipitatic acid	*Penicillium stipitatum* (68, 150, 165)

	Puberulonic acid	*Penicillium puberulum* (25, 81)

VII	Lecanoric acid	*Parmelia* spp. (lichens) (24)

	Gyrophoric acid	*Gyrophora esculenta* and other lichens (24)

VIII	Nidulin	*Aspergillus nidulans* (163)

formed from it by oxidation are more closely related biologically than are two differently substituted benzene compounds. The following division of the aromatic products synthesized by fungi, taken largely from Raistrick (430), should be considered as a formal classification only. Examples of the major types are illustrated in Table 4.

Group I, substituted benzenes, is the largest single group of aromatic compounds, and presents a bewildering array of possible biological interrelations. Some of the members of this group are soluble metabolites of the culture filtrate, others occur in the mycelium, and still others are associated with reproductive structures (214, 243).

Members of Group II, substituted benzoquinones, often have an obvious metabolic relation, as oxidation products, to phenolic compounds of Group I. Many are derivatives of toluquinone.

Anthraquinones, Group III, are pigments and are known also in lichens and in higher plants (280). The fungal anthraquinones may be considered as derivatives of chrysophanic acid.

Group IV, the xanthones, is represented in the fungi by only a few certain examples. Rubrofusarin, formed by *Fusarium* spp. (389), is probably the same methyl xanthone as asperxanthone of *Aspergillus niger* (355).

Group V comprises the naphthoquinones. In addition to javanicin, other fungal products of this type have been identified as products of *Fusarium* spp. (104, 451) and other fungi (40, 161). Solanione (552) and oxyjavanicin (21) are probably identical with, respectively, javanicin and fusarubin (63).

Derivatives of tropolone, Group VI in Table 4, are only quasibenzenoid, inasmuch as the ring contains seven carbons. Such higher plant products as thujaplicin and colchicine are tropolones (412). An origin of tropolones from phenolic compounds has been suggested (371).

The depsides, Group VII, are known so far only from lichens; it may be presumed, by analogy with other lichen products (112), that the fungus component of the lichen is responsible for their formation.

Nidulin illustrates the depsidones (Group VIII). The lichen depsidones are similar; some, e.g., gangaleoidin and diploicin, are chlorinated, most are not (24).

The physiological importance of the aromatic compounds is largely unknown, most effort to date having been concentrated on problems of identification. In what follows, three topics will be briefly considered: pathways of biosynthesis, enzymatic transformations, and the possible metabolic significance of the aromatic compounds.

The Biosynthesis of Aromatic Compounds. Although not all of the aromatic compounds of fungi have been proved to be formed from carbohydrate—some have been reported only from sporophores in nature—most of them are probably so formed; this is evidenced, for example, by the very high yields often obtained on synthetic media (95, 128, 252).

The origin of the aromatic ring from glucose has been investigated most successfully in connection with the biogenesis of the aromatic amino acids and *p*-aminobenzoic acid in bacteria. The current view of this process may be diagrammed as follows (162):

5-Dehydroquinic acid   Quinic acid

5-Dehydroshikimic acid   Shikimic acid

In this scheme, an unknown compound "V" arises from carbohydrate and is converted through the known materials shown to a second unidentified compound "Z_1", which is in turn ultimately transformed into the aromatic amino acids and *p*-aminobenzoic acid; the known later steps in the process are reviewed in Chapter 8. The initial steps of the reaction sequence are not known; preliminary evidence (162) suggests that the carbon chain of glucose is ruptured before incorporation of glucose carbon into shikimic acid.

A mutant of *Neurospora crassa* which requires *p*-aminobenzoic acid, tyrosine, phenylalanine, and tryptophan for growth is similar in these requirements to the bacterial mutants which have provided much of the evidence for the scheme just outlined, and appears to be blocked in the conversion of dehydroshikimic acid to shikimic acid (507). It accumulates protocatechuic acid, which is then oxidized by ring fission (p. 174). Protocatechuic acid is known as a metabolic product of *Phycomyces blakesleeanus* growing on a glucose-asparagine medium

(44) and is also formed by many fungi during the oxidation of quinic acid (53, 57).

Isotope studies on *Neurospora crassa* indicate that, as in bacteria, 3- and 4-carbon fragments derived from glucose—presumably via the phosphogluconate oxidation pathway (Chapter 7)—combine to form shikimic acid (506).

As discussed later, currently available information at least encourages the speculation that all aromatic compounds arise analogously to protocatechuic acid in *N. crassa*, i.e., that the normal pathway to aromatic amino acids is blocked or saturated and that the carbon of shikimic acid or its precursors is diverted to the synthesis of new aromatic structures. However, in *N. crassa* protocatechuic acid is oxidized with ring fission and does not give rise to other aromatic compounds.

Another possibility has been considered by Ehrensvärd (176), that pyrones might be intermediates in the conversion of glucose to aromatic compounds by *Penicillium urticae*. Evidence so far is limited to the action of pyranes, e.g., dehydracetic acid, on the synthesis of aromatic compounds.

Close structural relations among the aromatic compounds are numerous, both within and between species. Many are discussed by Raistrick (430); a few examples may be cited:

1. Simultaneous formation by one organism of a phenol and the corresponding quinone (14, 180).

2. Occurrence in the same organism of a compound and its dihydro derivative, e.g., cyclopolic and cyclopaldic acids (Table 4).

3. Formation of a compound and a hydroxy or methoxy derivative of it, e.g., gladiolic and cyclopaldic acids (Table 4) and methyl cinnamate and methyl-*p*-methoxycinnamate (74). The ability of fungi to introduce hydroxyl groups into a ring has been noted above in connection with steroid metabolism.

4. The close structural relationship, already mentioned, of all of the fungal anthraquinones, found in such diverse genera as *Aspergillus, Cortinarius, Helminthosporium,* and *Penicillium* (289). A possible origin of the anthraquinones from benzophenone is discussed by Tatum (505).

The foregoing examples refer to more or less static relations. In a dynamic and more conclusive experiment it has been shown that the ratio of patulin to gentisyl alcohol is controlled by the concentration of iron in the medium (Figure 7). Similarly, *Penicillium urticae* in a low-zinc medium forms predominantly 6-methylsalicylic

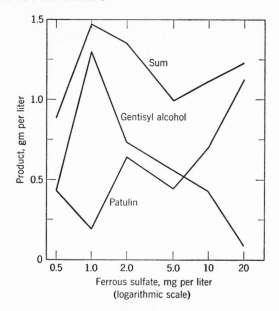

Figure 7. The effect of iron on the formation of patulin and gentisyl alcohol by *Penicillium* sp. From data of Brack (93).

acid, but at higher concentrations of zinc this compound is replaced by a mixture of gentisyl alcohol, patulin, and toluquinone (176). This type of analysis, in which an environmental modification causes a shift in metabolic products, is extremely promising.

Penicillium brevi-compactum produces several related phenols. Both the temporal sequence of appearance of these compounds (409) and the observation that the organism when fed one compound produces others (230) support the proposition that these structurally related molecules are related biologically as well.

A role of the polyphenol oxidases in the conversion of phenols to other compounds is probable but has not been investigated in the fungi; Mason (371) reviews several theories on the function of these enzymes in the origin of aromatic products of higher plants.

Enzymatic Transformations of Aromatic Compounds. The major known types of attack on aromatic compounds may be summarized as: (1) the oxidation of aliphatic side chains, (2) the oxidation of phenols, (3) the oxidative fission of the aromatic ring, and (4) the hydrolysis of depsides.

The side chain of phenylacetic acid is oxidized by *Penicillium chrysogenum;* benzaldehyde is formed during the oxidation and is thought to be an intermediate (279). The process therefore resembles the oxidation of substituted benzenes by bacteria (479) and higher plants (313), in which benzoic acid is the ultimate product:

$$CH_2COOH \qquad CHO \qquad COOH$$

$$\to\ ?\ \to \qquad\qquad \to \qquad\qquad (11)$$

Phenylacetic acid   Benzaldehyde   Benzoic acid

However, the entire sequence is not known in fungi, and the formation from phenylacetate of 2-hydroxyphenylacetate and 2,5-dihydroxyphenylacetate point to other possible modes of attack by fungi and actinomycetes (297, 320, 544). Benzoic acid is formed in culture by *Penicillium roseo-purpureum* (427a).

The oxidation of vanillin and ferulic acid by fungi appears to be of the same general type as that of phenylacetate, the side chain being oxidized in one or more steps to a carboxyl group (268).

There occurs in bacterial metabolism an oxidative fission of the aromatic ring of catechol to yield *cis-cis*-muconic acid (480):

OH
OH

$$+\ O_2 \to HOOC—CH=CH—CH=CH—COOH \quad (12)$$

Catechol   *Cis-cis*-muconic acid

This over-all reaction has been hypothecated for *Aspergillus niger* (57), and *Penicillium* sp. accumulates *cis-cis*-muconate during the oxidation of catechol (333). The aromatic ring of phenylacetic acid is split by *Penicillium chrysogenum,* but the details of the process are not known, except that an induced enzyme system is responsible and that compounds of the tricarboxylic acid cycle appear in the medium during oxidation (294, 296).

It has been mentioned that a mutant of *Neurospora crassa* accumulates and then oxidizes protocatechuic acid. The ultimate product is β-ketoadipic acid and the enzymatic steps involved are similar to but not identical with those known in *Pseudomonas fluorescens* (250, 481). The first step is the conversion of procatechuic acid to *cis, cis*-β-carboxymuconic acid, analogously to the reaction of Equation 12, by an inducible oxidase system (250, 251).

The oxidation of phenols to quinones is a special problem, and much more data are available on it than on other phases of aromatic metabolism.

The enzymes responsible for the oxidation of phenols are the polyphenol oxidases, of which two have been separated:

1. Tyrosinase, which oxidizes both monophenols (tyrosine, *p*-cresol, etc.) and polyphenols (catechol, pyrogallol, etc.). Oxidation of tyrosine leads, by a complex series of enzymatic and non-enzymatic reactions, to the formation of black pigments, the melanins (Chapter 8).

2. Laccase, which oxidizes polyphenols but not monophenols. In contrast to tyrosinase, laccase is sensitive to carbon monoxide and has a somewhat different substrate range.

Both enzymes are copper proteins. The characteristic reaction, often used for assay, is the oxidation of catechol to *o*-benzoquinone:

$$\text{Catechol} + \tfrac{1}{2}O_2 \rightarrow \text{o-Benzoquinone} + H_2O \tag{13}$$

Although other polyphenol oxidases probably occur in fungi (108, 286), they have not been characterized. Most assays do not, indeed, discriminate between laccase and tyrosinase.

Interest in the polyphenol oxidases has been stimulated by the Bavendamm reaction (35) of the wood-rotting fungi: on an agar medium containing gallic or tannic acid the fungi causing white rots of wood and capable of utilizing lignin form a colored zone. The brown rot fungi in general do not form the zone. Several surveys of the wood-rotting fungi have established that the correlation between zone production and type of rot is high, although not perfect (86, 160, 397). The usual substrates do not distinguish between tyrosinase and laccase, but work with specific substrates and on the distribution of the enzymes between cells and medium indicates that extracellular laccase, rather than tyrosinase, is responsible for the Bavendamm reaction (274, 335, 343, 344).

Extracellular polyphenol oxidases are formed also by other basidiomycetes, including parasitic and mycorrhizal species and both coprophilic and litter-inhabiting saprophytes (340). Fungi other than basidiomycetes have been less well studied; tyrosinase is found in *Glomerella cingulata* (500) and *Neurospora crassa* (210, 287) and—judged by color reactions—in *Streptomyces scabies* (282) and in *Sclerotinia fructicola* and *Macrosporium sarcinaeforme* (445).

Polyphenol oxidases in the fungi are often present only at particular times in the culture cycle, especially during autolysis (188, 500), or only in particular morphological structures (342, 344). The medium used affects the production of the enzymes, both positively and negatively. Laccase formation by *Polyporus versicolor* is increased non-specifically by constituents of the medium and specifically by certain aromatic compounds which probably act as inducers (189, 190). Both carbon source and growth temperature affect enzyme synthesis in *Glomerella cingulata* (499). Negative effects of an interesting type have been found in studies on *Neurospora crassa* (287): in a medium containing the usual level of sulfate a sulfur-containing dialyzable tyrosinase inhibitor is formed, the result being that the conventional assay detects tyrosinase only in cultures grown in a low-sulfate medium. This finding requires that earlier negative reports be re-evaluated.

The tannins are esters of polyhydroxy phenols with aromatic acids, and are hydrolyzed by tannase, e.g.,

HO　　　　　HO　　OH　　　HO

HO—⟨ ⟩—CO—O—⟨ ⟩　→　2HO—⟨ ⟩—COOH　(14)

HO　　　　　　　　COOH　HO

　　　　　Digallic acid　　　　　　　　　　　Gallic acid

The enzyme, an esterase, also hydrolyzes other similar esters (498). The tannase of *Aspergillus niger* is inducible (322); its properties and purification are summarized by Dyckerhoff and Armbruster (175), and partial purification has been reported (519). Although most studies have been made on the tannase of *A. niger,* the enzyme has been reported in a few other fungi (36, 448, 574).

The Significance of Aromatic Compounds. Some of the aromatic compounds bulk rather large in the economy of the organism, amounting to an appreciable fraction of the glucose consumed (140) and of the dry weight produced (128). Those which have been studied in relation to the history of the culture appear to be first formed and then utilized (93, 95), to be more than inactive waste products of metabolism.

Possibly the most likely metabolic significance of these compounds is as products of an unbalanced nutrition and metabolism. Most of them have been isolated from fungi grown on media very high in carbon; thus, the glucose Czapek-Dox medium often used has a carbon : nitrogen ratio of 60. Under these conditions, it is not surprising that carbon may flow into new metabolic pools simply because of an insufficiency of nitrogen. We may visualize this type of process schematically:

$$\text{Glucose} \rightleftharpoons A \rightleftharpoons B \rightleftharpoons C \rightleftharpoons D \rightleftharpoons E \ldots \qquad (15)$$

$$
\begin{array}{ccc}
\updownarrow & \updownarrow & \nearrow \\
A' & B' & -NH_2 \\
\updownarrow & \updownarrow & \\
A'' & B'' &
\end{array}
$$

If compound D, for example, cannot be synthesized because of a relative nitrogen deficiency, enzymatic equilibria and factors of permeability and solubility will determine which of the potential alternative pathways is followed. In the specific instance of the benzenoid compounds and their oxidation products, it is imaginable that the synthesis of aromatic amino acids stops because nitrogen is no longer available, and that a precursor of these amino acids, e.g., shikimic acid, is then diverted to the synthesis of new compounds.

This view of the origin of aromatic compounds puts them in the same class as organic acids, fats, and polysaccharides, as products of what have been termed metabolic shunts (200). Physiologically, the model proposed above requires that the ratio of metabolic product to mycelial nitrogen should increase with increasing glucose concentration, at least over a certain range. This has not been tested; the ratio of product to dry weight of mycelium (243) is less informative, because of the likelihood that carbon components of the mycelium may also be products of metabolic shunts.

It has often been suggested that fungal quinones play a specific role in respiration, and the hypothesis is an attractive one. The frequent simultaneous occurrence of the reduced and oxidized forms in one organism suggests that the system could transport electrons and so function in terminal respiration. However, satisfactory proof of such a role in the intact cell has not been brought forward. Addition of quinones to a culture often elicits a respiratory response (214, 389), but this can only be taken as an indication that the compound could function, not that it does in fact function.

A respiratory role for the polyphenol oxidases of higher plants has often been proposed, and the question is still open. In *Glomerella cingulata* it appears that tyrosinase cannot be an essential respiratory enzyme, inasmuch as it is not detectable during the growth phase (500).

A pyridine nucleotide-menadione reductase occurs in *Aspergillus niger* (564), and a pyridine nucleotide-quinone reductase in other fungi (565). In principle, either of these could participate in a coupling mechanism between substrate dehydrogenation and a polyphenol oxidase system transferring electrons to oxygen.

Many of the quinonoid compounds of fungi are more or less inhibitory to other organisms, and it has been suggested (341) that this property may confer an ecological advantage. Whether highly reactive compounds like the quinones could persist long enough in soil to inhibit competing bacteria and fungi is, however, somewhat doubtful.

4. DERIVATIVES OF PYRONE

Several metabolic products may be considered together as derivatives of 1,4-pyrone, and as related structurally to the pyranose form of glucose. Kojic acid is typical:

$$
\begin{array}{ccc}
& \text{CO} & \\
\diagup & & \diagdown \\
\text{HO—C} & & \text{CH} \\
\| & & \| \\
\text{HC} & & \text{C—CH}_2\text{OH} \\
\diagdown & & \diagup \\
& \text{O} &
\end{array}
\qquad
\begin{array}{ccc}
& \text{CHOH} & \\
\diagup & & \diagdown \\
\text{HOHC} & & \text{CHOH} \\
| & & | \\
\text{HOHC} & & \text{CH—CH}_2\text{OH} \\
\diagdown & & \diagup \\
& \text{O} &
\end{array}
$$

Kojic acid   Glucopyranose

Kojic acid was first discovered, as a product of *Aspergillus oryzae*, by Saito (452); its structure was determined by Yabuta (568). Many species of *Aspergillus,* but only one of *Penicillium,* produce it in culture (71, 227, 242, 303). Kojic acid is weakly antibacterial (381).

Kojic acid is produced from most common carbon sources (71, 311), although strains differ somewhat in this regard (404). The number of compounds providing carbon for kojic acid synthesis is less for a preformed mycelium than for growing cells (504).

The data of Figure 8 show that, as would be expected, there is over a certain range an inverse relation between nitrogen supplied to a culture and kojic acid production per unit mycelial weight. These data can best be interpreted as showing that kojic acid synthesis per cell is maximal when growth is limited by a nitrogen deficiency, in accordance with the principle that metabolites accumulate when carbon is supplied in excess of that which can be incorporated into cellular material.

The formation of kojic acid is sensitive to pH; the yield from a preformed mycelium declines virtually to zero as the pH is raised from 2.2 to 6.0 (319). Ethylene chlorhydrin increases the formation of

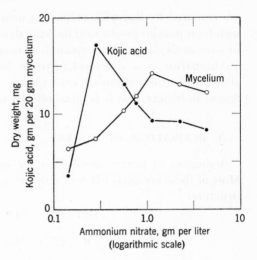

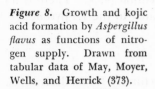

Figure 8. Growth and kojic acid formation by *Aspergillus flavus* as functions of nitrogen supply. Drawn from tabular data of May, Moyer, Wells, and Herrick (373).

kojic acid by *Aspergillus flavus,* but the effect appears to be on the entire metabolism of the organism rather than specifically on kojic acid synthesis (374).

The very high yields of kojic acid—up to 57 per cent of the glucose consumed by a growing culture (373) and up to 78 per cent of that used by preformed mycelium (319)—suggest that the acid may be formed directly from glucose. This is borne out by the isotope studies of Arnstein and Bentley (18). Degradation of kojic acid derived from glucose-1-C^{14} shows that the bulk of the acid is formed from glucose without splitting of the carbon chain. The occurrence of small amounts of C^{14} in other positions is adequately explained by the postulate that a minor fraction of the carbon of kojic acid is derived from compounds of the phosphogluconate oxidation respiratory pathway (19, 283).

The details of the conversion of glucose to kojic acid are not known; Arnstein and Bentley (18) discuss some possibilities. The fact that a preformed mycelium does not require added phosphate for kojic acid synthesis (242) is irrelevant to the problem of whether or not phosphorylative steps are involved in synthesis, since the endogenous phosphate reserves of the cell would without question be adequate for a cyclic process.

Patulin is a pyrone derivative, the structure of which is largely known (181, 563). It has been isolated several times independently under different names—clavacin, claviformin, expansin, and clavatin —from species of *Penicillium* and *Aspergillus;* its history and synonymy are reviewed by Raistrick (430). As mentioned earlier, the effects of metals on patulin production indicate that it is biosynthetically related to some of the aromatic compounds of fungi.

Alternariol is a dibenzo-1,2-pyrone formed by *Alternaria tenuis* after long-continued growth on a glucose medium (435). There is no reason to believe that it is metabolically related to the 1,4-pyrones.

5. DERIVATIVES OF FURAN

A number of fungal metabolites are structurally furan derivatives. Most of these are derivatives of tetronic acid and have in common the structure:

$$
\begin{array}{c}
\text{HO}\!-\!\text{C}\!=\!=\!\text{C}\!-\!\text{R}_1 \\
\mid \qquad\quad \mid \\
\text{R}_2\!-\!\text{C} \qquad \text{C}\!=\!\text{O} \\
\diagdown \quad \diagup \\
\text{O}
\end{array}
$$

One organism, *Penicillium charlesii,* forms five related compounds of this type: γ-methyltetronic acid, carlic acid, carlosic acid, carolinic acid, and carolic acid (140, 143). Other compounds of the same general class are terrestric acid of *Penicillium terrestre* (82), dehydro-carolic acid of *P. cinerascens* (94), and penicillic acid of *Penicillium* spp. and *Aspergillus* spp. (6, 78, 227).

L-Ascorbic acid, well known as a product of higher plants, has been isolated from the culture filtrate of *Aspergillus niger* (223). Its relation to the tetronic acids is shown by its structure:

$$
\begin{array}{c}
\text{HO}\!-\!\text{C}\!=\!=\!\text{C}\!-\!\text{OH} \\
\mid \qquad\qquad \mid \\
\text{CH}_2\text{OH}\!-\!\text{CHOH}\!-\!\text{C} \qquad \text{C}\!=\!\text{O} \\
\diagdown \quad \diagup \\
\text{O}
\end{array}
$$

Ascorbic acid

Studies on higher plants indicate that ascorbic acid is synthesized from glucose without rupture of the carbon chain and that L-galactono-γ-lactone is an important intermediate (367). It is also striking, in view of the formation of oxalic acid by *Aspergillus niger,* that oxalic acid is an end product of ascorbate metabolism in the guinea pig (99). Reports of ascorbic acid in fungi other than *Aspergillus niger* are summarized by Van Lanen and Tanner (531).

An ascorbic acid oxidase of the higher plant type, containing copper, has not been reported from fungi. *Myrothecium verrucaria* spores oxidize ascorbate, but the reaction is believed to be mediated by a new enzyme, probably located on the spore surface (365, 366).

Two other derivatives of furan—not derivatives, however, of tetronic acid—are known: 2-hydroxy-5-furan carboxylic acid, from *Aspergillus* spp. (496, 497) and zymonic acid, from yeasts (493).

The thiophen or thiofuran ring differs from the furan in that a sulphur atom replaces the oxygen. A single compound of this type, junipal, is known in the fungi, from *Daedalea juniperina* (69).

6. BIOLOGICAL METHYLATION

The transfer of intact methyl groups from one molecule to another has been most intensively studied in animal materials. The synthesis of methionine may be taken as an example:

$$CH_2-SH$$
$$|$$
$$CH_2$$
$$|$$
$$(CH_3)_3-\overset{+}{N}-CH_2-COO^- + H_2N-CH-COOH \rightarrow$$

Betaine　　　　　　　　　　　Homocysteine

$$CH_2-S-CH_3$$
$$|$$
$$CH_2$$
$$|$$
$$H_2N-CH-COOH + (CH_3)_2-N-CH_2-COOH \qquad (16)$$

Methionine　　　　　　　　　Dimethylglycine

In this reaction, details of which are neglected in the above over-all formulation, betaine functions as the methyl donor. Methionine can in turn donate a methyl group to other molecules, e.g., in the stepwise methylation of aminoethanol to choline.

Studies on *Neurospora crassa* mutants which require methionine show that the final step in methionine synthesis is the conversion of homocysteine to methionine, as in Equation 16 above (285). The methyl donor in the fungus system is not known.

In a particularly important application of biochemical genetics, Horowitz (284) showed that *Neurospora crassa* synthesizes choline by the stepwise methylation of aminoethanol, that is:

Aminoethanol → monomethylaminoethanol →
$$\text{dimethylaminoethanol} \rightarrow \text{choline} \qquad (17)$$

Here it is to be presumed that methionine or formate is the source of methyl groups. The ultimate source for those fungi—perhaps all naturally occurring fungi—which do not require preformed methyl groups in the medium is, of course, carbohydrate; that is, most or all fungi can synthesize methyl groups from the products of glucose metabolism.

Early in the nineteenth century, it was recognized that an arsenical poisoning of humans by volatile compounds is associated with the action of fungi on wallpaper or other building materials containing arsenical pigments. The history of this problem is reviewed by Challenger (117); the toxic material was finally identified as trimethylarsine (121). The ability of certain fungi to form methylated compounds of arsenic and other elements has since been investigated vigorously by the group at the University of Leeds. Some examples of the products identified are listed in Table 5; these and others are reviewed

Table 5. Methylated Products of Fungi

Substrate	Product	Organism
Na methylarsenate	Trimethylarsine	*Scopulariopsis brevicaulis* (121)
Na cacodylate	Trimethylarsine	*S. brevicaulis* (121)
Arsenous oxide	Trimethylarsine	*S. brevicaulis* (121)
Diethylarsonic acid	Methyldiethylarsine	*S. brevicaulis* (120)
K tellurite	Dimethyl telluride	*S. brevicaulis*, *Penicillium* spp. (62)
Na selenate	Dimethyl selenide	*Aspergillus niger* (170)
		Penicillium spp. (62)
		Scopulariopsis brevicaulis (123)
Na selenite	Dimethyl selenide	*S. brevicaulis* (123)
Ethyl disulfide	Methyl ethyl sulfide	*S. brevicaulis* (124)
Inorganic sulfate	Methyl mercaptan, dimethyl sulfide	*Schizophyllum commune* (76, 119)

by Challenger (118). It should be noted that the methods used permit only identification of the final product. Obviously, many steps in addition to methylation must be assumed in the conversion of the highly oxidized selenate ion, for example, to the reduced dimethyl selenide.

Evidence is now at hand that these products do in fact arise by transmethylation. Isotope experiments (122, 170) show that the methyl groups of dimethyl selenide and trimethylarsine originate from methionine in *Scopulariopsis brevicaulis* and *Aspergillus niger*. Betaine does not serve as a methyl donor; carbon from formate and choline enters the system, probably through methionine.

7. BIOLOGICAL CHLORINATION

Chloride ion is commonly present in culture media simply as an accompaniment of essential ions. With the discovery of geodin and erdin in *Aspergillus terreus* (433, 434), it was realized that chlorine may be incorporated into organic compounds by fungi. Subsequent investigations have shown many chlorinated metabolites; a partial list includes:

1. *p*-Methoxy-tetrachlorophenol of *Drosophila subatrata* (8).
2. Chlorinated depsidones, e.g., nidulin (Table 4). Chlorinated depsidones are also known in the lichens (24); they are presumably synthesized by the fungus component.
3. Griseofulvin, a complex benzenoid compound of uncertain structure, produced by *Penicillium* spp. (96, 256, 411).
4. Chlortetracycline (aureomycin), an antibiotic of *Streptomyces aureofaciens* (487).
5. Chloramphenicol (chloromycetin) (Table 4). Here the chlorine is attached to a side chain carbon; chloramphenicol is also unusual in its nitrobenzene structure.
6. Nalgiolaxin, a chlorinated anthraquinone of *Penicillium nalgiovensis*, occurring in association with its dechloro analogue nalgiovensin (436).
7. Caldariomycin of *Caldariomyces fumago* (*Fumago vagans*), probably a cyclopentane with two chlorine atoms attached to a ring carbon (141). Terrein, of *Aspergillus terreus*, not a chlorine compound, is the only other cyclopentane derivative known in fungi (32, 255).

In a survey of 139 fungi, it was found that strains of *Absidia spinosa, Alternaria tenuis, Aspergillus* spp., *Caldariomyces fumago, Penicillium* spp., *Syncephalastrum racemosum,* and *Trichoderma viride* incorporate 15 per cent or more of the available chlorine into organic combinations (141).

Frequently a compound and its dechloro derivative occur together in one organism, e.g., griseofulvin and dechlorogriseofulvin in *Penicillium* spp. (362). The antibiotics tetracycline and chlortetracycline are produced by different species of *Streptomyces*, the related oxytetracycline by a third (61). The substitution of bromide for chloride in the medium has specific effects of two kinds: either the organism forms the bromo analogue of a chlorine compound (363), or chlorination is suppressed and the dechloro derivative is formed (468). The incorporation of chlorine into tetracycline is also suppressed by copper-complexing agents, e.g., thiourea (468), which are known to interfere with iodination of tyrosine in the thyroid (551); presumably, the chlorination step requires copper.

8. PENICILLIN

The discovery by Fleming (197) of an organism producing penicillin initiated a new field of medical and biological investigation, the study of the formation and clinical use of antibiotics. The history of the exploitation of Fleming's discovery has been told elsewhere (1); in general, although extensive application of our knowledge of fungal physiology was essential to the development of methods of production, the physiological studies were less dramatic than the genetic, and few new principles of physiology or biochemistry have emerged from the work on penicillin and other antibiotics.

The penicillins are produced by several different fungi, including *Penicillium* spp., *Aspergillus* spp., and a thermophilic organism tentatively identified as *Malbranchea pulchella* (441). Strains of the *Penicillium chrysogenum* series, including *P. notatum,* are the most active, and supply the penicillin of commerce.

The penicillins are alike in their basic chemical structure, but differ in the side chain (R in the formula):

$$
\begin{array}{c}
S \\
\diagup \quad \diagdown \quad \diagup CH_3 \\
R-CO-NH-CH-CH \qquad C \\
\mid \qquad \mid \qquad \mid \diagdown CH_3 \\
CO-N----CH-COOH
\end{array}
$$

The natural penicillins whose structures have been determined include:

1. 2-Pentenylpenicillin (penicillin I, penicillin F)
2. Benzylpenicillin (penicillin II, penicillin G)
3. *p*-Hydroxybenzylpenicillin (penicillin III, penicillin X)
4. *n*-Amylpenicillin (dihydro penicillin F)
5. *n*-Heptylpenicillin (penicillin IV, penicillin K)
6. 4-Amino-4-carboxy-*n*-butylpenicillin (cephalosporin N) (393).

It is likely that other penicillins formed only in small amounts have not been identified. Benzylpenicillin, now available in crystalline form, is the penicillin of medical practice.

Extensive information on the metabolism of penicillin-producing fungi, reviewed by Chain (115) and Perlman (417), is available, but it must be said that there is no correlation of any other metabolic process with penicillin formation. It is possible to specify fairly exactly the optimal conditions for penicillin formation by a given strain, but not possible to define the way in which these conditions act.

The metabolic changes which take place during penicillin production are conveniently divided into three phases: an initial phase of rapid growth and metabolic activity, with assimilation of the more available nutrients, a second phase of slower growth with carbohydrate utilization, and a third phase of autolysis and low metabolic activity. These are illustrated in Figure 9. Penicillin formation begins late in the first phase and is most vigorous during the second. Rates differ, but in broad outline this pattern is followed by different strains in both complex and synthetic media, with various carbon sources, and under diverse conditions of aeration (31, 209, 217, 239, 300, 324). Lactose or other slowly utilizable carbohydrates yield both a favorable rate of growth and a favorable pH for penicillin formation (385, 484).

Penicillin production is also directly affected by aeration (483). The metal requirement for maximal penicillin formation by a strain of

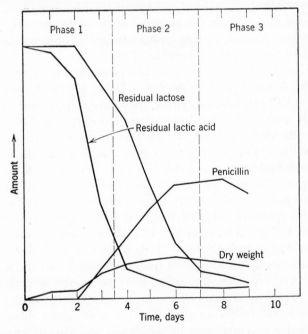

Figure 9. Metabolic changes accompanying penicillin formation by *Penicillium notatum* in shaken flasks in a corn steep liquor–lactose medium. Redrawn from Koffler, Emerson, Perlman, and Burris (323), by permission of the Williams and Wilkins Company.

P. chrysogenum is somewhat higher, particularly as to iron and phosphorus, than that for growth (301).

Corn steep liquor, a complex mixture of organic substances derived by bacterial action on maize (339), probably has more than one role in penicillin production; its principal function, however, appears to be as a source of β-phenylethylamine and related compounds (375), which are specific precursors of benzylpenicillin. In the biosynthesis of mixed penicillins, phenylacetic acid and its derivatives shift the balance of natural penicillins toward benzylpenicillin (273). Similarly, *p*-hydroxyphenylacetate increases the relative amount of *p*-hydroxybenzylpenicillin. Although only a small fraction of the phenylacetate supplied is incorporated into the molecule (295), isotope studies have shown that it is incorporated without dilution, i.e., that the intact benzyl group enters as such into penicillin (38, 240, 467).

Not only are close relatives of phenylacetic acid incorporated into benzylpenicillin, but many other substituted acetic acids can serve as precursors for new "biosynthetic" penicillins (37). Fatty acids, especially those which are not rapidly broken down by the fungus, are incorporated into both natural and new penicillins (380, 516).

The sulfur of penicillin can be supplied by inorganic sulfate; sulfur of methionine, cysteine, cystine, or glutathione is, however, utilized in preference to that of inorganic sulfate (490).

The origin of the main part of the penicillin molecule has been clarified by Arnstein and Grant (22). Using C^{14}-labeled valine and triply (N^{15}, C^{14}, S^{35}) labeled cystine, they have shown that: (1) cystine —probably after conversion to cysteine—is incorporated directly into the penicillin molecule, and (2) the remaining five carbons are supplied by valine. This is consistent with earlier work on the incorporation of small molecules into penicillin (368, 489, 517). The molecule of benzylpenicillin may be viewed, therefore, as made of three metabolic units, one formed directly from phenylacetic acid, one directly from cystine (probably via cysteine), and one supplied, directly or indirectly, by valine. The steps by which these structures are combined remain for future investigation. It is to be expected that energy is necessary for penicillin formation from these units, and the inhibitory effect of 2,4-dinitrophenol suggests that the energy is derived from oxidative phosphorylations (449).

The extensive studies on penicillin precursors have made it clear that although a precursor may be specifically and directly incorporated into a molecule, provision of the precursor does not necessarily increase the final yield of product. It is only when the formation of the precursor is so slow as to be rate-limiting to the total process that such increases in yield are found. This general principle obviously applies to all biosynthetic studies with putative precursors.

Penicillinase is produced by many bacteria and probably by actinomycetes; it is not certain whether any fungus forms it (116). Its action is to convert penicillins to penicilloic acids by hydrolysis and opening of the β-lactam ring.

Penicillin amidase, found in the mycelium of *Penicillium chrysogenum* and *Aspergillus oryzae*, splits off the benzyl side chain from benzylpenicillin; like penicillinase, it attacks a peptide (amide) linkage (459).

BIBLIOGRAPHY

1. Abraham, E. P., et al. 1949. In H. W. Florey et al. (eds.), *Antibiotics*, Vol. 2, p. 631–671. London: Oxford Univ. Press.
2. Acklin, O. 1929. *Biochem. Z.* 204: 253–274.
3. Akamatsu, S. 1923. *Biochem. Z.* 142: 186–187.
4. Allsopp, A. 1937. *New Phytologist* 36: 327–356.
5. Allsopp, A. 1950. *J. Exp. Botany* 1: 71–81.
6. Alsberg, C. L. and O. F. Black. 1913. *U. S. Dept. Agr. Bur. Plant Ind. Bull.* 270: 1–48.
7. Ammonn, R. and M. Jaarma. 1950. In J. B. Sumner and K. Myrbäck (eds.), *The Enzymes*, Vol. 1 (1), p. 390–442. New York: Academic Press.
8. Anchel, M. 1952. *J. Am. Chem. Soc.* 74: 2943.
9. Anchel, M. 1953. *Arch. Biochem. Biophys.* 43: 127–135.
10. Anchel, M. 1955. *Science* 121: 607–608.
11. Anchel, M. and M. P. Cohen. 1954. *J. Biol. Chem.* 72: 318–326.
12. Anchel, M., A. Hervey, F. Kavanagh, J. Polatnick, and W. J. Robbins. 1948. *Proc. Natl. Acad. Sci. U. S.* 34: 498–502.
13. Angeletti, A. and C. F. Cerruti. 1930. *Ann. chim. appl.* 20: 424–433.
14. Anslow, W. K. and H. Raistrick. 1938a. *Biochem. J.* (*London*) 32: 687–696.
15. Anslow, W. K. and H. Raistrick. 1838b. *Biochem. J.* (*London*) 32: 803–806.
16. Anslow, W. K. and H. Raistrick. 1938c. *Biochem. J.* (*London*) 32: 2282–2289.
17. Armstrong, G. I. 1929. *Protoplasma* 8: 222–260.
18. Arnstein, H. R. V. and R. Bentley. 1953. *Biochem. J.* (*London*) 54: 493–508, 508–516, 517–522.
19. Arnstein, H. R. V. and R. Bentley. 1956. *Biochem. J.* (*London*) 62: 403–411.
20. Arnstein, H. R. V. and A. H. Cook. 1947. *J. Chem. Soc.* (*London*) 1947: 1021–1028.
21. Arnstein, H. R. V., A. H. Cook, and M. S. Lacey. 1946. *Brit. J. Exp. Pathol.* 27: 349–355.
22. Arnstein, H. R. V. and P. T. Grant. 1954. *Biochem. J.* (*London*) 57: 353–359, 360–368.
23. Asahina, Y. and S. Shibata. 1939. *Ber. deut. chem. Ges.* 72B: 1531–1533.
24. Asahina, Y. and S. Shibata. 1953. *Chemistry of Lichen Substances*. Tokyo: Japan Society for the Promotion of Science, pp. 240.
25. Aulin-Erdtman, G. 1951. *Acta Chem. Scand.* 5: 301–315.
26. Baba, S. and K. Sakaguchi. 1942. *Bull. Agr. Chem. Soc. Japan* 18: 93–94.
27. Bach, D. and J. Fournier. 1935. *Compt. rend.* (*Paris*) 201: 982–984.
28. Baker, G. E. 1945. *Mycologia* 37: 582–600.

28a. Ball, S., C. J. Bessell, and A. Mortimer. 1957. *J. Gen. Microbiol.* 17: 96–103.
29. Barnett, H. L., V. G. Lilly, and R. F. Krause. 1956. *Science* 123: 141.
30. Barron, E. S. G. and F. Ghiretti. 1953. *Biochim. et Biophys. Acta* 12: 239–249.
31. Bartholomew, W. H., E. O. Karow, M. R. Spat, and R. H. Wilhelm. 1950. *Ind. Eng. Chem.* 42: 1810–1815.
32. Barton, D. H. R. and E. Miller. 1955. *J. Chem. Soc. (London)* 1955: 1028–1029.
33. de Bary, A. 1886. *Botan. Ztg.* 44: 393–404.
34. Bauer, R. 1938. *Zentr. Bakteriol. Parasitenk. Abt. II,* 98: 133–167.
35. Bavendamm, W. 1927. *Ber. deut. bot. Ges.* 45: 357–367.
36. Bazzigher, G. 1955. *Phytopathol. Z.* 23: 265–282.
37. Behrens, O. K. 1949. In H. T. Clarke, J. R. Johnson, and R. Robinson (eds.), *The Chemistry of Penicillin,* p. 657–679, Princeton, N. J.: Princeton Univ. Press.
38. Behrens, O. K., et al. 1948. *J. Biol. Chem.* 175: 765–769.
39. Belin, P. 1926. *Bull. soc. chim. Biol.* 8: 1081–1102.
40. Bendz, G. 1951. *Acta Chem. Scand.* 5: 489–490.
41. Bentley, R. and C. P. Thiessen. 1957. *J. Biol. Chem.* 226: 673–687, 689–702, 703–720.
42. Bergel, F., A. L. Morrison, A. R. Moss, and H. Rinderknecht. 1944. *J. Chem. Soc. (London)* 1944: 415–421.
43. Bernhard, K. 1948. *Cold Spring Harbor Symposia Quant. Biol.* 13: 26–28.
44. Bernhard, K. and H. Albrecht. 1947. *Helv. Chim. Acta* 30: 627–632.
45. Bernhard, K. and H. Albrecht. 1948. *Helv. Chim. Acta* 31: 2214–2220.
46. Bernhauer, K. 1926a. *Biochem. Z.* 172: 313–323.
47. Bernhauer, K. 1926b. *Biochem. Z.* 172: 324–349.
48. Bernhauer, K. 1928. *Biochem. Z.* 197: 278–286.
49. Bernhauer, K. 1934. *Ergeb. Enzymforsch.* 3: 185–226.
50. Bernhauer, K. 1943. *Ergeb. Enzymforsch.* 9: 297–360.
51. Bernhauer, K. and N. Böckl. 1932. *Biochem. Z.* 253: 16–24.
52. Bernhauer, K., N. Böckl, and H. Siebenäuger. 1932. *Biochem. Z.* 253: 37–41.
53. Bernhauer, K. and B. Görlich. 1935. *Biochem. Z.* 280: 394–395.
54. Bernhauer, K., J. Rauch, and J. N. Miksch. 1949. *Biochem. Z.* 320: 178–188.
55. Bernhauer, K. and Z. Scheuer. 1932. *Biochem. Z.* 253: 11–15.
56. Bernhauer, K. and H. Thole. 1936. *Biochem. Z.* 287: 167–171.
57. Bernhauer, K. and H. H. Waelsch. 1932. *Biochem. Z.* 249: 223–226.
58. Bernhauer, K. and H. Wolf. 1928. *Z. physiol. Chem. Hoppe-Seyler's.* 177: 270–279.
58a. Bertrand, D. and A. De Wolf. 1955. *Compt. Rend. (Paris)* 241: 1877–1880.
59. Biale, J. B. and A. D. Shepherd. 1941. *Am. J. Botany* 28: 263–270.
60. Bier, M. 1955. In S. P. Colowick and N. O. Kaplan (eds.), *Methods in Enzymology,* Vol. 1, p. 627–642. New York: Academic Press.
61. Binkley, S. B. 1955. *Ann. Rev. Biochem.* 24: 596–626.
61a. Birch, A. J. and F. W. Donovan. 1954. *Chem. & Ind.* 1954: 1047–1048.
62. Bird, M. L. and F. Challenger. 1939. *J. Chem. Soc. (London)* 1939: 163–168.
63. Birkinshaw, J. H. 1953. *Ann. Rev. Biochem.* 22: 371–398.
64. Birkinshaw, J. H., A. Bracken, and W. P. K. Findlay. 1944. *Biochem. J. (London)* 38: 131–132.
65. Birkinshaw, J. H., A. Bracken, E. N. Morgan, and H. Raistrick. 1948. *Biochem. J. (London)* 43: 216–223.
66. Birkinshaw, J. H., A. Bracken, and H. Raistrick. 1943. *Biochem. J. (London)* 37: 726–728.
67. Birkinshaw, J. H., A. Bracken, and H. Raistrick. 1945. *Biochem. J. (London)* 39: 70–72.
68. Birkinshaw, J. H., A. R. Chambers, and H. Raistrick. 1942. *Biochem. J. (London)* 36: 242–251.

69. Birkinshaw, J. H. and P. Chaplen. 1955. *Biochem. J.* (*London*) 60: 255–261.
70. Birkinshaw, J. H., J. H. V. Charles, A. C. Hetherington, and H. Raistrick. 1931. *Phil. Trans. Roy. Soc. London Ser. B* 220: 153–171.
71. Birkinshaw, J. H., J. H. V. Charles, C. H. Lilly, and H. Raistrick. 1931. *Phil. Trans. Roy. Soc. London Ser. B* 220: 127–138
72. Birkinshaw, J. H., J. H. V. Charles, and H. Raistrick. 1931. *Phil. Trans. Roy. Soc. London Ser. B* 220: 355–362.
73. Birkinshaw, J. H., J H. V. Charles, H. Raistrick, and J. A. R. Stoyle. 1931. *Phil. Trans. Roy. Soc. London Ser. B* 220: 27–54.
74. Birkinshaw, J. H. and W. P. K. Findlay. 1940. *Biochem. J.* (*London*) 34: 82–88.
75. Birkinshaw, J. H., W. P. K. Findlay, and R. A. Webb. 1940. *Biochem. J.* (*London*) 34: 906–916.
76. Birkinshaw, J. H., W. P. K. Findlay, and R. A. Webb. 1942. *Biochem. J.* (*London*) 36: 526–529.
77. Birkinshaw, J. H., E. N. Morgan, and W. P. K. Findlay. 1952. *Biochem. J.* (*London*) 50: 509–516.
78. Birkinshaw, J. H., A. E. Oxford, and H. Raistrick. 1936. *Biochem J.* (*London*) 30: 394–411.
79. Birkinshaw, J. H. and H. Raistrick. 1931a. *Phil. Trans. Roy. Soc. London Ser. B* 220: 245–254.
80. Birkinshaw, J H. and H. Raistrick. 1931b. *Phil. Trans. Roy. Soc. London Ser. B* 220: 331–353.
81. Birkinshaw, J. H. and H. Raistrick. 1932. *Biochem. J.* (*London*) 26: 441–453.
82. Birkinshaw, J. H. and H. Raistrick. 1936. *Biochem. J.* (*London*) 30: 2194–2200.
83. Birkinshaw, J. H., H. Raistrick, and D. J. Ross. 1952. *Biochem. J.* (*London*) 50: 630–634.
84. Birkinshaw, J. H., H. Raistrick, D. J. Ross, and C. E. Stickings. 1952. *Biochem. J.* (*London*) 50: 610–628.
85. Birkinshaw, J. H., H. Raistrick, and G. Smith. 1942. *Biochem. J.* (*London*) 36: 829–835.
86. Boidin, J. 1951. *Rev. mycol.* (*Paris*) 16: 173–197.
87. Bolcato, V. and P. Tono. 1939. *Enzymologia* 7: 146–156.
88. Bomstein, R. A. and M. J. Johnson. 1952. *J. Biol. Chem.* 198: 143–153.
89. Bonner, J., A. Sandoval, Y. W. Tang, and L. Zechmeister. 1946. *Arch. Biochem.* 10: 113–123.
90. Boothroyd, B., J. A. Thorn, and R. H. Haskins. 1955. *Can. J. Biochem. Physiol.* 33: 289–296.
91. Bowers, A., T. G. Halsall, E. R. H. Jones, and A. J. Lemin. 1953. *J. Chem. Soc.* (*London*) 1953: 2548–2560.
92. Bowers, A., T. G. Halsall, and G. C. Sayer. 1954. *J. Chem. Soc.* (*London*) 1954: 3070–3084.
93. Brack, A. 1947. *Helv. Chim. Acta* 30: 1–8.
94. Bracken, A. and H. Raistrick. 1947. *Biochem. J.* (*London*) 41: 569–574.
95. Breen, J., J. C. Dacre, H. Raistrick, and G. Smith. 1955. *Biochem. J.* (*London*) 60: 618–626.
96. Brian, P. W., P. J. Curtis, and H. G. Hemming. 1949. *Trans. Brit. Mycol. Soc.* 32: 30–33.
97. Bu'Lock, J. D., E. R. H. Jones, and P. R. Leeming. 1955. *J. Chem. Soc.* (*London*) 1955: 4270–4276.
98. Bu'Lock, J. D. and E. F. Leadbeater. 1956. *Biochem. J.* (*London*) 62: 476–480.
99. Burns, J. J., H. B. Burch, and C. G. King. 1951. *J. Biol. Chem.* 191: 501–514.
100. Burton, H. S., E. P. Abraham, and H. M. E. Caldwell. 1956. *Biochem. J.* (*London*) 62: 171–176.

101. Butkewitsch, W. 1924. *Biochem. Z.* 154: 177–190.
102. Butkewitsch, W. and M. W. Fedoroff. 1929. *Biochem. Z.* 207: 302–318.
103. Butkewitsch, W. (Butkevich, V. S.) and A. G. Timofeeva. 1934. *Mikrobiologiya* 3: 574–584.
104. Cajori, F. A., T. T. Otani, and M. A. Hamilton. 1954. *J. Biol. Chem.* 208: 107–114.
105. Calam, C. T., A. E. Oxford, and H. Raistrick. 1939. *Biochem J. (London)* 33: 1488–1495.
106. Cantino, E. C. 1949. *Am. J. Botany* 36: 95–112.
107. Cantino, E. C. 1951. *Am. J. Botany* 38: 579–585.
108. Cantino, E. C. and E. A. Horenstein. 1955. *Physiol. Plantarum* 8: 189–221.
109. Carson, S. F., J. W. Foster, W. E. Jefferson, E. F. Phares, and D. S. Anthony. 1951. *Arch. Biochem. Biophys.* 33: 448–458.
110. Carson, S. F., E. H. Mosbach, and E. F. Phares. 1951. *J. Bacteriol.* 62: 235–238.
111. Casida, L. E., Jr. and S. G. Knight. 1954. *J. Bacteriol.* 67: 171–175.
112. Castle, H. and F. Kubsch. 1949. *Arch. Biochem.* 23: 158–160.
113. Celmer, W. D. and I. A. Solomons. 1953. *J. Am. Chem. Soc.* 75: 1372–1376.
114. Chaikoff, I. L. and G. W. Brown, Jr. 1954. In D. M. Greenberg (ed.), *Chemical Pathways of Metabolism*, Vol. 1, p. 277–347. New York: Academic Press.
115. Chain, E. 1949. In H. W. Florey et al. (eds.), *Antibiotics*, Vol. 2, p. 749–767. London: Oxford Univ. Press.
116. Chain, E., H. W. Florey, N. G. Heatley, and M. A. Jennings. 1949. In H. W. Florey et al. (eds.), *Antibiotics*, Vol. 2, p. 1090–1110. London: Oxford Univ. Press.
117. Challenger, F. 1945. *Chem. Revs.* 36: 315–361.
118. Challenger, F. 1951. *Advances in Enzymol.* 12: 429–491.
119. Challenger, F. and P. T. Charlton. 1947. *J. Chem. Soc. (London)* 1947: 424–429.
120. Challenger, F. and L. Ellis. 1935. *J. Chem. Soc. (London)* 1935: 396–400.
121. Challenger, F., C. Higginbottom, and L. Ellis. 1933. *J. Chem. Soc. (London)* 1933: 95–101.
122. Challenger, F., D. B. Lisle, and P. B. Dransfield. 1954. *J. Chem. Soc. (London)* 1954: 1760–1771.
123. Challenger, F. and H. E. North. 1934. *J. Chem. Soc. (London)* 1934: 68–71.
124. Challenger, F. and A. A. Rawlings. 1937. *J. Chem. Soc. (London)* 1937: 868–875.
125. Challenger, F., V. Subramaniam, and T. K. Walker. 1927a. *J. Chem. Soc. (London)* 1927: 200–208.
126. Challenger, F., V. Subramaniam, and T. K. Walker. 1927b. *Nature (London)* 119: 674.
127. Champeau, M.-F. and P.-J. Luteraan. 1946. *Ann. parasitol. humaine et comparée* 21: 345–355.
128. Charles, J. H. V., H. Raistrick, R. Robinson, and A. R. Todd. 1933. *Biochem. J. (London)* 27: 499–511.
129. Chesters, C. G. C. and G. N. Rolinson. 1951a. *Biol. Revs. Cambridge Phil. Soc.* 26: 239–252.
130. Chesters, C. G. C. and G. W. Rolinson. 1951b. *J. Gen. Microbiol.* 5: 553–558.
131. Chichester, C. O., P. S. Wong, and G. Mackinney. 1954. *Plant Physiol.* 29: 238–241.
132. Chrząszcz, T. 1901. *Centr. Bakteriol. Parasitenk. Abt. II*, 7: 326–338.
133. Chrząszcz, T. and R. Schillak. 1936. *Biochem. Z.* 288: 359–368.
134. Chrząszcz, T. and D. Tiukow. 1929. *Biochem. Z.* 204: 106–124.
135. Chrząszcz, T. and D. Tiukow. 1931. *Biochem. Z.* 242: 137–148.
136. Chrząszcz, T., D. Tiukow, and M. Zakomorny. 1932. *Biochem. Z.* 250: 254–269.

137. Chrząszcz, T. and M. Zakomorny. 1935. *Biochem. Z.* 279: 64–75.

138. Claes, H. 1954. *Z. Naturforsch.* 9b: 461–469.

138a. Cleland, W. W. and M. J. Johnson. 1956. *J. Biol. Chem.* 220: 595–606.

139. Clutterbuck, P. W. 1936. *J. Soc. Chem. Ind. (London)* 55: 55T–61T.

140. Clutterbuck, P. W., W. N. Haworth, H. Raistrick, G. Smith, and M. Stacey. 1934. *Biochem. J. (London)* 28: 94–110.

141. Clutterbuck, P. W., S. L. Mukhopadhyay, A. E. Oxford, and H. Raistrick. 1940. *Biochem. J. (London)* 34: 664–677.

142. Clutterbuck, P. W., A. E. Oxford, H. Raistrick, and G. Smith. 1932. *Biochem. J. (London)* 26: 1441–1458.

143. Clutterbuck, P. W., H. Raistrick, and F. Reuter. 1935. *Biochem. J. (London)* 29: 300–321, 871–883, 1300–1309.

144. Cochrane, V. W. 1952. *J. Bacteriol.* 63: 459–471.

145. Cochrane, V. W. and I. Dimmick. 1949. *J. Bacteriol.* 58: 723–730.

146. Coleman, R. J., M. Cefola, and F. F. Nord. 1952. *Arch. Biochem. Biophys.* 40: 102–110.

147. Collins, F. D. 1954. *Biol. Revs. Cambridge Phil. Soc.* 29: 453–477.

148. Contardi, A. and A. Ercoli. 1935. *Arch. sci. biol. (Bologna)* 21: 1–44.

149. Coppock, P. D., V. Subramaniam, and T. K. Walker. 1928. *J. Chem. Soc. (London)* 1928: 1422–1427.

150. Corbett, R. E., A. W. Johnson, and A. R. Todd. 1950. *J. Chem. Soc. (London)* 1950: 147–149.

151. Cort, L. A. et al. 1954. *J. Chem. Soc. (London)* 1954: 3713–3721.

151a. Cort, W. M. et al. 1956. *Arch. Biochem. Biophys.* 63: 477–478.

152. Crasemann, J. M. 1954. *Am. J. Botany* 41: 302–310.

153. Crewther, W. G. and F. G. Lennox. 1953. *Australian J. Biol. Sci.* 6: 410–427.

154. Cross, L. C., C. G. Eliot, I. M. Heilbron, and E. R. H. Jones. 1940. *J. Chem. Soc. (London)* 1940: 632–636.

155. Currie, J. N. 1917. *J. Biol. Chem.* 31: 15–37.

156. Currie, J. N. and C. Thom. 1915. *J. Biol. Chem.* 22: 287–293.

157. Dakin, H. D. 1906. *J. Biol. Chem.* 1: 271–278.

158. Damm, H. 1943. *Chemiker-Ztg.* 67: 47–49.

159. Dammann, E., O. T. Rotini, and F. F. Nord. 1938. *Biochem. Z.* 297: 185–202.

160. Davidson, R. W., W. A. Campbell, and D. Blaisdell. 1938. *J. Agr. Research* 57: 683–695.

161. Davies, J. E., F. E. King, and J. C. Roberts. 1955. *J. Chem. Soc. (London)* 1955: 2782–2786.

162. Davis, B. D. 1955. *Advances in Enzymol.* 16: 246–312.

163. Dean, F. M., J. C. Roberts, and A. Robertson. 1954. *J. Chem. Soc. (London)* 1954: 1432–1439.

164. Deuel, H. J., Jr. 1951. *The Lipids,* Vol. 1. New York: Interscience Publishers, pp. 982.

165. Dewar, M. J. S. 1945. *Nature (London)* 155: 50–51.

166. Dimond, A. E., G. H. Plumb, E. M. Stoddard, and J. G. Horsfall. 1949. *Conn. (New Haven) Agr. Exp. Sta. Bull.* 531: 1–69.

167. Dimond, A. E. and P. E. Waggoner. 1953. *Phytopathology* 43: 663–669.

168. Dingle, J. and G. L. Solomons. 1952. *J. Appl. Chem. (London)* 2: 395–399.

169. Doelger, W. P. and S. C. Prescott. 1934. *Ind. Eng. Chem.* 26: 1142–1149.

170. Dransfield, P. B. and F. Challenger. 1955. *J. Chem. Soc. (London)* 1955: 1153–1160.

171. Dulaney, E. L. and D. Perlman. 1947. *Bull. Torrey Botan. Club* 74: 504–511.

172. Dulaney, E. L. et al. 1955a. *Appl. Microbiol.* 3: 336–340.

173. Dulaney, E. L. et al. 1955b. *Appl. Microbiol.* 3: 372–374.

174. Dulaney, E. L. et al. 1955c. *Mycologia* 47: 464–474.
175. Dyckerhoff, H. and R. Armbruster. 1933. *Z. physiol. Chem. Hoppe-Seyler's.* 219: 38–56.
176. Ehrensvärd, G. 1955. *Exp. Cell Research,* Suppl. 3: 102–109.
177. Ehrlich, F. 1911. *Ber. deut. chem. Ges.* 44: 3737–3742.
178. Emerson, R. and D. L. Fox. 1940. *Proc. Roy. Soc. (London) B* 128: 275–293.
179. Enebo, L., L. G. Anderson, and H. Lundin. 1946. *Arch. Biochem.* 11: 383–395.
180. Engel, B. G. and W. Brzeski. 1947. *Helv. Chim. Acta* 30: 1472–1478.
181. Engel, B. G., W. Brzeski, and P. A. Plattner. 1949. *Helv. Chim. Acta* 32: 1166–1175, 1752–1758.
182. Engel, B. G., J. Würsch, and M. Zimmerman. 1953. *Helv. Chim. Acta* 36: 1771–1776.
182a. Eppstein, S. H., P. D. Meister, H. C. Murray, and D. H. Peterson. 1956. *Vitamins and Hormones* 14: 359–432.
183. Erdtman, H. 1948. *Acta Chem. Scand.* 2: 209–219.
184. Erikson, D. and J. W. Porteous. 1953. *J. Gen. Microbiol.* 8: 464–474.
185. Erkama, J., B. Hägerstrand, and S. Junkkonen. 1949. *Acta Chem. Scand.* 3: 862–866.
186. Erkama, J., I. Heikkenen, and B. Hägerstrand. 1949. *Acta Chem. Scand.* 3: 858–861.
187. Eyre, J. C. 1932. *Ann. Appl. Biol.* 19: 351–369.
188. Fåhraeus, G. 1952. *Physiol. Plantarum* 5: 284–291.
189. Fåhraeus, G. 1954. *Physiol. Plantarum* 7: 704–712.
190. Fåhraeus, G. and G. Lindeberg. 1953. *Physiol. Plantarum* 6: 150–158.
191. Fairbairn, D. 1948. *J. Biol. Chem.* 173: 705–714.
192. Falck, R. and S. N. Kapur. 1924. *Ber. deut. chem. Ges.* 57B: 920–923.
193. Fink, H., G. Haenseler, and M. Schmidt. 1937. *Z. Spiritusind.* 60: 74, 76–77, 81–82. (*Chem. Abstr.* 31: 7926. 1937.)
194. Fiore, J. V. 1948. *Arch. Biochem.* 16: 161–168.
195. Fiore, J. V. and F. F. Nord. 1950. *Arch. Biochem.* 26: 382–400.
196. Fitz, A. 1873. *Ber. deut. chem. Ges.* 6: 48–58.
197. Fleming, A. 1929. *Brit. J. Exp. Pathol.* 10: 226–236.
198. Fodor, P. J. and A. Chari. 1939. *Enzymologia* 13: 258–267.
199. Forsyth, F. R. 1955. *Can. J. Botany* 33: 363–373.
200. Foster, J. W. 1949. *Chemical Activities of Fungi.* New York: Academic Press, pp. 648.
201. Foster, J. W. 1951. *Ann. Rev. Microbiol.* 5: 101–120.
202. Foster, J. W. and S. F. Carson. 1950. *Proc. Natl. Acad. Sci. U. S.* 36: 219–229.
203. Foster, J. W., S. F. Carson, D. S. Anthony, J. B. Davis, W. E. Jefferson, and M. V. Long. 1949. *Proc. Natl. Acad. Sci. U. S.* 35: 663–672.
204. Foster, J. W., S. F. Carson, S. Ruben, and M. D. Kamen. 1941. *Proc. Natl. Acad. Sci. U. S.* 27: 590–596.
205. Foster, J. W. and J. B. Davis. 1948. *J. Bacteriol.* 56: 329–338.
206. Foster, J. W. and J. B. Davis. 1949. *Arch. Biochem.* 21: 135–142.
207. Foster, J. W. and S. A. Waksman. 1939a. *J. Am. Chem. Soc.* 61: 127–135.
208. Foster, J. W. and S. A. Waksman. 1939b. *J. Bacteriol.* 37: 599–617.
209. Foster, J. W., H. B. Woodruff, and L. E. McDaniel. 1943. *J. Bacteriol.* 46: 421–433.
210. Fox, A. S. and W. D. Gray. 1950. *Proc. Natl. Acad. Sci. U. S.* 36: 538–546.
211. Francioli, M. 1935. *Fermentforschung* 14: 493–501.
212. Franke, W. and M. Deffner. 1939. *Ann. Chem. Liebigs* 541: 117–150.
213. Frey, A. 1931. *Arch. Mikrobiol.* 2: 272–309.
214. Friedheim, E. A. H. 1933. *Compt. rend. soc. biol.* 112: 1030–1032.
215. Friend, J. and T. W. Goodwin. 1954. *Biochem. J. (London)* 57: 434–437.

BIBLIOGRAPHY

193

216. Fruton, J. S. and S. Simmonds. 1953. *General Biochemistry.* New York: John Wiley and Sons, pp. 940.
217. Gailey, F. B., J. J. Stefaniak, B. H. Olson, and M. J. Johnson. 1946. *J. Bacteriol.* 52: 129–140.
218. Gardner, J. F., L. V. James, and S. D. Rubbo. 1956. *J. Gen. Microbiol.* 14: 228–237.
219. Garton, G. A., T. W. Goodwin, and W. Lijinsky. 1951. *Biochem. J.* (*London*) 48: 154–163.
220. Gascoigne, R. M., J. S. E. Holker, B. J. Ralph, and A. Robertson. 1951. *J. Chem. Soc.* (*London*) 1951: 2346–2352.
221. Gastrock, E. A., N. Porges, P. A. Wells, and A. J. Moyer. 1938. *Ind. Eng. Chem.* 30: 782–789.
222. Gayet, J. 1949. *Bull. soc. chim. biol.* 31: 792–795.
223. Geiger-Huber, M. and H. Galli. 1945. *Helv. Chim. Acta* 28: 248–250.
224. Gentile, A. C. 1954. *Plant Physiol.* 29: 257–261.
225. Gibbs, M., V. W. Cochrane, L. M. Paege, and H. Wolin. 1954. *Arch Biochem. Biophys.* 50: 237–242.
226. Gibbs, M. and R. Gastel. 1953. *Arch Biochem. Biophys.* 43: 33–38.
227. Gill-Carey, D. 1949. *Brit. J. Exp. Pathol.* 30: 119–123.
228. Godin, P. 1953a. *Biochim. et Biophys. Acta* 11: 114–118.
229. Godin, P. 1953b. *Biochim. et Biophys. Acta* 11: 119–121.
230. Godin, P. 1955. *Antonie van Leeuwenhoek J. Microbiol. Serol.* 21: 215–224.
231. Golueke, C. G. 1957. *J. Bacteriol.* 74: 337–344.
232. Goodwin, T. W. 1952a. *The Comparative Biochemistry of the Carotenoids.* London: Chapman and Hall, pp. 356.
233. Goodwin, T. W. 1952b. *Biochem. J.* (*London*) 50: 550–558.
234. Goodwin, T. W. 1953a. *Biochem. J.* (*London*) 53: 538–540.
235. Goodwin, T. W. 1953b. *J. Sci. Food Agr.* 4: 209–220.
236. Goodwin, T. W. 1955. *Ann. Rev. Biochem.* 24: 497–522.
237. Goodwin, T. W., W. Lijinsky, and J. S. Willmer. 1953. *Biochem. J.* (*London*) 53: 208–212.
238. Goodwin, T. W. and J. S. Willmer. 1952. *Biochem. J.* (*London*) 51: 213–217.
239. Gordon, J. J. et al. 1947. *J. Gen. Microbiol.* 1: 187–202.
240. Gordon, M., S. C. Pan, A. Virgona, and P. Numerof. 1953. *Science* 118: 43.
241. Gordon, M. A. 1950. *Mycologia* 42: 167–185.
242. Gould, B. S. 1938. *Biochem. J.* (*London*) 32: 797–802.
243. Gould, B. S. and H. Raistrick. 1934. *Biochem. J.* (*London*) 28: 1640–1656.
244. Grant, J. K. and A. C. Brownie. 1955. *Biochim. et Biophys. Acta* 18: 433–434.
245. Green, D. E. 1954. In D. M. Greenberg (ed.), *Chemical Pathways of Metabolism*, Vol. 1, p. 27–65. New York: Academic Press.
246. Gripenberg, J. 1952. *Acta Chem. Scand.* 6: 580–586.
247. Grob, E. C. and R. Bütler. 1954. *Helv. Chim. Acta* 37: 1908–1912.
248. Grob, E. C. and R. Bütler. 1955. *Helv. Chim. Acta* 38: 1313–1316.
248a. Grob, E. C. and R. Bütler. 1956. *Helv. Chim. Acta* 39: 1975–1980.
249. Grob, E. C., V. Grundbacher, and W. H. Schopfer. 1954. *Experientia* 10: 378–379.
250. Gross, S. R., R. D. Gafford, and E. L. Tatum. 1956. *J. Biol. Chem.* 219: 781–796.
251. Gross, S. R. and E. L. Tatum. 1955. *Science* 122: 1141.
252. Grosser, A., H. Kundtner-Schwarzkopf, and K. Bernhauer. 1950. *Z. Naturforsch. B* 5: 28–30.
253. Grove, J. F. 1952. *Biochem. J.* (*London*) 50: 648–666.

254. Grove, J. F. 1953. *Biochem. J. (London)* 54: 664–673.
255. Grove, J. F. 1954. *J. Chem. Soc. (London)* 1954: 4693–4694.
256. Grove, J. F. and J. C. McGowan. 1947. *Nature (London)* 160: 574.
257. Guider, J. M., T. G. Halsall, R. Hodges, and E. R. H. Jones. 1954. *J. Chem. Soc. (London)* 1954: 3234–3238.
258. Gyllenberg, H. and A. Raitio. 1952. *Physiol. Plantarum* 5: 367–371.
259. Halliwell, G. 1953. *J. Exp. Botany* 4: 369–376.
260. Halsall, T. G. and R. Hodges. 1954. *J. Chem. Soc. (London)* 1954: 2385–2391.
261. Hamada, M. 1940. *Japan. J. Botany* 10: 387–458.
262. Harrold, C. E. and M. Fling. 1952. *J. Biol. Chem.* 194: 399–406.
263. Haskins, R. H., J. A. Thorn, and B. Boothroyd. 1955. *Can. J. Microbiol.* 1: 749–756.
264. Haxo, F. 1955. *Fortschr. der Chemie org. Naturstoffe* 12: 169–197.
265. Hayasida, A. 1938. *Biochem. Z.* 198: 169–178.
266. Heim. P. 1946a. *Compt. rend. (Paris)* 222: 1354–1355.
267. Heim, P. 1946b. *Compt. rend. (Paris)* 223: 1170–1172.
268. Henderson, M. E. K. and V. C. Farmer. 1955. *J. Gen Microbiol.* 12: 37–46.
269. Herrick, H. T. and O. E. May. 1928. *J. Biol. Chem.* 77: 185–195.
270. Hesse, A. 1949. *Advances in Enzymol.* 9: 653–704.
270a. Hesseltine, C. W. and R. F. Anderson. 1957. *Mycologia* 49: 449–452.
271. Heugshem, C. and M. Welsch. 1949. *Bull. soc. chim. biol.* 31: 282–286.
272. Hida, T. 1935. *J. Shanghai Sci. Inst. Sect. IV, 1:* 201–214.
273. Higuchi, K., F. G. Jarvis, W. H. Peterson, and M. J. Johnson. 1946. *J. Am. Chem. Soc.* 68: 1669–1670.
274. Higuchi, T. and K. Kitamura. 1953. *J. Japan. Forestry Soc.* 35: 350–354. (*Chem. Abstr.* 48: 12875. 1954.)
275. Hirata, Y. and K. Nakanishi. 1950. *J. Biol. Chem.* 184: 135–143.
276. Hirsch, H. M. and G. I. Wallace. 1951. *Rev. can. biol.* 10: 191–214.
277. Hiura, M. and Y. Nagata. 1954. *Research Bull. Fac. Agr. Gifu Univ. (Japan)* No. 3: 98–99.
278. Hockenhull, D. J. D., M. Herbert, A. D. Walker, G. D. Wilkin, and F. G. Winder. 1954. *Biochem. J. (London)* 56: 73–82.
279. Hockenhull, D. J. D., A. D. Walker, G. D. Wilkin, and F. G. Winder. 1952. *Biochem. J. (London)* 50: 605–609.
280. Hoffman-Ostenhoff, O. 1950. *Fortschr. der Chemie org. Naturstoffe* 6: 154–241.
281. Holker, J. S. E. et al. 1953. *J. Chem. Soc. (London)* 1953: 2422–2429.
282. Hollis, J. P. 1952. *Phytopathology* 42: 273–276.
283. Horecker, B. L., M. Gibbs, H. Klenow, and P. Z. Smyrniotis. 1954. *J. Biol. Chem.* 207: 393–403.
284. Horowitz, N. H. 1946. *J. Biol. Chem.* 162: 413–419.
285. Horowitz, N. H. 1947. *J. Biol. Chem.* 171: 255–264.
286. Horowitz, N. H. and M. Fling. 1953. *Genetics* 38: 360–374.
287. Horowitz, N. H. and S-C. Shen. 1952. *J. Biol. Chem.* 197: 513–520.
288. Horowitz-Wlassowa, L. M. and M. J. Livschitz. 1935. *Zentr. Bakteriol. Parasitenk. Abt. II,* 92: 424–435.
289. Howard, B. H. and H. Raistrick. 1950. *Biochem. J. (London)* 46: 49–53.
290. Howard, B. H. and H. Raistrick. 1955. *Biochem. J. (London)* 59: 475–484.
291. Howell, A., Jr. and L. Pine. 1956. *J. Bacteriol.* 71: 47–53.
292. Ingraham, J. L. and R. Emerson. 1954. *Am. J. Botany* 41: 146–152.
293. Irvine, G. N., M. Golobchuk, and J. A. Anderson. 1954. *Can. J. Agr. Sci.* 34: 234–239.
294. Isono, M. 1953a. *J. Agr. Chem. Soc. Japan* 27: 198–207.
295. Isono, M. 1953b. *J. Agr. Chem. Soc. Japan* 27: 255–259.

296. Isono, M. 1953c. *J. Agr. Chem. Soc. Japan* 27: 297–301.
297. Isono, M. 1954. *J. Agr. Chem. Soc. Japan* 28: 475–479.
298. Itto, G. 1933. *J. Agr. Chem. Soc. Japan* 9: 552–562. (*Chem. Abstr.* 27: 5141. 1933.)
299. Jacquot, R. 1938. *Ann. fermentations* 4: 284–294, 346–362.
300. Jarvis, F. G. and M. J. Johnson. 1947. *J. Am. Chem. Soc.* 69: 3010–3017.
301. Jarvis, F. G. and M. J. Johnson. 1950. *J. Bacteriol.* 59: 51–60.
302. Jefferson, W. E. and J. W. Foster. 1953. *J. Bacteriol.* 65: 587–592.
303. Jennings, M. A. and T. I. Williams. 1945. *Nature (London)* 155: 302.
304. Johnston, J. A., D. W. Racusen, and J. Bonner. 1954. *Proc. Natl. Acad. Sci. U. S.* 40: 1031–1037.
305. Jones, E. R. H. and J. D. Bu'Lock. 1953. *J. Chem. Soc. (London)* 1953: 3719–3720.
306. Jones, E. R. H. and T. G. Halsall. 1955. *Fortschr. der Chemie org. Naturstoffe* 12: 44–130.
307. Kardo-Syssojewa, H. 1936. *Zentr. Bakteriol. Parasitenk. Abt. II,* 93: 264–277.
308. Karow, E. O. and S. A. Waksman. 1947. *Ind. Eng. Chem.* 39: 821–825.
309. Karrer, P. and F. Haab. 1948. *Helv. Chim. Acta* 31: 795–798.
310. Karrer, P. and E. Krause-Voith. 1948. *Helv. Chim. Acta* 31: 802–803.
311. Katagiri, H. and K. Kitahara. 1929. *Bull. Agr. Chem. Soc. Japan* 5: 38–47. (*Chem. Abstr.* 24: 3813–3814. 1930.)
312. Kavanagh, F., A. Hervey, and W. J. Robbins. 1950. *Proc. Natl. Acad. Sci. U. S.* 36: 102–106.
313. Kenten, R. H. 1953. *Biochem. J. (London)* 55: 350–360.
314. Kinoshita, K. 1931a. *Botan. Mag. (Tokyo)* 45: 45–61.
315. Kinoshita, K. 1931b. *Acta Phytochim. (Japan)* 5: 271–287.
316. Kirsh, D. 1935a. *Botan. Gaz.* 97: 321–333.
317. Kirsh, D. 1935b. *J. Biol. Chem.* 108: 421–430.
318. Kleinzeller, A. 1948. *Advances in Enzymol.* 8: 299–341.
319. Kluyver, A. J. and L. H. C. Perquin. 1933. *Biochem. Z.* 266: 82–95.
320. Kluyver, A. J. and J. C. M. van Zijp. 1951. *Antonie van Leeuwenhoek J. Microbiol. Serol.* 17: 315–324.
321. Knobloch, H. and H. Mayer. 1941. *Biochem. Z.* 307: 285–292.
322. Knudson, L. 1913. *J. Biol. Chem.* 14: 159–184, 185–202.
323. Koffler, H., R. L. Emerson, D. Perlman, and R. H. Burris. 1945. *J. Bacteriol.* 50: 517–548.
324. Koffler, H., S. G. Knight, W. C. Frazier, and R. H. Burris. 1946. *J. Bacteriol.* 51: 385–392.
325. Kögl, F. and H. Becker. 1928. *Ann. Chem. Liebigs* 465: 211–242.
326. Kögl, F., H. Erxleben, and L. Jänicke. 1930. *Ann. Chem. Liebigs.* 482: 105–119.
327. Kögl, F. and J. J. Postowsky. 1925. *Ann. Chem. Liebigs* 444: 1–7.
328. Kögl, F. and G. C. van Wessem. 1944. *Rec. trav. chim.* 63: 5–12.
329. Krámli, A. and J. Horvath. 1948. *Nature (London)* 162: 619.
330. Krámli, A. and J. Horvath. 1949. *Nature (London)* 163: 219.
331. Kresling, E. and E. Stern. 1936. *Zentr. Bakteriol. Parasitenk. Abt. II,* 95: 327–340.
332. Kusnetzov, S. J. 1931. *Zentr. Bakteriol. Parasitenk. Abt. II,* 83: 37–52.
333. Landa, S., V. Solín, and J. Palatý. 1953. *Chem. listy* 47: 1066–1070. (*Chem. Abstr.* 48: 4043. 1954.)
334. Larsen, H. and K. E. Eimhjellen. 1955. *Biochem. J. (London)* 60: 135–139.
335. Law, K. 1950. *Ann. Botany* 14: 69–78.
336. Lein, J., T. A. Puglisi, and P. S. Lein. 1953. *Arch. Biochem. Biophys.* 45: 434–442.
337. Lewis, K. F. and S. Weinhouse. 1951a. *J. Am. Chem. Soc.* 73: 2500–2503.

338. Lewis, K. F. and S. Weinhouse. 1951b. *J. Am. Chem. Soc.* 73: 2906–2909.
339. Liggett, R. W. and H. Koffler. 1948. *Bacteriol. Revs.* 12: 297–311.
340. Lindeberg, G. 1948. *Physiol. Plantarum* 1: 196–205, 401–409.
341. Lindeberg, G. 1949. *Svensk Botan. Tidskr.* 43: 438–447.
342. Lindeberg, G. 1950. *Nature (London)* 166: 739.
343. Lindeberg, G. and G. Fåhraeus. 1952. *Physiol. Plantarum* 5: 277–283.
344. Lindeberg, G. and G. Holm. 1952. *Physiol. Plantarum* 5: 100–114.
345. Lindner, P. 1922. *Z. angew. Chem.* 35: 110–114.
346. Lipmann, F. 1954. *Science* 120: 855–865.
347. Lloyd, G., A. Robertson, G. B. Sankey, and W. B. Whalley. 1955. *J. Chem. Soc. (London)* 1955: 2163–2165.
348. Lockwood, L. B. and G. E. N. Nelson. 1946. *Arch. Biochem.* 10: 365–374.
349. Lockwood, L. B., K. B. Raper, A J. Moyer, and R. D. Coghill. 1945. *Am. J. Botany* 32: 214–217.
350. Lockwood, L. B. and M. D. Reeves. 1945. *Arch. Biochem.* 6: 455–469.
351. Lockwood, L. B., J. J. Stubbs, and C. E. Senseman. 1938. *Zentr. Bakteriol. Parasitenk. Abt. II,* 98: 167–171.
352. Lockwood, L. B. and G. E. Ward. 1945. *Ind. Eng. Chem.* 37: 405–406.
353. Lockwood, L. B., G. E. Ward, and O. E. May. 1936. *J. Agr. Research* 53: 849–857.
354. Loesecke, H. W. von. 1945. *Chem. Eng. News* 23: 1952–1959.
355. Lund, N. A., A. Robertson, and W. B. Whalley. 1953. *J. Chem. Soc. (London)* 1953: 2434–2439.
356. Lutz, L. 1931. *Bull. soc. chim. biol.* 13: 436–457.
357. Luz, G. 1934. *Phytopathol. Z.* 7: 585–638.
358. Maas-Förster, M. 1955. *Arch. Mikrobiol.* 22: 115–144.
359. McCallan, S. E. A. and F. Wilcoxon. 1936. *Contribs. Boyce Thompson Inst.* 8: 151–165.
360. McEown, J. M. 1952. Thesis, Univ. of California. pp. 116.
361. Mackinney, G., C. O. Chichester, and P. S. Wong. 1953. *Arch. Biochem. Biophys.* 53: 479–483.
362. MacMillan, J. 1953. *J. Chem. Soc. (London)* 1953: 1697–1702.
363. MacMillan, J. 1954. *J .Chem. Soc. (London)* 1954: 2585–2587.
364. Mamoli, L. and A. Vercellone. 1937. *Z. physiol. Chem. Hoppe-Seyler's.* 245: 93–95.
365. Mandels, G. R. 1953a. *Arch. Biochem. Biophys.* 42: 164–173.
366. Mandels, G. R. 1953b. *Arch. Biochem. Biophys.* 44: 362–377.
367. Mapson, L. W. 1955. *Vitamins and Hormones* 13: 71–100.
368. Martin, E. et al. 1953. *J. Biol. Chem.* 203: 239–250.
369. Martin, S. M., P. W. Wilson, and R. H. Burris. 1950. *Arch. Biochem.* 26: 103–111.
370. Martin, W. R. and J. W. Foster. 1955. *J. Bacteriol.* 70: 405–414.
371. Mason, H. S. 1955. *Advances in Enzymol.* 16: 105–184.
372. May, O. E., H. T. Herrick, C. Thom, and M. B. Church. 1927. *J. Biol. Chem.* 75: 417–422.
373. May, O. E., A. J. Moyer, P. A. Wells, and H. T. Herrick. 1931. *J. Am. Chem. Soc.* 53: 774–782.
374. May, O. E., G. E. Ward, and H. T. Herrick. 1932. *Zentr. Bakteriol. Parasitenk. Abt. II,* 86: 129–134.
375. Mead, T. H. and M. V. Stack. 1948. *Biochem. J. (London)* 42: xviii.
376. Mininger, R. F., M. E. Wall, R. G. Dworschack, and R. W. Jackson. 1956. *Arch. Biochem. Biophys.* 60: 427–432.
377. Miyaji, K. 1930. *Research Bull. Gifu Imp. Coll. Agr. (Japan)* No. 10: 1–5.
378. Miller, E. V., J. R. Winston, and D. F. Fisher. 1940. *J. Agr. Research* 60: 269–277.
379. Molliard, M. 1922. *Compt. rend. (Paris)* 174: 881–883.

380. Mortimer, D. C. and M. J. Johnson. 1952. *J. Am. Chem. Soc.* 74: 4098–4102.
381. Morton, H. E., W. Kocholaty, R. Junowicz-Kocholaty, and A. Kelner. 1945. *J. Bacteriol.* 50: 579–584.
382. Moses, V. 1955. *J. Gen. Microbiol.* 13: 235–251.
383. Moyer, A. J. 1953. *Appl. Microbiol.* 1: 1–7.
384. Moyer, A. J. and R. D. Coghill. 1945. *Arch. Biochem.* 7: 167–183.
385. Moyer, A. J. and R. D. Coghill. 1946. *J. Bacteriol.* 51: 57–78.
386. Moyer, A. J., E. J. Umberger, and J. J. Stubbs. 1940. *Ind. Eng. Chem.* 32: 1379–1383.
387. Mukherjee, S. 1951. *Arch. Biochem. Biophys.* 33: 364–376.
388. Mukherjee, S. 1952. *Arch. Biochem. Biophys.* 35: 23–33, 34–59.
389. Mull, R. P. and F. F. Nord. 1944. *Arch. Biochem.* 4: 419–433.
390. Munekata, H. 1953. *J. Biochem. (Tokyo)* 40: 451–460.
391. Nagata, Y., A. Matuda, and M. Hiura. 1954. *Research Bull. Fac. Agr. Gifu Univ. (Japan)* No. 3: 100–101.
392. Nakayama, T., G. Mackinney, and H. J. Phaff. 1954. *Antonie van Leeuwenhoek J. Microbiol. Serol.* 20: 217–228.
393. Newton, G. G. F., E. P. Abraham, and C. W. Hale. 1954. *Biochem. J. (London)* 58: 103–111.
394. Nickerson, W. J. 1948. *Arch. Biochem.* 17: 225–233.
395. Nishikawa, H. 1939. *Acta Phytochim. (Japan)* 11: 167–185.
396. Nishikawa, H. 1940. *Bull. Agr. Chem. Soc. Japan* 16: 97–98.
397. Nobles, M. K. 1948. *Can. J. Research C* 26: 281–431.
398. Nord, F. F. 1940. *Chem. Revs.* 26: 422–472.
399. Nord, F. F. and W. Engel. 1938. *Biochem. Z.* 296: 153–170.
400. Nord, F. F. and L. J. Sciarini. 1946. *Arch. Biochem.* 9: 419–437.
401. Nord, F. F. and J. C. Vitucci. 1947. *Arch. Biochem.* 14: 229–241.
402. Nord, F. F. and J. C. Vitucci. 1948. *Advances in Enzymol.* 8: 253–298.
403. Nord, F. F. and S. Weiss. 1951. In J. B. Sumner, and K. Myrbäck (eds.), *The Enzymes,* Vol. 2 (1), p. 684–790.
404. Ohara, Y. 1952. *J. Agr. Chem. Soc. Japan* 26: 547–551.
405. Olson, J. A. 1954. *Nature (London)* 174: 695–696.
406. Oroshnik, W., L. C. Vining, A. D. Mebane, and W. A. Taber. 1955. *Science* 121: 147–149.
407. Ottke, R. C., E. L. Tatum, I. Zabin, and K. Bloch. 1951. *J. Biol. Chem.* 189: 429–443.
408. Oxford, A. E. and H. Raistrick. 1932. *Biochem. J. (London)* 26: 1902–1906.
409. Oxford, A. E. and H. Raistrick. 1933. *Biochem. J. (London)* 27: 1473–1478.
410. Oxford, A. E. and H. Raistrick. 1934. *Biochem. J. (London)* 28: 1321–1324.
411. Oxford, A. E., H. Raistrick, and P. Simonart. 1939. *Biochem. J. (London)* 33: 240–248.
412. Pauson, P. L. 1955. *Chem. Revs.* 55: 9–136.
413. Pearson, L. K. and H. S. Raper. 1927. *Biochem. J. (London)* 21: 875–879.
414. Perlman, D. 1948. *Am. J. Botany* 35: 360–363.
415. Perlman, D. 1949. *Am. J. Botany* 36: 180–184.
416. Perlman, D. 1950a. *Am. J. Botany* 37: 237–241.
417. Perlman, D. 1950b. *Botan. Rev.* 16: 449–523.
418. Perlman, D. 1950c. *Bull. Torrey Botan. Club* 77: 103–109.
419. Perlman, D. 1951. *Am. J. Botany* 38: 652–658.
420. Perlman, D., D. A. Kita, and W. H. Peterson. 1946. *Arch. Biochem.* 11: 123–129.
421. Perlman, D. and E. O'Brien. 1953. *Bacteriol. Proc. (Soc. Am. Bacteriologists)* 1953: 20.
422. Perwozwansky, W. W. 1930. *Zentr. Bakteriol. Parasitenk. Abt. II,* 81: 372–392.
423. Peterson, D. H. and H. C. Murray. 1952. *J. Am. Chem. Soc.* 74: 1871–1872.

424. Plotho, O. von. 1940. *Arch. Mikrobiol.* 11: 33–72.
425. Pontillon, C. 1930. *Compt. rend.* (*Paris*) 191: 1148–1151.
426. Porges, N. 1932. *Botan. Gaz.* 94: 197–205.
427. Porter, J. W. and R. E. Lincoln. 1950. *Arch. Biochem.* 27: 390–403.
427a. Posternak, T. 1940. *Helv. Chim. Acta* 23: 1046–1053.
428. Prill, E. A., P. R. Wenck, and W. H. Peterson. 1935. *Biochem. J.* (*London*) 29: 21–33.
429. Raaf, H. 1941. *Arch. Mikrobiol.* 12: 131–182.
430. Raistrick, H. 1950. *Proc. Roy. Soc.* (*London*) B 136: 481–508.
431. Raistrick, H., R. Robinson, and D. E. White. 1936. *Biochem. J.* (*London*) 30: 1303–1314.
432. Raistrick, H. and P. Simonart. 1933. *Biochem. J.* (*London*) 27: 628–633.
433. Raistrick, H. and G. Smith. 1935. *Biochem. J.* (*London*) 29: 606–611.
434. Raistrick, H. and G. Smith. 1936. *Biochem. J.* (*London*) 30: 1315–1322.
435. Raistrick, H., C. E. Stickings, and R. Thomas. 1953. *Biochem. J.* (*London*) 55: 421–433.
436. Raistrick, H. and J. Ziffer. 1951. *Biochem. J.* (*London*) 49: 563–574.
437. Ralph, B. J. and A. Robertson. 1950. *J. Chem. Soc.* (*London*) 1950: 3380–3383.
438. Ramachandran, K. and T. K. Walker. 1951. *Arch. Biochem. Biophys.* 31: 224–233.
439. Ramachandran, K. and T. K. Walker. 1952. *Arch. Biochem. Biophys.* 35: 195–203.
440. Ramakrishnan, C. V. and B. N. Banerjee. 1952. *Arch. Biochem. Biophys.* 37: 131–135.
441. Raper, K. B. and C. Thom. 1949. *A Manual of the Penicillia.* Baltimore: The Williams and Wilkins Co., pp. 875.
442. Raveux, R. 1948. *Bull. soc. chim. biol.* 30: 346–357, 357–366.
443. Raveux, R. 1954. *Compt. rend.* (*Paris*) 238: 1150–1152.
444. Rebstock, M. C., H. M. Crooks, Jr., J. Controulis, and Q. R. Bartz. 1949. *J. Am. Chem. Soc.* 71: 2458–2462.
444a. Ribéreaux-Gayon, J. et al. 1955. *Bull. soc. chim. biol.* 37: 1055–1076.
445. Rich, S. and J. G. Horsfall. 1954. *Proc. Natl. Acad. Sci. U. S.* 40: 139–145.
446. Rippel, A. 1940. *Arch. Mikrobiol.* 11: 271–284.
447. Rippel, A. and G. Behr. 1934. *Arch. Mikrobiol.* 5: 561–577.
448. Rippel, A. and J. Keseling. 1930. *Arch. Mikrobiol.* 1: 60–77.
449. Rolinson, G. N. 1954. *J. Gen. Microbiol.* 11: 412–419.
450. Rotini, O. T., E. Dammann, and F. F. Nord. 1936. *Biochem. Z.* 288: 414–420.
451. Ruelius, H. W. and A. Gauhe. 1950. *Ann. Chemie Liebigs* 569: 38–59.
452. Saito, K. 1907. *Botan. Mag.* (*Tokyo*) 21: 7–11.
453. Saito, K. 1911. *Centr. Bakteriol. Parasitenk. Abt. II,* 29: 289–290.
454. Sakaguchi, K., T. Asai, and H. Munekata. 1942. *Bull. Agr. Chem. Soc. Japan* 18: 60.
455. Sakaguchi, K. and S. Baba. 1942a. *Bull. Agr. Chem. Soc. Japan* 18: 85–86.
456. Sakaguchi, K. and S. Baba. 1942b. *Bull. Agr. Chem. Soc. Japan* 18: 95.
457. Sakaguchi, K. and T. Inoue. 1940. *Bull. Agr. Chem. Soc. Japan* 16: 158.
458. Sakaguchi, K., T. Inoue, and S. Tada. 1939. *Zentr. Bakteriol. Parasitenk. Abt. II,* 100: 302–307.
459. Sakaguchi, K. and S. Murao. 1950. *J. Agr. Chem. Soc. Japan* 23: 411.
460. Sakaguchi, K., H. Takahashi, and J. Kataoka. 1951. *J. Agr. Chem. Soc. Japan* 25: 180–185.
461. Satina, S. and A. F. Blakeslee. 1928. *Proc. Natl. Acad. Sci. U. S.* 14: 308–316.
462. Schatz, A., K. Savard, and I. J. Pintner. 1949. *J. Bacteriol.* 58: 117–125.
463. Schopfer, W. H. and E. C. Grob. 1952. *Experientia* 8: 140.
464. Schreyer, R. 1928. *Biochem. Z.* 202: 131–158.
465. Schreyer, R. 1931. *Biochem Z.* 240: 295–325.

466. Schulz, G. 1937. *Planta* 27: 196–218.
467. Sebek, O. K. 1953. *Proc. Soc. Exp. Biol. Med.* 84: 170–172.
468. Sekizawa, Y. 1955. *J. Biochem.* (*Tokyo*) 42: 217–219.
469. Sheng, T. C. and C. Sheng. 1952. *Genetics* 37: 264–269.
470. Shimazono, H. 1955. *J. Biochem.* (*Tokyo*) 42: 321–340.
471. Shipe, W. F., Jr. 1951. *Arch. Biochem.* 30: 165–179.
472. Shu, P. and M. J. Johnson. 1948a. *Ind. Eng. Chem.* 40: 1202–1205.
473. Shu, P. and M. J. Johnson. 1948b. *J. Bacteriol.* 56: 577–585.
474. Simonart, P. and P. Godin. 1951. *Bull. soc. chim. Belges* 60: 446–448.
475. Singh, J. and T. K. Walker. 1956. *Biochem. J.* (*London*) 62: 286–289.
476. Sisler, H. D. and C. E. Cox. 1954. *Am. J. Botany* 41: 338–345.
477. Smith, R. A. and I. C. Gunsalus. 1955. *Nature* (*London*) 175: 774–775.
478. Smith, V. M. 1949. *Arch. Biochem.* 22: 275–287.
479. Stanier, R. Y. 1948. *J. Bacteriol.* 55: 447–493.
480. Stanier, R. Y. and O. Hayaishi. 1951. *Science* 114: 326–330.
481. Stanier, R. Y. and J. L. Ingraham. 1954. *J. Biol. Chem.* 210: 799–808.
482. Stärkle, M. 1924. *Biochem. Z.* 151: 371–415.
483. Stefaniak, J. J., F. B. Gailey, C. S. Brown, and M. J. Johnson. 1946. *Ind. Eng. Chem.* 38: 666–671.
484. Stefaniak, J. J., F. B. Gailey, F. G. Jarvis, and M. J. Johnson. 1946. *J. Bacteriol.* 52: 119–128.
485. Steinberg, M. P. and Z. J. Ordal. 1954. *J. Agr. Food Chem.* 2: 873–877.
486. Steiner, M. and H. Heinemann. 1954. *Naturwiss.* 41: 40–41.
487. Stephens, C. R. et al. 1954. *J. Am. Chem. Soc.* 76: 3568–3575.
488. Stern, A. M., Z. J. Ordal, and H. O. Halvorson. 1954. *J. Bacteriol.* 68: 24–27.
489. Stevens, C. M., P. Vohra, and C. W. DeLong. 1954. *J. Biol. Chem.* 211: 297–300.
490. Stevens, C. M., P. Vohra, E. Inamine, and O. A. Roholt, Jr. 1953. *J. Biol. Chem.* 205: 1001–1006.
491. Stewart, W. D., W. L. Wachtel, J. J. Shipman, and J. A. Yanko. 1955. *Science* 122: 1271–1272.
492. Stodola, F. H., M. Friedkin, A. J. Moyer, and R. D. Coghill. 1945. *J. Biol. Chem.* 161: 739–742.
493. Stodola, F. H., O. L. Shotwell, and L. B. Lockwood. 1952. *J. Am. Chem. Soc.* 74: 5415–5418.
494. Stokoe, W. N. 1928. *Biochem. J.* (*London*) 22: 80–93.
495. Subramaniam, V., H. B. Stent, and T. K. Walker. 1929. *J. Chem. Soc.* (*London*) 1929: 2485–2492.
496. Sumiki, Y. 1929. *Bull. Agr. Chem. Soc. Japan* 5: 10–13.
497. Sumiki, Y. 1931. *Bull. Agr. Chem. Soc. Japan* 7: 62–63.
498. Sumner, J. B. and G. F. Somers. 1953. *Enzymes,* 3d ed. New York: Academic Press, pp. 462.
499. Sussman, A. S., P. Coughey, and J. C. Strain. 1955. *Am. J. Botany* 42: 810–815.
500. Sussman, A. S. and C. L. Markert. 1953. *Arch. Biochem. Biophys.* 45: 31–40.
501. Takahashi, T. and T. Asai. 1932. *J. Agr. Chem. Soc. Japan* 8: 652–658. (*Chem. Abstr.* 26: 5602. 1932.)
502. Takahashi, T. and T. Asai. 1933. *Zentr. Bakteriol. Parasitenk. Abt. II,* 89: 81–84.
503. Takahashi, T. and K. Sakaguchi. 1927. *Bull. Agr. Chem. Soc. Japan* 3: 59–62.
504. Tamiya, H. 1932. *Acta Phytochim.* (*Japan*) 6: 1–129.
505. Tatum, E. L. 1944. *Ann. Rev. Biochem.* 13: 667–704.
506. Tatum, E. L. and S. R. Gross. 1956. *J. Biol. Chem.* 219: 797–807.
507. Tatum, E. L., S. R. Gross, G. Ehrensvärd, and L. Garnjobst. 1954. *Proc. Natl. Acad. Sci. U. S.* 40: 271–276.
508. Terroine, E. F., R. Bonnet, G. Kopp, and J. Véchot. 1927. *Bull. soc. chim. biol.* 9: 605–620.

509. Thaler, H. and G. Geist. 1939. *Biochem. Z.* 302: 121–136.
510. Thaler. H., A. Schottmayer, I. Stählin, and H. Beck. 1949. *Biochem. Z.* 320: 87–98.
511. Thaler, H. and I. Stählin. 1949. *Biochem. Z.* 320: 84–86.
512. Thibodeau, R. and H. Macy. 1942. *Minn. Univ. Agr. Exp. Sta. Tech. Bull.* 152: 1–56.
513. Thies, W. 1930. *Zentr. Bakteriol. Parasitenk. Abt. II,* 82: 321–347.
514. Thies, W. 1931. *Ber. deut. chem. Ges.* 64B: 214–218.
515. Thom, C. and J. N. Currie. 1916. *J. Agr. Research* 7: 1–15.
516. Thorn, J. A. and M. J. Johnson. 1950. *J. Am. Chem. Soc.* 72: 2052–2058.
517. Tome, J., H. D. Zook, R. B. Wagner, and R. W. Stone. 1953. *J. Biol. Chem.* 203: 251–255.
518. Tomlinson, N., J. J. R. Campbell, and P. C. Trussell. 1951. *J. Bacteriol.* 61: 17–25.
519. Tóth, G. and G. Bársony. 1943. *Enzymologia* 11: 19–23.
520. Treccani, V., N. Walker, and G. H. Wiltshire. 1954. *J. Gen. Microbiol.* 11: 341–348.
521. Turfitt, G. E. 1943. *Biochem. J. (London)* 37: 115–117.
522. Turfitt, G. E. 1944a. *Biochem. J. (London)* 38: 492–496.
523. Turfitt, G. E. 1944b. *J. Bacteriol.* 47: 487–493.
524. Turfitt, G. E. 1946. *Biochem. J. (London)* 40: 79–81.
525. Turfitt, G. E. 1947. *J. Bacteriol.* 54: 557–562.
526. Turfitt, G. E. 1948. *Biochem. J. (London)* 42: 376–383.
527. Turian, G. 1952. *Experientia* 8: 302.
528. Turian, G. and F. T. Haxo. 1952. *J. Bacteriol.* 63: 690–691.
529. Turian, G. and F. T. Haxo. 1954. *Botan. Gaz.* 115: 254–260.
530. Tytell, A. A. et al. 1955. *Antibiotics Annual 1954/55:* 716–718.
531. Van Lanen, J. M. and F. W. Tanner, Jr. 1948. *Vitamins and Hormones* 6: 163–224.
532. Vercellone, A. and L. Mamoli. 1937. *Z. physiol. Chem. Hoppe-Seyler's.* 248: 277–279.
533. Verujski, D. 1887. *Ann. inst. Pasteur* 1: 369–391.
534. Vining, L. C., W. A. Taber, and F. J. Gregory. 1955. *Antibiotics Annual 1954/55:* 980–987.
535. Wain, R. L. and E. H. Wilkinson. 1946. *Ann. Appl. Biol.* 33: 401–405.
536. Waksman, S. A. and I. J. Hutchings. 1937. *J. Am. Chem. Soc.* 59: 545–547.
537. Wald, G. 1951. *Science* 113: 287–291.
538. Walker, T. K. 1949. *Advances in Enzymol.* 9: 537–584.
539. Walker, T. K., V. Subramaniam, and F. Challenger. 1927. *J. Chem. Soc. (London)* 1927: 3044–3054.
540. Ward, G. E., L. B. Lockwood, O. E. May, and H. T. Herrick. 1935. *Ind. Eng. Chem.* 27: 318–322.
541. Ward, G. E., L. B. Lockwood, O. E. May, and H. T. Herrick. 1936. *J. Am. Chem. Soc.* 58: 1286–1288.
542. Ward, G. E., L. B. Lockwood, B. Tabenkin, and P. A. Wells. 1938. *Ind. Eng. Chem.* 30: 1233–1235.
543. Webley, D. M. and P. C. DeKock. 1952. *Biochem. J. (London)* 51: 371–375.
544. Webley, D. M., R. B. Duff, and V. C. Farmer. 1955. *J. Gen. Microbiol.* 13: 361–369.
545. Wehmer, C. 1891. *Botan. Ztg.* 49: 233–246, 249–257, 271–280, 289–298, 305–313, 321–332, 337–346, 353–363, 369–374, 385–396, 401–407, 417–428, 433–439, 449–455, 465–478, 511–518.
546. Wehmer, C. 1893a. *Bull. soc. chim. biol.,* 3 Sér. 9: 728–730.
547. Wehmer, C. 1893b. *Compt. rend. (Paris)* 117: 332–333.
548. Wehmer, C. 1897. *Chem. Ztg.* 21: 1022–1023.

549. Wehmer, C. 1918. *Ber. deut. chem. Ges.* 51B: 1663–1668.
550. Wehmer, C. 1928. *Biochem. Z.* 197: 418–432.
551. Weiss, B. 1953. *J. Biol. Chem.* 201: 31–43.
552. Weiss, S., J. V. Fiore, and F. F. Nord. 1947. *Arch. Biochem.* 15: 326–328.
553. Wells, P. A., A. J. Moyer, and O. E. May. 1936. *J. Am. Chem Soc.* 58: 555–558.
554. Wells, P. A. et al. 1937. *Ind. Eng. Chem.* 29: 653–656.
555. Welsch, M. and C. Heugshem. 1948. *Compt. rend soc. biol.* 142: 1074–1076.
556. Wenck, P. R., W. H. Peterson, and H. C. Greene. 1935. *Zentr. Bakteriol. Parasitenk. Abt. II*, 92: 324–330.
557. Wettstein, A. 1955. *Experientia* 11: 465–479.
558. Whitfield, G. B. et al. 1955. *J. Am. Chem. Soc.* 77: 4799–4801.
559. Williamson, C. E. 1950. *Phytopathology* 40: 205–208.
560. Witter, R. F. and E. Stotz. 1946. *Arch. Biochem.* 9: 331–339.
561. Woodbine, M., M. E. Gregory, and T. K. Walker. 1951. *J. Exp. Botany* 2: 204–211.
562. Woodruff, H. B. and J. W. Foster. 1943. *Arch. Biochem.* 2: 301–315.
563. Woodward, R. B. and G. Singh. 1949. *J. Am. Chem. Soc.* 71: 758–759.
564. Wosilait, W. D. and A. Nason. 1954. *J. Biol. Chem.* 206: 255–270.
565. Wosilait, W. D., A. Nason, and A. J. Terrell. 1954. *J. Biol. Chem.* 206: 271–282.
566. Wright, B. E. 1951. *Arch. Biochem. Biophys.* 31: 332–333.
567. Wünschendorff, H. and C. Killian. 1928. *Compt. rend. (Paris)* 187: 572–574.
568. Yabuta, T. 1924. *J. Chem. Soc. (London)* 125: 575–587.
569. Yamamoto, G. 1950. *Symposium Enzyme Chemistry (Japan)* 5: 74–81. (*Chem. Abstr.* 45: 8079. 1951.)
570. Yasuda, S., H. Hori, and A. Hibiya. 1951. *J. Agr. Chem. Soc. Japan* 25: 357–361.
571. Young, R. E., H. K. Pratt, and J. B. Biale. 1951. *Plant Physiol.* 26: 304–310.
572. Zalokar, M. 1954. *Arch. Biochem. Biophys.* 50: 71–80.
573. Zalokar, M. 1955. *Arch. Biochem. Biophys.* 56: 318–325.
574. Zeller, S. M. 1916. *Ann. Missouri Botan. Garden* 3: 439–509.
575. Zellner, J. 1907. *Chemie der höheren Pilze.* Leipzig: W. Engelmann, pp. 257.
576. Zellner, J. and E. Zikmunda. 1930. *Monatsh. Chem.* 56: 200–203.
577. ZoBell, C. E. 1950. *Advances in Enzymol.* 10: 443–486.

7. Respiration

R̲espiration in the most general sense includes all cellular oxidations which yield energy, or could yield energy, to the cell. In this chapter, after touching on a few general problems, we shall consider primarily those reactions which are or may be part of organized respiratory systems. Many individual reactions described in the preceding chapter undoubtedly yield energy, but their relation to the major pathways of respiration is not yet known.

Respiration may be aerobic or anaerobic. Aerobic respiration is defined by the fact that the ultimate hydrogen acceptor is molecular oxygen; in anaerobic respiration, or fermentation, hydrogen from substrate is transferred to compounds other than oxygen (107). Use of the term "fermentation" to describe an aerobic process is misleading.

The maximum energy available from a reaction or sequence of reactions is, of course, the free energy change; thus, complete aerobic oxidation of glucose to carbon dioxide and water involves a change in free energy of approximately $-700,000$ calories per mole under standard conditions. Some fraction of this energy is trapped by the cell and used for energy-requiring reactions. So far as we now know, the size of the fraction so trapped depends on the ability of the organism to couple the oxidation to phosphorylation of adenosine monophosphate or adenosine diphosphate to yield adenosinetriphosphate (ATP). In turn, the hydrolysis of ATP is coupled to energy-requiring reactions. The common practice of describing ATP and similar compounds as having "high energy" phosphate bonds is ambiguous (103). In general, most of the oxidative phosphorylations associated with glucose or other substrate oxidations are carried out at the cofactor level; electrons from substrate are passed along a chain of respiratory carriers to oxygen and in the process, in ways still unknown in detail, the energy released in electron transfer is used to form ATP. Substrate-level phosphorylations occur in the anaerobic conversion of glucose to ethanol and carbon dioxide—the Embden-Meyerhof pathway—and, possibly, in the oxidative decarboxylation of α-ketoglutaric acid.

As described briefly in Chapter 9, fungi during growth transform inorganic into organic phosphate. Organic phosphorus compounds which have been identified in fungi and actinomycetes include sugar phosphates (38, 94, 134), adenosine phosphates (9, 162, 219), and various of the other known nucleotides (9). A mycelial extract of *Rhizopus nigricans* has myokinase activity (228), catalyzing the reversible transphosphorylation:

$$2 \text{ adenosine diphosphate} \rightleftharpoons \text{adenosinetriphosphate} +$$
$$\text{adenosinemonophosphate} \qquad (1)$$

The utilization of ATP to phosphorylate organic molecules is implicit in the two major respiratory pathways for glucose, both of which start with glucose-6-phosphate. There is very suggestive evidence that ATP generated by oxidative processes is involved in the streaming of the myxomycete *Physarum polycephalum* as it is in muscular contraction (3, 177, 303, 304, 305).

1. PROBLEMS OF METHOD

The respiration of whole cells and of extracts is usually measurable in terms of gas exchange—oxygen uptake or carbon dioxide formation. The basic instrument in most laboratories is the Warburg-Barcroft constant-volume manometer, described in the manuals of Dixon (77) and Umbreit et al. (308). Macrorespirometers with larger capacity have been designed (170, 188, 282, 328), and a few studies on fungi have been performed with more sensitive manometric apparatus (78, 214, 324). An amperometric procedure for measuring oxygen utilization has been applied successfully in studies on *Penicillium chrysogenum* (52).

Dye reduction methods have a more limited application but are useful in some problems. The best known is that of Thunberg (298), which depends on the reduction of methylene blue coupled to oxidation of substrate:

Substrate + oxidized dye → oxidized substrate + reduced dye   (2)

The Thunberg method has been used to demonstrate the presence of respiratory enzymes in cell-free extracts from fungi (182, 226). Methylene blue is often inhibitory (271) and other dyes, e.g., 2,6-dichlorophenolindophenol, are in general to be preferred (30, 207, 216, 225).

Spectrophotometric methods are both more powerful and more quantitative. The most generally useful of these relies upon the fact that the reduced forms of the coenzymes diphosphopyridine nucleotide (DPN) and triphosphopyridine nucleotide (TPN) absorb strongly at 340 mμ; the change in density can be followed easily and rapidly after addition of substrate to a suitable system (312). Examples of the use of this method in studies of fungi and actinomycetes include work on the enzymes of *Neurospora crassa* (81, 301), *Aspergillus niger* (148), *Fusarium lini* (62), and *Streptomyces coelicolor* (66).

Spectrophotometric measurements can, of course, be used whenever a component of the system changes its light absorption as a consequence of an enzymatic reaction. Oxidation and reduction of cytochrome c can be followed at 550 mμ (46, 47, 71, 280), or reducible dyes may be used (50).

Like all other sensitive measurements, the spectrophotometric requires a certain amount of judgment. Too often, a crude enzyme preparation contains unsuspected activities which complicate a given determination. For example, an extract may reduce both DPN and TPN when fructose-1,6-diphosphate is added. The DPN reduction is straightforward: aldolase forms triose phosphate, which is then oxidized with concurrent reduction of the coenzyme. The reduction of TPN is not, however, as might first be thought, the same process; instead, fructose-1,6-diphosphate is first converted to glucose-6-phosphate, which is oxidized by glucose-6-phosphate dehydrogenase and TPN to 6-phosphogluconate. The crude experiment falsely suggests that triose phosphate dehydrogenase can react with either DPN or TPN.

These manometric and spectrophotometric methods are general in their application and therefore stand in contrast to the problem of preparing cells and extracts of fungi for respirometric study. In a certain sense, each organism is a problem in itself, but it may be useful here to mention some of the methods which have been used in particular instances. Discs of growing mycelium from a surface culture may be transferred to a respirometer flask (36, 78, 214, 313), but most workers have preferred to use when possible the more homogeneous mycelium obtained from shaken or aerated cultures (65, 70, 102, 163). The mycelium from such cultures is often in the form of small pellets; if these are too large, above 0.4 mm. for *Myrothecium verrucaria* (70), the rate of diffusion of oxygen into the interior of the pellet may be limiting. Either surface or shake culture mycelium may be homogenized briefly, but there is a considerable risk that mechanical injury may reduce respiratory capacity (70, 80).

The preparation of active cell-free extracts from fungi is an even more vexing problem. We may list here, in outline, some of the methods which have been successful:

1. Hand grinding with abrasives (7, 44, 50, 65, 71, 140, 182, 301).
2. Acetone drying (14, 129, 212, 288).
3. Physical drying, with or without a preliminary freezing (89, 155, 204, 218, 331).
4. Mechanical disruption in a ball mill (240) or in a motor-driven homogenizer (46, 274).
5. Freezing, followed by grinding with abrasives or by homogenization (190, 201, 258, 274).
6. Sonic oscillation (210, 264).
7. Disruption in the Hughes press (142) or in a small-orifice press (55, 200, 228).
8. Treatment of frozen mycelium with dilute ammonium hydroxide, followed by mild pressure (148).

Of these, the most generally useful appear to be hand grinding with sand or powdered glass, sonic oscillation, and treatment in the Hughes or similar presses. Hugo (143) reviews the methods available for the preparation of extracts from bacteria.

Suspending media for extraction may be water, phosphate buffer, or salt mixtures. Protective materials are often essential—both cysteine (62, 209) and ethylenediaminetetraacetate (110) protect against inactivation of enzymes by heavy metals liberated during the extraction process.

During the preparation of cell-free extracts the terminal respiratory system is usually disrupted and must be replaced by an added hydrogen carrier or hydrogen acceptor. Methylene blue, 2,6-dichlorophenol-indophenol, and other dyes have often been used; phenazine derivatives (76), ferricyanide (134, 235), and manganese dioxide (133) are of value for the same purpose.

2. FACTORS IN RESPIRATION

In general, it is probable that the most important factor in respiration is the species. Few comparative data are available, but we may assume that fungi which can grow on a given substrate can also oxidize it (291), so that the omnivorous saprophytes, e.g., *Aspergillus* spp., may be expected to oxidize a greater variety of compounds than do nutritionally more specialized forms. Within a given species, age and developmental status are the primary non-environmental factors; the permeability of the cell is also presumed to be important by the usual indirect evidence. The principal external factors are acidity, temperature, oxygen pressure, carbon dioxide, and accessory nutrients.

Age and Developmental Status. As mentioned in Chapter 1, the highest respiratory activity is usually found during the period of most rapid growth. Subsequent to this period, respiration, especially endogenous respiration, falls off with increasing age. This may, of course, reflect only the fact that more and more dead cells accumulate in the older mycelium; quite possibly, the respiration of the growing tips of the thallus is independent of the age of the culture so long as nutrients are available.

The data of Figure 1 are typical, and many others of the same type have been reported in studies of fungi and aerobic actinomycetes (52, 70, 95, 96, 115, 134, 163, 249). *Ustilago zeae* appears unusual, in that once the maximum respiratory rate is reached it is maintained (260).

Spore respiration is considered briefly in Chapter 12; there is as yet no reason to think that it differs fundamentally from that of mycelium, although it would not be surprising to find generally higher activity in germinating spores than in older cultures. The yeast phase of *Blastomyces brasiliensis* exhibits an endogenous oxygen uptake greater than that of the mycelial form (215), and the same relation prevails between cell types of *Mucor guillermondii* (179). In *Blastocladiella emersonii* the two different types of mature thallus differ in their content of important respiratory enzymes and, presumably, in their respiratory pathways (44). Oxygen consumption of *Dictyostelium discoideum* is in part a function of developmental stage (116).

Cell Permeability. It is difficult to distinguish between intrinsic inability of a cell to respire an exogenous substrate and failure of the compound to penetrate to the interior of the cell. As in the utilization of organic acids for growth (Chapter 3), it is often found that a low pH is required for or accelerates the oxidation of organic acids

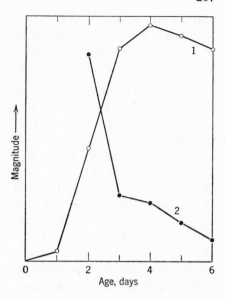

Figure 1. The effect of culture age on the endogenous respiration of *Fusarium solani* mycelium. Curve 1, dry weight of culture; curve 2, respiratory rate, in μl oxygen per milligram dry cells per hour.

(93) or that provision of an ester of the acid increases its biological effect (13). Or, intact cells of a fungus may fail to oxidize a substrate while cell-free extracts do so rapidly (13, 65, 89, 258). All of these types of evidence suggest that the intact cell is impermeable to the substrate. In general, ionizable substances, e.g., phosphorylated compounds and organic acids, are the most likely to be excluded by a permeability barrier.

However, failure of exogenous substrate to be utilized cannot always be ascribed to membrane impermeability. Thus, in yeast, frozen cells are permeable to citrate but metabolize it only after further treatment with chloroform (90). It is possible for enzymes in the cell to be inaccessible by virtue of subcellular organization; in most cases we cannot distinguish between this situation and true membrane effects.

Induction of Respiratory Enzymes. The enzymes of whatever fundamental respiratory pathways an organism has are probably always present whatever the substrate. But it is often observed that some compounds are oxidized only after a long lag or only if the cells have previously been grown in contact with them. This suggests that certain enzymes, probably those concerned in the preliminary steps of respiratory breakdown, are not constitutive but are induced by substrate. The oxidation of phenylacetic acid is an example (Chapter 6), and attack on other aromatic compounds by *Hormodendrum* sp.

appears also to require the formation of inducible enzymes (127). In *Streptomyces coelicolor* gluconic acid and pentoses are oxidized only by specifically adapted cells (66). In none of these cases just cited, however, has the specific enzyme been isolated and studied as such.

Acidity and Respiration. In most experiments reported, the pH of the suspending medium has little effect on endogenous metabolism over the range pH 5 to 8 (3, 70, 187), and the data of Figure 2 are typical of many. Exceptions to this general rule have, however, occasionally been found (93, 127, 214). Acidity is more apt to be important in substrate respiration, e.g., the oxidation of phenylacetic acid by *Penicillium chrysogenum* (135) and of glucose by *Streptomyces griseus* (134). Since the internal pH of the intact cell is probably protected against all but the most extreme changes in the medium, it seems likely that pronounced pH effects on respiration of undissociated compounds or of very weak acids signify that surface-located enzymes are involved in the total process of metabolism.

Phosphate buffers are the most generally satisfactory for respirometric studies; others, particularly acetate, are often toxic (Chapter 1).

Temperature. Most respirometric studies of saprophytic fungi and actinomycetes are performed at moderate temperature, 20–30°C; higher temperatures are more suitable for the fungi pathogenic to animals (215). Carbon dioxide evolution from growing mycelium of *Aspergillus niger* has a high Q_{10} at low temperature, e.g., 312 over the range 7–17°; the Q_{10} drops as the temperature is raised, and is only 1.7 over the range 27–37° (217).

Oxygen and Carbon Dioxide Pressure. The response of aerobic respiration to oxygen pressure varies with the organism studied (3, 72,

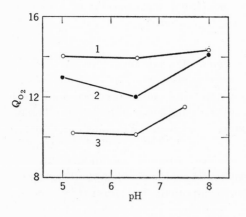

Figure 2. pH and the endogenous respiration of *Streptomyces coelicolor* (curve 1), *Myrothecium verrucaria* (curve 2) and *Fusarium solani* (curve 3) mycelium.

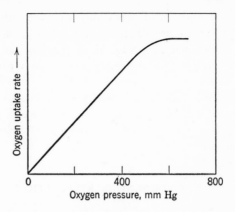

Figure 3. The effect of oxygen pressure on the rate of respiration of *Aspergillus niger.* Redrawn from P. Shu, *Journal of Agricultural and Food Chemistry,* Vol. 1, p. 1119, November 25, 1953. Copyright 1953 by the American Chemical Society and reprinted by permission of the copyright owner.

259, 260, 291). Respiration depends immediately upon dissolved oxygen, which in turn is proportional to the partial pressure of oxygen in the gas phase. Finn (83) defines C_{crit} as the concentration of dissolved oxygen above which cell respiration is independent of the oxygen concentration; data from several sources show that C_{crit} for *Penicillium chrysogenum* is about 0.022 millimoles per liter (equivalent to an oxygen tension of 16 mm of mercury), that for yeast and *Escherichia coli* considerably lower. Amperometric measurements show that the rate of oxygen utilization is independent of oxygen pressure down to very low values (52). It follows, therefore, that the requirement of many fungi, e.g., *Aspergillus niger* (Figure 3), for relatively high oxygen pressure for maximal respiratory rate means that other factors must be operative. Studies on the respiration of mycelium of *Myrothecium verrucaria* indicate that the rate of oxygen consumption by these rather active cells is limited in part by the rate at which oxygen reaches the interior of the cell mass (70).

The oxygen uptake of *Micromonospora vulgaris* is reduced by high oxygen pressure (315), but this effect is not usually encountered in the fungi.

Little evidence is available on the influence of carbon dioxide pressure on fungus respiration. Most respirometric techniques involve removal of metabolic carbon dioxide during measurement of oxygen uptake. In many bacteria oxygen uptake is in fact depressed by such removal of carbon dioxide (119). Two methods are available to determine if this occurs with any given organism: use of Warburg's "indirect" method (308) or use of diethanolamine as a carbon dioxide "buffer" (166, 231).

Nutrients. Potassium, phosphorus, and magnesium are usually supplied to respiring cells, although it is likely that endogenous reserves of these and other minerals are sufficient. Aerobic oxidation with exogenous substrate is generally markedly increased if a source of nitrogen is provided (199, 265, 275); this, of course, converts the preparation at least potentially to a growing culture carrying on amino acid or even protein synthesis with an attendant demand upon energy and upon metabolic intermediates of the citric acid cycle. The effect of such organic materials as yeast extract may be the same, but there is the added complication that respirable materials are also being supplied.

3. ENDOGENOUS RESPIRATION

Endogenous respiration, or "autorespiration," defines the metabolism of the cell in the absence of an external substrate insofar as it is expressed by gas exchange. In yeast there is normally no anaerobic endogenous carbon dioxide liberation (270), although 2,4-dinitrophenol initiates fermentation of carbohydrate reserves (251). *Fusarium lini*, on the other hand, has a vigorous endogenous fermentation (98).

The substrate of endogenous respiration in fungi is not known; respiratory quotients are consistent with lipid oxidation (186, 230), but suitable analytical data to discriminate between this and other possibilities are not available. Cell-free extracts of *Neurospora crassa* are stimulated in endogenous respiration by triphosphopyridine nucleotide (301).

Scopulariopsis brevicaulis cells are unable to assimilate nitrogen in the absence of exogenous substrate, i.e., the endogenous respiration cannot be coupled to amino acid or protein synthesis (186). This is in contrast to both *Chlorella vulgaris* (284) and *Torulopsis utilis* (332).

The high endogenous rate characteristic of many fungi and actinomycetes complicates experimental study; obviously, if some limiting terminal system is fully saturated by the endogenous system, then an addition of substrate will not cause any further increase in oxygen uptake. However, it cannot be assumed that under these circumstances the exogenous substrate is inert—conceivably some of it will be oxidized in competition with the oxidation of endogenous materials. Partial responses are also possible: if, for example, the terminal system were 50 per cent saturated by endogenous metabolism, addition of substrate could at most double the oxygen uptake rate. But—and this may be a real problem—one can imagine that in fact the substrate is competing on, say, equal terms with the endogenous metabolism for the terminal system. Were this so, not 50 per cent but 75 per cent of the total metabolism would be substrate metabolism; put another way, the endogenous system would be suppressed 50 per cent.

Barker (11) proposed a method to determine whether or not substrate utilization does suppress endogenous respiration. The method relies essentially on the assumption that the oxygen uptake per mole of substrate consumed is not affected by the concentration of substrate. Application of this technique to *Penicillium chysogenum* indicates that glucose does not suppress endogenous respiration (272). In yeast, on the other hand, suppression of endogenous respiration by acetate occurs with agar-grown cells but not with cells grown in a liquid medium (322).

A second approach to this problem is to use cells the endogenous reserves of which have been labeled by cultivation on a carbon-14 substrate (37, 244). It is essential that all of the reserves be labeled by growth from a very early stage on the isotopic substrate; a short exposure to labeled acetate, for example, may not succeed in marking all of the reserves. This method has received only a limited trial to date (25, 63, 101, 128, 203), and it is, of course, open to the criticism that not enough is known of the composition and dynamics of the many metabolic pools involved. Experimentally, it is only necessary to determine what the total activity of carbon dioxide from labeled cells is and whether or not this activity is affected by the simultaneous oxidation of substrate.

Amino acids have been reported as affecting endogenous respiration both positively (17) and negatively (93). These findings cannot at present be interpreted, since the presence of amino nitrogen in the system and the possibility of amino acid toxicity unduly complicate the picture.

Experimentally, it is often desirable or even essential to reduce the level of endogenous respiration. Starving the cells for a period of time prior to measuring their respiratory response to an exogenous substrate has been successful with some fungi and actinomycetes (34, 70, 316, 320). Others, however, lose substrate respiratory capacity during the starvation period (14, 134, 195). There is also the danger that the starvation period may result in developmental changes in the organism (145). Since endogenous respiration is affected by the composition of the growth medium (254), the better approach would seem to be an attempt to find a medium in which the cells do not accumulate reserve materials in large amounts (102). Many of the media commonly used for fungi are so concentrated that accumulation of such reserves is almost forced upon the organism.

4. OXIDATIVE ASSIMILATION

Oxidation of carbon compounds by many organisms is not accompanied by the oxygen uptake theoretically necessary to account for the known disappearance of substrate. This has been explained as the result of the assimilation of part of the utilized carbon into reserves, presumably carbohydrate in nature, of the cell (59).

Oxidative assimilation occurs in yeast (234, 322), actinomycetes (254), and fungi (70, 80, 253). Its extent may be rather high; for *Penicillium chrysogenum* (272), the data fit the equation:

$$C_6H_{12}O_6 + O_2 \rightarrow 5(CH_2O) + CO_2 + H_2O \tag{3}$$

Thus, in this organism about 83 per cent of the glucose disappearing is assimilated.

Fermentative, i.e., anaerobic, assimilation is known in yeast and bacteria (297). In what is presumably the same process, *Aspergillus niger* forms intracellular mannitol and carbohydrate anaerobically (255). Fermentative accumulation may account for the finding (154, 247) that *A. niger* forms less ethanol from glucose than the theoretical amount expected from a fermentation of the yeast type.

5. THE EMBDEN-MEYERHOF PATHWAY

The anaerobic breakdown of glucose by yeast is diagrammed in part in Figure 4. This series of reactions is of very general, although probably not universal, occurrence in microorganisms (79, 118). In muscle the reactions, termed glycolysis, are similar, except that pyruvic acid is reduced to lactic acid in the final step and that the starting material is glycogen.

Since the filamentous fungi require oxygen for growth (Chapter 1), there has been a tendency to discount the possible importance of the Embden-Meyerhof pathway. First, it should be realized that the products of glucose metabolism by other routes may feed into the pathway; thus the phosphogluconate oxidation pathway, as discussed later, forms triose phosphate. Second, the Embden-Meyerhof pathway is not restricted to anaerobic conditions; it is entirely possible for a portion of it to function simultaneously with aerobic processes or to be coupled to terminal aerobic reactions. Finally, some fungi seem to be able to ferment sugar anaerobically even though they require oxygen for growth.

Although in the bacteria there are routes of ethanol formation other

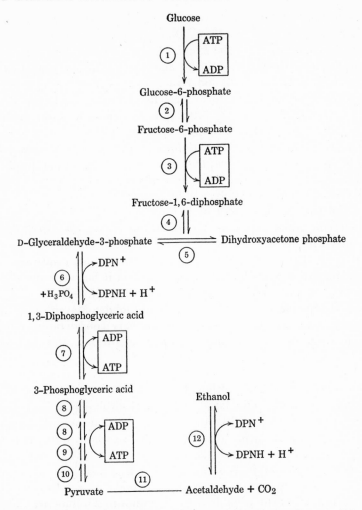

Figure 4. Schematic outline of the Embden-Meyerhof pathway of yeast. Abbreviations: ATP = adenosine triphosphate, ADP = adenosine diphosphate, DPN⁺ = diphosphopyridine nucleotide, DPNH = reduced diphosphopyridine nucleotide. Enzymes are numbered as follows:

1. Hexokinase
2. Phosphohexoisomerase
3. Phosphofructokinase
4. Aldolase
5. Triosephosphate isomerase
6. Triosephosphate dehydrogenase

7. Phosphoglyceryl kinase
8. Phosphoglyceryl mutase
9. Enolase
10. Phosphoenolpyruvic transphosphorylase
11. Pyruvic carboxylase
12. Alcohol dehydrogenase

214   RESPIRATION

than the Embden-Meyerhof, we may consider ethanol production as
at least suggestive of the pathway. Formation of ethanol from glucose
is rather common among the fungi. Early work, chiefly with species
of *Aspergillus, Fusarium, Mucor,* and *Penicillium,* is reviewed by
Wehmer (317), Czapek (69), and Foster (84). A number of the wood-
destroying basidiomycetes form detectable amounts of ethanol in
culture (178, 221, 232, 233, 319); other ethanol producers include
Ashbya gossypii (194), *Rhizopus* spp. (121, 310, 314), *Diplodia
tubericola* (121), *Dematium pullulans* (278), *Mortierella* spp. (233),
Neurospora crassa (232), *Stemphylium radicinum* (178), and, probably,
several of the Fungi Imperfecti (20). The most active producers are
in the genus *Fusarium,* and, as will be seen later, a functional Embden-
Meyerhof pathway is present in *F. lini.*

Under the usual experimental conditions ethanol is oxidized concurrently with its formation, so that an accurate stoichiometry is impossible (5, 194, 255). However, under anaerobic conditions not
permitting either growth or ethanol oxidation it has been possible to
show that the production of alcohol and carbon dioxide from glucose
follows the quantitative predictions of the Embden-Meyerhof pathway
(62, 290, 302). Species of a given genus vary considerably in their
accumulation of alcohol under growth conditions; this has been
studied especially in *Aspergillus* (21, 292, 333).

Ethanol production by fungi is generally favored by restricted
aeration (168, 285, 290), although even under conditions of rapid
aeration some fungi form large amounts of alcohol (176, 314). The
accumulation of ethanol, like that of other carbon-containing metabolites, is greatest in media relatively high in carbohydrate (146) and
low in nitrogen and minerals (243).

Ethanol oxidation in *Fusarium lini* is a special case of a more
general capacity to oxidize primary and secondary alcohols (111, 112);
ethanol is oxidized to acetaldehyde, 2-butanol to 2-butanone, and 2,3-
butylene glycol to acetoin.

Acetaldehyde, the precursor of ethanol in the yeast fermentation, is
formed, sometimes in appreciable amounts, by growing cultures or
resting preformed mats of several fungi (16, 22, 27, 171, 176, 211, 221,
255, 257, 279, 286). Most of these forms are ethanol producers, and
the acetaldehyde may be formed either as a precursor of ethanol or
during oxidation of it (112).

In the yeast fermentation small amounts of glycerol are formed;
more is produced in the presence of sulfite or at alkaline pH. The
same observations have been made with fungi (211, 287).

Pyruvic acid is frequently produced in isolatable amounts by fungi and actinomycetes (60, 131, 237, 238, 257); the presence of nitrite increases pyruvate formation by *Fusarium* spp. (220). Added thiamine decreases pyruvate accumulation (273, 323), presumably by reason of its function in diphosphothiamine, the coenzyme of pyruvic carboxylase.

The formation of ethanol, acetaldehyde, and pyruvic acid is consistent with the functioning of a pathway of the yeast type, as is the appearance of other minor products (53, 109, 237, 255, 281), but does not prove the occurrence of the pathway in any sense.

The occurrence of lactic acid among fungi has been reviewed in the preceding chapter. Among the phycomycetes, the only true fungi to form large amounts of lactate from glucose, there appear to be two different types of metabolic pattern. The lower phycomycetes so far investigated anaerobically convert virtually all of the glucose consumed to lactic acid (40, 41, 114, 145). This immediately suggests comparison to the metabolism of muscle and of the homofermentative bacteria, in both of which glucose is converted anaerobically to two moles of lactic acid via the Embden-Meyerhof pathway. The comparison must, of course, be only tentative in the absence of further data; the demonstration of a diphosphopyridine-linked lactic dehydrogenase would be of especial interest.

Members of the genus *Rhizopus* constitute the second group of lactate-forming fungi. Under anaerobiosis glucose is converted to lactic acid in 50 per cent yield; Waksman and Foster (310) suggest the over-all reaction:

$$\text{Glucose} \rightarrow \text{lactic acid} + \text{ethanol} + CO_2 \tag{4}$$

The data of Table 1 show that *R. oryzae* ferments labeled glucose as expected from the Embden-Meyerhof sequence, that is, the path of glucose carbon is presumably, in outline:

$$
\begin{array}{lll}
 & \text{C3,4} & \\
 & \text{C2,5} & \\
\text{C1} & \nearrow \text{C1,6} & \\
\text{C2} \quad \text{C3,4} & \text{Lactic acid} & \\
\text{C3} \rightarrow \text{C2,5} & & \tag{5}\\
\text{C4} \quad \text{C1,6} & & \\
\text{C5} & \searrow \text{C2,5} + \text{C3,4} & \\
\text{C6} & \text{C1,6} & \\
\text{Glucose Pyruvic acid} & \text{Ethanol} \qquad CO_2 &
\end{array}
$$

This implies that all products arise from a common pool of triose phosphate, leaving open the problem of how the 1:1 ratio of lactic acid to ethanol (Equation 4) is maintained. The conversion of pyruvate to lactate has been shown (84), and carbon-14 data suggest that a direct reduction occurs (48). *Leuconostoc mesenteroides* yields the same products as *Rhizopus* spp., but the mechanism of this heterolactic fermentation is entirely different (75).

Table 1.   The Distribution of Glucose Carbon among the Fermentation Products of *Rhizopus oryzae**

			Ethanol		Lactic Acid		
Exp.	Substrate	CO_2	CH_3	CH_2OH	COOH	CHOH	CH_3
1	Glucose-1-C^{14}	—	—	—	0.5	0.5	16.0
2	Glucose-1-C^{14}	0.5	14.1	0.9	0.2	0.2	3.8
3	Glucose-3,4-C^{14}	13.0	0	0	13.2	0.35	0.5
4	Glucose-3,4-C^{14}	—	—	—	14	0.2	0.2

* Figures represent millimicrocuries of carbon-14 in each carbon atom.   From M. Gibbs and R. Gastel, *Arch. Biochem. Biophys.* 43: 33–38 (1953), by permission of The Academic Press, Inc.

Purely enzymatic studies can establish only the possibility of the Embden-Meyerhof pathway, since most of the enzymes of the sequence are also used for disposing of the triose phosphate formed in the phosphogluconate oxidation pathway and since the enzymes, even if present, are not necessarily functional.   Pyruvic carboxylase has been detected in several fungi (62, 88, 148, 230, 274).   *Aspergillus niger* extracts contain virtually the complete battery of enzymes necessary for the conversion of glucose to ethanol and carbon dioxide (148); this is consistent with the data cited earlier indicating that some species of *Aspergillus* produce ethanol.   Several of the same enzymes appear in extracts of *Penicillium chrysogenum* (264) and *P. notatum* (182). Aldolase, one of the enzymes which is characteristic of the Embden-Meyerhof sequence, is found in *Aspergillus* spp. (7, 15a, 149, 150), *Neurospora crassa* (277), *Fusarium lini* (62), *Penicillium* spp. (182, 264), *Streptomyces coelicolor* (61), and *Tilletia caries* (212).

Ethanol production in *Fusarium* spp. has already been mentioned. Carbon balance studies, enzymatic analyses, and isotope distribution experiments agree that anaerobically the Embden-Meyerhof pathway is functional and that no other anaerobic mechanism need be postulated (62, 125).   Balance and fermentation data on *Ashbya gossypii* also implicate the yeast system (194).

Streptomyces coelicolor is unable to form either carbon dioxide or acids anaerobically; it contains, however, the enzymes necessary to convert glucose to pyruvic acid by way of the Embden-Meyerhof pathway.   The explanation for its failure to ferment seems to be that no enzymes are present which can anaerobically metabolize pyruvate and regenerate diphosphopyridine nucleotide from its reduced form (61). This biochemical lesion occurs also in certain of the bacteria (132). These data suggest that failure of certain of the true fungi, e.g., *Myrothecium verrucaria,* to ferment glucose may ultimately be traced to the same enzymatic deficiency.

In summary, the cumulative evidence for the Embden-Meyerhof pathway in at least some of the filamentous fungi is impressive. There are, however, several different variations of the pattern. *Fusarium* spp. and, probably, *Aspergillus* spp. appear to resemble yeast most closely. The enzymatic basis of the two types of lactic acid formation in the phycomycetes remains unknown, and at present it is only on the basis of comparative biochemistry that we regard these as subtypes of the Embden-Meyerhof sequence. Finally, it is possible that non-fermentative forms can utilize the pathway by coupling it to an aerobic process in which reduced coenzyme is regenerated by an oxidase system and pyruvate is metabolized via the citric acid cycle.

6. THE PHOSPHOGLUCONATE OXIDATION PATHWAY

Studies carried out during the decade 1930–1940 by Dickens, Lipmann, and Warburg and more recently by Horecker, Racker, and many others have established the occurrence of a second sequence of respiratory reactions, variously known as the "hexosemonophosphate shunt," the "direct oxidative pathway," and the "pentose phosphate cycle." The system appears to be widespread in nature, occurring in animals, plants, and microorganisms (238).

For convenience and to avoid unnecessary detail, we may, following Racker (236), divide the pathway into two phases. The first is an oxidative phase, in which glucose-6-phosphate is transformed to pentose phosphate via 6-phosphogluconic acid; carbon atom 1 of glucose, the aldehyde carbon, is converted to carbon dioxide in the process:

Glucose-6-phosphate $+ \text{TPN}^+ \rightarrow$ 6-phosphogluconic acid
$$+ \text{TPNH} + \text{H}^+ \qquad (6)$$

6-Phosphogluconic acid $+ \text{TPN}^+ \rightarrow$ pentose phosphate
$$+ \text{TPNH} + \text{H}^+ + \text{CO}_2 \qquad (7)$$

The key enzymes of this phase are glucose-6-phosphate dehydrogenase (Equation 6) and 6-phosphogluconic acid dehydrogenase (Equation 7); both are linked to triphosphopyridine nucleotide (TPN). Reaction 7 is probably the sum of two reactions. It is assumed that the aerobic reoxidation of reduced coenzyme (TPNH) occurs and that in the process the energy of the oxidation is utilized for synthesis of adenosine triphosphate or related compounds. The phosphogluconate pathway is an aerobic system; evidence for an analogous fermentative pathway is summarized by Gunsalus et al. (118).

The first pentose phosphate formed, i.e., the product of Equation 7, is ribulose-5-phosphate; this rapidly comes into enzymatic equilibrium with two other pentose phosphates, ribose-5-phosphate and xylulose-5-phosphate.

The second phase of the sequence is a complex series of non-oxidative conversions of the pentose phosphates into other phosphorylated sugars. Direct intermediates in this phase include sedoheptulose-7-phosphate, glyceraldehyde-3-phosphate, a tetrose-4-phosphate (probably erythrose-4-phosphate), and fructose-6-phosphate. Since glucose-6-phosphate is regenerated, this second phase may be summarized:

$$6 \text{ Pentose phosphate} \rightarrow 5 \text{ glucose-6-phosphate} \qquad (8)$$

The key enzymes in this phase are transketolase and transaldolase. In the presence of enzymes of the Embden-Meyerhof sequence, still other sugar phosphates, fructose-1,6-diphosphate and sedoheptulose-1,7-diphosphate, appear; in addition a greater or less amount of the triose phosphate formed may be converted to pyruvic acid and thereby removed from the system under discussion.

It was natural to investigate the fungi for an aerobic system of this type, but so far comparatively little progress has been made toward an organized and coherent picture of the role of this cycle in the oxidative metabolism of the fungi. The evidence at hand includes three types of study: demonstration of particular enzymes, demonstration of one or more of the characteristic sugar phosphates, and study of the distribution of isotope from specifically labeled glucose.

The two dehydrogenases of the oxidative phase of the pathway have been identified in *Neurospora crassa* (213), *Tilletia caries* (212), and *Streptomyces coelicolor* (66). Extracts of *Aspergillus niger* contain glucose-6-phosphate dehydrogenase (147).

The conversion of pentose phosphate to hexose phosphate and the formation of sedoheptulose phosphate and other known intermediates are easily demonstrated in cell-free preparations of both fungi and actinomycetes (64, 212, 263).

A variety of methods depending on the formation of metabolites from carbon-14 labeled glucose have been devised in an attempt to assay the quantitative importance of the phosphogluconate oxidation pathway. One group of methods is based upon the fact that operation of the phosphogluconate oxidation pathway results in a preferential liberation of the aldehyde carbon of glucose as carbon dioxide. The limitation of this approach is that glucose goes through many more metabolic pools and is more diluted in the Embden-Meyerhof than in the oxidative pathway before liberation of carbon dioxide; this results in a bias which may exaggerate the contribution of the oxidative pathway. Application of various modifications of this method indicates that there is a substantial flow of carbon over some pathway preferentially liberating carbon-1 of glucose as carbon dioxide in *Penicillium chrysogenum* (80, 124), *Aspergillus oryzae* (6), *Streptomyces coelicolor* (66), and *Neurospora crassa* (293). A modification of this method indicates that in growing mycelium of *Penicillium chrysogenum* about 60 per cent of the glucose carbon goes over the oxidative pathway (124), while in *Fusarium lini* a minimum of 17 per cent of the glucose catabolic mechanism involves preferential liberation of carbon-1 (125).

A more promising method involves determination of acetate, ethanol, pyruvate, or compounds derived therefrom during aerobic respiration of specifically labeled glucose (26, 318). Application of this technique to *Penicillium chrysogenum* suggests that the Embden-Meyerhof pathway is the principal route of glucose breakdown (172). Still other methods may be applicable but have not yet been tested in the fungi (18, 19, 23, 24, 105, 139, 156, 236, 268). Wood (327) discusses the methods critically and points out their limitations.

In *Aspergillus niger* the distribution of isotope in citric acid indicates that the Embden-Meyerhof sequence accounts for 80 per cent of the total aerobic glucose catabolism (261). Similarly, in *Ustilago zeae* the labeling of the carbohydrate moiety of the glucolipid ustilagic acid is consistent with the resynthesis of glucose from triose phosphate and consequently with the operation of the Embden-Meyerhof pathway (29). The labeling of kojic acid formed by *Aspergillus flavus* from pentose is, on the other hand, suggestive of a preliminary conversion of pentose, through the non-oxidative phase of the phosphogluconate pathway, to hexose (8).

The various approaches which attempt to utilize labeled sugars each has its own difficulties and ambiguities, and we should regard the data collected so far as preliminary and tentative. Some attempt should be made to see whether two different methods agree with regard to the same material before reliance can be placed on any single method. There seems little doubt that the phosphogluconate oxidation pathway is utilized by many fungi and actinomycetes, and it is not unreasonable to anticipate that for some it may be a major pathway of respiration or of pentose biogenesis. It is also clear that in some organisms both the oxidative and the Embden-Meyerhof systems are present and presumably complete for glucose metabolism (64). It is to be expected that cells in different physiological states will strike different balances between the two systems.

7. THE NON-PHOSPHORYLATIVE OXIDATION OF GLUCOSE

The single reaction of this type known is the oxidation of free glucose to gluconic acid (the first product is in fact glucono-δ-lactone) by the enzyme usually described as glucose oxidase or notatin. It is debatable whether this reaction can be classed as respiratory, since we know neither the subsequent metabolic history of the gluconic acid nor the way in which energy from the oxidation can be used by the cell. However, it seems likely that further study will reveal a genuine respiratory pathway.

The enzyme responsible for the oxidation of free glucose was discovered by D. Müller (205, 206) in *Aspergillus niger* and named glucose oxidase; earlier results of Maximov (193) probably involve this enzyme. Interest in it was revived by the later discovery that an antibiotic effect of *Penicillium resticulosum* and *P. notatum* is traceable to the hydrogen peroxide generated by the reaction:

$$\text{Glucose} + O_2 + H_2O \rightarrow \text{gluconic acid} + H_2O_2 \qquad (9)$$

As an antibiotic, and before its identity with the enzyme was known, the material was variously named penicillin B, notatin, and penatin.

The enzyme is a flavoprotein with two flavin adenine dinucleotide groups per molecule (158). It is highly specific for β-D-glucose; purified preparations are virtually inactive toward other common sugars (160), although 2-deoxyglucose is oxidized (267). The specificity has been taken advantage of in a manometric assay for glucose (159) and in the demonstration of the mutarotase of *Penicillium notatum* (161).

Studies with isotopic oxygen show that the enzyme transfers hydrogen from glucose to oxygen (15). It is therefore a dehydrogenase rather than an oxidase, and the name glucose aerodehydrogenase is to be preferred.

The enzyme differs from the glucose dehydrogenases of liver (120) and of *Pseudomonas fluorescens* (330), neither of which is a flavoprotein. Claims that other glucose dehydrogenases are present in fungi (207, 224, 225) have been disputed (91), and it appears that only one such enzyme is involved in the organisms studied.

The importance of the oxidation of free glucose is difficult to assess. A relatively large number of fungi form gluconic acid (Chapter 6) and we may reasonably assume that the same reaction is involved in all. However, the known glucose aerodehydrogenase has been found only in the fungi mentioned above and in *Penicillium glaucum,* apparently not occurring in *Aspergillus fumigatus, Mucor racemosus, Rhizopus nigricans,* or *Dematium pullulans* (92). As mentioned earlier, the availability of the energy of the reaction to the cell is uncertain; the hydrogen peroxide formed could, in the presence of catalase, serve as an oxidizing agent for other cell metabolites (157, 294). The further metabolism of gluconic acid is similarly obscure; the likeliest possibilities are that the gluconate is phosphorylated and enters the hexose monophosphate pathway, or that there is a continued non-phosphorylative metabolism after the pattern of the bacterial genera *Pseudomonas* and *Acetobacter* (297, 329); discovery of 2-keto-gluconic acid in small amounts in the culture fluid of *Penicillium brevi-compactum* (Chapter 6) suggests that the bacterial pathway may be worth investigation.

8. PENTOSE FERMENTATION AND OXIDATION

The fermentation of pentoses by fungi has been studied primarily as it occurs in the genus *Fusarium,* although other fungi can carry out at least a slow fermentation of pentose (221). Early results and theories on the reaction are reviewed by Foster (84), and are of historical interest only.

Resting cells of *Fusarium lini* ferment xylose in accordance with the equation:

$$C_5H_{10}O_5 \rightarrow C_2H_5OH + CH_3COOH + CO_2 \qquad (10)$$

Xylose   Ethanol   Acetate

With xylose-1-C[14] as substrate, virtually all of the label appears in the methyl carbon of acetate (98). This system resembles that of *Lactobacillus* spp. (169), with the difference that the lactic acid characteristic of the bacterial fermentation is replaced by ethanol and carbon dioxide. In *Lactobacillus pentosus* preparations the pentose chain is split between carbons 2 and 3, yielding triose phosphate and acetyl phosphate (35, 123). Presumably in *F. lini* the triose phosphate is then metabolized to ethanol and carbon dioxide—the enzymes necessary for this transformation are all present (62).

The pentose fermentation by *F. lini* is striking in another connection: there does not seem to be any conversion of pentose to hexose by the non-oxidative reactions of the phosphogluconate oxidation pathway, as described earlier for other fungi and actinomycetes and as is common in yeast and bacterial pentose metabolism (4, 99).

The oxidative breakdown of pentose by fungi has not been intensively investigated. It has been mentioned in the preceding chapter that there is one report of the oxidation of pentoses to pentonic acids; the more recent and better documented report (175) that *Pseudomonas* spp. form pentonic acids from pentose suggests that a re-examination of the problem in fungi would be of interest. *Streptomyces coelicolor* extracts oxidize xylose and ribose only if the cells have been grown on the particular sugar; indirect evidence suggests that these pentoses must be phosphorylated and that the kinase responsible is an inducible enzyme not present in glucose-grown cells (66).

9. THE CITRIC ACID CYCLE

In animal tissues the functioning of a respiratory cycle, the citric acid cycle (also called the tricarboxylic acid cycle or the Krebs cycle) is well established. The historical development of the concept has been reviewed by Krebs (165); other valuable general reviews are those of Wood (326) and Ochoa (222).

In Figure 5 the principal reactions of the citric acid cycle are outlined. It can be seen, first, that the net effect of one turn of the cycle is the complete oxidation of a 2-carbon fragment, $CH_3CO—$, to carbon dioxide and water. This acetyl fragment is known to be attached to coenzyme A, forming acetyl-coenzyme A. The first reaction in the cycle is the transfer of the acetyl fragment to oxaloacetic acid, forming citric acid. In subsequent reactions, two molecules of carbon dioxide are split off and oxaloacetic acid is regenerated. In principle, therefore, only one molecule of oxaloacetate is required, to initiate the cycle, after which the reaction becomes self-sustaining. In fact, of course, carbon is drawn off, especially for the synthesis of amino acids, so that steady state operation of the cycle under normal conditions presumably requires that 4-carbon dicarboxylic acids be formed *de novo* continually. Mechanisms are known in bacteria by which pyruvic acid, phosphoenolpyruvic acid, and propionic acid can be carboxylated by carbon dioxide fixation (118); in addition, the possibility of malate synthesis from acetate has been raised by work with bacteria (p. 227).

Viewed strictly as a respiratory system, the net effect of the cycle shown in Figure 5 is the oxidation of pyruvic acid:

$$CH_3—CO—COOH + 2.5\ O_2 \rightarrow 3\ CO_2 + 2\ H_2O \qquad (11)$$

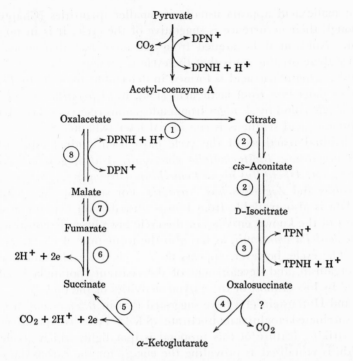

Figure 5. Schematic and simplified outline of the citric acid cycle. Abbreviations: $DPN^+ = $ diphosphopyridine nucleotide, DPNH = reduced diphosphopyridine nucleotide, $TPN^+ = $ triphosphopyridine nucleotide, TPNH = reduced triphosphopyridine nucleotide. Enzymes are numbered as follows:

1. Condensing enzyme
2. Aconitase
3. Isocitric dehydrogenase
4. Oxalosuccinic decarboxylase (?)

5. Complex system
6. Succinic dehydrogenase
7. Fumarase
8. Malic dehydrogenase

Free acetate may enter the cycle and be oxidized, by 2 moles of oxygen.

The occurrence of the cycle is well established in animal cells, and there is good evidence that it is at least potentially functional in yeast, bacteria, and higher plants. There is, however, a real question whether its major metabolic importance is in supplying the carbon skeleton of amino acids (167, 248) or whether it has an additional role in providing energy to the cell (74, 283). With the probable exception of the oxidative decarboxylation of α-ketoglutaric acid, the phosphorylations associated with the citric acid cycle are at the cofactor level.

The organic acids of the citric acid cycle which are formed in substantial amounts by fungi include succinic, citric, fumaric, and acetic acids; malic acid appears usually in smaller quantities (Chapter 6). Although their occurrence is suggestive of the cycle, it is in no sense proof. Nor can it be argued from the mere fact that intact cells oxidize these organic acids that the cycle is present.

Alpha-ketoglutaric acid is formed in detectable amounts by *Penicillium chrysogenum* from lactic acid (136), by *Aspergillus oryzae* from glucose (252), and by *A. niger* from endogenous reserves (311). Its role in glutamic acid synthesis is considered later (Chapter 8).

Individual reactions of the cycle have been studied especially in seven organisms: *Blastocladiella emersonii, Ashbya gossypii, Neurospora crassa, Aspergillus niger, Penicillium chrysogenum, Streptomyces coelicolor,* and *Zygorhynchus moelleri.* For some of these more or less data is also available from isotope distribution experiments.

Most of the known enzymes of the cycle have been demonstrated in *Blastocladiella emersonii,* as has also the formation of citrate (43, 46, 47). The cycle, however, appears to be at best weakly functional in this organism, and development of the resistant sporangia is accompanied by loss of most of the enzyme activities of the cycle (43). Cantino and Horenstein (45) have suggested that in *B. emersonii* a reductive succinate-ketoglutarate-isocitrate (S.K.I.) cycle is operative; the most striking feature of this proposal is that light, which accelerates growth, is visualized as providing the energy for the carboxylation of succinate and α-ketoglutarate.

In *Ashbya gossypii* acetate oxidation is accelerated by dicarboxylic acids, citrate is synthesized from acetate and oxalacetate, and citrate accumulation is increased by malonate (195).

Several of the characteristic enzyme activities of the cycle have been demonstrated in extracts of *Neurospora crassa* (82, 213, 258, 275). Incorporation of carbon-14 from several substrates into aspartic and glutamic acids indicates that in this fungus the citric acid cycle plays a major role in the synthesis of these amino acids (248).

Aspergillus niger is of particular interest in that some strains accumulate citric acid (Chapter 6) and in that tracer studies have been made. Enzymatic analyses are the most complete for any fungus, and show that all of the known enzymes of the citric acid cycle are present in extracts made from mycelium (190, 239, 240, 241). The enzyme systems acting upon tricarboxylic acids are rather complex: there is evidence for an aconitase of the usual type, an aconitic hydrase converting aconitate only to citrate (73, 210), and two isocitric dehydrogenases (241). Excellent agreement between the enzymatic content of cells and the accumulation of citric acid affords further evidence for the role of an interrupted tricarboxylic acid cycle in the biogenesis of citric acid (242).

Extensive studies of the incorporation of isotopic carbon into the citric acid molecule lend further and decisive support to the idea that bulk citric acid synthesis in *Aspergillus niger* occurs via the citric acid cycle. The labeling of citrate formed in the presence of $C^{14}O_2$ is consistent with fixation of carbon dioxide into oxalacetate and condensation of the oxalacetate with an acetyl fragment (191, 192, 198). Lewis and Weinhouse (174) showed experimentally that the symmetrical citric acid molecule is asymmetrically synthesized, as first suggested by Ogston (223).

Experiments with the metabolism of labeled acetic acid (28, 49, 173) similarly implicate the known initial reactions of the citric acid cycle in the synthesis of citrate by *A. niger*. A study of the incorporation of glucose-3,4-C^{14} into citrate provides evidence that pyruvate, arising from glucose, is converted to oxalacetate and an acetyl fragment, and that these condense to yield citrate with almost theoretical incorporation of carbon dioxide and little or no randomization of the carboxyl carbons of oxalacetate (58). The last observation is important in showing that oxalacetate does not equilibrate with a symmetrical acid like fumaric or succinic.

Although it has been suggested (85) that a condensation of 2-carbon fragments may yield the 4-carbon dicarboxylic acid skeleton for citrate synthesis, work with isotopic acetate indicates that this pathway is at best of minor significance (28, 173), and the studies of Cleland and Johnson (58) with labeled glucose afford no evidence at all for such a reaction.

For *Penicillium chrysogenum* there is good evidence of the formation of citrate from acetyl phosphate and oxalacetate and for the presence of enzyme systems oxidizing citrate, isocitrate, α-ketoglutarate, succinate, and malate (51, 126, 229). A partially purified succinic dehydrogenase is inhibited by malonate (110), and acetate oxidation is depressed by the same poison (13). The incorporation of acetate carbon into glutamic acid conforms to that expected if the citric acid cycle is responsible for the metabolism of acetate (113).

Extracts of *Streptomyces coelicolor* carry out the major reactions of the cycle, including the formation of citrate, the oxidation of α-ketoglutarate and other acids, and the decarboxylation of oxalacetate (65). The incorporation of labeled carbon dioxide and acetate into amino acids by *S. griseus* is also consistent with the operation of the cycle (39, 104).

Most of the enzymes of the cycle are demonstrable in extracts of *Zygorhynchus moelleri* (201), and isotope distribution experiments indicate that the cycle plays a major role in energy metabolism (202).

Apart from these more intensively studied species, individual enzyme activities have been determined in many other fungi and actinomycetes. These include oxalacetic decarboxylase (87, 306), α-ketoglutaric acid oxidase (46), "oxalosuccinic decarboxylase" (183), enzyme systems oxidizing succinic acid (46, 89, 137, 182, 216), and isocitric dehydrogenase and condensing enzyme (12).

In conclusion, it is evident that the enzymes of the citric acid cycle are of quite general occurrence among fungi and actinomycetes and, indeed, that further enzyme surveys can add little to our understanding. The more important question is the physiological role of the citric acid cycle. Two such roles may be envisaged: provision of energy to the cell, and provision of carbon skeletons for amino acid synthesis. The second of these is reasonably certainly a real function of the cycle in *Neurospora crassa, Penicillium chrysogenum,* and *Streptomyces griseus.* A role in energy metabolism is more difficult to establish, but would be of great interest. Citric acid accumulation seems to result directly from an interruption of the cycle, under special nutritional conditions, at the citric acid stage.

We must also recall from Chapter 6 that isocitritase, catalyzing the conversion of isocitrate to succinic and glyoxylic acids, is known to occur in fungi; its activity may contribute to some of the complexities of the metabolic data.

10. DICARBOXYLIC ACIDS IN RESPIRATION

Apart from their role in the citric acid cycle, it has long been speculated that the 4-carbon dicarboxylic acids (succinic, fumaric, malic, and oxalacetic) may be components of another respiratory cycle in which acetate is oxidized to carbon dioxide. The initial reaction of such a cycle would be the reductive condensation of acetate, first suggested by Thunberg (298):

$$2 \text{ CH}_3\text{COOH} \rightarrow \text{HOOC—CH}_2\text{—CH}_2\text{—COOH} + 2 \text{ [H]} \qquad (12)$$

Further reactions can be imagined whereby the succinate so formed is converted to 1 mole of acetate and 2 moles of carbon dioxide, the acetate re-entering the cycle. The net effect would be the oxidation of one mole of acetate for each turn of the cycle. Possible dicarboxylic acid cycles are described by Ajl (1), Ochoa (222), and Umbreit (307); Siegel (262) discusses energy relations.

The formation of 4-carbon dicarboxylic acids has often been as-cribed to the Thunberg condensation solely on the basis that resting or growing cells given acetate form one or more of the dicarboxylic acids. By itself, this observation is of no significance and cannot be offered as evidence for the Thunberg reaction.

The most effective evidence for some sort of Thunberg reaction in fungi comes from studies on the formation of fumaric acid by *Rhizopus nigricans,* and consists of the finding that the organism forms fumarate from ethanol in yields so high as to make it unlikely that the citric acid cycle is the pathway responsible (89). The reaction may be written:

$$2C^*H_3CH_2OH + O_2 \rightarrow 2C^*H_3COOH$$
$$\rightarrow HOOC—C^*H{=}C^*H—COOH \qquad (13)$$

As indicated in the equation, the methyl carbons of ethanol appear as the methine carbons of fumarate. However, in this instance the dis-tribution of isotope is not of critical value, i.e., the labeling results do not require us to postulate the Thunberg reaction (2, 283, 309); the entrance of formic acid into the methyl group of pyruvate also com-plicates the interpretation of the isotope data (151, 152).

It has been suggested that an "acetic dehydrogenase" of *Aspergillus fumigatus* carries out the Thunberg reaction (12), but the products of the reaction have not been isolated.

Studies on bacteria offer a possible model for the results on *Rhizopus nigricans.* The enzyme malate synthetase of *Escherichia coli* carries out the reaction (325):

$$\text{Acetyl phosphate} + \text{glyoxylate} \rightarrow \text{malate} \qquad (14)$$

Kornberg and Madsen (164) find the same enzyme in *Pseudomonas* sp. and suggest the following sequence of reactions:

Acetate + oxalacetate → citrate	(15a)
Citrate → isocitrate	(15b)
Isocitrate → succinate + glyoxalate	(15c)
Acetate + coenzyme A → acetyl-CoA	(15d)
Acetyl-CoA + glyoxylate → malate + CoA	(15e)
Malate → oxalacetate + 2[H]	(15f)
2 Acetate → succinate + 2[H]	(15)

This complex system requires condensing enzyme (15a), aconitase (15b), isocitritase (15c), some mechanism generating acetyl-coenzyme A (15d), malate synthetase (15e), and malic dehydrogenase (15f). Although the accumulation of malate or of fumarate by such a system can be imagined, the cyclical character of the system as written would not be maintained. Most of the enzymes required for Equation 15 are known in fungi, and it will be of considerable interest to see if some such series of reactions participates in energy metabolism or in the synthesis of dicarboxylic acids. A comparable reaction system in *Tetrahymena pyriformis* converts succinate reversibly to acetyl phosphate (256).

11. CARBON DIOXIDE FIXATION

Evidence for a physiological role of carbon dioxide in the growth of fungi appears first in relatively crude experiments on *Fusarium* spp. (180); retardation of early growth in the absence of carbon dioxide has been observed in many other fungi (245, 246, 250). The carbon dioxide requirement is enhanced by mineral deficiencies (269).

An apparent effect of carbon dioxide on dehydrogenations (130) has been shown to be exerted in fact on endogenous methylene blue reduction (97).

Carbon dioxide stimulation of growth could, of course, be ascribed to other phenomena than fixation. However, in *Penicillium chrysogenum* there is good evidence that fixation is related to the essentiality of carbon dioxide (106). In this organism, fixation is negligible unless both carbon and nitrogen sources are provided; this situation, coupled with the fact that carbon dioxide is not essential in a complex medium and that aspartic and glutamic acids are labeled very early by C^{14} from isotopic carbon dioxide, suggests strongly that the physiological role of carbon dioxide is in the synthesis of essential amino acids via the citric acid cycle. Carbon dioxide fixation in *Neurospora crassa* is similarly enhanced by provision of nitrogen (275) and carbon (128).

It has been mentioned earlier in this chapter that under appropriate conditions there is extensive incorporation of carbon dioxide into citric acid. Labeled carbon dioxide is also incorporated into the carboxyl group of pyruvic acid by *Rhizopus nigricans* (86), in the carboxyl of lactate by *R. oryzae* (100), in oxalic acid by *Aspergillus niger* (174), in succinic acid by *Streptomyces coelicolor* (60), in streptomycin by *S. griseus* (144), and in unidentified cell constituents by several fungi (181).

In organisms generally there are several different pathways by which carbon dioxide is fixed (10, 118, 309). Indirect and not entirely conclusive evidence suggests that fixation occurs into oxalacetate in

Rhizopus nigricans (86) and *Neurospora crassa* (276). We have already noted the proposal that the light-stimulated carbon dioxide fixation in *Blastocladiella emersonii* reflects the reductive carboxylation of succinate and α-ketoglutarate (45). The pathway of fixation can presumably only be detected with finality in experiments with active cell-free preparations.

12. TERMINAL RESPIRATION

In aerobic organisms the ultimate oxidizing agent is molecular oxygen; the reaction or sequence of reactions by which the electrons withdrawn from the substrate are transferred to oxygen is denoted terminal respiration. Conventionally the process is visualized as transfer of hydrogen from substrate to oxygen. The transfer is mediated by a system in which substances of increasingly positive oxidation-reduction potential form a chain of carriers.

The simplest system involves only one carrier, the flavoprotein prosthetic group of an enzyme; examples are the amino acid oxidases and glucose aerodehydrogenase. More usually, the pyridine nucleotides—diphosphopyridine nucleotide or triphosphopyridine nucleotide—are the first hydrogen carriers of the sequence. Perhaps the most common terminal pathway involves a pyridine nucleotide, a flavoprotein, and the cytochrome system in succession, that is, the flow of hydrogen (electrons) is over the pathway:

$$\text{Substrate} \rightarrow \text{pyridine nucleotide} \rightarrow \text{flavoprotein} \rightarrow \text{cytochromes}$$
$$\rightarrow \text{oxygen} \qquad (16)$$

The cytochrome system is complex and there is considerable doubt whether what is known of animal systems can be applied directly to microorganisms. The flavoprotein is probably always a metalloenzyme (141).

Under some conditions, e.g., a high partial pressure of oxygen, flavoproteins may react directly with oxygen without the intervention of the cytochrome system (295).

The cytochrome system appears to be general in the fungi, as judged in the first instance by spectroscopic observations (32, 33, 56, 117, 122, 197, 227, 291, 300). However, it should be noted that experience with bacterial cytochromes indicates that it is not possible from simple spectroscopic measurements to state with precision whether the components of a new system are the same as those of the more familiar yeast and animal systems (266, 321). Consequently, it is well to reserve judgment for the time being as to whether the fungal cytochromes are the same as those of yeast, and to be content with the generalization that cytochromes are generally present in fungi. The cytochrome c of *Ustilago sphaerogena,* for example, has a spectrum like beef heart cytochrome c, but has a higher molecular weight and a lower isoelectric point (208). In this organism, too, the conditions of culture, especially the supply of zinc and of thiamine, markedly affect the concentrations of the cytochromes (117).

Exogenously supplied cytochrome, from animal sources, functions as an electron carrier for the aerobic lactic dehydrogenase of *Penicillium chrysogenum* (50) and for the succinoxidase systems of all forms tested (13, 190, 258).

Cytochrome oxidase may be assayed either manometrically or spectrophotometrically (Figure 6), usually with animal cytochrome c as substrate. The enzyme, operationally defined by these assays, seems to be of universal occurrence in the fungi; experiments have covered representatives of all of the major taxonomic groups (31, 32, 33, 46, 47, 57, 71, 117, 213, 230, 300). As in other organisms, cytochrome oxidase activity is associated with the insoluble and sedimentable fraction of homogenates (57, 71, 122, 258, 299). In bacteria, this fraction is apparently the cytoplasmic membrane or a similar structure (266).

The flavin components of the terminal system which proceeds over the cytochromes (Equation 16) have not been systematically investigated. Reductases linking cytochrome c with the pyridine nucleotide coenzymes and with succinate occur in *Neurospora tetrasperma* (57).

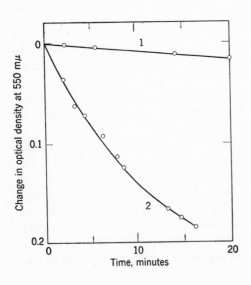

Figure 6. Cytochrome oxidase in *Blastocladiella* sp. Curve 1, in presence of cyanide; curve 2, action of the enzyme. Redrawn, from E. C. Cantino, "The Role of Metabolism and alpha-Ketoglutarate Oxidase in the Growth and Differentiation of the Aquatic Phycomycete, *Blastocladiella Emersonii,*" *Transactions of The New York Academy of Sciences,* Series II, Vol. 15, No. 5, p. 159-163 (1953), by permission of the New York Academy of Sciences.

It is of some interest whether the cytochrome system is responsible for the entire terminal respiration, or whether other systems may also be important. Elsewhere (Chapter 6) it has been noted that a role of the polyphenol oxidases or of quinone reductases is not yet established. The other alternative is a flavin system, and this possibility has received some attention.

The cytochrome system is poisoned by cyanide, azide, and carbon monoxide. In general, the aerobic respiration of intact cells of fungi is also inhibited by these poisons (31, 108, 189, 194, 324). However, both in *Myrothecium verrucaria* (71) and *Ustilago sphaerogena* (117) cell respiration is not affected by cyanide or carbon monoxide at concentrations which inhibit cytochrome oxidase. This suggests—although there are other possibilities—that some system other than the cytochrome is operative in intact cells. Cells of *Gelasinospora tetrasperma*, on the other hand, are as sensitive to these poisons as is the extracted oxidase (31); in this and in some other fungi (32, 57) the activity of the cytochrome system is sufficient to explain mycelial respiration.

There is some possibility that slow-growing strains of *Neurospora crassa* possess a terminal respiratory system other than the cytochromes. The "poky" strain, the distinctive features of which are inherited cytoplasmically, is relatively insensitive to cytochrome inhibitors, more responsive than the normal strain to oxygen pressure, and has a high content of flavin adenine dinucleotide (122, 301). A similar but gene-determined strain lacks cytochrome oxidase activity and is insensitive to azide and cyanide (300). Finally, although the "poky" character is suppressed by a nuclear gene, the cytochrome system is not increased along with the return to normal growth rate; this suggests that the effect of the gene is to open up some pathway alternative to the cytochrome route of terminal respiration (196). These observations all point toward a terminal system involving flavin enzymes.

Tamiya (291) summarizes the Japanese literature which suggests that in *Aspergillus oryzae* the respiration of mycelium from submerged (aerated or shaken) culture is mediated by the cytochromes, that of mycelium from still culture by some other, possibly flavin, system. This perhaps merits re-examination with the improved methods now available, although there are some contradictions (313).

Catalase, an iron-containing enzyme of the hydroperoxidase group (296), is present in all fungi which have been examined for it. Catalyzing the breakdown of hydrogen peroxide, the enzyme may serve only to protect the organism against hydrogen peroxide or may have a broader function in the oxidation of organic molecules (54, 157). The catalase of *Aspergillus oryzae* appears in the medium during autolysis (67), and the enzyme may have more than one component (68, 153). Peroxidases, which utilize hydrogen peroxide for the oxidation of other compounds, are especially active in some of the wood-destroying basidiomycetes (184, 185). *Neurospora tetrasperma* contains a cytochrome c peroxidase (57).

BIBLIOGRAPHY

1. Ajl, S. J. 1951. *Bacteriol. Revs.* 15: 211–244.
2. Ajl, S. J. and D. T. O. Wong. 1955. *Arch. Biochem. Biophys.* 54: 474–485.
3. Allen, P. J. and W. H. Price. 1950. *Am. J. Botany* 37: 393–402.
4. Altermatt, H. A., F. J. Simpson, and A. C. Neish. 1955. *Can. J. Biochem. and Physiol.* 33: 615–621.
5. Anderson, A. K. 1924. *Stud. Biol. Sci. Univ. Minnesota* 5: 237–280.
6. Arnstein, H. R. V. and R. Bentley. 1953a. *Biochem. J.* (*London*) 54: 493–508.
7. Arnstein, H. R. V. and R. Bentley. 1953b. *Biochem. J.* (*London*) 54: 508–516.
8. Arnstein, H. R. V. and R. Bentley. 1956. *Biochem. J.* (*London*) 62: 403–411.
9. Ballio, A., C. Casinori, and G. Serlupi-Crescenzi. 1956. *Biochim. et Biophys. Acta* 20: 414–415.
10. Bandurski, R. S. 1955. *J. Biol. Chem.* 217: 137–150.
11. Barker, H. A. 1936. *J. Cellular Comp. Physiol.* 8: 231–250.
12. Barron, E. S. G. and F. Ghiretti. 1953. *Biochim. et Biophys. Acta* 12: 239–249.
13. Beevers, H., E. P. Goldschmidt, and H. Koffler. 1952. *Arch. Biochem. Biophys.* 39: 236–238.
14. Bentley, M. L. 1953. *J. Gen. Microbiol.* 8: 365–377.
15. Bentley, R. and A. Neuberger. 1949. *Biochem. J.* (*London*) 45: 584–590.
15a. Bentley, R. and C. P. Thiessen. 1957. *J. Biol. Chem.* 226: 689–702.
16. Bernhauer, K. and H. Thelen. 1932. *Biochem. Z.* 253: 30–36.
17. Bernheim, F. 1942. *J. Bacteriol.* 44: 533–539.
18. Bernstein, I. A. 1956. *J. Biol. Chem.* 221: 873–878.
19. Bernstein, I. A. et al. 1955. *J. Biol. Chem.* 215: 137–152.
20. Birkinshaw, J. H., J. H. V. Charles, A. C. Hetherington, and H. Raistrick. 1931. *Phil. Trans. Roy. Soc.* (*London*). *Ser. B* 220: 99–125.
21. Birkinshaw, J. H., J. H. V. Charles, H. Raistrick, and J. A. R. Stoyle. 1931. *Phil. Trans. Roy. Soc.* (*London*). *Ser. B* 220: 27–54.
22. Birkinshaw, J. H. and H. Raistrick. 1931. *Phil. Trans. Roy. Soc.* (*London*). *Ser. B* 220: 331–353.
23. Bloom, B. 1955. *J. Biol. Chem.* 215: 467–472.
24. Bloom, B., F. Eisenberg, Jr., and D. Stetten, Jr. 1955. *J. Biol. Chem.* 215: 461–466.
25. Blumenthal, H. J., H. Koffler, and E. P. Goldschmidt. 1952. *Science* 116: 475–477.
26. Blumenthal, H. J., K. F. Lewis, and S. Weinhouse. 1954. *J. Am. Chem. Soc.* 76: 6093–6097.
27. Bolcato, V. and P. Tono. 1939. *Enzymologia* 7: 146–156.
28. Bomstein, R. A. and M. J. Johnson. 1952. *J. Biol. Chem.* 198: 143–153.
29. Boothroyd, B., J. A. Thorn, and R. H. Haskins. 1955. *Can. J. Biochem. and Physiol.* 33: 289–296.
30. Bose, S. 1947. *J. Indian Chem. Soc.* 24: 327–337.
31. Boulter, D. 1957. *J. Gen. Microbiol.* 16: 305–316.

32. Boulter, D. and A. Burges. 1955. *Experientia* 11: 188–189.
33. Boulter, D. and E. Derbyshire. 1957. *J. Exp. Botany* 8: 313–318.
34. Brown, D. H. and E. C. Cantino. 1955. *Am. J. Botany* 42: 337–341.
35. Burma, D. P. and B. L. Horecker. 1957. *Biochim. et Biophys. Acta* 24: 660–661.
36. Burnet, J. H. 1953. *New Phytologist* 52: 58–64.
37. Burris, R. H. 1949. In W. W. Umbreit, R. H. Burris, and J. F. Stauffer (eds.), *Manometric Techniques and Tissue Metabolism*, 2nd ed., p. 96–97. Minneapolis: Burgess Publishing Co.
38. Buston, H. W. and A. H. Khan. 1956. *J. Gen. Microbiol.* 14: 655–660.
39. Butterworth, E. M., C. M. Gilmour, and C. H. Wang. 1955. *J Bacteriol.* 69: 725–727.
40. Cantino, E. C. 1949. *Am. J. Botany* 36: 95–112.
41. Cantino, E. C. 1951. *Antonie van Leeuwenhoek J. Microbiol. Serol.* 17: 59–96.
42. Cantino, E. C. 1953. *Trans. N. Y. Acad. Sci.* II, 15: 159–163.
43. Cantino, E. C. 1956. *Mycologia* 48: 225–240.
44. Cantino, E. C. and E. A. Horenstein. 1955. *Physiol. Plantarum* 8: 189–221.
45. Cantino, E. C. and E. A. Horenstein. 1956. *Mycologia* 48: 777–799.
46. Cantino, E. C. and M. T. Hyatt. 1953a. *Am. J. Botany* 40: 688–694.
47. Cantino, E. C. and M. T. Hyatt. 1953b. *J. Bacteriol.* 66: 712–720.
48. Carson, S. F., J. W. Foster, W. E. Jefferson, E. F. Phares, and D. S. Anthony. 1951. *Arch. Biochem. Biophys.* 33: 448–458.
49. Carson, S. F., E. H. Mosbach, and E. F. Phares. 1951. *J. Bacteriol.* 62: 235–238.
50. Casida, L. E., Jr. and S. G. Knight. 1954a. *J. Bacteriol.* 67: 171–175.
51. Casida, L. E., Jr. and S. G. Knight. 1954b. *J. Bacteriol.* 67: 658–661.
52. Chain, E. B. and G. Gualandi. 1954. *Rend. ist. super. sanità* (English ed.) 17: 5–60.
53. Challenger, F., L. Klein, and T. K. Walker. 1931. *J. Chem. Soc.* (*London*) 1931: 16–23.
54. Chance, B. 1951. In J. B. Sumner and K. Myrbäck (eds.), *The Enzymes*, Vol. 2 (1), p. 428–453. New York: Academic Press.
55. Chattaway, F. W., C. C. Thompson, and A. G. E. Barlow. 1954. *Biochim. et Biophys. Acta* 14: 583–584.
56. Chauvet, J. 1943. *Enzymologia* 10: 57–69.
57. Cheng, S-C. 1954. *Plant Physiol.* 29: 458–467.
58. Cleland, W. W. and M. J. Johnson. 1954. *J. Biol. Chem.* 208: 679–689.
59. Clifton, C. E. 1952. In J. B. Sumner and K. Myrbäck (eds.), *The Enzymes*, Vol. 2 (2), p. 912–928. New York: Academic Press.
60. Cochrane, V. W. 1952. *J. Bacteriol.* 63: 459–471.
61. Cochrane, V. W. 1955. *J. Bacteriol.* 69: 256–263.
62. Cochrane, V. W. 1956. *Mycologia* 48: 1–12.
63. Cochrane, V. W. and M. Gibbs. 1951. *J. Bacteriol.* 61: 305–307.
64. Cochrane, V. W. and P. L. Hawley. 1956. *J. Bacteriol.* 71: 308–314.
65. Cochrane, V. W. and H. D. Peck, Jr. 1953. *J. Bacteriol.* 65: 37–44.
66. Cochrane, V. W., H. D. Peck, Jr., and A. Harrison. 1953. *J. Bacteriol.* 66: 17–23.
67. Crewther, W. G. and F. G. Lennox. 1953a. *Australian J. Biol. Sci.* 6: 410–427.
68. Crewther, W. G. and F. G. Lennox. 1953b. *Australian J. Biol. Sci.* 6: 428–446.
69. Czapek, F. 1922. *Biochemie der Pflanzen*, 3rd ed., Vol. 1, p. 316–338. Jena: Gustav Fischer.
70. Darby, R. T. and D. R. Goddard. 1950a. *Am. J. Botany* 37: 379–387.
71. Darby, R. T. and D. R. Goddard. 1950b. *Physiol. Plantarum* 3: 435–446.
72. DeBoer, S. R. 1928. *Rec. trav. Botan. Néerl.* 25: 117–240.

73. Deffner, M. 1942. *Ann. Chem. Liebigs.* 522: 191–202.
74. DeMoss, J. A., H. E. Swim, and L. O. Krampitz. 1955. *Bacteriol. Proc.* (*Soc. Am. Bacteriologists*) 1955: 114.
75. DeMoss, R. D. 1953. *J. Cellular Comp. Physiol.* 41, Suppl. 1: 207–224.
76. Dickens, F. and H. McIlwain. 1938. *Biochem. J.* (*London*) 32: 1615–1625.
77. Dixon, M. 1951. *Manometric Methods,* 3rd ed. Cambridge: Cambridge University Press, pp. 165.
78. Edwards, G. A., C. B. Buell, and W. H. Weston. 1947. *Am. J. Botany* 34: 551–555.
79. Elsden, S. R. 1952. In J. B. Sumner and K. Myrbäck (eds.), *The Enzymes,* Vol. 2 (2), p. 791–843. New York: Academic Press.
80. deFiebre, C. W. and S. G. Knight. 1953. *J. Bacteriol.* 66: 170–172.
81. Fincham, J. R. S. 1951. *J. Gen. Microbiol.* 5: 793–806.
82. Fincham, J. R. S. and J. B. Boylen. 1957. *J. Gen. Microbiol.* 16: 438–448.
83. Finn, R. K. 1954. *Bacteriol. Revs.* 18: 254–274.
84. Foster, J. W. 1949. *Chemical Activities of Fungi.* New York: Academic Press. pp. 648.
85. Foster, J. W. and S. F. Carson. 1950. *Proc. Natl. Acad. Sci. U. S.* 36: 219–229.
86. Foster, J. W. and J. B. Davis. 1948. *J. Bacteriol.* 56: 329–338.
87. Foster, J. W. and J. B. Davis. 1949. *Arch. Biochem.* 21: 135–142.
88. Foster, J. W. and F. W. Denison, Jr. 1950. *Nature* (*London*) 166: 833–834.
89. Foster, J. W. et al. 1949. *Proc. Natl. Acad. Sci. U. S.* 35: 663–672.
90. Foulkes, E. C. 1954. *J. Bacteriol.* 68: 505.
91. Franke, W. 1944. *Ann. Chemie Liebigs.* 555: 111–132.
92. Franke, W. and M. Deffner. 1939. *Ann. Chem. Liebigs.* 541: 117–150.
93. Ganguly, S. and S. C. Roy. 1955. *Arch. Biochem. Biophys.* 59: 45–51.
94. Ganguly, S. and S. C. Roy. 1956. *Arch. Biochem. Biophys.* 63: 26–31.
95. Garner, H. H. et al. 1953. *Am. J. Botany* 40: 289–296.
96. Gentile, A. C. 1954. *Plant Physiol.* 29: 257–261.
97. Gest, H. and J. L. Stokes. 1952. *Antonie van Leeuwenhoek J. Microbiol. Serol.* 18: 55–62.
98. Gibbs, M., V. W. Cochrane, L. M. Paege, and H. Wolin. 1954. *Arch. Biochem. Biophys.* 50: 237–242.
99. Gibbs, M., J. M. Earl, and J. L. Ritchie. 1955. *J. Biol. Chem.* 217: 161–168.
100. Gibbs, M. and R. Gastel. 1953. *Arch. Biochem. Biophys.* 43: 33–38.
101. Gibbs, M. and W. A. Wood. 1952. *Bacteriol. Proc.* (*Soc. Am. Bacteriologists*) 1952: 11.
102. Giese, A. C. and E. L. Tatum. 1946. *Arch. Biochem.* 9: 1–13.
103. Gillespie, R. J., G. A. Maw, and C. A. Vernon. 1953. *Nature* (*London*) 171: 1147–1149.
104. Gilmour, C. M., E. M. Butterworth, E. P. Noble, and C. H. Wang. 1955. *J. Bacteriol.* 69: 719–724.
105. Gilvarg, C. 1952. *J. Biol. Chem.* 199: 57–64.
106. Gitterman, C. O. and S. G. Knight. 1952. *J. Bacteriol.* 64: 223–231.
107. Goddard, D. R. 1945. *Science* 101: 352–353.
108. Goddard, D. R. and P. E. Smith. 1938. *Plant Physiol.* 13: 241–264.
109. Godin, P. 1953. *Biochim. et Biophys. Acta* 11: 119–121.
110. Godzeski, C. and R. W. Stone. 1955. *Arch. Biochem. Biophys.* 59: 132–144.
111. Goepfert, G. J. 1941. *J. Biol. Chem.* 140: 525–534.
112. Goepfert, G. J. and F. F. Nord. 1942. *Arch. Biochem.* 1: 289–301.
113. Goldschmidt, E. P., I. Yall, and H. Koffler. 1956. *J. Bacteriol.* 72: 436–446.
114. Golueke, C. G. 1957. *J. Bacteriol.* 74: 337–344.
115. Gottlieb, D. 1953. *Intern. Congr. Microbiol., 6th Congr. Rome,* 5: 122–136.
116. Gregg, J. H. 1950. *J. Exp. Zool.* 114: 173–196.
117. Grimm, P. W. and P. J. Allen. 1954. *Plant Physiol.* 29: 369–377.

118. Gunsalus, I. C., B. L. Horecker, and W. A. Wood. 1955. *Bacteriol. Revs.* 19: 79–128.
119. Harris, J. O. 1953. *Bacteriol. Proc. (Soc. Am. Bacteriologists)* 1953: 90.
120. Harrison, D. C. 1931. *Biochem. J. (London)* 25: 1016–1027.
121. Harter, L. L. and J. L. Weimer. 1921. *J. Agr. Research* 21: 211–226.
122. Haskins, F. A., A. Tissieres, H. K. Mitchell, and M. B. Mitchell. 1953. *J. Biol. Chem.* 200: 819–826.
123. Heath, E. C., J. Hurwitz, and B. L. Horecker. 1956. *J. Am. Chem. Soc.* 78: 5449.
124. Heath, E. C. and H. Koffler. 1956. *J. Bacteriol.* 71: 174–181.
125. Heath, E. C., D. Nasser, and H. Koffler. 1956. *Arch. Biochem. Biophys.* 64: 80–87.
126. Heberling, R. L. and R. W. Stone. 1957. *Bacteriol. Proc. (Soc. Am. Bacteriologists)* 1957: 127.
127. Henderson, M. K. 1956. *J. Gen. Microbiol.* 14: 684–691.
128. Heplar, J. Q. and E. L. Tatum. 1954. *J. Biol. Chem.* 208: 489–494.
129. Herzog, R. O. and A. Meier. 1908. *Z. physiol. Chem. Hoppe-Seyler's.* 57: 35–42.
130. Hes, J. W. 1938. *Nature (London)* 141: 647.
131. Hida, T. 1935. *J. Shanghai Sci. Inst. Sect. IV*, 1: 201–214.
132. Hill, R. L. and R. C. Mills. 1954. *Arch. Biochem. Biophys.* 53: 174–183.
133. Hochster, R. M. and J. H. Quastel. 1952. *Arch Biochem. Biophys.* 36: 132–146.
134. Hockenhull, D. J. D., K. H. Fantes, M. Herbert, and B. Whitehead. 1954. *J. Gen. Microbiol.* 10: 353–370.
135. Hockenhull, D. J. D., A. D. Walker, G. D. Wilkin, and F. G. Winder. 1952. *Biochem. J. (London)* 50: 605–609.
136. Hockenhull, D. J. D., G. D. Wilkin, and F. G. Winder. 1951. *Nature (London)* 168: 1043.
137. Holter, H. and B. M. Pollock. 1952. *Compt. rend. trav. lab. Carlsberg. Sér. chim.* 28: 221–245.
138. Horecker, B. L. 1953. *Brewers Dig.* 28: 214–219.
139. Horecker, B. L. and A. H. Mehler. 1955. *Ann. Rev. Biochem.* 24: 207–274.
140. Horowitz, N. H. 1944. *J. Biol. Chem.* 154: 141–149.
141. Huennekens, F. M. 1956. *Experientia* 12: 1–6.
142. Hughes, D. E. 1951. *Brit. J. Exp. Pathol.* 32: 97–109.
143. Hugo, W. B. 1954. *Bacteriol. Revs.* 18: 87–105.
144. Hunter, G. D., M. Herbert, and D. J. D. Hockenhull. 1954. *Biochem. J. (London)* 58: 249–254.
145. Ingraham, J. L. and R. Emerson. 1954. *Am. J. Botany* 41: 146–152.
146. Jacquot, R. and R. Raveux. 1943. *Compt. rend. (Paris)* 216: 318–319.
147. Jagannathan, V., P. N. Rangachari, and M. Damodaran. 1956. *Biochem. J. (London)* 64: 477–481.
148. Jagannathan, V. and K. Singh. 1953. *Enzymologia* 16: 150–160.
149. Jagannathan, V. and K. Singh. 1954. *Biochim. et Biophys. Acta* 15: 138.
150. Jagannathan, V., K. Singh, and M. Damodaran. 1956. *Biochem. J. (London)* 63: 94–105.
151. Jefferson, W. E. and J. W. Foster. 1953. *J. Bacteriol.* 65: 587–592.
152. Jefferson, W. E., J. W. Foster, E. F. Phares, and S. F. Carson. 1952. *J. Am. Chem. Soc.* 74: 1477–1478.
153. Jermyn, M. A. 1953. *Australian J. Biol. Sci.* 6: 77–97.
154. Johnson, E. M., E. C. Knight, and T. K. Walker. 1937. *Biochem. J. (London)* 31: 903–908.
155. Karrer, P. and F. Haab. 1948. *Helv. Chim. Acta* 31: 795–798.
156. Katz, J., S. Abraham, R. Hill, and I. L. Chaikoff. 1955. *J. Biol. Chem.* 214: 853–868.

157. Keilin, D. and E. F. Hartree. 1945. *Biochem. J. (London)* 39: 293–301.
158. Keilin, D. and E. F. Hartree. 1948a. *Biochem. J. (London)* 42: 221–229.
159. Keilin, D. and E. F. Hartree. 1948b. *Biochem. J. (London)* 42: 230–238.
160. Keilin, D. and E. F. Hartree. 1952a. *Biochem. J. (London)* 50: 331–341.
161. Keilin, D. and E. F. Hartree. 1952b. *Biochem. J. (London)* 50: 341–348.
162. Kita, D. A. and W. H. Peterson. 1953. *J. Biol. Chem.* 203: 861–868.
163. Koffler, H., R. L. Emerson, D. Perlman, and R. H. Burris. 1945. *J. Bacteriol.* 50: 517–548.
164. Kornberg, H. L. and N. B. Madsen. 1957. *Biochim. et Biophys. Acta* 24: 651–653.
165. Krebs, H. A. 1950. *The Harvey Lectures, 1948–49,* p. 165–199. Springfield, Ill.: C. C. Thomas.
166. Krebs, H. A. 1951. *Biochem. J. (London)* 48: 349–359.
167. Krebs, H. A., S. Gurin, and L. V. Eggleston. 1952. *Biochem. J. (London)* 51: 614–628.
168. Kusnetzow, S. J. 1932. *Microbiologiya* 1: 3–18, 83.
169. Lampen, J. O. 1953. *J. Cellular Comp. Physiol.* 41, Suppl. 1: 183–205.
170. Laties, G. G. 1949. *Arch. Biochem.* 22: 8–15.
171. Letcher, H. and J. J. Willaman. 1926. *Phytopathology* 16: 941–949.
172. Lewis, K., H. J. Blumenthal, C. E. Wenner, and S. Weinhouse. 1954. *Federation Proc.* 13: 252.
173. Lewis, K. F. and S. Weinhouse. 1951a. *J. Am. Chem. Soc.* 73: 2500–2503.
174. Lewis, K. F. and S. Weinhouse. 1951b. *J. Am. Chem. Soc.* 73: 2906–2909.
175. Lockwood, L. B. and G. E. N. Nelson. 1946. *J. Bacteriol.* 52: 581–586.
176. Lockwood, L. B., J. J. Stubbs, and C. J. Senseman. 1938. *Zentr. Bakteriol. Parasitenk. Abt. II,* 98: 167–171.
177. Loewy, A. G. 1952. *J. Cellular Comp. Physiol.* 40: 127–156.
178. Lopez-Ramos, B. and W. J. Schubert. 1955. *Arch. Biochem. Biophys.* 55: 566–577.
179. Lüers, H., R. Kühles, and H. Fink. 1930. *Biochem. Z.* 217: 253–278.
180. Lundegårdh, H. 1923. *Botan. Notiser* 1923: 25–52.
181. Lynch, V. H. and M. Calvin. 1952. *J. Bacteriol.* 63: 525–531.
182. Lynen, F. and H. P. Hoffmann-Walbeck. 1948. *Ann. Chem. Liebigs.* 559: 153–168.
183. Lynen, F. and H. Scherer. 1948. *Ann. Chem. Liebigs.* 560: 163–190.
184. Lyr, H. 1955. *Planta* 46: 408–413.
185. Lyr, H. 1956. *Planta* 48: 239–265.
186. MacMillan, A. 1956. *Physiol. Plantarum* 9: 533–545.
187. Mandels, G. R. and A. B. Norton. 1948. *Research Rept. Quartermaster Gen. Labs., Microbiol. Ser.* 11: 1–50 (mimeographed).
188. Mandels, G. R. and R. G. H. Siu. 1950. *J. Bacteriol.* 60: 249–262.
189. Mann, T. 1944. *Biochem. J. (London)* 38: 339–345.
190. Martin, S. M. 1954. *Can. J. Microbiol.* 1: 6–11.
191. Martin, S. M. and P. W. Wilson. 1951. *Arch. Biochem. Biophys.* 32: 150–157.
192. Martin, S. M., P. W. Wilson, and R. H. Burris. 1950. *Arch. Biochem.* 26: 103–111.
193. Maximov, N. A. 1904. *Ber deut. botan. Ges.* 22: 225–235.
194. Mickelson, M. N. 1950. *J. Bacteriol.* 59: 659–666.
195. Mickelson, M. N. and M. N. Schuler. 1953. *J. Bacteriol.* 65: 297–304.
196. Mitchell, M. B. and H. K. Mitchell. 1956. *J. Gen. Microbiol.* 14: 84–89.
197. Mitchell, M. B., H. K. Mitchell, and A. Tissieres. 1953. *Proc. Natl. Acad. Sci. U. S.* 39: 606–613.
198. Mosbach, E. H., E. F. Phares, and S. F. Carson. 1952. *Arch. Biochem. Biophys.* 35: 435–442.
199. Moses, V. 1954. *Biochem. J. (London)* 57: 547–556.

200. Moses, V. 1955a. *Ann. Botany* 19: 211–223.
201. Moses, V. 1955b. *J. Gen. Microbiol.* 13: 235–251.
202. Moses, V. 1957. *J. Gen. Microbiol.* 16: 534–549.
203. Moses, V. and P. J. Syrett. 1955. *J. Bacteriol.* 70: 201–204.
204. Mukherjee, S. 1951. *Arch. Biochem. Biophys.* 33: 364–376.
205. Müller, D. 1926. *Chem. Ztg.* 50: 101.
206. Müller, D. 1928. *Biochem. Z.* 199: 136–170.
207. Müller, D. 1941. *Enzymologia* 10: 40–47.
208. Neilands, J. B. 1952. *J. Biol. Chem.* 197: 701–708.
209. Neilson, N. E. 1955. *Biochim. et Biophys. Acta* 17: 139–140.
210. Neilson, N. E. 1956. *J. Bacteriol.* 71: 356–361.
211. Neuberg, C. and C. Cohen. 1921. *Biochem. Z.* 122: 204–224.
212. Newburgh, R. W., C. A. Claridge, and V. H. Cheldelin. 1955. *J. Biol. Chem.* 214: 27–35.
213. Nicholas, D. J. D., A. Nason, and W. D. McElroy. 1954. *J. Biol. Chem.* 207: 341–351.
214. Nickerson, W. J. and J. B. Chadwick. 1946. *Arch. Biochem.* 10: 81–100.
215. Nickerson, W. J. and G. A. Edwards. 1949. *J. Gen. Physiol.* 33: 41–55.
216. Nickerson, W. J. and R. R. Mohan. 1953. *Intern Congr. Microbiol., 6th Congr. Rome,* 5: 137–146.
217. Nielsen, N. and D. Dresden. 1939. *Compt. rend. trav. lab. Carlsberg. Sér. physiol.* 22: 287–300.
218. Nord, F. F., E. Dammann, and H. Hofstetter. 1936. *Biochem. Z.* 285: 241–269.
219. Nord, F. F., H. Hofstetter, and E. Dammann. 1937. *Biochem. Z.* 293: 231–255.
220. Nord, F. F. and R. P. Mull. 1945. *Advances in Enzymol.* 5: 165–205.
221. Nord, F. F. and L. J. Sciarini. 1946. *Arch. Biochem.* 9: 419–437.
222. Ochoa, S. 1952. *The Harvey Lectures, 1950–51,* p. 153–180. Springfield, Ill.: C. C. Thomas.
223. Ogston, A. G. 1948. *Nature (London)* 162: 963.
224. Ogura, Y. 1939. *Acta Phytochim. (Japan)* 11: 127–143.
225. Ogura, Y. 1951. *J. Biochem. (Tokyo)* 38: 75–84.
226. Ogura, Y. and M. Nagahisa. 1937. *Botan. Mag. (Tokyo)* 54: 597–612.
227. Ohta, J. 1954. *J. Biochem. (Tokyo)* 41: 489–497.
228. Oliver, I. T. and J. L. Peel. 1956. *Biochim. et Biophys. Acta* 20: 390–392.
229. Olson, J. A. 1954. *Nature (London)* 174: 695–696.
230. Owens, R. G. 1955. *Contribs. Boyce Thompson Inst.* 18: 125–144, 145–152.
231. Pardee, A. B. 1949. *J. Biol. Chem.* 179: 1085–1091.
232. Perlman, D. 1949. *Am. J. Botany* 36: 180–184.
233. Perlman, D. 1950. *Am. J. Botany* 37: 237–241.
234. Pickett, M. J. and C. E. Clifton. 1943. *J. Cellular Comp. Physiol.* 21: 77–94.
235. Quastel, J. H. and A. H. M. Wheatley. 1938. *Biochem. J. (London)* 32: 936–943.
236. Racker, E. 1957. *The Harvey Lectures, Series 51:* 143–174. New York: Academic Press.
237. Ramachandran, K. and T. K. Walker. 1951. *Arch. Biochem. Biophys.* 31: 224–233.
238. Ramachandran, K. and T. K. Walker. 1952. *Arch. Biochem. Biophys.* 35: 195–203.
239. Ramakrishnan, C. V. 1954. *Enzymologia* 17: 169–174.
240. Ramakrishnan, C. V. and S. M. Martin. 1954. *Can. J. Biochem. and Physiol.* 32: 434–439.
241. Ramakrishnan, C. V. and S. M. Martin. 1955. *Arch. Biochem. Biophys.* 55: 403–407.

242. Ramakrishnan, C. V., R. Steel, and C. P. Lentz. 1955. *Arch. Biochem. Biophys.* 55: 270–273.
243. Raveux, R. 1950. *Compt. rend. (Paris)* 238: 729–731, 1006–1008, 1107–1108.
244. Reiner, J. M., H. Gest, and M. D. Kamen. 1949. *Arch. Biochem.* 20: 175–177.
245. Rippel, A. and H. Bortels. 1927. *Biochem. Z.* 184: 237–244.
246. Rippel, A. and F. Heilmann. 1930. *Arch. Mikrobiol.* 1: 119–136.
247. Rippel, A. and H. Wiangke. 1941. *Arch. Mikrobiol.* 12: 124–127.
248. Roberts, R. B. et al. 1955. *Carnegie Inst. Wash. Publ.* 607: 1–521.
249. Robinson, R. 1926. *Trans. Brit. Mycol. Soc.* 10: 307–314.
250. Rockwell, G. E. and J. H. Highberger. 1927. *J. Infectious Diseases* 40: 438–446.
251. Rothstein, A. and H. Berke. 1952. *Arch. Biochem. Biophys.* 36: 195–201.
252. Sakaguchi, K., H. Takahashi, and H. Morino. 1953. *J. Agr. Chem. Soc. Japan* 27: 591–595.
253. Schade, A. L. and K. V. Thimann. 1940. *Am. J. Botany* 27: 659–670.
254. Schatz, A., G. S. Trelawney, V. Schatz, and R. R. Mohan. 1956. *Mycologia* 48: 883–885.
255. Schmidt-Lorenz, W. 1956. *Arch. Mikrobiol.* 25: 137–165.
256. Seaman, G. R. and M. D. Naschke. 1955. *J. Biol. Chem.* 217: 1–12.
257. Semeniuk, G. 1944. *Iowa State Coll. J. Sci.* 18: 325–358.
258. Shepherd, C. J. 1951. *Biochem. J. (London)* 48: 483–486.
259. Shibata, K. and H. Tamiya. 1930. *Acta Phytochim. (Japan)* 5: 23–97.
260. Shu, P. 1953. *J. Agr. Food Chem.* 1: 1119–1123.
261. Shu, P., A. Funk, and A. C. Neish. 1954. *Can. J. Biochem. and Physiol.* 32: 68–80.
262. Siegel, B. V. 1950. *Proc. Natl. Acad. Sci. U. S.* 36: 515–517.
263. Sih, C. J., P. B. Hamilton, and S. G. Knight. 1957. *J. Bacteriol.* 73: 447–451.
264. Sih, C. J. and S. G. Knight. 1956. *J. Bacteriol.* 72: 694–699.
265. Sisler, H. D. and C. E. Cox. 1954. *Am. J. Botany* 41: 338–345.
266. Smith, L. 1954. *Bacteriol. Revs.* 18: 106–130.
267. Sols, A. and G. de la Fuente. 1957. *Biochim. et Biophys. Acta* 24: 206–207.
268. Sowden, J. C., S. Frankel, B. H. Moore, and J. E. McClary. 1954. *J. Biol. Chem.* 206: 547–552.
269. Steinberg, R. A. 1942. *Plant Physiol.* 17: 129–132.
270. Stickland, H. 1956. *Biochem. J. (London)* 64: 498–503.
271. Stokes, J. L. 1950. *Bacteriol. Proc. (Soc. Am. Bacteriologists)* 1950: 119.
272. Stout, H. A. and H. Koffler. 1951. *J. Bacteriol.* 62: 253–268.
273. Strauss, B. S. 1952. *Arch. Biochem. Biophys.* 36: 33–47.
274. Strauss, B. S. 1953. *Arch. Biochem. Biophys.* 44: 200–210.
275. Strauss, B. S. 1956. *J. Gen. Microbiol.* 14: 494–511.
276. Strauss, B. S. 1957. *J. Biol. Chem.* 225: 535–544.
277. Strauss, B. S. and S. Pierog. 1954. *J. Gen. Microbiol.* 10: 221–235.
278. Sumiki, Y. 1929. *Bull. Agr. Chem. Soc. Japan* 5: 14–16.
279. Sumiki, Y. 1931. *Bull. Agr. Chem. Soc. Japan* 7: 62–63.
280. Sussman, A. S. and C. L. Markert. 1953. *Arch. Biochem. Biophys.* 45: 31–40.
281. Suthers, A. J. and T. K. Walker. 1932. *Biochem. J. (London)* 26: 317–322.
282. Swaby, R. J. and B. I. Passey. 1953. *Australian J. Agr. Research* 4: 334–339.
283. Swim, H. E. and L. O. Krampitz. 1954. *J. Bacteriol* 67: 419–425.
284. Syrett, P. J. 1953. *Ann. Botany* 17: 1–36.
285. Takahashi, T. and T. Asai. 1933a. *Zentr. Bakteriol. Parasitenk. Abt. II,* 88: 376–384.
286. Takahashi, T. and T. Asai. 1933b. *Zentr. Bakteriol. Parasitenk. Abt. II,* 89: 81–84.
287. Takahashi, T. and T. Asai. 1933c. *J. Agr. Chem. Soc. Japan* 9: 443–448. (*Chem. Abstr.* 27: 4273. 1933.)

288. Takahashi, T., K. Sakaguchi, and T. Asai. 1927. *Bull. Agr. Chem. Soc. Japan* 3: 87–92.
289. Tamiya, H. 1927. *Acta Phytochim. (Japan)* 3: 51–173.
290. Tamiya, H. 1928. *Acta Phytochim. (Japan)* 4: 77–213.
291. Tamiya, H. 1942. *Advances in Enzymol.* 2: 183–238.
292. Tamiya, H. and Y. Miwa. 1929. *Z. Botan.* 21: 417–432.
293. Tatum, E. L. and S. R. Gross. 1956. *J. Biol. Chem.* 219: 797–807.
294. Tauber, H. 1954. *Enzymologia* 16: 311–316.
295. Theorell, H. 1951a. In J. B. Sumner and K. Myrbäck (eds.), *The Enzymes*, Vol. 2 (1), p. 335–356. New York: Academic Press.
296. Theorell, H. 1951b. In J. B. Sumner and K. Myrbäck (eds.), *The Enzymes*, Vol. 2 (1), p. 397–427. New York: Academic Press.
297. Thimann. K. V. 1955. *The Life of Bacteria.* New York: The Macmillan Co. pp. 775.
298. Thunberg, T. 1920. *Skand. Arch. Physiol.* 40: 1–91.
299. Tissieres, A. 1954. *Biochem. J. (London)* 58: 142–146.
300. Tissieres, A. and H. K. Mitchell. 1954. *J. Biol. Chem.* 208: 241–249.
301. Tissieres, A., H. K. Mitchell, and F. A. Haskins. 1953. *J. Biol. Chem.* 205: 423–433.
302. Tomlinson, T. G. 1937. *New Phytologist* 36: 418–434.
303. Ts'o, P. O. P., J. Bonner, L. Eggman, and J. Vinograd. 1956. *J. Gen. Physiol.* 39: 325–347.
304. Ts'o, P. O. P., L. Eggman, and J. Vinograd. 1956a. *J. Gen. Physiol.* 39: 801–812.
305. Ts'o, P. O. P., L. Eggman, and J. Vinograd. 1956b. *Arch. Biochem. Biophys.* 66: 64–70.
306. Tytell, A. A. and B. S. Gould. 1941. *J. Bacteriol.* 42: 513–526.
307. Umbreit, W. W. 1952. *J. Cellular Comp. Physiol.* 41, Suppl. 1: 39–66.
308. Umbreit, W. W., R. H. Burris, and J. F. Stauffer. 1949. *Manometric Techniques and Tissue Metabolism,* 2nd ed. Minneapolis: Burgess Publishing Co., pp. 227.
309. Utter, M. F. and H. G. Wood. 1951. *Advances in Enzymol.* 12: 41–151.
310. Waksman, S. A. and J. W. Foster. 1938. *J. Agr. Research* 57: 873–899.
311. Walker, T. K., A. N. Hall, and J. W. Hopton. 1951. *Nature (London)* 168: 1042–1043.
312. Warburg, O. 1938. *Ergeb. Enzymforsch.* 7: 210–245.
313. Warburg, O. and F. Kubowitz. 1929. *Biochem. Z.* 214: 24–25.
314. Ward, G. E., L. B. Lockwood, B. Tabenkin, and P. A. Wells. 1938. *Ind. Eng. Chem.* 30: 1233–1235.
315. Webley, D. M. 1954. *J. Gen. Microbiol.* 11: 114–121.
316. Webley, D. M. and P. C. DeKock. 1952. *Biochem. J. (London)* 51: 371–375.
317. Wehmer, C. 1907. In *Lafar's Handbuch der technischen Mykologie*, Vol. 4, p. 506–528.
318. Wenner, C. E. and S. Weinhouse. 1956. *J. Biol. Chem.* 219: 691–704.
319. Whitaker, D. R. and P. E. George. 1951. *Can. J. Botany* 29: 176–181.
320. Wikén, T. and H. Somm. 1952. *Experientia* 8: 140–142.
321. Wilson, T. G. G. and P. W. Wilson. 1955. *J. Bacteriol.* 70: 30–34.
322. Winzler, R. J. 1940. *J. Cellular Comp. Physiol.* 15: 343–354.
323. Wirth, J. C. and F. F Nord. 1942. *Arch. Biochem.* 1: 143–163.
324. Wolf, F. T. 1947. *Arch. Biochem.* 13: 83–92.
325. Wong, D. T. O. and S. J. Aji. 1956. *J. Am. Chem. Soc.* 78: 3230–3231.
326. Wood, H. G. 1946. *Physiol. Revs.* 26: 198–246.
327. Wood, H. G. 1955. *Physiol. Revs.* 35: 841–859.
328. Wood, H. G., C. R. Brewer, M. N. Mickelson, and C. H. Werkman. 1940. *Enzymologia* 8: 314–317.

329. Wood, W. A.   1955.   *Bacteriol. Revs.* 19: 223–233.
330. Wood, W. A. and R. F. Schwerdt.   1953.   *J. Biol. Chem.* 201: 501–511.
331. Yanofsky, C. and J. L. Reissig.   1953.   *J. Biol. Chem.* 202: 567–577.
332. Yemm, E. W. and B. F. Folkes.   1954.   *Biochem. J. (London)* 57: 495–508.
333. Yuill, J. L.   1928.   *Biochem. J. (London)* 22: 1504–1507.

8. Nitrogen Nutrition and Metabolism

With the exception of certain problems in amino acid biosynthesis, the nitrogen metabolism of the fungi has been relatively neglected. Numerous surveys of nitrogen nutrition have been made, unfortunately too often without a clear conception of the physiological problems involved. As will be seen, little is known of the mechanism of nitrogen assimilation into amino acids and proteins, the synthesis of specific peptides, and the metabolism of purines and pyrimidines.

There is no optimum amount of nitrogen for a culture; the demand depends in the first instance upon the carbon supply, but in principle, at least, any factor may change the apparent optimum concentration of the nitrogen source. The dependence upon carbon is illustrated in Figure 1; in this organism, *Aspergillus niger,* enough is known of other cultural factors so that a strict proportionality between carbohydrate supply and nitrogen demand can be demonstrated (496).

No single pattern of nitrogen assimilation can be described to apply to all fungi. In general, however, inorganic or organic nitrogen is taken up rapidly during the phase of growth. Even in this phase, however, there may be a back movement of ammonia nitrogen from the cells to the medium (211), reflecting the permeability of the cell to ammonia. Certain enzymes also begin to appear in the medium during this period (115, 278), and in at least some organisms amino acids and other soluble nitrogen compounds are liberated (139, 181, 374, 413). The major liberation of proteins and other nitrogenous

241

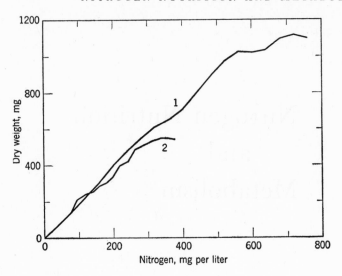

Figure 1. The relation between growth of *Aspergillus niger* and nitrogen supply (ammonium nitrate) in media containing sucrose at 50 gm per liter (curve 1) and 25 gm per liter (curve 2). Drawn from data of Steinberg and Bowling (496).

compounds occurs, of course, in the phase of autolysis (Chapter 1).

Studies of *Scopulariopsis brevicaulis* indicate that upon exhaustion of the utilizable nitrogen of the medium, there is a mobilization and reutilization of at least part of the nitrogen from older hyphae to support development of new mycelium (374).

1. INORGANIC SOURCES OF NITROGEN

Primary attention must be devoted here to three inorganic forms of nitrogen: ammonium salts, nitrites, and nitrates. Other inorganic nitrogen compounds have been little studied but appear in general to be utilized only if easily or spontaneously converted to one of the types above-named (278, 494). Cyanide as a nutrient and metabolite is considered separately.

The Utilization of Nitrate Nitrogen. Nitrates are excellent sources of nitrogen for many fungi (30, 221, 326, 459). Inability to utilize nitrate is especially common in some groups, e.g., the higher basidiomycetes (221, 234, 275, 327, 397, 546), the Saprolegniaceae (55, 434, 562), and the Blastocladiales so far as known (90). Nitrate utilization, or at least nitrate reduction, is common in the actinomycetes, although one could ask for more quantitative data (15, 306, 419, 534, 569, 570), but some strains definitely cannot grow with nitrate as the sole source of nitrogen (138, 144, 393, 541).

It is unlikely in the extreme that inability to use nitrate can serve as a phylogenetic criterion. Within a genus, individual species differ in nitrate utilization (150, 327, 397, 610). The capacity to use nitrate can be lost by mutation (250, 255, 420, 428, 455), and survival in nature of strains carrying this mutation is presumably governed by their ecological situation rather than their taxonomic position.

Failure to utilize nitrate is usually presumed to be absolute, but there has been little exploration of the possibility that nitrate can be metabolized once growth is initiated on another more readily available nitrogen source. When spores of *Streptomyces griseus* are inoculated into a synthetic nitrate medium, no growth occurs, but a pregrown mycelium uses nitrate readily (105).

As mentioned below, nitrite may be toxic in an acid medium. It follows that the kind and the concentration of the carbon source, insofar as these affect the pH, will decisively influence the response of some organisms, e.g., *Streptomyces coelicolor* (107), to nitrate.

Ammonium nitrate is often used in media, and it is of interest to ask whether there is preferential utilization of either ion. The frequent experience that utilization of ammonium nitrate is accompanied by a pH drop (227, 256, 409, 415, 529) is presumptive evidence for preferential utilization of the ammonium ion. More direct evidence is provided, however, by analytical studies. In *Scopulariopsis brevicaulis* and other fungi, nitrate utilization does not begin until virtually all the ammonium has disappeared from the medium (Figure 2); this is

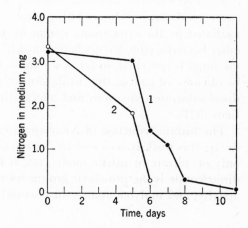

Figure 2. The utilization of ammonium and nitrate by *Scopulariopsis brevicaulis* in a medium containing glucose, succinate, and ammonium nitrate. Curve 1, nitrate concentration in the medium; curve 2, ammonium concentration in the medium. From tabular data of Morton and MacMillan (375).

also true of *Neurospora crassa* (511). Detailed study of the phenomenon (345, 373, 375) brings out that nitrate utilization is completely stopped by the addition of ammonium salts, provided the ammonia is assimilated, i.e., that a carbon source is available. Since nitrite utilization is not blocked by ammonium, it must be assumed that in these fungi ammonium prevents the reduction of nitrate to nitrite; this is borne out by enzymatic studies, which show that the nitratase system declines in quantity soon after ammonia assimilation begins.

Analytical data on utilization of ammonium nitrate by *Helminthosporium gramineum* show a different relation: ammonium ion is used much more rapidly than nitrate, but there is a slight assimilation of nitrate even in the early stages of growth (110). This relation is stated to prevail in some other fungi (375).

The preferential utilization of ammonia from ammonium nitrate is influenced by pH. Foster (163) reviews several studies in *Aspergillus niger,* all of which agree that at very low pH ammonium utilization is reduced and at least some nitrate is assimilated. Attempts have been made to explain this phenomenon as one of permeability or as based on the adsorption capacity of cell colloids (86, 264); neither of these explanations is convincing, and it would appear desirable to reinvestigate the phenomenon itself before speculating on its theoretical implications. As shown later (Figure 3), the optimum pH for nitrate uptake in *Scopulariopsis brevicaulis* is about 6.0, far above the "critical" pH at which *Aspergillus niger* is claimed to assimilate nitrate (439).

Nitrate reduction in the fungi is believed to be strictly assimilatory in nature, that is, to occur only in the incorporation of nitrate nitrogen into the cell. This process is in contrast to that of the bacteria, many of which reduce nitrate without assimilation of the nitrogen; nitrate, if it has an essential function, is acting as a hydrogen acceptor for substrate oxidations (556). This "nitrate respiration" appears to be mediated by the cytochrome system in *Micrococcus denitrificans* and other bacteria (460, 557); whereas, as will be seen, nitrate reduction in the fungi is mediated, so far as we know, by flavin enzymes. It should be obvious, of course, that utilization of nitrate in fungi does depend upon substrate oxidations and affects, therefore, the respiratory quotient (521).

The nitrate reductase of *Neurospora crassa* has been studied intensively; this work is reviewed by Nason (384). The enzyme is formed only on nitrate or nitrite media, i.e., it is inducible. Flavin adenine dinucleotide is the prosthetic group; sulfhydryl groups are essential to activity, and molybdenum is an essential factor in electron transport.

The passage of electrons is visualized:

Reduced triphosphopyridine nucleotide → flavin
adenine dinucleotide → molybdenum → nitrate   (1)

That is, nitrate is reduced with concurrent oxidation of some other, presumably carbon, compound by a triphosphopyridine-linked dehydrogenase. The enzyme of *Hansenula anomala* differs in that either di- or triphosphopyridine nucleotide is functional (483).

Two other flavin enzymes of *Neurospora crassa,* nitrite reductase and hydroxylamine reductase, also inducible metal-dependent enzymes, have not as yet been separated. Together, and possibly with the aid of a third enzyme, they catalyze the reduction of nitrite to ammonia (384, 385, 451).

From these enzymatic studies, and from the somewhat uncertain occurrence of hydroxylamine in nitrate cultures (322, 396, 494), an inorganic pathway of nitrogen reduction has been proposed (384):

$$NO_3^- \rightarrow NO_2^- \rightarrow ? \rightarrow NH_2OH \rightarrow NH_3 \qquad (2)$$

The unknown intermediate, possibly hyponitrite, is included on the assumption that the four-electron change from nitrite to hydroxylamine is unlikely to be a single reaction.

Whether this inorganic pathway is the sole and obligatory sequence of nitrate reduction in fungi is not yet certain. Since molybdenum deficiency reduces both nitrate reductase content and the ability to grow on nitrate in *N. crassa* and *Aspergillus niger,* it seems probable that the first proposed step is essential. Genetic studies bear out this conclusion (484). However, we cannot be sure that succeeding steps are necessarily inorganic in nature, as implied in Equation 2; incorporation into organic combination may occur at an oxidation level above that of ammonia (220, 338, 484).

A nitroaryl reductase system in *Neurospora crassa* catalyzes the reduction of *m*-dinitrobenzene by reduced pyridine nucleotides to *m*-nitroaniline (384). This system, although possibly not specific, is of interest as a model of the reduction of organic nitro compounds as an alternative to the inorganic pathway of Equation 2.

The increased toxicity of thiourea to *Aspergillus niger* in nitrate media suggests that the poison interferes with assimilation (158); chlorate toxicity is also more evident in nitrate media (203). Fluoride causes the accumulation of nitrite in fungi, presumably acting specifically on the nitrite reductase system (373).

The Utilization of Nitrite Nitrogen. Nitrite serves more or less well as the sole source of nitrogen for a number of fungi, e.g., *Fusarium niveum* (622), *Coprinus* spp. (165), *Phymatotrichum omnivorum* (520), *Scopulariopsis brevicaulis* (375), and *Rhizophlyctis rosea* (424). Different species of *Aspergillus* use it well, poorly, or not at all (305, 457, 494). Failure to utilize nitrite, which is the more common situation in fungi, is explained on the basis of its known toxicity (233, 402, 623). The fact that growth in the presence of nitrite is best in alkaline media (107, 402, 454) indicates that it is the free unionized acid, rather than the nitrite ion, which is the toxic species. Nitrite toxicity to *Fusarium lini* is evidenced by accumulation of pyruvic acid (396); induction by nitrite of morphological variants in *Aspergillus* spp. also suggests toxicity (495, 497, 498).

The Utilization of Ammonium Nitrogen. Studies on *Scopulariopsis brevicaulis* (336, 338, 375) provide the best general view of the physiology of ammonium utilization. Both oxygen and an exogenous carbon source are required, i.e., assimilation depends on respiratory energy or glucose breakdown products or both. Ammonium utilization increases with pH, and, unlike nitrate absorption, has no definite pH optimum (Figure 3). Ammonia enters and leaves the cell by passive diffusion of the undissociated NH_3 molecule; the requirement for respiration is not therefore an indication of accumulation against a gradient.

In organisms generally (123, 558), in *Torulopsis utilis* in particular (620), it is believed that the major and primary reaction of ammonium assimilation is the formation of glutamic acid. Other

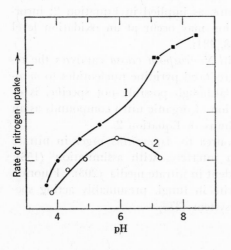

Figure 3. The rate of uptake of ammonia and nitrate by *Scopulariopsis brevicaulis* as a function of pH. Curve 1, ammonia (two buffers); curve 2, nitrate. From Morton and MacMillan (375), by permission of the Oxford University Press.

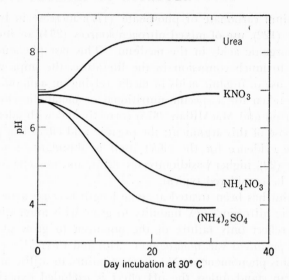

Figure 4. The effect of nitrogen assimilation on pH in *Karlingia (Rhizophlyctis)* *rosea*. Redrawn from Haskins and Weston (227), by permission of the *American Journal of Botany.*

amino acids can be formed from glutamate by transamination (p. 267). Secondary roles in ammonium assimilation may be filled by reactions which incorporate free ammonia into alanine, aspartic acid or glutamine. Respiratory breakdown of glucose is obviously necessary to supply the carbon skeleton.

One of the best established physiological correlates of ammonium assimilation from such salts as the sulfate, nitrate, or chloride is the rapid and often quantitatively large drop in pH consequent upon preferential utilization of the cation. Typical data are shown in Figure 4. The generality of this reaction may be emphasized by listing a few of the fungi in which careful observation demonstrates the phenomenon beyond question:

Alternaria solani (391), *Aspergillus niger* (496), *Chaetomium funicola* (477), *Choanephora cucurbitarum* (43), *Chytridium* sp. (113), *Diplocarpon rosae* (482), *Entomophthora* spp. (604), *Myrothecium verrucaria* (122), *Mycosphaerella pinodes* (45), *Penicillium* spp. (119, 254), *Phymatotrichum omnivorum* (520), *Piricularia oryzae* (406), *Psalliota bispora* (546), *Pythium* spp. (459), *Polyporus* spp. (221), *Verticillium* spp. (221, 256), *Xylaria mali* (221).

In many, if not most, of the instances cited the decrease in pH was sufficient to reduce growth. Practically, several remedies exist: use of ammonium carbonate or phosphate (477), increase in buffer concentration (122), use of mixed nitrogen sources (254), or inclusion of utilizable organic acids in the medium. This last phenomenon has given rise to much confusion in the literature, the improvement of growth by use of organic acids in media relying on ammonium nitrogen being taken for a specific nutritional or metabolic effect of the acid. Morton and MacMillan (375) correctly and with adequate evidence dispose of this argument; the organic acid effect is a pH effect. Illustrative evidence for the effect itself is abundant—work on the Mucorales (29), higher basidiomycetes (275), and miscellaneous fungi (221) may be considered typical.

This point has been treated at some length because a requirement for "organic nitrogen," i.e., inability to grow with ammonium nitrogen, may reflect only failure of the organism to grow at low pH. *Allomyces javanicus* var. *macrogynus* (340) and *Chytridium* sp. (113) illustrate this phenomenon. No claim of failure to utilize ammonium nitrogen can stand unless the pH effect is excluded experimentally.

Other possibilities of error in claims for a non-specific organic nitrogen requirement may be mentioned. The amino acids which appear to be essential may be acting to reduce, by complex formation, the inhibitory effect of heavy metals present in the basal medium; copper is especially likely to be removed by amino acids (16, 17), and histidine specifically antidotes cobalt toxicity (411, 462). Apparently essential sources of organic nitrogen may be effective by virtue of their content of vitamins (234, 591).

The apparent glutamic acid requirement of *Allomyces javanicus* var. *macrogynus* disappears when the concentrations of glucose, potassium, and minor elements are changed and sulfate is eliminated from the medium (339).

It seems therefore that many reports of failure to utilize ammonium nitrogen (318, 343, 359, 506) must remain *sub judice*. There does appear, however, to be in some of the lower phycomycetes—*Blastocladiella emersonii* (42), *Sapromyces elongatus* (204) and, probably, *Leptomitus lacteus* (463)—a genuine inability to grow with ammonium as the sole nitrogen source, but no specific amino acid requirement. Contradictory and only semi-quantitative data on *Apodachlya brachynema* (200, 461) do not permit of a decision. Finally, the relatively few naturally occurring fungi with specific amino acid requirements (p. 259) and the many known deficient mutants are, of course, exceptions to the rule that fungi as a group can, at least under specified conditions, grow with ammonium ion as the sole source of nitrogen.

Ammonia in high concentrations is toxic (332) and may even find limited use as a fungicide (218, 388). Abnormalities in growth (458), spore germination (169), and development (108) have been traced to ammonia toxicity; especially in media with large amounts of organic nitrogen, ammonia may accumulate to an inhibitory level and contribute to the so-called staling effect (421). The toxicity of high ammonium ion concentration to *Allomyces javanicus* var. *macrogynus* is alleviated by phosphate (340).

Nitrogen Fixation. From the earliest days of microbiology, claims have been made that fungi are able, like certain bacteria, to convert gaseous nitrogen to combined nitrogen. These studies have been reviewed several times in the last generation (18, 137, 163, 202, 478). The evidence is overwhelmingly against the occurrence of nitrogen fixation in saprophytic fungi. Results with mycorrhizal fungi, particularly *Phoma* spp., have been more often positive, but isotope results fail to corroborate earlier claims (601). There is, therefore, at present no good evidence for fixation of nitrogen by the fungi. Nitrogen fixation occurs in root nodules of *Alnus glutinosa* (426), but it is not yet known what microorganism is involved; the causal agent has been variously assigned to the bacteria, the actinomycetes, the filamentous fungi, and, most recently, the Plasmodiophorales (228). Until the organism can be cultivated, both its identity and its role in nitrogen fixation will remain uncertain.

Oxidation of Inorganic Nitrogen Compounds. Heterotrophic oxidation of inorganic nitrogen compounds is effected by a few bacteria (126); this is to be distinguished from the better known autotrophic oxidation of ammonium and nitrite. Among the true fungi, *Aspergillus aureus* and *A. batatae* are reported to form nitrate from nitrite during growth (457). *Aspergillus flavus* growing on a glucose-peptone-yeast extract medium produces small amounts of nitrite and rather larger amounts of nitrate (468). This finding, if confirmed, has importance to soil microbiology. Color tests suggest that *A. niger* oxidizes ammonia to hydroxylamine (494).

Among the actinomycetes, *Nocardia corallina* oxidizes pyruvic oxime and hydroxylamine to nitrite (277, 321). An unusual species of *Streptomyces, S. nitrificans,* has been studied by Schatz and coworkers (257, 258, 464, 465). This organism utilizes urethan as the sole source of both carbon and nitrogen, and forms nitrite during growth on carbamates and during metabolism of urea or ammonium carbonate. Activity of cell-free preparations suggests a pyridine nucleotide-linked ammonium dehydrogenase. Nitrate is not formed.

Cyanide as a Metabolite. Cyanide is, of course, an effective respiratory poison, acting on iron enzymes. It has also, however, been reported to provide assimilable nitrogen to preformed mycelium of *Aspergillus niger* (271) and to cause an apparent increase in growth of *Fusarium lini* (395, 437). Data so far available, however, are not adequate for a final conclusion on the utilizability of cyanide as a nitrogen source; it is to be noted that Chughtai and Walker (104) found that the growth-promoting effect of cyanide is not duplicated by nitrate; they suggest a metabolic disturbance which diverts more carbon into dry matter. An unidentified soil organism, probably an aerobic actinomycete, makes visible growth with cyanide as the sole source of both carbon and nitrogen (578).

The liberation of hydrogen cyanide from the fruit bodies of basidiomycetes has been noted repeatedly; reports are reviewed by Bach (38), Müller (379), Robbins et al. (444), and Zellner (629). An unidentified *Mucor* sp. was reported in 1916 to form both cyanide and benzaldehyde (219). Cyanide is produced in culture, but apparently only during autolysis, not during growth (444). Fruit bodies of *Pholiota aurea* do not contain free cyanide when freshly collected, and circumstantial evidence indicates that it is released from another compound by an enzymatic reaction (37).

Production of cyanide by an unidentified basidiomycete growing under snow cover is apparently responsible for crown rot in alfalfa; the fungus in culture produces cyanide at low temperature (319, 320).

2. PROTEINS AND PEPTIDES

Nutritional Aspects. The fungi and actinomycetes as a group are active in the decomposition of proteins in soil and other materials (1, 568, 571, 572, 573). In pure culture it appears that proteins such as gelatin, casein, and egg albumin can serve as sources of nitrogen for at least the common saprophytic fungi and actinomycetes (278, 574); much more data are available on enzymatic destruction of common proteins than on their use for growth. Utilization of keratin is common only among dermatophytic fungi and, possibly, chytrids (Chapter 3). Whether fungi can attack highly purified proteins in the absence of any other nitrogen source is in doubt.

Commercial peptone—a mixture of peptides of varying chain length—is generally utilizable, but in recent years has been replaced in culture media meant for physiological studies by materials of known composition. Dipeptides and tripeptides support the growth of *Aspergillus* spp. (2, 531) and *Ustilago* spp. (62, 470); the histidine requirement of *Trichophyton rosaceum* is met by carnosine and histidylhistidine (136). The widespread occurrence of enzymes hydrolyzing peptides to amino acids indicates that in general at least the simple linear peptides will be found to be adequate sources of nitrogen for most fungi. *Tricholoma gambosum* is unusual in that growth is tripled by glycylglycine, unaffected by glycine (398).

The requirement of some Myxomycetes for protein has been mentioned elsewhere (Chapter 10).

Enzymatic Breakdown of Proteins and Peptides. Following current usage (487) we distinguish two general types of enzyme which attack peptide bonds:

1. Endopeptidases (proteinases), acting on peptide bonds either in simple peptides or in the interior of a protein chain.

2. Exopeptidases, acting only on peptide bonds which are adjacent to a free α-amino or a free carboxyl group and therefore restricted generally to hydrolysis of small peptides.

Both these types are subsumed under the general term protease.

Surveys of the activity of culture filtrates indicate than an enzyme or enzymes able to hydrolyze gelatin is extremely common among the Fungi Imperfecti (129, 130, 142, 351) and *Streptomyces* spp. (130, 276). Generalization as to other fungi is difficult; gelatin hydrolysis is, however, effected by some ascomycetes (130) and basidiomycetes (53, 629). Among the Mucorales, *Rhizopus* sp. grows upon and hydrolyzes several proteins (574), and *Mortierella renispora* forms active proteases (587, 588).

However, surveys limited to studies of the culture filtrate cannot be taken as final evidence of lack of a protease. The distribution of proteolytic enzymes between mycelium and culture fluid is conditioned both by age (185) and by the medium (208). This may explain some apparent disagreements (130, 142).

The most extensive study of the utilization of proteins by fungi and actinomycetes is that of Waksman and Starkey (574). *Streptomyces violaceus-ruber* and *Rhizopus* sp. grow upon and decompose casein, zein, gliadin, fibrin, gelatin, and egg albumin; *Trichoderma koningi* utilizes edestin, zein, gliadin, and casein. In culture, proteins are used more rapidly if there is no other carbon source, but the liberation of ammonia under these conditions is large.

Other less comprehensive studies show that fungi and actinomycetes generally hydrolyze fibrin (19, 185, 469, 567) and casein (262, 333, 485, 489, 524, 567). Keratin-hydrolyzing preparations have been obtained from *Streptomyces* sp. (399), and it may be assumed that the destruction of keratin by dermatophytic fungi is carried out by an extra-cellular enzyme (491, 492, 555). A protease of *Penicillium* sp. converts trypsinogen to trypsin, but is distinct from the enterokinase which carries out this reaction in animal tissues (312).

Fungal endopeptidases cannot be identified with known exocellular animal enzymes. However, it is reasonable to believe that studies of purified enzymes acting on synthetic substrates will eventually support a rational classification. For the present, a few general observations must suffice:

1. Crude and purified preparations from a fungus usually have their pH optimum somewhat on the alkaline side of neutrality (142, 185, 283, 335, 485), but particular activities may have an optimum as low as 4.5 (115).

2. Substrate and inhibition studies suggest that endopeptidases of the trypsin type occur in *Streptomyces* sp. (377), and in *Trichophyton gypseum* (185) and other fungi (335); a purified enzyme from *Streptomyces proteolyticus* acts on pepsin substrates but at a pH very different from that of the animal enzyme (549).

3. Crude and highly purified preparations alike consist of mixtures of different enzymes (116, 279, 335, 588, 589, 621); enzymes of even closely related strains show differences in rate of attack on different proteins (142).

Endopeptidases of *Aspergillus oryzae* have been studied thoroughly (115, 116, 198). Three different enzymes acting on proteins have been separated. The major component probably acts on most proteins, in-cluding those which lack aromatic acids, and has been obtained in a crystalline, although not completely pure, state (114, 198).

Culture filtrates of *Streptomyces* spp. lyse bacterial cells. Lysis of heat-killed Gram-negative bacteria has been attributed to a protease (67, 285, 376, 519). Lysis of Gram-positive bacterial cells by different species of *Streptomyces* is effected, however, by an enzyme similar to lysozyme, i.e., a mucopolysaccharase (333, 334), or by the combined action of a ribonuclease and a protease (376, 378).

The formation of exocellular protein-hydrolyzing enzymes by some fungi and actinomycetes proceeds in synthetic media with inorganic nitrogen sources (131, 185, 352); for other species a more complex medium may be required (131). There is as yet no good evidence of enzyme induction by substrate, although use of protein media may increase yields (53, 530). A study of cultural conditions as they affect endopeptidase formation by *Aspergillus oryzae* shows, as expected, optima for carbon source, salts, iron, and temperature (352).

Culture filtrates or mycelial extracts of fungi commonly, perhaps universally, hydrolyze peptides. However, it is hazardous at present to identify this activity with particular exopeptidases known from other sources or even to state categorically that endopeptidase activity has been excluded in many of the reports. *Aspergillus parasiticus* forms four exopeptidases, including an aminopeptidase which is activated by zinc and by reducing agents (284); these same activators affect the aminopeptidase of *Penicillium* spp. (52). A number of fungi—*Aspergillus* spp., *Penicillium* spp., *Cunninghamella* sp., *Coprinus radians*, and *Agaricus campestris*—form a dipeptidase, an aminopeptidase, and a carboxypeptidase; many of these fungi also elaborate an aminotripeptidase assayed with triglycine, and a glycylglycine dipeptidase (53). A similar range of activities is reported for *Mortierella renispora*, *Chaetomium* sp., and other fungi (336).

Glycylglycine dipeptidase of *Aspergillus oryzae* is activated by cobalt (115), as is the same enzyme from other sources (487). Dipeptidases also are produced by *Physarum polycephalum* (244), *Piricularia oryzae* (259), *Penicillium notatum* (263) and other fungi (336, 403).

Hydrolysis of some amides may be effected by enzymes which also act on peptides or proteins; "hippuricase," for example, may be identical with a carboxypeptidase (182).

It appears, in summary, that fungi produce a battery of enzymes attacking peptides of low molecular weight. Information is at present too fragmentary for a detailed classification of the fungal exopeptidases; the availability of synthetic test substrates (487) makes the development of such a classification a possible enterprise.

Peptides of Fungi and Actinomycetes. Following Bricas and Fromageot (76), we may define peptides as compounds of low molecular weight which contain two or more amino acids and peptide or peptidoid bonds. This excludes certain compounds such as pantothenic acid and biocytin (Chapter 10), in which one amino acid and a non-amino acid moiety are joined by a peptide linkage. The naturally occurring peptides may be classified as homeomeric—consisting only of amino acids—and heteromeric—consisting of amino acids and a non-amino acid moiety.

Glutathione perhaps deserves first place in this discussion because of its probable ubiquity in living cells, its vital role in triose phosphate dehydrogenase, and its probable role in peptide synthesis (76). Using an iodometric method of possibly doubtful specificity, Miller and Stone (366) report the presence of glutathione in mycelium of *Neurospora sitophila* and other fungi. The common occurrence in fungi of triose phosphate dehydrogenase (Chapter 7), of which glutathione is the prosthetic group (308), indicates that the peptide is at least widespread among fungi and actinomycetes. A mutant of *Glomerella* sp. requires glutathione, and nutritional evidence suggests that it is deficient in the ability to form the component dipeptide γ-glutamylcysteine (348).

The actinomycins form a group of related antibiotics first discovered by Waksman and Woodruff (575) and produced by *Streptomyces* spp. (79) and by *Micromonospora* sp. (157). Chemically they are heteromeric peptides; all contain the same chromophore, or despeptido-actinomycin, of the structure (81):

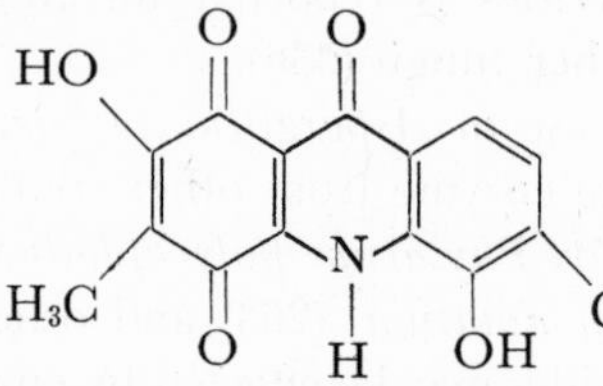

The peptide chain distinguishes the various actinomycins, very many of which have been described (78, 79); the identity of the individual actinomycins is much in doubt, since it appears that many of the isolated fractions are in fact different mixtures of the same components (452). A given strain may produce one type or mixture early, another later, in the culture cycle (210).

Several other antibiotics of *Streptomyces* spp. are or contain peptide chains; examples include viomycin, streptothricin and streptolin (76), and the less completely characterized amphomycin (230) and levomycin (95). Polypeptide antibiotics are very common also among the true bacteria. Such compounds are not usual among the filamentous fungi, although penicillin (Chapter 6) may be considered as a heteromeric cyclic peptide, and the toxin of *Helminthosporium victoriae* is probably a polypeptide (421a).

Lycomarasmin, reviewed by Gäumann (190), is a peptide produced by *Fusarium oxysporum* f. *lycopersici;* although it is able to cause wilting of plants, its role in natural pathogenesis in the wilt diseases is in dispute. It appears in quantity in the medium fairly late in the culture cycle, after autolysis has begun (Figure 5). A heteromeric peptide, its structure has been determined (609) to be N-(α-[α-hydroxypropionic acid])-glycyl-asparagine.

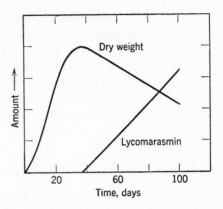

Figure 5. Growth and lycomarasmin formation (in the culture medium) in *Fusarium oxysporum* f. *lycopersici.* Redrawn from Dimond and Waggoner (127), by permission of *Phytopathology.*

Lycomarasmin forms a complex with iron, and it is the complex which is responsible for all or most of its toxicity to higher plants (190, 564). Both free lycomarasmin and the iron complex are relatively unstable in solution (128).

Two heteromeric peptides, enniatin A and enniatin B, are also produced by *Fusarium* spp. (190, 417, 418) and, like lycomarasmin, cause wilting of plants (193).

Aspergillus fumigatus and *Streptomyces* spp. release into the culture medium a diketopiperazine, the anhydride of L-leucyl-L-proline, previously known only from animal sources (280).

Lastly, the toxins of *Amanita* spp. may be mentioned; they have been reviewed most recently by Block, Stephens, and Murrill (61). Originally, the hemolytic nitrogenous glucoside phallin was separated from "amanitin" (8, 466); later, it was discovered that the second material is in fact three closely related peptides, now known as α-amanitine, β-amanitine, and phalloidine. The European form of *Amanita phalloides* contains all three of these compounds, amounting in total to about 0.005 per cent of its fresh weight (596). Other species of *Amanita* have only one or two of the peptides, and most species have none (61). A complete structure has been proposed only for phalloidine (597), although the three toxins have been separated and purified (60, 594, 596). The suggested structure, that of a bicyclic hexapeptide, is unusual in that two amino acids are joined by a sulfur bridge.

The excretion of unidentified nitrogenous compounds, primarily peptides, into the medium during growth has been studied by Morton and Broadbent (374). This excretion occurs in *Scopulariopsis brevicaulis* during the period of rapid growth, i.e., it is not an autolytic phenomenon in the usual sense; about 25 per cent of the nitrogen supplied appears in the medium, and it is not reutilized.

The enzymatic basis of peptide synthesis in fungi is at present unknown. Extracts of *Neurospora crassa* mycelium show γ-glutamyl transferase activity; conceivably this system could function in the synthesis of peptides of glutamic acid (563). In *Bacillus subtilis* glutamyl di- and tripeptides are synthesized by transfer reactions of this general type (600).

3. UTILIZATION OF AMINO ACIDS AND AMIDES

Amino Acids and Amides in Nutrition. The specificity of response to different amino acids indicates that in fungi as in other organisms amino acids are assimilated primarily as such, and that conversion to ammonia before assimilation of the nitrogen is at best a secondary pathway (44, 542). It can be shown by analysis that amino acids are assimilated at varying rates from a complex medium and that they exist in part, as mentioned earlier (Chapter 2), as free acids in the mycelium. Typically, the amino acid content of a medium drops as the acids are taken up, then rises again as they are liberated during autolysis (181, 413, 423).

The value of individual amino acids for fungi is customarily assayed by growth on media containing the amino acid of interest as the sole nitrogen source. Studies of this type are numerous but generalization from them is difficult; we find that a given amino acid allows very good growth of one organism and only very little growth of another, but we are not able to say whether this reflects permeability, enzymatic capacities, or merely such secondary problems as acidity changes consequent upon utilization. In addition, amino acids and amides from natural sources may be contaminated with vitamins and there may also be metabolic consequences of the chelation of inorganic ions by amino acids.

Most investigations more or less agree that glycine, asparagine, glutamic acid, and aspartic acid are the most likely to support good growth. However, it is relatively easy to find fungi which grow only poorly with asparagine (164, 252, 440, 625), aspartate (110, 278), or glutamate (275, 278). Conversely, leucine is generally not an adequate source of nitrogen (409), but for *Trichophyton persicolor* it is one of the most easily utilizable of the amino acids (506); tryptophan, usually not well utilized, supports normal growth of *Streptomyces coelicolor* (106). Examples of this type could be multiplied to establish the point that, although generalizations may be made which fit most

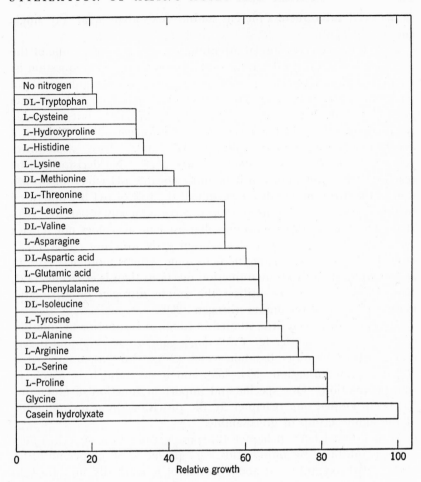

Figure 6. The growth of *Venturia inaequalis* in media with amino acids as the source of nitrogen. Each value is the mean of 27 observations (3 concentrations, 3 incubation periods, and 3 replicates). Growth on casein hydrolyzate has been given a relative value of 100. Drawn from tabular data of Pelletier and Keitt (409).

fungi, they will not necessarily apply to any one fungus which happens to be of interest.

The data of Figure 6 show the range of utilizability of the common amino acids for *Venturia inaequalis*. Statistical analysis of these and other data shows that the apparent relative value of different amino acids is affected by the period of incubation, the nature of the basal medium, and the concentrations of amino acids used (409). Figure 6 also brings out the point that growth is usually better with a natural or artificial mixture of different amino acids than with any single amino acid (442).

Asparagine deserves special attention, since it is so often one of the best sources of nitrogen for fungi and actinomycetes. The question is: does the amide have some particular value, or is asparagine merely a source of aspartic acid and extra nitrogen? Asparagine and aspartate are about equivalent for many fungi (25, 46, 275, 604), but the amide is superior to the acid for *Tricholoma imbricatum* (398), *Piricularia oryzae* (406), and *Leptographium* sp. (317), and, at least as sole nitrogen source, for *Phycomyces blakesleeanus* (323). No decision can be reached at this time, nor can it be until possible pH effects of utilization of the two compounds are excluded; the role of pH is emphasized by the response of *Coprinus hiascens* to asparagine and aspartate (165). It is significant in this connection that aspartic acid does not replace the asparagine requirement of a mutant of *Neurospora crassa* (523). It is also known that asparagine is in some systems more active as an amino group donor to transamination reactions than is aspartate (354, 355). *Piricularia oryzae* utilizes the amide nitrogen of asparagine more rapidly than the amino nitrogen (260).

Glutamine has been little studied in fungi; it is superior to glutamic acid as a nitrogen source for *Tricholoma gambosum* (398) and is generally utilized by other basidiomycetes (275). Like asparagine, it is active in transamination (354, 355), and it may also have a role in transpeptidation. One specific and important function of glutamine has been pointed out (Chapter 5), the provision, by transamidation, of the amino group of glucosamine.

As mentioned later (Chapter 12) spore germination of *Neurospora crassa* is inhibited by amino acids, e.g., glycine at 50 μg per milliliter (453). Hydroxyproline at about this level is markedly inhibitory to *Trichophyton* spp. and other dermatophytic fungi (443, 471). Hydroxyproline is not toxic to other fungi; its action on *Trichophyton mentagrophytes* is partially reversed by L-proline (443). Methionine and phenylalanine are also inhibitory to *Trichophyton* spp. (506), methionine to other fungi (169). The possibility that toxicity is exerted at the cell surface deserves exploration, in view of studies on histidine mentioned below.

The aliphatic amides, although possibly acted upon by fungal enzymes (p. 265), are not generally utilizable; acetamide may be an exception (39, 63, 120).

Utilization of the D-isomers of the amino acids is specific; thus, *Apodachlya brachynema* utilizes D-leucine, but *Leptomitus lacteus* does not (463), and *Ustilago scabiosae* can grow with D-valine, D-isoleucine, or D-alanine, but not with D-leucine or D-phenylalanine as nitrogen source (62).

It seems likely that utilization of the D-amino acids depends upon oxidative deamination by D-amino acid oxidase (p. 260); ammonia liberated by the oxidase system is then presumed to be incorporated into L-acids (245). Specific racemases effecting direct interconversion of the D- and L-forms, are known in bacteria (22, 28, 286, 383, 608), not as yet in fungi. Presumably a second factor in utilization of the D-amino acids is their occasional toxicity (149).

Specific amino acid requirements appear with reasonable frequency as induced mutations in fungi. They are, however, uncommon in nature and, when found, are more apt to be conditioned or partial deficiencies than absolute requirements. Thus, *Mycena rubromarginata* responds in growth to tyrosine or phenylalanine, but grows without either (169), and *Cenococcum graniforme* has a partial requirement for histidine (358). *Eremothecium ashbyii* requires several amino acids only in acid media (619). An absolute requirement for histidine has been reported in *Trichophyton* spp. (135, 136, 196), as has a requirement for arginine in *T. tonsurans* (515); these reports are based on responses in agar media. *Labryinthula minuta* var. *atlantica* requires leucine (559), *Lentinus omphalodes* tryptophan (171).

Requirements for methionine or cysteine are assumed to be related to sulfur rather than nitrogen metabolism, and are considered in Chapter 9; cysteine may also promote the growth of an organism requiring a low oxidation-reduction potential (275).

Transport of Amino Acids into the Cell. In the present context, the main purpose of this section must be to call attention to a problem which has been only tentatively explored in the fungi, and for the solution of which promising experimental techniques are available. We know that a free amino acid pool exists in fungal cells, that transport across the membrane occurs in both directions, and that proteins and peptides are synthesized. In bacteria, yeast, and animal cells there is good evidence that some or all amino acids enter the cell by an active transport mechanism requiring an expenditure of metabolic energy, but different organisms cannot at present be fitted into any single pattern (100, 183, 188); lysine accumulation, for example, appears to be independent of an energy source in Gram-positive bacteria, but glutamic acid enters only if glucose is being respired. Histidine enters the cells of *Neurospora crassa* against a concentration gradient; the uptake is inhibited by arginine and methionine, which are, consequently, toxic to a histidine-requiring mutant (350). An analogous interaction accounts for the toxicity to *Lactobacillus arabinosus* of D-alanine (293). Threonine uptake is possibly inhibited in *N. crassa* by other amino acids, but this is not yet certain (566).

Catabolism of Amino Acids. The breakdown of amino acids and amides may be reviewed under two general headings, the processes which lead to removal of nitrogen and the processes which alter the carbon skeleton. These two categories of biochemical change are reviewed by Cohen (109) and Greenberg (214), respectively. We must restrict this discussion largely to the fungi, and only a very incomplete picture of amino acid metabolism will emerge, inasmuch as many important reactions known in other organisms have not yet been investigated in the fungi.

One approach to amino acid catabolism is to determine what compounds are either oxidized or deaminated by resting cells, using manometric data or ammonia determinations as criteria. *Penicillium chrysogenum,* for example, oxidizes glutamic acid, proline, and alanine rapidly, other amino acids more slowly or not at all, as judged by oxygen uptake (603). Washed cells of *Streptomyces venezuelae* liberate ammonia from glutamate, arginine, proline, and other amino acids, not from tyrosine, trytophan, leucine or cysteine; only those amino acids which are attacked can serve as sole sources of nitrogen for growth (212). *Leptomitus lacteus* oxidizes and deaminates L-alanine, glycine, and L-leucine (463).

A second avenue of investigation of amino acid catabolism is the study of particular enzymatic activities in cell-free preparations or as reflected in activities of intact cells. Most efforts of this type have been focused on amino acid oxidase (dehydrogenase) systems; scattered information on other reactions is available but difficult to systematize.

The D- and L-amino acid oxidases are flavoproteins known and studied in animal systems; their general properties are reviewed by Cohen (109) and Meister (355). The usual manometric system, employing crude extracts which contain catalase, may be formulated as follows:

$$R—CH(NH_2)—COOH + \tfrac{1}{2} O_2 \rightarrow R—CO—COOH + NH_3 \quad (3)$$

Amino acid   α-Keto acid

In the absence of catalase, the keto acid is decarboxylated and the over-all reaction then proceeds:

$$R—CH(NH_2)—COOH + O_2 \rightarrow R—COOH + NH_3 + CO_2 \quad (4)$$

The D-amino acid oxidase of *Neurospora crassa* acts at varying rates on a number of amino acids (Figure 7); detailed comparison with the

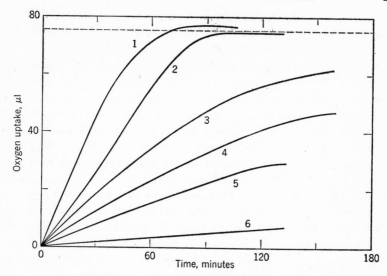

Figure 7. The oxidation of some amino acids by the D-amino acid oxidase system of *Neurospora crassa*. Curves 1 to 6 represent, in sequence, the rate of oxidation of methionine, leucine, isoleucine, valine, lysine, and ornithine. The broken horizontal line is drawn at the theoretical value for the complete oxidation of the D-isomer. Redrawn from Horowitz (245), by permission of the *Journal of Biological Chemistry*.

corresponding enzyme of sheep kidney reveals that the rates of attack on amino acids and the response to inhibitors of the two systems are somewhat different (47). The enzyme exhibits maximal activity at pH 8.0–8.5 (245). The same or a very similar enzyme is found in mycelial extracts of *Aspergillus niger* and three *Penicillium* spp., not in *P. sanguineum* (143). The different fungal preparations differ somewhat in their substrate preferences (47, 143). *Penicillium chrysogenum* forms much more of the enzyme in a synthetic than in a complex medium (143).

An oxidase system acting on L-amino acids has been shown in *Neurospora* spp. (47, 87, 536), both in cells and in the medium (48). The enzyme has a somewhat broader substrate specificity than the L-amino acid oxidase of cobra venom (47). Indirect evidence supports the assumption that the prosthetic group is flavin adenine dinucleotide (87). Enzyme yield is increased by cultivation with casein hydrolyzate, but this presumed induction occurs only in a low-biotin medium (536). Endogenous amino acids interfere with detection of the enzyme (536).

The L-amino acid oxidase of *Neurospora crassa* converts lysine to its keto analogue, which exists in a cyclic form as, probably, Δ'-dehydro-pipecolic acid; this compound may be either reduced to pipecolic acid or reconverted to lysine (476).

Although several other fungi show L-amino acid oxidase activity (51, 87, 99, 224, 299), it is not yet certain that the enzyme is identical in all forms. The formation of α-keto acids by growing or resting cells supplied with the corresponding L-amino acid is often observed, and may be taken as presumptive evidence for an L-amino acid oxidase (551, 552, 602). The formation of isoamyl alcohol from leucine (422) probably reflects oxidative conversion of the amino acid to a keto acid, followed by decarboxylation and reduction.

It should be stressed that chemical attack on an L-amino acid does not, by itself, prove that an L-amino acid oxidase is present. A combination of transaminase and glutamic dehydrogenase activities could —and probably does in mammalian tissues (355)—bring about oxidative deamination without the participation of an oxidase, and the over-all stoichiometry would be identical with Equation 3.

Glutamic dehydrogenase has a wide distribution in nature, and has been found in extracts of *Neurospora crassa* mycelium (152). Unlike the oxidases, it is specific to L-glutamic acid and requires the participation of a pyridine nucleotide. The reaction may be formulated:

$$HOOC—(CH_2)_2—CH(NH_2)COOH + TPN+$$
L-Glutamic acid

$$\leftrightharpoons HOOC—(CH_2)_2—CO—COOH$$
$$+ TPNH + H^+ + NH_3 \qquad \text{\scriptsize α-Ketoglutaric acid} \qquad (5)$$

Glutamic dehydrogenase is probably the key to synthesis of amino acids (see below) and to the entrance of ammonia into organic combination; its possible role in deamination of other amino acids has just been mentioned.

Non-oxidative deamination of L-serine and L-threonine is effected by serine dehydrase of *Neurospora crassa* (435, 618); the products are, respectively, pyruvate and α-ketobutyrate. Another pyridoxal phosphate enzyme of *N. crassa* deaminates D-serine (617). Neither D-serine nor D-threonine is attacked by the *N. crassa* D-amino acid oxidase (47).

Aspartase, converting aspartate non-oxidatively to fumaric acid and ammonia, is also reported to be formed by *Neurospora crassa* (480) and *Penicillium notatum* (547).

Transamination results, of course, in the deamination of the donor amino acid; the process is considered later, in connection with amino acid biosynthesis.

Catabolism of the carbon chain of amino acids by fungi can be considered at present only on the basis of fragments of information, many of which, however, are suggestive of breakdown pathways known in other organisms.

Tyrosine in at least some fungi and actinomycetes is attacked by tyrosinase, a polyphenol oxidase (Chapter 6). The sequence of reactions in *Neurospora crassa* (248) appears to be at least in general the same as in mammalian systems (324): tyrosine is oxidized via 2,4-dihydroxyphenylalanine ("dopa") through a red hallochrome pigment to an insoluble black pigment, a melanin. The pigment of *Streptomyces scabies* probably—although evidence is incomplete—is formed by this same pathway (15, 133, 242, 243), and it is usually assumed that black insoluble pigments as a group are products of tyrosinase action.

In mammalian liver, tyrosine is oxidized to acetoacetic acid and fumaric acid by the following sequence of reactions (214):

$$\text{Tyrosine} \rightarrow p\text{-hydroxyphenylpyruvic acid} \rightarrow$$
$$2,5\text{-dihydroxyphenylpyruvic acid} \rightarrow \text{homogentisic}$$
$$\text{acid} \rightarrow \text{acetoacetate} + \text{fumarate} \tag{6}$$

The last reaction—actually three reactions (300)—is not known in fungi. Homogentisic acid can be isolated as a product of the tyrosine metabolism of *Aspergillus niger* and *Penicillium* spp. (261, 298, 554); inhibition data implicate p-hydroxyphenylpyruvate in the tyrosine metabolism of *Neurospora crassa* (125).

The isolation of tyramine from *Aspergillus niger* cultures (552) suggests another type of tyrosine breakdown, by decarboxylation, as in bacterial systems.

Tryptophan catabolism in fungi has been studied principally in relation to nicotinic acid biogenesis (Chapter 10). Other pathways are known in bacteria (14, 121, 214, 493) involving indole, catechol, kynurenic acid, or 5-hydroxytryptophan. A preparation from *Neurospora crassa* converts 3-hydroxykynurenine, an intermediate in nicotinic acid biosynthesis, to xanthurenic acid (353).

Indoleacetic acid (auxin), a growth regulator for higher plants, is produced by several fungi, including *Aspergillus niger, Phycomyces nitens,* and *Rhizopus suinus,* and by soil actinomycetes and bacteria (72, 73, 236, 302, 394, 446, 448). Its obvious structural relation to tryptophan and the effect of the amino acid in stimulating its formation by fungi indicate that the auxin is formed from tryptophan (537, 605). Production by *Rhizopus suinus* is increased by aeration (538). Detailed enzymatic studies of the synthesis have not appeared, but it has been suggested that oxidative deamination, decarboxylation, and oxidation reactions occur as follows (353, 584):

$$\text{Tryptophan} \rightarrow \text{indolepyruvic acid} \rightarrow$$
$$\text{indoleacetaldehyde} \rightarrow \text{indoleacetic acid} \tag{7}$$

Although from time to time it is reported that indoleacetic acid increases the growth of fungi, most studies have not shown this (367, 438, 584) or show it only under special circumstances (235). However, acceleration of the maturation of the meiosporangium of *Allomyces arbuscula* on agar media, perhaps by an effect on the sporangium wall, indubitably occurs (341). Growth inhibition by indoleacetate is common (71, 235, 438, 449); in *Nectria galligena* inhibition is reduced by biotin (400, 401). It has been argued, on the basis of inhibition studies alone, that indoleacetate is an essential metabolite of *Diplodia natalensis* (195); the evidence, however, is subject to other interpretations.

Destruction of indoleacetic acid occurs in the cultures in which it is produced (584), and cell-free enzyme systems of several basidiomycetes inactivate the auxin (77, 148, 479, 545). The enzyme of *Omphalia flavida* is highly specific, oxidizing indoleacetate with equimolar amounts of oxygen at pH 3.5; the first product of the reaction is not known (430, 431).

Threonine is cleaved by *Neurospora crassa* to glycine and acetaldehyde (565); this non-oxidative reaction occurs also in animal systems (214).

The breakdown of histidine in bacterial and animal preparations proceeds via urocanic and glutamic acids (339, 516); this system has not been studied in fungi, although glutamate does accumulate during histidine breakdown by *Streptomyces venezuelae* (212). Histidine decarboxylase could not be detected in *Claviceps purpurea* or *Aspergillus* spp. (585).

The oxidation of cysteine sulfur is mentioned in Chapter 9, and the role of methionine as a methyl donor in Chapter 6. No other significant information on the breakdown of the carbon chains of these compounds by fungi is available. Cysteine desulfhydrase is not detectable in *Penicillium chrysogenum;* its occurrence in bacteria is reviewed by Fromageot (180).

Arginine is broken down in the urea cycle, discussed later. *Streptomyces griseus* extracts contain an inducible enzyme which converts arginine to guanidinobutyramide (539, 540).

Glutamic acid is probably the principal donor of amino groups in transaminations (p. 267); in the process it is converted to α-ketoglutaric acid. Hence its carbon chain may be assumed to be oxidized by the tricarboxylic acid cycle. Glutamic decarboxylase, presumably yielding γ-aminobutyric acid, has been detected in *Penicillium chrysogenum* (201) and *Endomycopsis vernalis* (290).

It might be at first glance surprising that proline, a ring compound, is generally an excellent source of nitrogen for fungi (275, 278, 409, 412). The answer conceivably lies in a ready conversion of proline to glutamic acid, i.e., reversal of the steps in the synthesis of proline from glutamate (p. 268).

Hydrolysis of Acyl Amino Acids and Amides. Nitrogen-acylated amino acids are hydrolyzed, liberating the free amino acid, by preparations from *Aspergillus* spp. and *Penicillium* spp. (263, 364, 389, 405). Although these reactions may be referred to as acylase activity, it must be realized that there is in fungi no clear separation of acylases, amidases, and peptidases, all of which act on the —C—O—N< bond.

Hippuricase (histozyme) splits hippuric acid (N-benzoylglycine) to benzoic acid and glycine. Its identity and relation to other acylases and to peptidases is still obscure; certain other N-benzoylated L-α-amino acids are attacked (325). It has most recently been studied in *Penicillium* spp. (263, 456); reports of its occurrence in other fungi are reviewed by Leuthardt (325).

Asparaginase, hydrolyzing asparagine to aspartic acid and ammonia, has received some attention, although it has not been purified. Activity is found in *Aspergillus niger* (467), *Penicillium* spp. (134, 456, 535), *Microsporum* spp. (51), and *Piricularia oryzae* (260). The optimum pH is about 8 (32, 51, 467). The enzyme of *A. niger* is liberated into the medium only on autolysis (33), is not easily solubilized in sand-ground preparations (35), is unstable (36, 630), and is formed in cells grown on a synthetic medium (467).

Amidase activity against glutamine is found in yeast, bacteria, and higher animals (630); it is probably common in the fungi, but has been reported so far only in *Neurospora crassa* (523).

Several early reports, reviewed by Foster (163), suggest that fungal enzymes also act on aliphatic or aromatic amides, e.g., acetamide and benzamide. In view of the negative results of Schmalfuss and Mothes (467) it is perhaps best to suspend judgment, although aliphatic amides are hydrolyzed by *Torula utilis* (630). Penicillinase and penicillin amidase, both acting on amide linkages, have been mentioned briefly in Chapter 6.

4. BIOSYNTHESIS OF AMINO ACIDS

The formation of amino acids by fungi may be considered for our purposes from three aspects: (1) the entrance of nitrogen into the amino acid pool, (2) transfer of the nitrogen from one amino acid to another, and (3) biosynthesis of the carbon chains of known amino acids either before or after incorporation of nitrogen.

Most attention has been directed toward the synthesis of the protein amino acids. Even a superficial survey reveals that many other amino acids are formed by fungi either free or in combined form. Gamma-aminobutyric acid, probably arising from glutamate by decarboxylation, is rather common (374, 380, 486, 612). Djenkolic acid is found free in extracts and culture fluids of *Tilletia caries* (380). Beta-lysine occurs in several actinomycete antibiotics (56, 76, 382). Antibiotics of fungi and actinomycetes yield on hydrolysis numerous N-methyl amino acids, for example, sarcosine, N-methylvaline, and N-methyliso-leucine (78, 417). Alpha-hydroxy amino acids occur combined in ly-comarasmin (609) and in ergot compounds (76), while D-α-methylserine is a constituent of the antibiotic amicetin (160).

Entrance of Nitrogen into the Amino Acid Pool. We have observed that most fungi utilize ammonium nitrogen as the major or sole nitrogen source; other inorganic forms are, we may assume with certain reservations, converted to ammonia before assimilation. The best-established reaction is the amination of α-ketoglutaric acid derived from carbohydrate via the tricarboxylic acid cycle, to form glutamic acid, i.e., by the reversal of Equation 5. As mentioned, the only fungus in which this enzyme has been unequivocally demonstrated is *Neurospora crassa;* distribution of carbon-14 in glutamate is consistent with the operation of this reaction in *Streptomyces griseus* (89, 199).

Reversal of aspartase action occurs in bacteria (145, 183) and the enzyme is known in fungi (p. 262). It is not yet, however, known whether the reverse reaction:

$$\text{Fumaric acid} + \text{NH}_3 \rightarrow \text{D-aspartic acid} \tag{8}$$

makes a significant contribution to amino acid synthesis in fungi. This leaves us for the moment with only one mechanism for the entrance of nitrogen into amino acids. On grounds of comparative biochemistry, however, it seems likely that future work will uncover other mechanisms, especially in the synthesis of amides and of tryptophan, histidine, serine, and other amino acids. *Blastocladiella emersonii,* which will not grow with ammonia as sole nitrogen source, forms glutamate from labeled glucose, but isotopic equilibrium with α-ketoglu-tarate is not observed; this suggests that glutamic acid arises in some other way (91).

Transamination. In organisms generally, the amino group of glutamic acid can be transferred to various keto acids, yielding α-ketoglutaric acid and a new α-amino acid, thus:

$$HOOC-CH_2-CH_2-CH(NH_2)-COOH + R-CO-COOH$$

L-Glutamic acid α-Keto acid

$$\rightleftharpoons HOOC-CH_2-CH_2-CO-COOH$$

α-Ketoglutaric acid

$$+ R-CH(NH_2)COOH \qquad\qquad (9)$$

α-amino acid

Investigation of these enzymes in filamentous fungi has only begun, with the identification in *Neurospora crassa* of the transaminase reactions in which aspartate and alanine participate as the $R-CH(NH_2)COOH$ of Equation 9 (151). Mutants which lack glutamic dehydrogenase exhibit a requirement for any of several amino acids; the fact that so many different amino acids support growth argues for an extensive transaminase system in *N. crassa* (151, 152, 154).

Aspergillus fumigatus homogenates carry out the reaction (445):

$$H_2N-(CH_2)_3-COOH + HOOC-(CH_2)_2-CO-COOH \rightleftharpoons$$

γ-Aminobutyric acid α-Ketoglutaric acid

$$HOOC-(CH_2)_2-CH(NH_2)-COOH \qquad\qquad (10)$$

L-Glutamic acid

This represents the transfer of an ω-amino group, and is similar to the formation of glutamate from ornithine and α-keto-glutarate by extracts of *Neurospora crassa* (153, 155). *Endomycopsis vernalis* also forms glutamic acid by the reaction of Equation 10 (290). As in other organisms, transaminations in *N. crassa* are activated by pyridoxal phosphate (151).

A kynurenine transaminase, catalyzing the transfer of the α-amino group of kynurenine or 3-hydroxykynurenine to keto acids, has been partially purified from extracts of *Neurospora crassa;* again, pyridoxal phosphate is required (274).

Asparagine and glutamine participate also in transaminations; the amino nitrogen is transferred to any of several keto acids (355). This reaction has not been explored in the fungi.

Biosynthesis of Amino Acid Carbon Skeletons. Perhaps in no field of biochemistry have the techniques of biochemical genetics been more fruitfully employed than in that of amino acid synthesis; *Neurospora crassa* has been especially useful. In recent years, the application of isotype and enzymatic methods has provided additional valuable information. It is not always realized that there are serious pitfalls in all methods which seek to state unequivocally that this or that compound is an obligatory precursor of a given metabolite. Adelberg (11) has critically reviewed these problems with the conclusion that "present-day techniques are unable to establish metabolic intermediates with finality." In practice, one approaches certainty or conviction as more and more evidence from different types of experiment is accumulated (123).

It seems appropriate to include here only a sketch of the more important biosynthetic pathways which are known, or are likely, to be functional in one or more fungi. As will be seen, there is little evidence from fungi other than *Neurospora crassa*. Following Davis (123), we shall consider groups of amino acids which are known to be biosynthetically related.

A family of amino acids is derived more or less directly from glutamic acid. Omitting details, the following over-all formulation may be suggested (123, 500):

$$\text{Glutamic acid} \begin{array}{l} \nearrow \text{glutamine} \\ \searrow \text{proline} \rightarrow \text{hydroxyproline} \end{array} \qquad (11)$$

Evidence from fungi is, however, limited at present to the glutamate-proline interconversion (9, 64, 561, 624), and the appearance of Δ'-pyrroline-5-carboxylic acid, the immediate precursor of proline in Equation 11, in glutamate cultures of *Aspergillus oryzae* (486).

Ornithine biosynthesis in *Neurospora crassa* starts from glutamic acid also; the pathways, however, are not at all clear. Vogel (560) suggests the following sequence in *N. crassa* and *Torulopsis utilis:*

$$\text{Glutamic acid} \rightarrow \text{glutamic } \gamma\text{-semialdehyde} \rightarrow \text{ornithine} \qquad (12)$$

This is rather different from the *Escherichia coli* system (123), which depends upon acetylated intermediates. There may be in *N. crassa* some other pathway of ornithine biosynthesis than that of Equation 12 (153, 560).

Ornithine participates in the ornithine cycle, first worked out in animal systems (307) and later found to function in *Neurospora crassa* (156, 490). The basic elements of the cycle, leaving aside biochemical details, are schematized in Figure 8. *N. crassa,* although forming urease, does not liberate urea; we may suppose that the cycle here serves primarily to supply arginine for protein synthesis. Nutritional data suggest the same general pattern in *Penicillium chrysogenum* (64). Urea is a common product of fungi, but direct evidence implicating

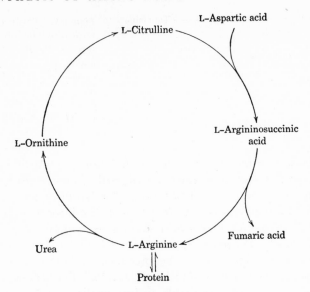

Figure 8. The ornithine cycle (429).

the ornithine cycle in net formation of urea has not yet appeared. Ornithine appears in the medium during breakdown of arginine by *Streptomyces venezuelae* (212).

Canavanine, a hydroxyguanidine derivative structurally related to arginine, inhibits the growth of some normal strains of *Neurospora crassa* (251). The inhibition has been traced (576) to the formation of a canavinino-succinate which blocks the splitting of arginino-succinate.

Of the short-chain amino acids—glycine, alanine, serine, and cysteine —only the first named has received much attention in fungi. A glycine-requiring mutant of *Neurospora crassa* can grow normally if given either glycolic or glyoxylic acids (613). This is in agreement with animal studies (356, 582), and suggests the following sequence:

$$\text{HOOC—CH}_2\text{OH} \rightarrow \text{HOOC—CHO} \rightarrow \text{HOOC—CH}_2\text{NH}_2 \quad (13)$$

Glycolic acid   Glyoxylic acid   Glycine

Drawing on experience with other organisms, we may suggest that the glycolate arises from pentose phosphate (583), and that the amino group is introduced by a transamination from glutamate or other amino donor.

Glycine and serine are closely related in *Penicillium notatum* (26) and *Eremothecium ashbyii* (206, 207). Both participate in a variety of biochemical reactions and are clearly related in their biosynthesis; it cannot yet be said which is formed first.

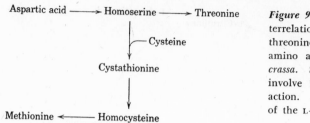

Figure 9. The probable interrelations of aspartic acid, threonine, and the sulfur amino acids in *Neurospora crassa*. Several of the steps involve more than one reaction. All amino acids are of the L-configuration.

Nutritional and metabolic studies on methionine-requiring mutants of *Neurospora crassa* established an over-all sequence leading from cysteine to methionine (159, 247, 533). A relation of threonine and methionine biosynthesis is suggested by both inhibition studies (132) and nutritional requirements of a single-gene mutant (533). These relations are schematized in Figure 9, to which has been added the postulate that aspartic acid is the precursor of both threonine and methionine, as it is in yeast and bacteria (59). The scheme is by no means complete; there is probably an intermediate between homocysteine and methionine (92), and the source of the methyl group of methionine is not yet clear. An enzyme converting homoserine to threonine occurs in fungi (578a).

Sulfur-methylcysteine is formed by *Neurospora crassa* and the isolated compound is utilizable as a source of sulfur (427).

Canavanine has been mentioned as an inhibitor of arginine synthesis. It has also been suggested that canavanine-resistant strains convert canavanine to homoserine (329); *Streptococcus faecalis* carries out this reaction (292). Such a conversion would explain why canavanine replaces threonine for some *N. crassa* mutants (532).

Isoleucine and valine are synthesized by *Neurospora crassa* from, respectively, α,β-dihydroxy-β-ethylbutyric acid and α,β-dihydroxy-β-methylbutyric acid (13). An observed double requirement for both isoleucine and valine (65) has been traced to a deficiency in the dehydrase—possibly dehydrases—which convert these dihydroxy acids to keto acids (381). There is some evidence that the precursors of valine and isoleucine ultimately arise from, respectively, pyruvic acid and threonine (12, 13, 565).

The keto analogue of leucine, α-ketoisocaproic acid, replaces leucine for a mutant of *Neurospora crassa*, and is considered therefore to be a precursor of it (432). Earlier steps in leucine biosynthesis by fungi are not known.

Studies on *Neurospora crassa* have shown that both α-aminoadipic acid and α-amino-ϵ-hydroxycaproic acid serve as precursors of lysine, probably both being converted to a semialdehyde (475, 611). Since *Ophiostoma multiannulatum* lysineless mutants utilize α-ketoadipic acid, it is probable that this compound is the precursor of α-aminoadipic acid (54).

A series of investigations of histidineless mutants of *Neurospora crassa* is reviewed by Ames (20); the following over-all pathway is suggested:

Imidazole glycerol phosphate → imidazole acetol phosphate →

L-histidinol phosphate → L-histidine (14)

Conventional nutritional techniques were of limited use in these studies, since the phosphorylated intermediates do not penetrate the cell. More reliance was placed on isolation of intermediates from blocked mutants and on direct enzymatic studies (20, 21).

The known early steps of the conversion of glucose to aromatic compounds have been diagrammed in Chapter 6. Figure 10 takes up the story from shikimic acid on; although this presentation is based in large part on studies of *Escherichia coli,* all of the available evidence from *Neurospora crassa* is in agreement with it. In particular, a multiple requirement for *p*-aminobenzoic acid, phenylalanine, tyrosine, and tryptophan is met by shikimic acid (526). Additional evidence is found in the accumulation of prephenic acid by a strain deficient for the three aromatic amino acids (361), and in the replacement of tyrosine by phenylpyruvic acid (125).

The suggestion that α-phenylglycine is a precursor of tyrosine and phenylalanine (222) has not been borne out by later work (124).

Tryptophan synthesis from anthranilic acid and indole by *Neurospora crassa* is indicated by nutritional responses of deficient mutants (66, 171, 525) and by studies with isotopic nitrogen (408). The conversion of indole to tryptophan is catalyzed by tryptophan synthetase (indole-serine ligase); this enzyme has been isolated and partially purified from *N. crassa* (616). The over-all reaction, which requires pyridoxal phosphate, may be written:

Indole + serine → tryptophan + H_2O (15)

The mechanism of this reaction is considered by Tatum and Shemin (528). Tryptophan synthesis in *Claviceps purpurea* is probably effected by the same system (548).

Presence or absence of the enzyme is controlled by a single gene in

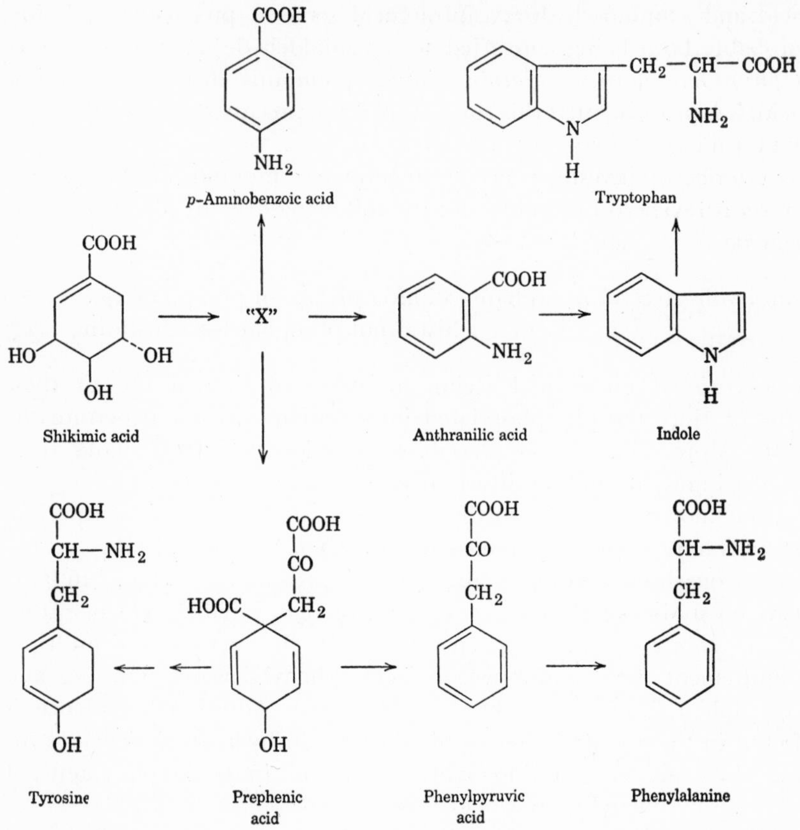

Figure 10. The biosynthesis of tryptophan, phenylalanine, tyrosine, and *p*-amino-benzoic acid. This is a general scheme based on data from several organisms but consistent with knowledge of *Neurospora crassa*. Many of the reactions shown are multiple.

Neurospora crassa (241). However, an antigenically related protein, possibly an enzyme precursor or possibly a complex of altered enzyme with an inhibitor, has been isolated from tryptophan-requiring mutants (514a). Cultivation of *N. crassa* in a medium deficient in zinc reduces the concentration of the synthesizing enzyme (386, 512).

This summary of amino acid synthesis may give a false impression of finality. There are, in fact, many complexities and uncertainties which cannot be considered here, and it is to be expected that our picture of these reactions will change as time goes on and more information becomes available.

5. AMINES

Although only one specific decarboxylase activity—glutamic decarboxylation, yielding γ-aminobutyric acid—is known in fungi (p. 265), the number of amines which occur and which presumably originate by decarboxylation of known amino acids is large. Sclerotia of *Claviceps purpurea* yield histamine, tyramine, isoamylamine, agmatine, putrescine and cadaverine (503, 508, 586). Occasional reports—not all certain—suggest that putrescine, phenylethylamine, isoamylamine, and cadaverine occur in fruit bodies of basidiomycetes (291, 310, 499, 580).

A mutant of *Aspergillus nidulans* requires putrescine for growth, and the requirement is not met by L-ornithine or by other amines (488). Several fungi act on histamine (585). Amines are in general poor or unavailable sources of nitrogen (278).

Muscarine, the toxin of *Amanita muscaria,* is an amine; Eugster (146) reviews earlier studies; a new structure has been confirmed by synthesis (301).

Choline has been found as a constituent of several fungi (508, 581); whether, however, it occurs in the free state or only in phospholipids (Chapter 2) has not been determined. A single report (147) suggests that acetyl choline is a constituent of ergot. Cyclic choline sulfate has been mentioned (Chapter 2).

Barley and other grains scabbed by *Fusarium graminearum* or other related *Fusarium* spp. contain a water-soluble material toxic to animals (101); identification of this substance with choline has been shown (473) to be in error.

Choline is required by mutants of *Neurospora crassa* (246), and a mutant can be used for the bioassay of choline (249, 527). The synthesis of choline by successive methylations of aminoethanol has been described (Chapter 6).

Trimethylamine has been isolated from numerous basidiomycetes, e.g., *Tilletia levis, Phallus impudicus,* and *Russula aurata* (225, 499, 580), and from *Claviceps purpurea* (508). In plants and in bacteria trimethylamine arises from choline (98), and the same origin may be proposed in fungi.

Betaine, $(CH_3)_3$—N^+—CH_2—COO^-, has been isolated from fungi (581), but, as with all the amines found in gross studies, there is some doubt as to whether it occurs as such or combined. One such combined form of betaine, ergothioneine, has the structure of the trimethyl betaine of thiolhistidine:

$$
\begin{array}{c}
\text{HC}\!-\!\!-\!\!\text{N} \\
\| \qquad \diagdown \\
\qquad \qquad \text{C}\!-\!\text{SH} \\
\diagup \\
\text{C}\!-\!\!-\!\!\text{N}\!-\!\text{H} \\
| \\
\text{CH}_2 \\
| \\
(\text{CH}_3)_3 - \overset{+}{\text{N}}\!-\!\text{CH}\!-\!\text{COO}^-
\end{array}
$$

Ergothioneine occurs in mammalian blood and seminal fluid (182), in sclerotia and in cultivated mycelium of *Claviceps purpurea* (40, 508), and in the mycelium of several common fungi (360). Experiments with carbon-14 indicate that ergothioneine and histidine are synthesized by the same pathway (229) and that histamine is not a precursor of either (599).

Amanita mappa fruit bodies contain an amine first called mappin but now known to be identical with bufotenine; its structure, 5-hydroxy-N-dimethyl tryptamine (595), suggests that it is biosynthetically derived from 5-hydroxytryptophan, an amino acid known in other organisms (353, 550) but not to date in fungi.

6. METABOLISM OF NUCLEIC ACIDS AND THEIR DERIVATIVES

Nucleic acids, nucleotides, and the purine bases can probably all be used more or less well as sources of nitrogen by fungi (606, 607), but the important aspects of nucleic acid metabolism are more narrowly metabolic: the breakdown of nucleic acids and their biosynthesis. Information on nucleic acid breakdown is rather scanty and bears almost exclusively on the purine ribonucleotides. Biosynthetic studies are even less definitive, and are limited primarily to nutritional studies of deficient mutants.

Catabolism of Nucleic Acids and Their Derivatives. That fungal enzymes attack nucleic acids has been known for some time. In early experiments liberation of phosphorus or of nitrogen bases, or utilization of nitrogen for growth were the criteria, so that it is not possible to specify what enzymes were involved (134, 265, 294, 357, 404).

On comparative grounds, we may suppose that fungi, like bacteria, attack nucleic acids first by nucleodepolymerase action, yielding primarily mononucleotides. A few such activities have been shown in fungi (Table 1).

The second step in the classical pathway of nucleic acid degradation is the dephosphorylation of nucleotides, yielding inorganic phosphate.

Table 1. Enzymes Acting on Nucleic Acids, Nucleotides, and Nucleosides *

Substrate	Type of Action	Occurrence
Ribonucleic acid	Depolymerization	*Streptomyces* spp. (67, 378), *Aspergillus oryzae* (311)
Deoxyribonucleic acid	Depolymerization	*Neurospora crassa* (627), *Streptomyces* sp. (378)
Nucleotides	Deamination	*Aspergillus* spp. (68, 69, 288, 311)
Nucleosides	Deamination	*Aspergillus oryzae* (288, 311, 370), *Neurospora crassa* (350)
Nucleosides	Hydrolysis	*Aspergillus oryzae* (311)

* Dephosphorylation of adenosine phosphates is summarized in Table 1 of Chapter 9.

This action is often, perhaps usually, carried out by non-specific phosphatases (316). Hydrolysis of adenosine phosphates, summarized in Chapter 9, and the dephosphorylation of riboflavin monophosphate by extracts of *Penicillium chrysogenum* (96) are presumably, although not necessarily, effected by such phosphatases. A phosphatase of *Streptomyces* sp. acts both on glycerophosphate and on nucleotides (378).

Diphosphopyridine nucleotide is attacked by a specific enzyme, diphosphopyridine nucleotidase, which splits off nicotinamide from the dinucleotide, leaving adenosine diphosphate ribose. The enzyme is formed by *Neurospora crassa* (289); its high concentration in the conidia suggests that it is formed only during sporulation (626). The concentration of enzyme in the mycelium is increased by deficiencies of zinc, nitrogen, or, usually, growth factors (386, 387). The enzyme of *N. crassa,* unlike the corresponding animal enzyme, is not inhibited by nicotinamide, except at very high concentration, and does not catalyze an exchange reaction between the dinucleotide and free nicotinamide (628).

Deamination of nucleotides and nucleosides is usually effected by specific enzymes, but an adenyl deaminase of *Aspergillus oryzae* acts on both types of compound, deaminating adenosine, adenosine-5'-phosphate, adenosine-3-phosphate, adenosine diphosphate and diphosphopyridine nucleotide (288).

These scattered data do not, of course, give a complete or coherent picture of nucleic acid breakdown; they do indicate that catabolism of the purine ribonucleotides in fungi is similar to that in other organisms. It seems likely, therefore, that the free purines adenine, hypoxanthine, and guanine are converted to xanthine, which is then oxidized by xanthine oxidase to uric acid (518), the further metabolism of which is described below.

In *Nocardia corallina* the pyrimidines thymine and uracil are metabolized by way of barbituric acid (315); the over-all process, presumably also responsible for the catabolism of cytosine and 5-methylcytosine, leads eventually in bacteria to urea and malonic acid (474).

Purines and Pyrimidines as Nutritional Factors. Naturally occurring fungi with a partial requirement for adenine have been reported (172, 174, 275, 625) among the basidiomycetes; exogenous adenine accelerates growth but has no effect on final yield (174). The effect of guanine and hypoxanthine on spore germination and early growth of *Phycomyces blakesleeanus* is mentioned in Chapter 12. Purine- and pyrimidine-requiring mutants have been obtained by conventional procedures in several fungi (166, 167, 170, 197, 331, 410, 544), and have been adapted for bioassay (178, 330).

For both *Neurospora sitophila* and *Fusarium oxysporum* f. *nicotianae,* the purines are generally adequate sources of nitrogen, the pyrimidines poor sources, the methyl purines—caffeine and theophylline—unutilizable (606, 607). Xanthine as sole nitrogen source supports good growth of several unrelated fungi (517) and an isolate of *Nocardia corallina* can obtain both carbon and nitrogen from uracil (341).

Biosynthesis of Components of Nucleic Acids. It seems certain that purines as such are not synthesized; rather, a nucleoside or more complex molecule is probably the first stable compound to accumulate (215). Study of eight adenineless mutants of *Neurospora crassa* led Mitchell and Houlahan (368) to propose the following sequence of reactions:

$$\text{``X''} \rightarrow \text{Inosine} \rightarrow \text{Adenosine} \qquad (16)$$

Hypoxanthine replaces adenine for some mutants of *N. crassa* (414), *Ophiostoma multiannulatum* (166, 168, 176), and *Ustilago zeae* (410). These data on fungi are consistent with our knowledge of animal systems, in which the general pathway appears to be (433):

$$CO_2 + 3\,NH_3 + \text{glycine} + 2\,\text{``formate''} + \text{ribose-1-phosphate} \rightarrow$$
$$\text{inosine-5-phosphate} \rightleftharpoons \text{inosine} \rightleftharpoons \text{hypoxanthine} + \text{ribose-1-phosphate}$$
$$(17)$$

In *O. multiannulatum* there is some evidence for a role of 4-amino-5-imidazole carboxamide in purine biogenesis (176); purine reversal of sulfonamide toxicity to *Eremothecium ashbyii* (472) is consistent with this.

Guanosine (or guanylic acid) synthesis in *Ophiostoma multiannulatum* has been suggested to proceed from adenosine (or adenylic acid), i.e., by a further step or steps added to Equation 16 (173); 2,6-diaminopurine replaces guanine for some mutants of this organism, the corresponding riboside does not (175).

Adenylosuccinic acid has been proposed as a precursor of adenylic acid (93), and an adenine-requiring mutant of *Neurospora crassa* accumulates both this compound and its riboside (593).

Caffeine is inhibitory at low concentrations to *Ophiostoma multiannulatum;* since the inhibition is reversed not only by adenine but by structurally unrelated compounds the status of caffeine as a purine antimetabolite is doubtful (253). Inhibition of *Diplodia natalensis* by 8-azaguanine is reversed by adenine, suggesting an interconversion in this species of adenine and guanine or their derivatives (295). Other structural analogues of purines cause inhibition of growth in fungi (179, 184), but whether they act specifically on normal purine metabolism is uncertain.

Biosynthesis of pyrimidines in fungi is even less well understood than that of purines. Pyrimidineless mutants respond better to nucleosides than to the free pyrimidine bases (166, 170, 331), suggesting that ribosidation of a precursor precedes formation of the pyrimide ring. Orotic acid replaces a pyrimidine requirement in *Neurospora crassa* and the importance of this compound is underlined by the finding that pyrimidine-requiring mutants accumulate orotic acid or its nucleoside orotidine (362, 369). These findings, and the demonstrated incorporation of the carbamyl group of citrulline into pyrimidines of *N. crassa* (231), suggest that the following over-all pathway of uridylic acid biosynthesis, proposed largely on the basis of animal studies (93), is applicable to fungi:

Citrulline → L-ureidosuccinic acid → dihydroorotic acid →
    orotic acid → orotidine-5'-phosphate → uridine-5'phosphate   (18)

Cytidylic acid may then be formed by reactions at the triphosphate level, although there is some doubt about the occurrence of this interconversion in fungi (447).

7. UREA

Urea is generally recognized as a utilizable nitrogen source; it should be realized that only experiments with cold-sterilized urea are valid, since urea breaks down to ammonia on autoclaving. Such experiments show urea utilization by, for example, several of the Mucorales (31), *Coccidioides immitis* (39), and *Coprinus* spp. (165). Although urease is fairly common in actinomycetes, utilization of urea has been considered infrequent among *Streptomyces* spp. (211).

Urease, the enzyme hydrolyzing urea, is well known from higher plants and bacteria (514). It is evidently of very general occurrence among fungi, including *Aspergillus* spp. (34, 35, 36, 84, 115, 161, 392, 481, 522), *Penicillium* spp. (134, 371, 547), *Pythiacystis citrophthora* (296), several dermatophytic fungi (524), and most of the fleshy basidiomycetes which have been studied in this connection (70, 189, 209, 357). Both direct and indirect evidence indicate that urease is formed by at least some actinomycetes (10, 15, 240, 485).

The urease of *Aspergillus niger* is most active at pH 7.6 (34), although its production is favored to a marked degree by low pH (371). It is formed by *A. niger* on various media and appears in the medium after autolysis (34). In basidiomycete sporophores the enzyme is most abundant in the hymenium (209).

Urea is formed in the fruit bodies of the higher basidiomycetes (209, 268, 269, 579, 615), and by many saprophytic fungi and actinomycetes in pure culture (102, 194, 217, 266, 267, 579). Oxygen and exogenous ammonia increase urea formation by sporophores (272, 273). The function of urea—in some fungi very large amounts are reported (266, 268)—is presumably as a nitrogen reserve.

The biochemical origin of urea in fungi has not been definitely proved, and there are several possible processes. First among these is the breakdown of arginine in the ornithine cycle (p. 269). Urea biogenesis by this route is indicated by the finding that exogenous arginine increases urea accumulation in fungi (267, 522), and by the demonstration of urea formation from arginine by cell-free preparations from basidiomycete sporophores (273, 615).

Apart from the specific action of arginase on arginine, it appears that urea is also formed by one or more enzymes which act on guanidine and derivatives of it to form urea and ammonia; this activity is found in *Streptomyces griseus* (540) and in several saprophytic fungi (103, 270).

Formation of urea from calcium cyanamide by cell-free preparations of *Aspergillus niger* has been reported (314).

An origin of urea from purines is also possible in the fungi, by the general route:

Xanthine → uric acid → allantoin →

$$\text{allantoic acid} \rightarrow \text{glyoxylic acid} + \text{urea} \quad (19)$$

Evidence for this pathway is still incomplete, but may be summarized briefly:

1. Xanthine oxidase and uricase occur in several fungi (518). Uricase is an inducible enzyme in *Torulopsis utilis* (450).

2. Uric acid has been isolated, although possibly as a degradation product, from spores of *Aspergillus oryzae* (513).

3. Allantoinase, converting allantoin to allantoic acid, is found in cell-free extracts of basidiomycete sporophores (83) and *Aspergillus niger* (84). Allantoin serves as a nitrogen source for *Fusarium oxysporum* f. *nicotianae* (607).

4. Sporophores of basidiomycetes may contain significant amounts of allantoic acid (162).

Proof of the role of this sequence in a single organism, and demonstration of allantoicase and its products in a cell-free system are required for acceptance of the pathway as written in Equation 19.

8. ERGOT ALKALOIDS

At least since the Middle Ages, it has been known that the black sclerotia of the ergot fungus cause disease and often death if eaten (41). The alkaloids of the fungus now also occupy a place in pharmacology and have been intensively investigated as drugs (205, 436). Although the classical organism is *Claviceps purpurea*, there is reason to believe that sclerotia of other species of the genus, especially *C. paspali*, also contain the active materials (82).

Chemically, the known ergot alkaloids comprise three basic types, all amides of lysergic acid, which has the structure:

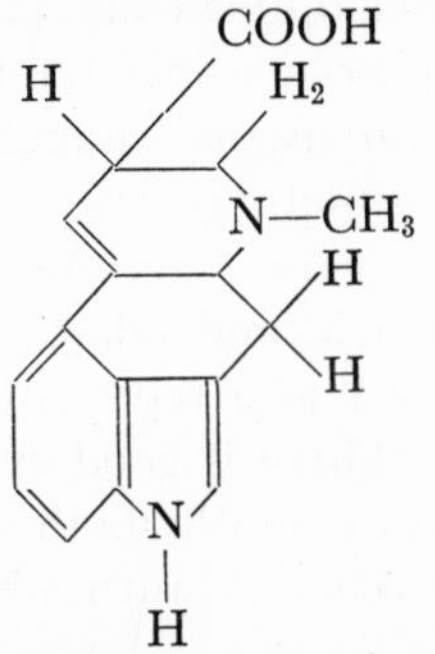

In the ergotamine and ergotoxine alkaloids, lysergic acid is linked to a peptide; ergonovine (ergometrine, ergobasine) is made up of lysergic acid and L-2-amino-1-propanol (508). A number of compounds closely related to the pharmacologically active materials are produced in culture by specific strains of *Claviceps* spp. (3, 509); the structure and possible biosynthetic relationships of these are reviewed by Stickings and Raistrick (504). Agroclavine production is greater in still than in shake culture (5, 6, 7). The ergot alkaloids, whether produced by the fungus or supplied exogenously, disappear in time from a culture (4, 363).

9. MISCELLANEOUS NITROGEN COMPOUNDS

Although the antibiotics of actinomycetes form a large share of the known nitrogenous metabolites, a number of fungal products are also known. Table 2 lists some representative compounds in a classification based on chemical similarity. Almost nothing is known of biochemical relationships.

Group I of Table 2 includes compounds more or less similar to amino acids. Azaserine is of some general interest by reason of its apparently specific blocking of a single step in the biogenesis of purine nucleotides (49, 543). Other serine derivatives include the antibiotic cycloserine and the non-antibiotic O-carbamyl-D-serine (223), both actinomycete products. Mycelianamide, produced by *Penicillium griseofulvum,* is structurally related, as an acylhydroxylamine, to cycloserine (57).

The structure of the related antibiotics thiolutin and aureothricin has been determined (97), and their resemblance to cystine has been noted (14).

Compounds more closely and obviously related to the amino acids include fumaryl-DL-alanine of *Penicillium resticulosum* (58), an unidentified ester of glutamine in *Lepiota naucina* (502), and the lichen product picroroccelin, a diketopiperazine (27).

The organic nitro group occurs only rarely in biological material; chloramphenicol (Chapter 6) is one example, β-nitropropionic acid another (Table 2). An antibiotic of *Streptomyces thiolutens* has the nitro group (238). *Neurospora crassa* forms an inducible enzyme acting on β-nitropropionic acid and related compounds (328).

Indigo is shown in Table 2 as a representative of Group III, compounds related to indole. There is good evidence that indole is the starting point for indigo formation by both soil bacteria (213) and in the mammalian gut (121); indole in turn, we may assume, arises from tryptophan.

The indole nucleus is found also in lysergic acid (p. 279), and in echinulin, a product of *Aspergillus glaucus* (425). Gliotoxin, produced by *Aspergillus fumigatus, Penicillium* spp., and *Trichoderma viride* (74), is believed to have a reduced indole nucleus (281). *Penicillium terlikowski,* earlier identified as *P. obscurum,* forms both gliotoxin and its monoacetate (282).

Fusaric acid is the sole representative of Group IV, pyridine deriva-

Table 2. Representative Nitrogenous Compounds of Fungi and Actinomycetes

Group*	Compound	Organisms
I	Azaserine	*Streptomyces* sp. (186, 187, 372, 505)

$$N^+ \equiv N^- = CH - CO - O - CH_2 - CH - COOH$$
$$\underset{NH_2}{}$$

| | Cycloserine (oxamycin) | *Streptomyces* spp. (226, 237, 309) |

$$H_2N - CH \underline{} C = O$$
$$\overset{|}{CH_2} \qquad \overset{|}{NH}$$
$$\diagdown \qquad \diagup$$
$$O$$

| II | Beta-nitropropionic acid | *Aspergillus flavus*† (88) |

$$O_2N - CH_2 - CH_2 - COOH$$

| III | Indigo (indigotin) | *Schizophyllum commune* (365) |

| IV | Fusaric acid | *Fusarium* spp., *Gibberella fujikuroi*, *Nectria cinnabarina* (191, 192, 416, 507, 614) |

| V | Viridicatin | *Penicillium* spp. (75, 117) |

* See p. 280.
† Also known in higher plants (94).

Table 2 (*continued*)

Group*	Compound	Organisms
VI	Aspergillic acid 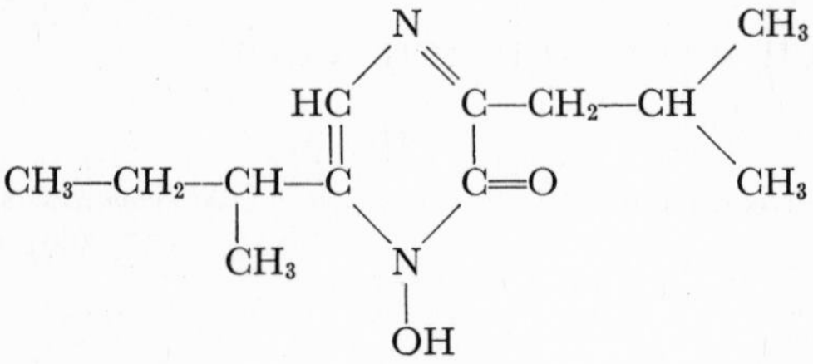	*Aspergillus flavus* (141, 390, 591)

$$CH_3-CH_2-CH-C \quad HC \quad N \quad C-CH_2-CH \quad CH_3$$
$$\underset{CH_3}{|} \qquad \quad C=O \quad CH_3$$
$$N$$
$$OH$$

| VII | Cordycepin 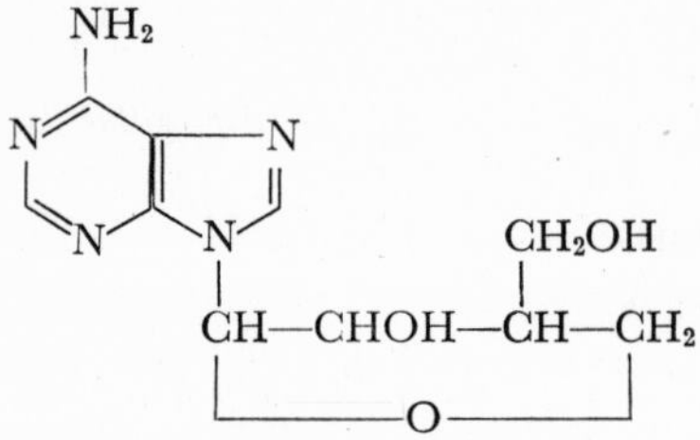 | *Cordyceps militaris* (50, 118) |

$$NH_2$$

CH—CHOH—CH—CH$_2$
CH$_2$OH
O

| VIII | Cycloheximide 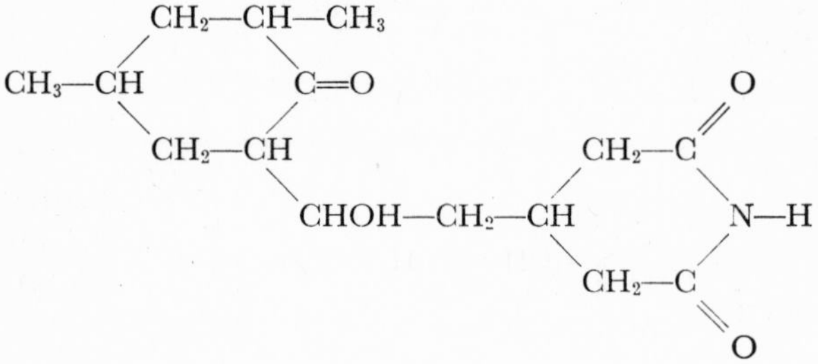 | *Streptomyces* spp. (112, 304, 313, 590) |

$$CH_2-CH-CH_3$$
$$CH_3-CH \qquad C=O$$
$$CH_2-CH$$
$$CHOH-CH_2-CH$$
$$CH_2-C \qquad O$$
$$N-H$$
$$CH_2-C \qquad O$$

| IX | Actithiazic acid 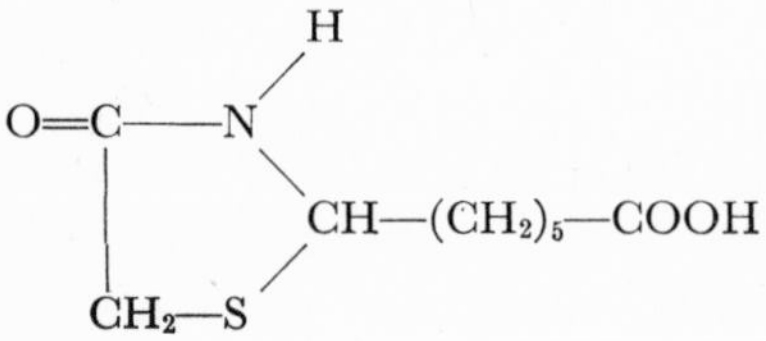 | *Streptomyces* spp. (352) |

$$O=C-N \quad H$$
$$CH-(CH_2)_5-COOH$$
$$CH_2-S$$

tives, although lysergic acid also has a reduced N-methyl pyridine structure. Fusaric acid is a potential wilt toxin in diseases caused by *Fusarium* spp. and related fungi. Its production by *F. vasinfectum* is narrowly controlled by the zinc content of the medium (287). *Gibberella fujikuroi* also forms dehydrofusaric acid (510).

Viridicatin (Group V, Table 2) is a derivative of quinoline; quinolinic acid is noted later (Chapter 10) as a possible intermediate in the biosynthesis of nicotinic acid from tryptophan. Some strains of *Penicillium cyclopium* form viridicatin, but in one it is replaced by the related cyclopenin (75).

Aspergillic acid, one tautomeric form of which is displayed in Table 2, represents a sixth group, derivatives of pyrazine. Gliotoxin, mentioned above as an indole derivative, also contains this grouping, as does pulcherriminic acid, the iron salt of which, pulcherrimin, is the red pigment of *Candida pulcherrima* (111, 297). *Aspergillus flavus* forms, in addition to aspergillic acid, the compound flavocol, a diisobutyl derivative of deoxyaspergillic acid (140).

The structure of the pyrazines strongly suggests a biosynthetic origin from leucine and isoleucine (74).

Cordycepin yields adenine on hydrolysis. Achromycin, an antibiotic of *Streptomyces albo-niger*, also is an adenine derivative (577). Another actinomycete antibiotic, amicetin, incorporates the pyrimidine cytosine (501).

Nitrogenous quinones include the azanthraquinone chromophore of the actinomycins (p. 254), cycloheximide (Table 2), and the pigment phomazarin of *Phoma terrestris* (239, 303).

Thiazolidine derivatives are represented only by the antibiotic actithiazic acid. Evidence has been presented indicating that this may act as an antimetabolite of biotin (553).

Polyacetylenic compounds of fungi have been considered briefly (Chapter 6). Of these, two—agrocybin (85) and diatetryne 1 (23)—are amides and a third, diatetryne 2 (24), is a nitrile.

Most pigments so far investigated have proved not to contain nitrogen but several do. To those already mentioned may be added as examples the pigments of *Trametes cinnabarina* (216), *Streptomyces coelicolor* (79a), and *S. limosus* (80).

BIBLIOGRAPHY

1. Abbott, E. V. 1923. *Soil Sci.* 16: 207–216.
2. Abderhalden, A. and Y. Teruuchi. 1906. *Z. Physiol. Chem. Hoppe-Seyler's* 47: 394–396.

3. Abe, M. 1949a. *J. Agr. Chem. Soc. Japan* 23: 135–139.
4. Abe, M. 1949b. *J. Agr. Chem. Soc. Japan* 23: 212–219.
5. Abe, M., T. Yamano, Y. Kozu, and M. Kusumoto. 1951. *J. Agr. Chem. Soc. Japan* 24: 416–422.
6. Abe, M., T. Yamano, Y. Kozu, and M. Kusumoto. 1953. *J. Agr. Chem. Soc. Japan* 27: 18–23.
7. Abe, M., T. Yamano, and M. Kusumoto. 1953. *J. Agr. Chem. Soc. Japan* 27: 617–620.
8. Abel, J. J. and W. W. Ford. 1907. *J. Biol. Chem.* 2: 273–288.
9. Abelson, P. H. and H. J. Vogel. 1955. *J. Biol. Chem.* 213: 355–364.
10. Adachi, M. and T. Imamura. 1933. *J. Soc. Trop. Agr. (Taiwan)* 5: 121–130. (*Biol. Abstr.* 8: 16055. 1934).
11. Adelberg, E. A. 1953. *Bacteriol. Revs.* 17: 253–267.
12. Adelberg, E. A. 1955a. *J. Biol. Chem.* 216: 431–437.
13. Adelberg, E. A. 1955b. In W. D. McElroy and H. B. Glass (eds.), *A Symposium on Amino Acid Metabolism*, p. 419–430. Baltimore: The Johns Hopkins Press.
14. Adelberg, E. A. and M. Rabinovitz. 1956. *Ann. Rev. Biochem.* 25: 349–396.
15. Afanasiev, M. M. 1937. *Nebraska Univ. Agr. Exp. Sta. Research Bull.* 92: 1–63.
16. Albert, A. 1950. *Biochem. J. (London)* 47: 531–538.
17. Albert, A. 1952. *Biochem. J. (London)* 50: 690–697.
18. Allison, F. E., S. R. Hoover, and H. J. Morris. 1934. *J. Agr. Research* 49: 1115–1123.
19. Amatayakul, T. 1955. *Ohio J. Sci.* 55: 343–353.
20. Ames, B. N. 1955. In W. D. McElroy and H. B. Glass (eds.), *A Symposium on Amino Acid Metabolism*, p. 357–372. Baltimore: The Johns Hopkins Press.
21. Ames, B. N. and B. L. Horecker. 1956. *J. Biol. Chem.* 220: 113–128.
22. Amos, H. 1954. *J. Am. Chem. Soc.* 76: 3858.
23. Anchel, M. 1953. *J. Am. Chem. Soc.* 75: 4621–4622.
24. Anchel, M. 1955. *Science* 121: 607–608.
25. Anderson, A. K. 1924. *Studies Biol. Sci. Univ. Minn.* 5: 237–280.
26. Arnstein, H. R. V. and P. T. Grant. 1954. *Biochem. J. (London)* 57: 353–359.
27. Asahina, Y. and S. Shibata. 1953. *Chemistry of Lichen Substances.* Tokyo: Japan Society for the Promotion of Science, pp. 240.
28. Ayengar, P. and E. Roberts. 1952. *J. Biol. Chem.* 197: 453–460.
29. Bach, D. 1927a. *Compt. rend. (Paris)* 184: 766–768.
30. Bach, D. 1927b. *Compt. rend. (Paris)* 184: 1578–1579.
31. Bach, D. 1927c. *Compt. rend. (Paris)* 185: 1309–1310.
32. Bach, D. 1929a. *Bull soc. chim. biol.* 11: 119–145.
33. Bach, D. 1929b. *Bull soc. chim. biol.* 11: 995–1006.
34. Bach, D. 1929c. *Bull. soc. chim. biol.* 11: 1007–1015.
35. Bach, D. 1929d. *Bull. soc. chim. biol.* 11: 1016–1024.
36. Bach, D. 1929e. *Compt. rend. soc. biol.* 100: 831–833.
37. Bach, E. 1948. *Physiol. Plantarum* 1: 387–389.
38. Bach, E. 1949. *Friesia* 3: 377–378.
39. Baker, E. E. and C. E. Smith. 1942. *J. Infectious Diseases* 70: 51–53.
40. Ban, R. W. and E. C. Stowell, Jr. 1956. *Arch. Biochem. Biophys.* 63: 259–260.
41. Barger, G. 1931. *Ergot and Ergotism.* London: Gurney and Jackson, pp. 279.
42. Barner, H. D. and E. C. Cantino. 1952. *Am. J. Botany* 39: 746–751.
43. Barnett, H. L. and V. G. Lilly. 1956. *Mycologia* 48: 617–627.
44. Barton-Wright, E. C. 1952. *Wallerstein Labs. Commun.* 15: 115–131.

45. Baumann, G. 1953. *Kühn-Archiv* 67: 305–383.
46. Beckman, C. H., J. E. Kuntz, and A. J. Riker. 1953. *Phytopathology* 43: 441–447.
47. Bender, A. E. and H. A. Krebs. 1950. *Biochem. J.* (*London*) 46: 210–219.
48. Bender, A. E., H. A. Krebs, and N. H. Horowitz. 1949. *Biochem. J.* (*London*) 45: xxi–xxii.
49. Bennett, L. L., Jr., F. M. Schabel, Jr., and H. E. Skipper. 1956. *Arch. Biochem. Biophys.* 64: 423–436.
50. Bentley, H. R., K. G. Cunningham, and F. S. Spring. 1951. *J. Chem. Soc.* (*London*) 1951: 2301–2305.
51. Bentley, M. L. 1953. *J. Gen. Microbiol.* 8: 365–377.
52. Berger, J. and M. J. Johnson. 1939. *J. Biol. Chem.* 130: 641–654.
53. Berger, J., M. J. Johnson, and W. H. Peterson. 1937. *J. Biol. Chem.* 117: 429–438.
54. Bergström, S. and R. Rasmussen. 1951. *Physiol. Plantarum* 4: 421–423.
55. Bhargava, K. S. 1945. *J. Indian Botan. Soc.* 24: 67–72.
56. Binkley, S. B. 1955. *Ann. Rev. Biochem.* 24: 596–626.
57. Birch, A. J., R. A. Massy-Westropp, and R. W. Rickards. 1956. *J. Chem. Soc.* (*London*) 1956: 3717–3721.
58. Birkinshaw, J. H., H. Raistrick, and G. Smith. 1942. *Biochem. J.* (*London*) 36: 829–835.
59. Black, S. and N. G. Wright. 1955. In W. D. McElroy and H. B. Glass (eds.), *A Symposium on Amino Acid Metabolism*, p. 591–600. Baltimore: The Johns Hopkins Press.
60. Block, S. S., R. L. Stephens, A. Barreto, and W. A. Murrill. 1955. *Science* 121: 505–506.
61. Block, S. S., R. L. Stephens, and W. A. Murrill. 1955. *J. Agr. Food Chem.* 3: 584–587.
62. Blumer, S. and W. H. Schopfer. 1940. *Ber. schweiz. botan. Ges.* 50: 248–272.
63. Boas, F. 1919. *Ber. deut. botan. Ges.* 37: 57–62.
64. Bonner, D. M. 1946. *Am. J. Botany* 33: 788–791.
65. Bonner, D. M., E. L. Tatum, and G. W. Beadle. 1943. *Arch. Biochem.* 3: 71–91.
66. Bonner, D. M. and C. Yanofsky. 1951. *J. Nutrition* 44: 603–616.
67. Born, G. V. R. 1952. *J. Gen. Microbiol.* 6: 344–351.
68. Borsook, H. and J. W. Dubnoff. 1939a. *Enzymologia* 7: 256.
69. Borsook, H. and J. W. Dubnoff. 1939b. *J. Biol. Chem.* 131: 163–176.
70. Bose, S. R. 1939. *Ergeb. Enzymforsch.* 8: 266–276.
71. Bouillenné, R. and M. Bouillenné-Walrand. 1951. *Bull. classe sci., Acad. roy. Belg.* 37: 557–566, 567–582.
72. Boysen-Jensen, P. 1931. *Biochem. Z.* 239: 243–249.
73. Boysen-Jensen, P. 1932. *Biochem. Z.* 250: 270–280.
74. Bracken, A. 1955. *The Chemistry of Micro-Organisms.* London: Sir Isaac Pitman and Sons, Ltd., pp. 343.
75. Bracken, A., A. Pocker, and H. Raistrick. 1954. *Biochem. J.* (*London*) 57: 583–595.
76. Bricas, E. and C. Fromageot. 1953. *Advances in Protein Chem.* 8: 1–125.
77. Briggs, W. R. and P. M. Ray. 1956. *Plant Physiol.* 31: 165–167.
78. Brockmann, H. 1954. *Angew. Chem.* 66: 1–10.
79. Brockmann, H. and H. Gröne. 1954. *Chem. Ber.* 87: 1036–1051.
79a. Brockmann, H. and V. Loeschcke. 1955. *Chem. Ber.* 88: 778–788.
80. Brockmann, H. and H.-U. May. 1955. *Chem. Ber.* 88: 419–423.
81. Brockmann, H. and H. Muxfeldt. 1955. *Angew. Chem.* 67: 617–618.
82. Brown, H. B. 1916. *J. Agr. Research* 7: 401–406.
83. Brunel, A. 1931. *Compt. rend.* (*Paris*) 192: 442–444.

84. Brunel, A. 1939. *Bull. soc. chim. biol.* 21: 380–387.

85. Bu'Lock, J. D. et al. 1954. *Chem. & Ind.* 1954: 990–991.

86. Bünning, E. 1936. *Flora* (*N. F.*) 31: 87–112.

87. Burton, K. 1951. *Biochem. J.* (*London*) 50: 258–268.

88. Bush, M. T., O. Touster, and J. E. Brockman. 1951. *J. Biol. Chem.* 188: 685–693.

89. Butterworth, E. M., C. M. Gilmour, and C. H. Wang. 1955. *J. Bacteriol.* 69: 725–727.

90. Cantino, E. C. 1955. *Quart. Rev. Biol.* 30: 138–149.

91. Cantino, E. C. and E. A. Horenstein. 1956. *Mycologia* 48: 777–799.

92. Carlson, G. L. and R. A. McRorie. 1955. *Biochim. et Biophys. Acta* 18: 454–455.

93. Carter, C. E. 1956. *Ann. Rev. Biochem.* 25: 123–146.

94. Carter, C. L. and W. J. McChesney. 1949. *Nature* (*London*) 164: 575–576.

95. Carter, H. E., C. P. Schaffner, and D. Gottlieb. 1954. *Arch. Biochem. Biophys.* 53: 282–293.

96. Casida, L. E., Jr. and S. G. Knight. 1954. *J. Bacteriol.* 67: 658–661.

97. Celmer, W. D. and I. A. Solomons. 1955. *J. Am. Chem. Soc.* 77: 2861–2865.

98. Challenger, F. 1951. *Advances in Enzymol.* 12: 429–491.

99. Chattaway, F. W., C. C. Thompson, and A. G. E. Barlow. 1954. *Biochim. et Biophys. Acta* 14: 583–584.

100. Christensen, H. N. 1955. In W. D. McElroy and H. B. Glass (eds.), *A Symposium on Amino Acid Metabolism,* p. 63–106. Baltimore: The Johns Hopkins Press.

101. Christensen, J. J. and H. C. H. Kernkamp. 1936. *Minn. Univ. Agr. Exp. Sta. Tech. Bull.* 113: 1–28.

102. Chrząszcz, T. and M. Zakomorny. 1934. *Biochem. Z.* 273: 31–42.

103. Chrząszcz, T. and M. Zakomorny. 1935. *Biochem. Z.* 275: 97–105.

104. Chughtai, I. D. and T. K. Walker. 1954. *Biochem. J.* (*London*) 56: 484–487.

105. Cochrane, V. W. 1950. *Bull. Torrey Botan. Club* 77: 176–180.

106. Cochrane, V. W. and J. E. Conn. 1947. *J. Bacteriol.* 54: 213–218.

107. Cochrane, V. W. and J. E. Conn. 1950. *Bull. Torrey Botan. Club* 77: 10–18.

108. Cohen, A. L. 1953. *Proc. Natl. Acad. Sci. U. S.* 39: 68–74.

109. Cohen, P. P. 1954. In D. M. Greenberg (ed.), *Chemical Pathways of Metabolism,* Vol. 2, p. 1–46. New York: Academic Press.

110. Converse, R. H. 1953. *Mycologia* 45: 335–344.

111. Cook, A. H. and C. A. Slater. 1956. *J. Chem. Soc.* (*London*) 1956: 4130–4133, 4133–4135.

112. Corbaz, R., L. Ettlinger, W. Keller-Schierlein, and H. Zähner. 1957. *Arch. Mikrobiol.* 26: 192–208.

113. Crasemann, J. M. 1954. *Am. J. Botany* 41: 302–310.

114. Crewther, W. G. and F. G. Lennox. 1950. *Nature* (*London*) 165: 680.

115. Crewther, W. G. and F. G. Lennox. 1953a. *Australian J. Biol. Sci.* 6: 410–427.

116. Crewther, W. G. and F. G. Lennox. 1953b. *Australian J. Biol. Sci.* 6: 428–446.

117. Cunningham, K. G. and G. G. Freeman. 1953. *Biochem. J.* (*London*) 53: 328–332.

118. Cunningham, K. G., S. A. Hutchinson, W. Manson, and F. S. Spring. 1951. *J. Chem. Soc.* (*London*) 1951: 2299–2300.

119. Curtis, P. J., H. G. Hemming, and C. H. Unwin. 1951. *Trans. Brit. Mycol. Soc.* 34: 332–339.

120. Czapek, F. 1902. *Beitr. Chem. Physiol. Pathol.* 1: 538–560.

121. Dalgliesh, C. E. 1955. *Advances in Protein Chem.* 10: 33–150.

122. Darby, R. T. and G. R. Mandels. 1954. *Mycologia* 46: 276–288.

123. Davis, B. D. 1955. *Advances in Enzymol.* 16: 247–312.
124. De Busk, A. G. 1956. *Advances in Enzymol.* 17: 393–476.
125. De Busk, A. G. and R. P. Wagner. 1953. *J. Am. Chem. Soc.* 75: 5131.
126. Delwiche, C. C. 1956. In W. D. McElroy and B. Glass (eds.), *Symposium on Inorganic Nitrogen Metabolism,* p. 218–232. Baltimore: The Johns Hopkins Press.
127. Dimond, A. E. and P. E. Waggoner. 1953a. *Phytopathology* 43: 195–199.
128. Dimond, A. E. and P. E. Waggoner. 1953b. *Phytopathology* 43: 319–321.
129. Dingle, J. and G. L. Solomons. 1952. *J. Appl. Chem. (London)* 2: 395–399.
130. Dion, W. M. 1950a. *Can. J. Research C,* 28: 577–585.
131. Dion, W. M. 1950b. *Can. J. Research C,* 28: 586–599.
132. Doudney, C. O. and R. P. Wagner. 1952. *Proc. Natl. Acad. Sci. U. S.* 38: 196–205.
133. Douglas, R. J. and C. L. San Clemente. 1956. *Can. J. Microbiol.* 2: 407–415.
134. Dox, A. W. 1909. *J. Biol. Chem.* 6: 461–467.
135. Drouhet, E. 1952. *Ann. inst. Pasteur* 82: 348–355.
136. Drouhet, E. 1954. Congr. intern. botan., *8e Congr. Paris,* Rapps. et Communs. 8, Sect. 18–20: 112–113.
137. Duggar, B. M. and A. R. Davis. 1916. *Ann. Missouri Botan. Garden* 3: 413–437.
138. Dulaney, E. L. 1948. *J. Bacteriol.* 56: 305–313.
139. Dulaney, E. L., E. Bilinski, and W. B. McConnell. 1956. *Can. J. Biochem. and Physiol.* 34: 1195–1198.
140. Dunn, G., G. T. Newbold, and F. S. Spring. 1949. *J. Chem. Soc. (London)* 1949: 2586–2587.
141. Dutcher, J. D. 1947. *J. Biol. Chem.* 171: 321–339, 341–353.
142. Dworschack, R. G., H. J. Koepsell, and A. A. Lagoda. 1952. *Arch. Biochem. Biophys.* 41: 48–60.
143. Emerson, R. L., M. Puziss, and S. G. Knight. 1950. *Arch. Biochem.* 25: 299–308.
144. Erikson, D. 1952. *J. Gen. Microbiol.* 6: 286–294.
145. Erkama, J. and I. Virtanen. 1951. In J. B. Sumner and K. Myrbäck (eds.), *The Enzymes,* Vol. 1 (2), p. 1244–1249. New York: Academic Press.
146. Eugster, C. H. 1956. *Helv. Chim. Acta* 39: 1002–1023, 1023–1037.
147. Ewins, A. J. 1914. *Biochem. J. (London)* 8: 44–49.
148. Fåhraeus, G. and V. Tullander. 1956. *Physiol. Plantarum* 9: 494–501.
149. Fairley, J. L. 1954. *Federation Proc.* 13: 205–206.
150. Fergus, C. L. 1952. *Mycologia* 44: 183–189.
151. Fincham, J. R. S. 1950. *J. Biol. Chem.* 182: 61–73.
152. Fincham, J. R. S. 1951. *J. Gen. Microbiol.* 5: 793–806.
153. Fincham, J. R. S. 1953. *Biochem. J. (London)* 53: 313–320.
154. Fincham, J. R. S. 1954. *J. Gen. Microbiol.* 11: 236–246.
155. Fincham, J. R. S. and A. B. Boulter. 1956. *Biochem. J. (London)* 62: 72–77.
156. Fincham, J. R. S. and J. B. Boylen. 1957. *J. Gen. Microbiol.* 16: 438–448.
157. Fisher, W. P., J. Charney, and W. A. Bolhofer. 1951. *Antibiotics & Chemotherapy* 1: 571–572.
158. Fleury, C. 1948. *Ber. schweiz. botan. Ges.* 58: 462–477.
159. Fling, M. and N. H. Horowitz. 1951. *J. Biol. Chem.* 190: 277–285.
160. Flynn, E. H., J. W. Hinman, E. L. Caron, and D. D. Woolf, Jr. 1953. *J. Am. Chem. Soc.* 75: 5867–5871.
161. Fosse, R. 1916. *Ann. inst. Pasteur* 30: 739–755.
162. Fosse, R. and A. Brunel. 1933. *Compt. rend. (Paris)* 197: 288–290.
163. Foster, J. W. 1949. *Chemical Activities of the Fungi.* New York: Academic Press, pp. 648.
164. Fothergill, P. G. and R. Ashcroft. 1955. *J. Gen. Microbiol.* 12: 387–395.

165. Fries, L. 1955. *Svensk Botan. Tidskr.* 49: 475–535.
166. Fries, N. 1947. *Arkiv Botan.* 33A (7): 1–7.
167. Fries, N. 1948. *Hereditas* 34: 338–350.
168. Fries, N. 1949a. *Physiol. Plantarum* 2: 78–102.
169. Fries, N. 1949b. *Svensk Botan. Tidskr.* 43: 316–342.
170. Fries, N. 1950a. *Arkiv Botan.*, Ser. 2, 1: 271–287.
171. Fries, N. 1950b. *Physiol. Plantarum* 3: 185–196.
172. Fries, N. 1950c. *Svensk Botan. Tidskr.* 44: 379–386.
173. Fries, N. 1953. *J. Biol. Chem.* 200: 325–333.
174. Fries, N. 1954. *Svensk Botan. Tidskr.* 48: 559–578.
175. Fries, N. 1955. *Acta Chem. Scand.* 9: 1020.
176. Fries, N., S. Bergström, and M. Rottenberg. 1949. *Physiol. Plantarum* 2: 210–211.
178. Fries, N. and U. Björkman. 1949. *Physiol. Plantarum* 2: 212–215.
179. Fries, N. and A. Panders. 1950. *Arkiv Botan.*, Ser. 2, 1: 437–444.
180. Fromageot, C. 1951. In J. B. Sumner and K. Myrbäck (eds.), *The Enzymes,* Vol. 1 (2), p. 1237–1243. New York: Academic Press.
181. Fromageot, C., M. Jutisz, and P. Tessier. 1949. *Bull. soc. chim. biol.* 31: 689–695.
182. Fruton, J. S. and S. Simmonds. 1953. *General Biochemistry.* New York: John Wiley and Sons, pp. 940.
183. Fry, B. A. 1955. *The Nitrogen Metabolism of Micro-organisms.* London: Methuen and Co., pp. 166.
184. Fuerst, R., C. E. Somers, and T. C. Hsu. 1956. *J. Bacteriol.* 72: 387–393.
185. Fujii, T. 1955. *J. Biochem. (Tokyo)* 42: 257–265.
186. Fusari, S. A. et al. 1954a. *J. Am. Chem. Soc.* 76: 2878–2881.
187. Fusari, S. A. et al. 1954b. *J. Am. Chem. Soc.* 76: 2881–2883.
188. Gale, E. F. 1953. *Advances in Protein Chem.* 8: 285–391.
189. Garren, K. H. 1938. *Phytopathology* 28: 839–845.
190. Gäumann, E. 1951. *Advances in Enzymol.* 11: 401–437.
191. Gäumann, E. 1954. *Endeavour* 13: 198–204.
192. Gäumann, E., S. Naef-Roth, and H. Kobel. 1952. *Phytopathol. Z.* 20: 1–38.
193. Gäumann, E., S. Naef-Roth, P. Reusser, and A. Ammann. 1952. *Phytopathol. Z.* 19: 160–220.
194. Gentile, A. C. 1951. *Physiol. Plantarum* 4: 370–386.
195. Gentile, A. C. and R. M. Klein. 1955. *Physiol. Plantarum* 8: 291–299.
196. Georg, L. K. 1952. *Mycologia* 44: 470–492.
197. Giles, N. H. 1946. *J. Bacteriol.* 52: 504.
198. Gillespie, J. M. and E. F. Woods. 1953. *Australian J. Biol. Sci.* 6: 447–462.
199. Gilmour, C. M., E. M. Butterworth, E. P. Noble, and C. H. Wang. 1955. *J. Bacteriol.* 69: 719–724.
200. Gilpin, R. H. 1954. *Mycologia* 46: 702–707.
201. Gitterman, C. O. and S. G. Knight. 1952. *J. Bacteriol.* 64: 223–231.
202. Goddard, H. N. 1913. *Botan. Gaz.* 56: 249–305.
203. Goksøyr, J. 1951. *Physiol. Plantarum* 4: 498–513.
204. Golueke, C. G. 1957. *J. Bacteriol.* 74: 337–344.
205. Goodman, L. S. and A. Gilman. 1956. *The Pharmacological Basis of Therapeutics.* New York: The Macmillan Co., pp. 1831.
206. Goodwin, T. W. and O. T. G. Jones. 1956. *Biochem. J. (London)* 64: 9–13.
207. Goodwin, T. W. and S. Pendlington. 1954. *Biochem. J. (London)* 57: 631–641.
208. Gorbach, G. and O. G. Koch. 1955. *Arch. Mikrobiol.* 23: 265–283.
209. Goris, A. and P. Costy. 1922. *Compt. Rend. (Paris)* 175: 539–541, 998–999.
210. Goss, W. A., E. Katz, and S. A. Waksman. 1956. *Proc. Natl. Acad. Sci. U. S.* 42: 10–12.

211. Gottlieb, D. 1953. *Intern. Congr. Microbiol., 6th Congr. Rome,* 5: 122–136.
212. Gottlieb, D. and D. Ciferri. 1956. *Mycologia* 48: 253–263.
213. Gray, P. H. H. 1927. *Proc. Roy. Soc. (London) B,* 102: 263–280.
214. Greenberg, D. M. 1954. In D. M. Greenberg (ed.), *Chemical Pathways of Metabolism,* Vol. 2, p. 47–112. New York: Academic Press.
215. Greenberg, G. R. 1951. *J. Biol. Chem.* 190: 611–631.
216. Gripenberg, J. 1951. *Acta Chem. Scand.* 5: 590–595.
217. Guittoneau, G. 1924. *Compt. rend. (Paris)* 178: 1383–1385.
218. Gunther, F. A. et al. 1956. *Phytopathology* 46: 632–633.
219. Guyot, H. 1916. *Bull. soc. botan. Genève, Sér. 2,* 8: 80–82.
220. de la Haba, G. 1950. *Science* 112: 203–204.
221. Hacskaylo, J., V. G. Lilly, and H. L. Barnett. 1954. *Mycologia* 46: 691–701.
222. Haddox, C. H. 1952. *Proc. Natl. Acad. Sci. U. S.* 38: 482–489.
223. Hagemann, G., L. Penasse, and J. Teillon. 1955. *Biochim. et Biophys. Acta* 17: 240–243.
224. Hakamura, Y. and T. Shimomura. 1953. *J. Agr. Chem. Soc. Japan* 27: 694–699.
225. Hanna, W. F., H. B. Vickery, and G. W. Pucher. 1932. *J. Biol. Chem.* 97: 351–358.
226. Harris, D. A. et al. 1955. *Antibiotics & Chemotherapy* 5: 183–190.
227. Haskins, R. H. and W. H. Weston, Jr. 1950. *Am. J. Botany* 37: 739–750.
228. Hawker, L. E. and J. Fraymouth. 1951. *J. Gen. Microbiol.* 5: 369–386.
229. Heath, H. and J. Wildy. 1956. *Biochem. J. (London)* 64: 612–620.
230. Heinemann, B., M. A. Kaplan, R. D. Muir, and I. R. Hooper. 1953. *Antibiotics & Chemotherapy* 3: 1239–1242.
231. Heinrich, M. R., V. C. Dewey, and G. W. Kidder. 1954. *J. Am. Chem. Soc.* 76: 3102–3103.
232. Heppel, L. A. 1954. In D. M. Greenberg (ed.), *Chemical Pathways of Metabolism,* Vol. 2, p. 263–286. New York: Academic Press.
233. Herrick, J. A. 1940. *Ohio J. Sci.* 40: 123–129.
234. Herrick, J. A. and C. J. Alexopoulos. 1942. *Ohio J. Sci.* 42: 109–111.
235. Hessayon, D. G. 1952. *Nature (London)* 169: 803–804.
236. Heyn, A. N. J. 1935. *Proc. Konlinkl. Acad. Wetenschap Amsterdam* 38: 1074–1081.
237. Hidy, P. H. et al. 1955. *J. Am. Chem. Soc.* 77: 2345–2346.
238. Hirata, Y., K. Okuhara, and T. Naitô. 1954. *Nature (London)* 173: 1101.
239. Hoffman-Ostenhoff, O. 1950. *Fortschr. Chemie org. Naturstoffe* 6: 154–241.
240. Hofmann, E. and E. Latzko. 1950. *Biochem. Z.* 320: 269–272.
241. Hogness, D. S. and H. K. Mitchell. 1954. *J. Gen. Microbiol.* 11: 401–411.
242. Hollis, J. P. 1952. *Phytopathology* 42: 273–276.
243. Hollis, J. P. 1954. *Bull. Torrey Botan. Club* 81: 98–103.
244. Holter, H. and B. M. Pollock. 1952. *Compt. rend. trav. lab. Carlsberg. Sér. chim.* 28: 221–245.
245. Horowitz, N. H. 1944. *J. Biol. Chem.* 154: 141–149.
246. Horowitz, N. H. 1946. *J. Biol. Chem.* 162: 413–419.
247. Horowitz, N. H. 1947. *J. Biol. Chem.* 171: 255–264.
248. Horowitz, N. H. 1951. *Growth* 15 (Suppl.): 47–62.
249. Horowitz, N. H. and G. W. Beadle. 1943. *J. Biol. Chem.* 150: 325–333.
250. Horowitz, N. H., D. M. Bonner, H. K. Mitchell, E. L. Tatum, and G. W. Beadle. 1945. *Am. Naturalist* 79: 304–317.
251. Horowitz, N. H. and A. M. Srb. 1948. *J. Biol. Chem.* 174: 371–378.
252. How, J. E. 1940. *Ann. Botany* 4: 135–150.
253. Hultgren, B., B. Kihlman, and N. Fries. 1955. *Physiol. Plantarum* 8: 493–500.
254. Hultin, E. and L. Nordström. 1949. *Acta Chem. Scand.* 3: 1405–1417.

255. Iguchi, N. 1950. *J. Agr. Chem. Soc. Japan* 23: 357–360.
256. Isaac, I. 1949. *Trans. Brit. Mycol. Soc.* 32: 137–157.
257. Isenberg, H. D., A. Schatz, A. A. Angrist, V. Schatz, and G. S. Trelawny. 1954. *J. Bacteriol.* 68: 5–9.
258. Isenberg, H. D., G. S. Trelawny, and A. Schatz. 1953. *Bacteriol. Proc. (Soc. Am. Bacteriologists)* 1953: 17.
259. Ishizu, K. 1953. *Yamaguchi J. Sci. (Japan)* 4: 41–44. (*Chem. Abstr.* 48: 10830. 1954.)
260. Ishizu, K. 1954. *Yamaguchi J. Sci. (Japan)* 5: 49–55. (*Chem. Abstr.* 48: 12873. 1954.)
261. Isono, M. 1954. *J. Agr. Chem. Soc. Japan* 28: 196–200, 475–479.
262. Ito, Y. 1950a. *J. Biochem. (Tokyo)* 37: 51–63.
263. Ito, Y. 1950b. *J. Biochem. (Tokyo)* 37: 237–247.
264. Itzerott, D. 1936. *Flora (N. F.)* 31: 60–86.
265. Iwanoff, L. 1903. *Z. physiol. Chem. Hoppe-Seyler's* 39: 31–43.
266. Iwanoff, N. N. 1925a. *Biochem. Z.* 157: 231–242.
267. Iwanoff, N. N. 1925b. *Biochem. Z.* 162: 425–440.
268. Iwanoff, N. N. 1927. *Z. physiol. Chem. Hoppe-Seyler's* 170: 274–288.
269. Iwanoff, N. N. 1928. *Biochem. Z.* 192: 36–40.
270. Iwanoff, N. N. and A. N. Awetissowa. 1931. *Biochem. Z.* 231: 67–78.
271. Iwanoff, N. N. and L. K. Osnizkaja. 1934. *Biochem. Z.* 271: 22–31.
272. Iwanoff, N. N. and M. I. Smirnowa. 1928. *Biochem. Z.* 201: 1–12.
273. Iwanoff, N. N. and A. Toschewikowa. 1927. *Biochem. Z.* 181: 1–7.
274. Jakoby, W. B. and D. M. Bonner. 1956. *J. Biol. Chem.* 221: 689–695.
275. Jennison, M. W., M. D. Newcomb, and R. Henderson. 1955. *Mycologia* 47: 275–304.
276. Jensen, H. L. 1930. *Soil Sci.* 30: 59–77.
277. Jensen, H. L. 1951. *J. Gen. Microbiol.* 5: 360–368.
278. Jermyn, M. A. 1953a. *Australian J. Biol. Sci.* 6: 48–69.
279. Jermyn, M. A. 1953b. *Australian J. Biol. Sci.* 6: 77–97.
280. Johnson, J. L., W. G. Jackson, and T. E. Eble. 1951. *J. Am. Chem. Soc.* 73: 2947–2948.
281. Johnson, J. R. and J. B. Buchanan. 1953. *J. Am. Chem. Soc.* 75: 2103–2109.
282. Johnson, J. R., A. R. Kidwai, and J. S. Warner. 1953. *J. Am. Chem. Soc.* 75: 2110–2112.
283. Johnson, M. J. 1934. *Z. physiol. Chem. Hoppe-Seyler's* 224: 163–175.
284. Johnson, M. J. and J. Berger. 1942. *Advances in Enzymol.* 2: 69–92.
285. Jones, A. S., A. J. Swallow, and M. Webb. 1948. *Biochim. et Biophys. Acta* 2: 167–183.
286. Kallio, R. E. and A. D. Larsen. 1955. In W. D. McElroy and H. B. Glass (eds.), *Symposium on Amino Acid Metabolism*, p. 616–631. Baltimore: The Johns Hopkins Press.
287. Kalyanasundarum, R. and L. Saraswathi-Devi. 1955. *Nature (London)* 175: 945.
288. Kaplan, N. O., S. P. Colowick, and M. M. Ciotti. 1952. *J. Biol. Chem.* 194: 579–591.
289. Kaplan, N. O., S. P. Colowick, and A. Nason. 1951. *J. Biol. Chem.* 191: 473–483.
290. Kating, H. 1955. *Arch. Mikrobiol.* 22: 396–407.
291. Keil, W. and H. Bartmann. 1935. *Biochem. Z.* 280: 58–60.
292. Kihara, H., J. M. Prescott, and E. E. Snell. 1955. *J. Biol. Chem.* 217: 497–503.
293. Kihara, H. and E. E. Snell. 1952. *J. Biol. Chem.* 197: 791–800.
294. Kikkoji, T. 1907. *Z. physiol. Chem. Hoppe-Seyler's* 51: 201–206.

295. Klein, D. T. and R. M. Klein. 1955. *Plant Physiol.* 30: 410–413.
296. Klotz, J. 1927. *Hilgardia* 3: 27–40.
297. Kluyver, A. J., J. P. van der Walt, and A. J. van Triet. 1933. *Proc. Natl. Acad. Sci. U. S.* 39: 583–593.
298. Kluyver, A. J. and J. C. M. van Zijp. 1951. *Antonie van Leeuwenhoek J. Microbiol. Serol.* 17: 315–324.
299. Knight, S. G. 1948. *J. Bacteriol.* 55: 401–407.
300. Knox, W. E. 1955. In W. D. McElroy and H. B. Glass (eds.), *Symposium on Amino Acid Metabolism,* p. 836–866. Baltimore: The Johns Hopkins Press.
301. Kögl, F., H. C. Cox, and C. A. Salemink. 1957. *Experientia* 13: 137–138.
302. Kögl, F. and D. G. F. R. Kostermans. 1934. *Z. physiol. Chem. Hoppe-Seyler's* 228: 113–121.
303. Kögl, F. and J. Sparenburg. 1940. *Rec. trav. chim.* 59: 1180–1197.
304. Kornfeld, E. C., R. G. Jones, and T. V. Parke. 1949. *J. Am. Chem. Soc.* 71: 150–159.
305. Kostytschew, S. and E. Tswetkowa. 1920. *Z. physiol. Chem. Hoppe-Seyler's* 111: 171–200.
306. Krainsky, A. 1914. *Centr. Bakteriol. Parasitenk. Abt. II,* 41: 649–688.
307. Krebs, H. A. and K. Henseleit. 1932. *Z. physiol. Chem. Hoppe-Seyler's,* 210: 33–66.
308. Krimsky, I. and E. Racker. 1952. *J. Biol. Chem.* 198: 721–729.
309. Kuehl, F. A. et al. 1955. *J. Am. Chem. Soc.* 77: 2344–2345.
310. Küng, A. 1914. *Z. physiol. Chem. Hoppe-Seyler's,* 91: 241–250.
311. Kuninaka, A. 1955. *J. Agr. Chem. Soc. Japan* 29: 52–57, 797–800, 801–805.
312. Kunitz, M. 1938. *J. Gen. Physiol.* 21: 601–620.
313. Kupferberg, A. B., H. Styles, H. O. Singher, and S. A. Waksman. 1950. *J. Bacteriol.* 59: 523–526.
314. Lamaire, Y. and A. Brunel. 1951. *Compt. rend. (Paris)* 232: 872–873.
315. Lara, F. J. S. 1952. *J. Bacteriol.* 64: 271–277, 279–285.
316. Laskowski, M. 1951. In J. B. Sumner and K. Myrbäck (eds.), *The Enzymes,* Vol. 1 (2), p. 956–985. New York: Academic Press.
317. Leaphart, C. D. 1956. *Mycologia* 48: 25–40.
318. Leaver, F. W., J. Leal, and C. R. Brewer. 1947. *J. Bacteriol.* 54: 401–408.
319. Lebeau, J. B. and J. G. Dickson. 1953. *Phytopathology* 43: 581–582.
320. Lebeau, J. B. and J. G. Dickson. 1955. *Phytopathology* 45: 667–673.
321. Lees, H., J. R. Simpson, H. L. Jensen, and H. Sørensen. 1954. *Nature (London)* 173: 358.
322. Lemoigne, M. and R. Desveaux. 1935. *Compt. rend. (Paris)* 201: 239–241.
323. Leonian, L. H. and V. G. Lilly. 1940. *Am. J. Botany* 27: 18–26.
324. Lerner, A. B. 1953. *Advances in Enzymol.* 14: 73–128.
325. Leuthardt, F. 1951. In J. B. Sumner and K. Myrbäck (eds.), *The Enzymes,* Vol. 1 (2), p. 951–955. New York: Academic Press.
326. Lilly, V. G. and H. L. Barnett. 1951. *Physiology of the Fungi.* New York: McGraw-Hill Book Co., pp. 464.
327. Lindeberg, G. 1944. *Symbolae Botan. Upsalienses* 8 (2): 1–183.
328. Little, H. N. 1951. *J. Biol. Chem.* 193: 347–358.
329. Lockhart, W. R. and H. R. Garner. 1955. *Genetics* 40: 721–725.
330. Loring, H. S., G. L. Ordway, and J. G. Pierce. 1948. *J. Biol. Chem.* 176: 1123–1130.
331. Loring, H. S. and J. G. Pierce. 1944. *J. Biol. Chem.* 153: 61–69.
332. McCallan, S. E. A. and F. R. Weedon. 1940. *Contribs. Boyce Thompson Inst.* 11: 331–342.
333. McCarty, M. 1952a. *J. Exp. Med.* 96: 555–568.
334. McCarty, M. 1952b. *J. Exp. Med.* 96: 569–580.

335. McConnell, W. B. 1950. *Can. J. Research C,* 28: 600–612.
336. McConnell, W. B., E. Y. Spencer, and J. A. Trew. 1953. *Can. J. Chem.* 31: 697–704.
337. McElroy, W. D. and H. K. Mitchell. 1946. *Federation Proc.* 5: 376–379.
338. McElroy, W. D. and D. Spencer. 1956. In W. D. McElroy and B. Glass (eds.), *Symposium on Inorganic Nitrogen Metabolism,* p. 137–152. Baltimore: The Johns Hopkins Press.
339. Machlis, L. 1953a. *Am. J. Botany* 40: 189–195.
340. Machlis, L. 1953b. *Am. J. Botany* 40: 450–459.
341. Machlis, L. and E. Ossia. 1953. *Am. J. Botany* 40: 465–468.
342. McLamore, W. M. et al. 1953. *J. Am. Chem. Soc.* 75: 105–108.
343. MacLeod, D. M. 1954. *Ann. N. Y. Acad. Sci.* 60 (1): 58–70.
344. MacMillan, A. 1956a. *J. Exp. Botany* 7: 113–126.
345. MacMillan, A. 1956b. *Physiol. Plantarum* 9: 470–481.
346. MacMillan, A. 1956c. *Physiol. Plantarum* 9: 533–545.
347. Magasanik, B. and H. R. Bowser. 1955. In W. D. McElroy and H. B. Glass (eds.), *Symposium on Amino Acid Metabolism,* p. 398–406. Baltimore: The Johns Hopkins Press.
348. Markert, C. L. 1952. *Genetics* 37: 603–604.
349. Martin, J. K. and R. D. Batt. 1955. *Proc. Univ. Otago Med. School (New Zealand)* 33: 6–7.
350. Mathieson, M. J. and D. G. Catcheside. 1955. *J. Gen. Microbiol.* 13: 72–83.
351. Maxwell, M. E. 1950. *Australian J. Appl. Sci.* 1: 348–362.
352. Maxwell, M. E. 1952. *Australian J. Sci. Research, Ser. B,* 5: 42–55.
353. Mehler, A. H. 1955. In W. D. McElroy and H. B. Glass (eds.), *Symposium on Amino Acid Metabolism,* p. 882–908. Baltimore: The Johns Hopkins Press.
354. Meister, A. 1955a. *Advances in Enzymol.* 16: 185–246.
355. Meister, A. 1955b. In W. D. McElroy and H. B. Glass (eds.), *Symposium on Amino Acid Metabolism,* p. 3–32. Baltimore: The Johns Hopkins Press.
356. Meister, A., H. A. Sober, S. V. Tice, and P. E. Fraser. 1952. *J. Biol. Chem.* 197: 319–330.
357. Melin, E. and K. Helleberg. 1925. *Biochem. Z.* 157: 146–155.
358. Melin, E. and P. Mikola. 1948. *Physiol. Plantarum* 1: 109–112.
359. Melin, E. and B. Norkrans. 1948. *Physiol. Plantarum* 1: 176–184.
360. Melville, D. B., D. S. Genghof, E. Inamine, and V. Kovalenko. 1956. *J. Biol. Chem.* 223: 9–17.
361. Metzenberg, R. L. and H. K. Mitchell. 1956. *Arch. Biochem. Biophys.* 64: 51–56.
362. Michelson, A. M., W. Drell, and H. K. Mitchell. 1951. *Proc. Natl. Acad. Sci. U. S.* 37: 396–399.
363. Michener, H. D. and N. Snell. 1950. *Am. J. Botany* 37: 52–59.
364. Michi, K. and H. Nonaka. 1954. *J. Agr. Chem. Soc. Japan* 28: 343–346, 346–349.
365. Miles, P. G., H. Lund, and J. R. Raper. 1956. *Arch. Biochem. Biophys.* 62: 1–5.
366. Miller, T. E. and R. W. Stone. 1938. *J. Bacteriol.* 36: 248–249.
367. Mishra, J. N. 1953–54. *Proc. Bihar Acad. Agr. Sci. (India)* 1: 81–90. (*Chem. Abstr.* 48: 7709. 1954.)
368. Mitchell, H. K. and M. B. Houlahan. 1946. *Federation Proc.* 5: 370–375.
369. Mitchell, H. K., M. B. Houlahan, and J. F. Nyc. 1948. *J. Biol. Chem.* 172: 525–529.
370. Mitchell, H. K. and W. D. McElroy. 1946. *Arch. Biochem.* 10: 343–349, 351–358.
371. Miwa, T. and S. Yoshii. 1934. *Sci. Repts. Tokyo Bunrika Daigaku, Sect. B,* 1: 243–270. (*Japan J. Botany* 7: 183. 1934.)

372. Moore, J. A. et al. 1954. *J. Am. Chem. Soc.* 76: 2884–2887.
373. Morton, A. G. 1956. *J. Exp. Botany* 7: 97–112.
374. Morton, A. G. and D. Broadbent. 1955. *J. Gen. Microbiol.* 12: 248–258.
375. Morton, A. G. and A. MacMillan. 1954. *J. Exp. Botany* 5: 232–252.
376. Muggleton, P. W. and M. Webb. 1952a. *Biochim. et Biophys. Acta* 8: 431–441.
377. Muggleton, P. W. and M. Webb. 1952b. *Biochim. et Biophys. Acta* 8: 526–536.
378. Muggleton, P. W. and M. Webb. 1952c. *Biochim. et Biophys. Acta* 9: 343–355.
379. Müller, D. 1944. *Friesia* 3: 52–57.
380. Murray, H. C. and F. P. Zscheile. 1956. *Phytopathology* 46: 363–366.
381. Myers, J. W. and E. A. Adelberg. 1954. *Proc. Natl. Acad. Sci. U. S.* 40: 493–499.
382. Nakanishi, K. et al. 1954. *Bull. Chem. Soc. Japan* 27: 539–543.
383. Narrod, S. A. and W. A. Wood. 1952. *Arch. Biochem. Biophys.* 35: 462–463.
384. Nason, A. 1956. In W. D. McElroy and B. Glass (eds.), *Symposium on Inorganic Nitrogen Metabolism*, p. 109–136. Baltimore: The Johns Hopkins Press.
385. Nason, A., R. G. Abraham, and B. C. Averbach. 1954. *Biochim. et Biophys. Acta* 15: 159–161.
386. Nason, A., N. O. Kaplan, and S. P. Colowick. 1951. *J. Biol. Chem.* 188: 397–406.
387. Nason, A., N. O. Kaplan, and H. A. Oldewurtel. 1953. *J. Biol. Chem.* 201: 435–444.
388. Neal, D. C., R. E. Wester, and K. C. Gunn. 1933. *J. Agr. Research* 47: 107–118.
389. Neuberg, C. and I. Mandl. 1950. *Enzymologyia* 14: 128–133.
390. Newbold, G. T., W. Sharp, and F. S. Spring. 1951. *J. Chem. Soc. (London)* 1951: 2679–2682.
391. Newton, W. 1946. *Sci. Agr.* 26: 303–304.
392. Nicholson, W. N., M. Nierenstein, J. C. Pool, and N. V. Price. 1931. *Biochem. J. (London)* 25: 752–755.
393. Nickell. L. G. and P. R. Burkholder. 1947. *J. Am. Soc. Agron.* 39: 771–779.
394. Nielsen, N. 1930. *Jahrb. wiss. Botan.* 73: 125–191.
395. Nord, F. F. 1939. *Ergeb. Enzymforsch.* 8: 149–184.
396. Nord, F. F. and R. P. Mull. 1945. *Advances in Enzymol.* 5: 165–205.
397. Norkrans, B. 1950. *Symbolae Botan. Upsalienses* 11 (1): 1–126.
398. Norkrans, B. 1953. *Physiol. Plantarum* 6: 584–593.
399. Noval, J. J. and W. J. Nickerson. 1956. *Bacteriol. Proc. (Soc. Am. Bacteriologists)* 1956: 125–126.
400. Nysterakis, F. 1954a. *Compt. rend. (Paris)* 238: 143–145.
401. Nysterakis, F. 1954b. *Rev. gén. botan.* 61: 285–299, 337–385, 416–451.
402. Ohtsuki, T. 1936. *Japan. J. Botany* 8: 269–293.
403. Otani, H. 1934. *Acta Schol. Med. Univ. Imp. Kioto (Japan)* 17: 242–248, 249–259, 260–268, 269–287. (*Chem. Abstr.* 29: 2205. 1935.)
404. Otani, H. 1935a. *Acta Schol. Med. Univ. Imp. Kioto (Japan)* 17: 323–329. (*Chem. Abstr.* 29: 4032. 1935.)
405. Otani, H. 1935b. *Acta Schol. Med. Univ. Imp. Kioto (Japan)* 17: 330–333. (*Chem. Abstr.* 29: 4032. 1935.)
406. Otani, Y. 1952. *Ann. Phytopathol. Soc. Japan* 27: 9–15.
407. Page, R. M. 1952. *Am. J. Botany* 39: 731–739.
408. Partridge, C. W. H., D. M. Bonner, and C. Yanofsky. 1952. *J. Biol. Chem.* 194: 269–278.
409. Pelletier, R. L. and G. W. Keitt. 1954. *Am. J. Botany* 41: 362–371.
410. Perkins, D. D. 1949. *Genetics* 34: 607–626.

411. Perlman, D. 1949. *Am. J. Botany* 36: 180–184.
412. Peterson, E. A. and H. Katznelson. 1954. *Can. J. Microbiol.* 1: 190–197.
413. Pfennig, N. 1956. *Arch. Mikrobiol.* 25: 109–136.
414. Pierce, J. G. and H. S. Loring. 1945. *J. Biol. Chem.* 160: 409–415.
415. Pistor, R. 1930. *Zentr. Bakteriol. Parasitenk. Abt. II*, 80: 169–200.
416. Plattner, P. A., W. Keller, and A. Boller. 1954. *Helv. Chim. Acta* 37: 1379–1392.
417. Plattner, P. A. and U. Nager. 1948. *Helv. Chim. Acta* 31: 665–671, 2192–2203.
418. Plattner, P. A., U. Nager, and A. Boller. 1948. *Helv. Chim. Acta* 31: 594–602.
419. Plotho, O. von. 1940. *Arch. Mikrobiol.* 11: 33–72.
420. Pontecorvo, G. et al. 1953. *Advances in Genet.* 5: 141–238.
421. Pratt, C. A. 1924. Ann. Botany 38: 599–615.
421a. Pringle, R. B. and A. C. Braun. 1957. *Phytopathology* 47: 369–371.
422. Pringsheim, H. 1908. *Biochem. Z.* 8: 128–131.
423. Pyle, A. J. H. 1954. *J. Gen. Microbiol.* 11: 191–194.
424. Quantz, L. 1943. *Jahrb. wiss. Botan.* 91: 120–168.
425. Quilico, A., C. Cardani, and F. Piozzi. 1955. *Gazz. chim. ital.* 85: 3–33.
426. Quispel, A. 1954. *Acta Botan. Néerl.* 3: 495–511, 512–532.
427. Ragland, J. B. and J. L. Liverman. 1956. *Arch. Biochem. Biophys.* 65: 574–576.
428. Raper, K. B., R. D. Coghill, and A. Hollaender. 1945. *Am. J. Botany* 32: 165–176.
429. Ratner, S. 1955. In W. D. McElroy and H. B. Glass (eds.), *A Symposium on Amino Acid Metabolism,* p. 231–256. Baltimore: The Johns Hopkins Press.
430. Ray, P. M. 1956. *Arch. Biochem. Biophys.* 64: 193–216.
431. Ray, P. M. and K. V. Thimann. 1956. *Arch. Biochem. Biophys.* 64: 175–192.
432. Regnery, D. C. 1944. *J. Biol. Chem.* 154: 151–160.
433. Reichard, P. 1955. In E. Chargaff and J. N. Davidson (eds.), *The Nucleic Acids,* Vol. 2, p. 277–308. New York: Academic Press.
434. Reischer, H. S. 1951. *Mycologia* 43: 319–328.
435. Reissig, J. L. 1952. *Arch. Biochem. Biophys.* 36: 234–235.
436. Reynolds, A. K. 1955. In R. H. F. Manske (ed.), *The Alkaloids,* Vol. 5, p. 163–209. New York: Academic Press.
437. Reynolds, E. S. 1924. *Am. J. Botany* 11: 215–217.
438. Richards, R. R. 1949. *Botan. Gaz.* 110: 523–550.
439. Rippel, K. 1931. *Arch. Mikrobiol.* 2: 72–135.
440. Robbins, W. J. and A. Hervey. 1955. *Mycologia* 47: 155–162.
441. Robbins, W. J. and R. Ma. 1942. *Am. J. Botany* 29: 835–842.
442. Robbins, W. J. and R. Ma. 1945. *Am. J. Botany* 32: 509–523.
443. Robbins, W. J. and I. McVeigh. 1946. *Am. J. Botany* 33: 638–647.
444. Robbins, W. J., A. Rolnick, and F. Kavanagh. 1950. *Mycologia* 42: 161–166.
445. Roberts, E., P. Ayengar, and I. Posner. 1953. *J. Biol. Chem.* 203: 195–204.
446. Roberts, J. L. and E. Roberts. 1939. *Soil Sci.* 48: 135–139.
447. Roberts, M. and D. W. Visser. 1952. *J. Biol. Chem.* 194: 695–701.
448. Ronsdorf, L. 1935. *Arch. Mikrobiol.* 6: 309–325.
449. Rother, W. 1954. *Arch. Mikrobiol.* 20: 89–108.
450. Roush, A. H. and A. J. Domnas. 1956. *Science* 124: 125–126.
451. Roussos, G. G., H. Takahashi, and A. Nason. 1957. *J. Bacteriol.* 73: 594–595.
452. Roussos, G. G. and L. C. Vining. 1956. *J. Chem. Soc. (London)* 1956: 2469–2474.
453. Ryan, F. J. 1946. *Federation Proc.* 5: 366–369.
454. Sakaguchi, K. and W. Y. Chang. 1934. *J. Agr. Chem. Soc. Japan* 10: 459–476. (*Chem. Abstr.* 28: 5852–5853. 1934.)

455. Sakaguchi, K. and C. Ishitani. 1952. *J. Agr. Chem. Soc. Japan* 26: 279–285.
456. Sakaguchi, K. and S. Murao. 1950. *J. Agr. Chem. Soc. Japan* 23: 411.
457. Sakaguchi, K. and Y. Wang. 1936. *Bull. Agr. Chem. Soc. Japan* 12: 63–69.
458. Saksena, R. K. and K. S. Bhargava. 1943. *Proc. Indian Acad. Sci. 18B:* 45–51.
459. Saksena, R. K., S. K. Jain, and S. M. H. Jafri. 1953. *J. Indian Botan. Soc.* 31: 281–286.
460. Sato, R. 1956. In W. D. McElroy and B. Glass (eds.), *Symposium on Inorganic Nitrogen Metabolism,* p. 163–175. Baltimore: The Johns Hopkins Press.
461. Schade, A. L. 1940. *Am. J. Botany* 27: 376–384.
462. Schade, A. L. 1949. *J. Bacteriol.* 58: 811–822.
463. Schade, A. L. and K. V. Thimann. 1940. *Am. J. Botany* 27: 659–670.
464. Schatz, A. and R. R. Mohan. 1955. *J. Cellular Comp. Physiol.* 45: 331–342.
465. Schatz, A., G. S. Trelawney, V. Schatz, and R. R. Mohan. 1956. *Biochim. et Biophys. Acta* 21: 391–392.
466. Schlesinger, H. and W. W. Ford. 1907. *J. Biol. Chem.* 3: 279–283.
467. Schmalfuss, K. and K. Mothes. 1930. *Biochem. Z.* 221: 134–153.
468. Schmidt, E. L. 1954. *Science* 119: 187–189.
469. Schmitz, H. and S. M. Zeller. 1919. *Ann. Missouri Botan. Garden* 6: 193–200.
470. Schopfer, W. H. and S. Blumer. 1938. *Arch. Mikrobiol.* 9: 305–367.
471. Schopfer, W. H. and S. Blumer. 1943. *Ber. schweiz. botan. Ges.* 53: 409–456.
472. Schopfer, W. H. and M. Guilloud. 1946. *Helv. Physiol. Pharmacol. Acta* 4: 24–25.
473. Schroeter, G. and L. Strassberger. 1931. *Biochem. Z.* 232: 452–458.
474. Schulman, M. P. 1954. In D. M. Greenberg (ed.), *Chemical Pathways of Metabolism,* Vol. 2, p. 223–261. New York: Academic Press.
475. Schweet, R. S., J. T. Holden, and P. H. Lowy. 1954. *J. Biol. Chem.* 211: 517–529.
476. Schweet, R. S., J. T. Holden, and P. H. Lowy. 1955. In W. D. McElroy and H. B. Glass (eds.), *A Symposium on Amino Acid Metabolism,* p. 496–505, Baltimore: The Johns Hopkins Press.
477. Semeniuk, G. 1942. *Iowa State Coll. J. Sci.* 16: 337–348.
478. Senn, G. 1928. *Biol. Revs. Cambridge Phil. Soc.* 3: 77–91.
479. Sequeira, L. and T. A. Steeves. 1954. *Plant Physiol.* 29: 11–16.
480. Shepherd, C. J. 1951. *Biochem. J. (London)* 48: 483–486.
481. Shibata, K. 1904. *Beitr. Chem. Physiol. Pathol.* 5: 384–394.
482. Shirakawa, H. S. 1955. *Am. J. Botany* 42: 379–384.
483. Silver, W. S. 1957. *J. Bacteriol.* 73: 241–246.
484. Silver, W. S. and W. D. McElroy. 1954. *Arch. Biochem. Biophys.* 51: 379–394.
485. Simon, S. 1955. *Acta Microbiol. Acad. Sci. Hung.* 3: 53–65. (*Chem. Abstr.* 50: 7226. 1956.)
486. Simonart, P. and K. Y. Chow. 1953. *Antonie van Leeuwenhoek J. Microbiol. Serol.* 19: 121–134.
487. Smith, E. L. 1951. In J. B. Sumner and K. Myrbäck (eds.), *The Enzymes,* Vol. 1 (2), p. 793–872. New York: Academic Press.
488. Sneath, P. H. A. 1955. *Nature (London)* 175: 818.
489. Spitzer, G. and M. M. Diehm. 1931. *J. Agr. Research* 43: 223–229.
490. Srb, A. M. and N. H. Horowitz. 1944. *J. Biol. Chem,* 154: 129–139.
491. Stahl, W. H., B. McQue, G. R. Mandels, and R. G. H. Siu. 1950. *Textile Research J.* 20: 570-579.
492. Stahl, W. H., B. McQue, and R. G. H. Siu. 1950. *Arch. Biochem.* 27: 211–220.
493. Stanier, R. Y. and O. Hayaishi. 1951. *Science* 101: 326–330.
494. Steinberg, R. A. 1939. *J. Agr. Research* 59: 731–748.
495. Steinberg, R. A. 1944. *Science* 100: 10.
496. Steinberg, R. A. and J. D. Bowling. 1939. *J. Agr. Research* 58: 717–732.
497. Steinberg, R. A. and C. Thom. 1940. *J. Heredity* 31: 61–63.

498. Steinberg, R. A. and C. Thom. 1942. *J. Agr. Research* 64: 645–652.
499. Steiner, M. and E. Stein von Kamienski. 1953. *Naturwiss.* 40: 483.
500. Stetten, M. R. 1955. In W. D. McElroy and H. B. Glass (eds.), *Symposium on Amino Acid Metabolism*, p. 277–290. Baltimore: The Johns Hopkins Press.
501. Stevens, C. L., R. L. Gasser, T. K. Mukherjee, and T. H. Haskell. 1956. *J. Am. Chem. Soc.* 78: 6212.
502. Steward, F. C. and J. K. Pollard. 1956. In W. D. McElroy and B. Glass (eds.), *Symposium on Inorganic Nitrogen Metabolism*, p. 377–407. Baltimore: The Johns Hopkins Press.
503. Steward, F. C., R. M. Zacharius, and J. K. Pollard. 1955. *Ann. Acad. Sci. Fennicae, Ser. A, II, No. 60:* 321–366.
504. Stickings, C. E. and H. Raistrick. 1956. *Ann. Rev. Biochem.* 25: 225–256.
505. Stock, C. C. et al. 1954. *Nature (London)* 173: 71–72.
506. Stockdale, P. M. 1953. *J. Gen. Microbiol.* 8: 434–441.
507. Stodola, F. H. et al. 1955. *Arch. Biochem. Biophys.* 54: 240–245.
508. Stoll, A. 1952. *Fortschr. der Chemie org. Naturstoffe* 9: 114–174.
509. Stoll, A. et al. 1954. *Helv. Chim. Acta* 37: 1815–1825.
510. Stoll, C. 1954. *Phytopathol. Z.* 22: 233–274.
511. Strauss, B. S. 1951. *Arch. Biochem.* 30: 292–305.
512. Strauss, B. S. 1953. *Arch. Biochem. Biophys.* 44: 200–210.
513. Sumi, M. 1928. *Biochem. Z.* 195: 161–174.
514. Sumner, J. B. 1951. In J. B. Sumner and K. Myrbäck (eds.), *The Enzymes,* Vol. 1 (2), p. 873–892. New York: Academic Press.
514a. Suskind, S. R. 1957. *J. Bacteriol.* 74: 308–318.
515. Swartz, H. E. and L. K. Georg. 1955. *Mycologia* 47: 475–493.
516. Tabor, H. 1955. In W. D. McElroy and H. B. Glass (eds.), *Symposium on Amino Acid Metabolism*, p. 373–390. Baltimore: The Johns Hopkins Press.
517. Taha, E. E. M. and M. M. Sharabash. 1956. *Nature (London)* 177: 622–623.
518. Taha, E. E. M., L. Storck-Krieg, and W. Franke. 1955. *Arch. Mikrobiol.* 23: 67–78.
519. Tai, T. Y. and W. E. van Heyningen. 1951. *J. Gen. Microbiol.* 5: 110–120.
520. Talley, P. J. and L. M. Blank. 1942. *Plant Physiol.* 17: 52–68.
521. Tamiya, H. 1942. *Advances in Enzymol.* 2: 183–238.
522. Tamiya, H. and S. Usami. 1940. *Acta Phytochim. (Japan)* 11: 261–298.
523. Tanenbaum, S. W., L. Garnjobst, and E. L. Tatum. 1954. *Am. J. Botany* 41: 484–488.
524. Tate, P. 1929. *Parasitology* 21: 31–54.
525. Tatum, E. L., D. M. Bonner, and G. W. Beadle. 1943. *Arch. Biochem.* 3: 477–478.
526. Tatum, E. L., S. R. Gross, G. Ehrensvärd, and L. Garnjobst. 1954. *Proc. Natl. Acad. Sci. U. S.* 40: 271–276.
527. Tatum, E. L., M. G. Ritchey, E. V. Cowdry, and L. F. Wicks. 1946. *J. Biol. Chem.* 163: 675–682.
528. Tatum, E. L. and D. Shemin. 1954. *J. Biol. Chem.* 209: 671–675.
529. Tausson, W. O. 1925. *Biochem. Z.* 155: 356–368.
530. Tazawa, Y., K. Okuniki, and N. Urushima. 1947. *J. Penicillin (Japan)* 1: 355–359.
531. Tazawa, Y. and S. Yamagata. 1937. *Acta Phytochim. (Japan)* 9: 299–310.
532. Teas, H. J. 1951. *J. Biol. Chem.* 190: 369–375.
533. Teas, H. J., N. H. Horowitz, and M. Fling. 1948. *J. Biol. Chem.* 172: 651–658.
534. Tempel, E. 1931. *Arch. Mikrobiol.* 2: 40–71.
535. Thakur, A. K. and R. V. Norris. 1928. *J. Indian Inst. Sci. 11A:* 141–160. (*Chem. Abstr.* 23: 2459. 1929.)
536. Thayer, P. S. and N. H. Horowitz. 1951. *J. Biol. Chem.* 192: 755–767.

537. Thimann, K. V. 1935. *J. Biol. Chem.* 109: 279–291.

538. Thimann, K. V. and H. E. Dolk. 1933. *Biol. Zentr.* 53: 49–66.

539. Thoai, N. V., J. L. Hatt, and T. T. An. 1956. *Biochim. et Biophys. Acta* 22: 116–123.

540. Thoai, N. V., J. L. Hatt, T. T. An, and J. Roche. 1956. *Biochim. et Biophys. Acta* 22: 337–341.

541. Thornberry, H. H. and H. W. Anderson. 1948. *Arch. Biochem.* 16: 389–397.

542. Thorne, R. S. W. 1950. *Wallerstein Lab. Commun.* 13: 319–340.

543. Tomisek, A. J., H. J. Kelly, and H. E. Skipper. 1956. *Arch. Biochem. Biophys.* 64: 437–455.

544. Tomizawa, C. 1952. *Ann. Phytopathol. Soc. Japan* 27: 113–118.

545. Tonhazy, N. E. and M. J. Pelczar, Jr. 1954. *Science* 120: 141–142.

546. Treschow, C. 1944. *Dansk Botan. Arkiv* 11 (6): 1–180.

547. Tsuda, N. 1950. *Japan. J. Nutrition* 8: 108–110.

548. Tyler, V. E., Jr. and A. E. Schwarting. 1953. *Science* 118: 132–133.

549. Tytell, A. A., J. Charney, W. A. Bolhofer, and C. Curran. 1954. *Federation Proc.* 13: 312.

550. Udenfriend, S. and E. Titus. 1955. In W. D. McElroy and H. B. Glass (eds.), *A Symposium on Amino Acid Metabolism,* p. 945–949. Baltimore: The Johns Hopkins Press.

551. Uemura, T. 1937. *Bull. Agr. Chem. Soc. Japan* 13: 107, 108.

552. Uemura, T. 1939. *J. Agr. Chem. Soc. Japan* 15: 353–358. (*Chem. Abstr.* 33: 8671–8672. 1939.)

553. Umezawa, H., K. Oikawa, Y. Okami, and K. Maeda. 1953. *J. Bacteriol.* 66: 118–119.

554. Utkin, L. M. 1950. *Biokhimiya* 15: 330–333. (*Chem. Abstr.* 45: 216. 1951.)

555. Vanbreuseghem, R. 1952. *Mycologia* 44: 176–182.

556. Verhoeven, W. 1956. In W. D. McElroy and B. Glass (eds.), *Symposium on Inorganic Nitrogen Metabolism,* p. 61–86. Baltimore: The Johns Hopkins Press.

557. Verhoeven, W. and Y. Takeda. 1956. In W. D. McElroy and B. Glass (eds.), *Symposium on Inorganic Nitrogen Metabolism,* p. 159–162. Baltimore: The Johns Hopkins Press.

558. Virtanen, A. I. 1950. *Ann. Acad. Sci. Fennicae, Ser. A. II, No. 39:* 1–25.

559. Vishniac, H. S. 1955. *J. Gen. Microbiol.* 12: 455–463.

560. Vogel, H. J. 1955. In W. D. McElroy and H. B. Glass (eds.), *A Symposium on Amino Acid Metabolism,* p. 335–346. Baltimore: The Johns Hopkins Press.

561. Vogel, H. J. and D. M. Bonner. 1954. *Proc. Natl. Acad. Sci. U. S.* 40: 688–694.

562. Volkonsky, M. 1934. *Ann. inst. Pasteur* 52: 76–101.

563. Waelsch, H. 1952. *Advances in Enzymol.* 13: 237–319.

564. Waggoner, P. E. and A. E. Dimond. 1953. *Phytopathology* 43: 281–284.

565. Wagner, R. P. and A. Bergquist. 1955. *J. Biol. Chem.* 216: 251–262.

566. Wagner, R. P. and P. W. Ifland. 1956. *Compt. rend. trav. lab. Carlsberg. Sér physiol.* 26: 381–406.

567. Waksman, S. A. 1918a. *J. Bacteriol.* 3: 509–530.

568. Waksman, S. A. 1918b. *Soil Sci.* 6: 137–155.

569. Waksman, S. A. 1919. *Soil Sci.* 8: 71–215.

570. Waksman, S. A. 1920. *J. Bacteriol.* 5: 1–30.

571. Waksman, S. A. 1927. *Principles of Soil Microbiology.* Baltimore: Williams and Wilkins Co. pp. 897.

572. Waksman, S. A. 1944. *Soil Sci.* 58: 89–113.

573. Waksman, S. A. 1950. *The Actinomycetes.* Waltham, Mass.: The Chronica Botanica Co. pp. 230.

574. Waksman, S. A. and R. L. Starkey. 1932. *J. Bacteriol.* 23: 405–428.

575. Waksman, S. A. and H. B. Woodruff. 1940. *J. Bacteriol.* 40: 581–600.

576. Walker, J. B. 1953. *J. Biol. Chem.* 204: 139–146.
577. Waller, C. W., P. W. Fryth, B. L. Hutchings, and J. H. Williams. 1953. *J. Am. Chem. Soc.* 75: 2025.
578. Ware, G. C. and H. A. Painter. 1955. *Nature (London)* 175: 900.
578a. Watanabe, Y. and K. Shimura. 1955. *J. Biochem.* (Tokyo) 42: 181–192.
579. Wehmer, C. and M. Hadders. 1933a. In G. Klein (ed.), *Handbuch der Pflanzenanalyse,* Vol. 4 (1), p. 222–228.
580. Wehmer, C. and M. Hadders. 1933b. In G. Klein (ed.), *Handbuch der Pflanzenanalyse,* Vol. 4 (1), p. 247–253.
581. Wehmer, C. and M. Hadders. 1933c. In G. Klein (ed.), *Handbuch der Pflanzenanalyse,* Vol. 4 (1), p. 291–298.
582. Weinhouse, S. 1955. In W. D. McElroy and H. B. Glass (eds.), *A Symposium on Amino Acid Metabolism,* p. 637–657. Baltimore: The Johns Hopkins Press.
583. Weissbach, A. and B. L. Horecker. 1955. In W. D. McElroy and H. B. Glass (eds.), *A Symposium on Amino Acid Metabolism,* p. 741–742. Baltimore: The Johns Hopkins Press.
584. Went, F. W. and K. V. Thimann. 1937. *Phytohormones.* New York: The Macmillan Co. pp. 294.
585. Werle, E. 1941. *Biochem. Z.* 309: 61–76.
586. Werle, E. 1943. *Die Chemie (Angew. Chem.)* 56: 141–148.
587. Wetter, L. R. 1952. *Can. J. Botany* 30: 685–692.
588. Wetter, L. R. 1954a. *Can. J. Biochem. and Physiol.* 32: 20–26.
589. Wetter, L. R. 1954b. *Can. J. Biochem. and Physiol.* 32: 60–67.
590. Whiffen, A. J. 1948. *J. Bacteriol.* 56: 283–291.
591. White, E. C. and J. H. Hill. 1943. *J. Bacteriol.* 45: 433–442.
592. White, N. H. 1941. *J. Australian Council Sci. Ind. Research* 14: 137–146.
593. Whitfield, P. R. 1956. *Arch. Biochem. Biophys.* 65: 585–586.
594. Wieland, T. 1949. *Ann. Chem. Liebigs.* 564: 152–160.
595. Wieland, T., W. Motzel, and H. Merz. 1953. *Ann. Chem. Liebigs.* 581: 10–16.
596. Wieland, T., G. Schmidt, and L. Wirth. 1952. *Ann. Chem. Liebigs.* 577: 215–233.
597. Wieland, T. and W. Schön. 1955. *Ann. Chem. Liebigs.* 593: 157–178.
598. Wieland, T. and O. Weiberg. 1957. *Ann. Chem. Liebigs.* 607: 168–174.
599. Wildy, J. and H. Heath. 1957. *Biochem. J. (London)* 65: 220–223.
600. Williams, W. J., J. Litwin, and C. B. Thorne. 1955. *J. Biol. Chem.* 212: 427–438.
601. Wilson, P. W. 1951. In C. H. Werkman and P. W. Wilson (eds.), *Bacterial Physiology,* p. 467–499. New York: Academic Press.
602. Wirth, J. C. and F. F. Nord. 1943. *Arch. Biochem.* 2: 463–468.
603. Wolf, F. T. 1948. *Arch. Biochem.* 16: 143–149.
604. Wolf, F. T. 1951. *Bull. Torrey Botan. Club* 78: 211–220.
605. Wolf, F. T. 1952. *Proc. Natl. Acad. Sci. U. S.* 38: 106–111.
606. Wolf, F. T. 1953. *Mycologia* 45: 825–835.
607. Wolf, F. T. 1955. *Bull. Torrey Botan. Club* 82: 343–354.
608. Wood, W. A. and I. C. Gunsalus. 1951. *J. Biol. Chem.* 190: 403–416.
609. Woolley, D. W. 1948. *J. Biol. Chem.* 176: 1291–1298, 1299–1308.
610. Wooster, R. C. and V. H. Cheldelin. 1945. *Arch. Biochem.* 8: 311–320.
611. Work, E. 1955. In W. D. McElroy and H. B. Glass (eds.), *A Symposium on Amino Acid Metabolism,* p. 462–492. Baltimore: The Johns Hopkins Press.
612. Work, E. and D. L. Dewey. 1953. *J. Gen. Microbiol.* 9: 394–409.
613. Wright, B. E. 1951. *Arch. Biochem. Biophys.* 31: 332–333.
614. Yabuta, T., K. Kambe, and T. Hayashi. 1934. *J. Agr. Chem. Soc. Japan* 10: 1059–1068. (*Chem. Abstr.* 29: 1132. 1935.)
615. Yamamoto, S., A. Eritate, and T. Miwa. 1953. *Botan. Mag. (Tokyo)* 66: 234–238.

616. Yanofsky, C. 1952a. *J. Biol. Chem.* 194: 279–286.
617. Yanofsky, C. 1952b. *J. Biol. Chem.* 198: 343–352.
618. Yanofsky, C. and J. L. Reissig. 1953. *J. Biol. Chem.* 202: 567–577.
619. Yaw, K. E. 1952. *Mycologia* 44: 307–317.
620. Yemm, E. W. 1954. *Proc. Symposium Colston Research Soc.,* 7, p. 51–66. New York: Academic Press.
621. Yoshida, F. 1954. *J. Agr. Chem. Soc. Japan* 28: 66–70.
622. Yoshii, H. 1935. *Bull. Sci. Fakultato Terkultura, Kjuŝu Imp. Univ.* (*Japan*) 6: 312–330.
623. Yoshii, H. 1936. *Ann. Phytopathol. Soc. Japan* 6: 199–204.
624. Yura, T. and H. J. Vogel. 1955. *Biochim. et Biophys. Acta* 17: 582.
625. Yusef, H. 1953. *Bull. Torrey Botan. Club* 80: 43–64.
626. Zalokar, M. and V. W. Cochrane. 1956. *Am. J. Botany* 43: 107–110.
627. Zamenhof, S. and E. Chargaff. 1949. *J. Biol. Chem.* 180: 727–740.
628. Zatman, L. J., N. O. Kaplan, and S. P. Colowick. 1953. *J. Biol. Chem.* 200: 197–212.
629. Zellner, J. 1907. *Chemie der höheren Pilze.* Leipzig: Wilhelm Engelmann, pp. 257.
630. Zittle, C. A. 1951. In J. B. Sumner and K. Myrbäck (eds.), *The Enzymes,* Vol. 1 (2), p. 922–945. New York: Academic Press.

9. Inorganic Nutrition and Metabolism

Inorganic sources of nitrogen have been discussed in the preceding chapter; here we are concerned with the utilization of other elements. Fungi have relatively large requirements for phosphorus, potassium, sulfur, and magnesium and much smaller but definite requirements for at least five micronutrients (trace elements, minor elements). The known essential micronutrients are iron, zinc, copper, manganese, and molybdenum. The calcium requirement of fungi, if specific, is of the same order of magnitude as the micronutrient requirement, whereas calcium is a major nutrient for higher plants. Boron, required by green plants, is not known to be needed by fungi. The possibility of other micronutrient requirements in fungi must also be considered. Effects of sodium chloride have been assumed here to be non-specific, although it has been shown that sodium is required by *Anabaena cylindrica* (4).

The history of investigations on the mineral nutrition of fungi is reviewed by Foster (57). Early studies were primarily nutritional in nature and were severely hampered by methodological difficulties. More recent nutritional studies owe much to the pioneering work of R. A. Steinberg on both the techniques and the basic concepts of the field. Interest at the present time is shifting toward the problem of the metabolic function of the inorganic nutrients, with special attention to enzymatic processes in which metals play a role. A return to the exploration of still unknown requirements should be possible as purer chemicals and inert container materials come to the attention of the biologist.

1. PHOSPHORUS

In culture media a level of potassium phosphate (monobasic or dibasic) of 0.004 M is usually provided; reported optimum concentrations —affected, of course, by the carbon and nitrogen level—are of the order of magnitude of 0.001–0.003 M (75, 100, 187, 241). These levels are, however, too low to provide adequate buffering against appreciable organic acid formation.

Orthophosphate may be replaced, at least for some fungi, by other forms of inorganic phosphate (49), by phytic acid (220), by adenosine phosphates (223), or by casein (22). *Aspergillus niger* cannot utilize phosphite or hypophosphite (49); phosphites appear to be generally inert in biological systems (203).

Phosphate deficiencies cause several metabolic disturbances. The most easily observed, as one would expect, is a lowered rate of glucose utilization (33, 123, 130); other metabolic symptoms of deficiency are presumably secondary to this direct effect.

In the typical culture cycle, phosphorus is absorbed rapidly during

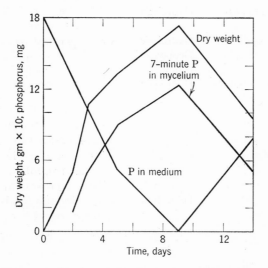

Figure 1. Growth and phosphorus changes in *Aspergillus niger*. From data of Mann (135). Seven-minute phosphorus is organic phosphorus mineralized by acid hydrolysis of 7 minutes duration.

the early stages of growth and is converted in the cells to organic compounds (69, 134). Absorption is dependent upon oxygen and a respirable substrate and is inhibited if respiration is poisoned (79, 134, 205). The rate of absorption is retarded if available carbon or nitrogen is

Table 1. Phosphatases of Fungi and Actinomycetes

Substrate	Action	Organisms
Beta-glycerophosphate, sugar phosphates, *p*-nitrophenyl phosphate, etc.	Hydrolysis at acid pH	*Actinomyces israeli* (90), *Aspergillus flavus** (251), *A. niger* (132, 134), *A. oryzae* (39, 41, 42, 179), *Candida albicans,*† *Cryptococcus* spp.,† *Geotrichum candidum,*† and *Torula cremoris*† (16), *Streptomyces coelicolor* (38), *Torulopsis utilis* (193)
Beta-glycerophosphate	Hydrolysis at alkaline pH	*Allomyces javanicus*† (248), *Aspergillus flavus** (251), *A. oryzae** (7), *Candida albicans*† (16), *Microsporum canis* (34), *Penicillium chrysogenum* (206, 207), *Torula cremoris*†, (16), *Trichophyton rubrum*† (172)
Glucosamine-6-phosphate	Hydrolysis	*Neurospora crassa* (24)
Adenosine triphosphate	Hydrolysis	*Aspergillus niger* (112, 134), *Penicillium chrysogenum* (110, 111)
Adenosine monophosphate	Hydrolysis	*Aspergillus niger* (132, 134), *Penicillium chrysogenum* (206)
Monoallyl phosphate	Hydrolysis	*Aspergillus niger* (8)
Colloidal polymetaphosphate	Depolymerization	*Aspergillus* spp., *Penicillium* spp.‡ (95, 96, 97, 98, 111, 132)
Low molecular weight metaphosphate	Hydrolysis	*Aspergillus* spp. (105, 106, 111, 112, 135)
Pyrophosphate	Hydrolysis	*Aspergillus* spp. (109, 132, 135, 159, 160, 164, 179), *Penicillium chrysogenum* (109, 206)
Triphosphate	Hydrolysis	*Aspergillus niger* (132), *A. oryzae*§ (159, 160, 161)
Polyphosphates	Hydrolysis	*Aspergillus niger* (111, 112, 113)
Phytic acid	Hydrolysis	*Aspergillus niger* (50, 134), *Penicillium chrysogenum* (206)
Thionophosphate	Hydrolysis	*Aspergillus* spp. (56)

* Two pH optima.

† Histochemical method.

‡ No depolymerization by extracts from *Phycomyces blakesleeanus*, *Rhizopus nigricans*, *Collybia velutipes*, *Marasmius* spp., *Merulius domesticus*, *Polyporus betulinus*, or *Tricholoma equestre*.

§ Two enzymes.

made limiting (71, 72) and, of course, if the external phosphate concentration is lowered (33, 70). When conidia appear, mycelial phosphorus enters the spores (10). Autolysis is marked by the appearance of phosphate, primarily inorganic, in the medium (33, 42, 143, 217); most of this appears to be derived from mycelial organic phosphorus, inasmuch as the inorganic mycelial phosphorus remains relatively constant during autolysis. Most of our information is from studies on *Aspergillus niger;* the data of Figure 1 are typical.

Combined forms of phosphate, organic and inorganic, are hydrolyzed by fungal enzymes, the phosphatases, the occurrence of which is summarized in Table 1. It may be that the acid and alkaline phosphatases of fungi are identical with phosphomonoesterases I and II of other organisms (204), but the specificity is very much in doubt. Indeed, there is no certainty in most of the examples of Table 1 that separate specific enzymes are involved.

Probably most or all fungi and actinomycetes form a phosphatase active at low pH against organic phosphates, although particular preparations have been reported to lack this activity (34, 206, 207).

2. POTASSIUM

Potassium is required by fungi; at the usual levels of carbohydrate, concentrations of 0.001–0.004 M are adequate (100, 187, 238). Surprisingly little information is available on the physiology of potassium in fungi; the most striking effect of potassium deficiency in *Aspergillus niger* is an increase in oxalic acid accumulation (29, 146, 196). A very low supply of the element is accompanied by poor sugar utilization (195), and it seems likely from work with organisms other than fungi that potassium has an essential function in carbohydrate metabolism (154, 176, 202). Certain enzymes, however, are more active in preparations from potassium-deficient cells (85).

Sodium can partially replace potassium in the nutrition of *Aspergillus niger* (73, 238), but the degree of replacement is small. Under some conditions, rubidium and cesium have slight effects (238), under others, none (149). In certain of the bacteria, rubidium and other alkali metals have a much more pronounced action, either as replacements for or competitors of potassium (55, 124, 130, 202, 247). It seems likely that studies of this problem in fungi other than *Aspergillus niger* would be rewarding. Rubidium can replace potassium in certain cell-free enzyme systems (126).

Figure 2 illustrates the typical growth response to the four major elements—potassium, magnesium, sulfur, and phosphorus.

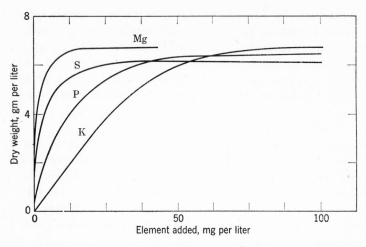

Figure 2. The response of *Cephalosporium salmosynnematum* to potassium, magnesium, phosphorus, and sulfur. Redrawn from Pisano et al. (187), by permission of the Williams and Wilkins Company.

3. SULFUR

Media in common use incorporate excess sulfur as magnesium sulfate; at moderate carbohydrate concentrations the sulfur requirement is about 0.0001–0.0006 M (13, 91, 228).

Most fungi can supply all their needs for sulfur from inorganic sulfate, i.e., they reduce the sulfate and incorporate it into organic molecules. The organic sulfur compounds known in fungi include amino acids (cysteine, cystine, and methionine), vitamins (thiamine and biotin), cyclic choline sulfate (Chapter 2), sulfur-containing antibiotics, e.g., penicillin and gliotoxin, and such miscellaneous compounds as junipal (Chapter 6), thiourea (177), and methyl mercaptan (Chapter 6). Sulfur incorporation into organic combinations is often very large; whether or not sulfur is released on autolysis appears to be determined by the species studied (84, 192, 197).

The fungi which as isolated from nature are unable to utilize sulfate sulfur are all aquatic phycomycetes: most Saprolegniales and all known members of the Blastocladiales (30, 31). Other phycomycetes—Chytridiales, Leptomitales, Peronosporales, and the Zygomycetes—utilize sulfate. Whether dependence on reduced sulfur is biochemically or ecologically related to the lower oxygen requirement or to the fermentative capacity of the Blastocladiales is still uncertain. Mutants requiring reduced sulfur have been obtained from *Neurospora crassa*

(89), *Aspergillus nidulans* (83, 188), *Penicillium chrysogenum* (82), *Ophiostoma multiannulatum* (64, 65), and *Ustilago zeae* (180).

Some nutritional studies on sulfur are summarized in Table 2, from which it appears that most or all fungi utilize sulfide, thiosulfate, and

Table 2. The Sulfur Nutrition of Some Fungi*

Source of Sulfur	*Saprolegnia delica* (22)	*Brevilegnia gracilis* (22)	*Pythium* spp. (208)	*Pestalotia malorum* (244)	*Aspergillus niger* (234)	*Penicillium chrysogenum* (82)
Sulfate	0	+	+	+	+	+
Persulfate	0	+	+	+	+	
Sulfite	0	+	+			+
Bisulfite	0	+	+	0	+	
Dithionate	0	0	0	+	0	
Hyposulfite	+	+	+	0	+	+
Thiosulfate	+	+	+	+	+	+
Sulfide†	+	+	+	+	+	+
Disulfide†				+	+	+
Cysteine	+	+	+	+	+	+
Cystine					+	+
Methionine					+	
Thiourea	+	+	+	+	0	+
Thiocyanate						+

* + = growth, 0 = no growth.
† See text.

the more oxidized forms of inorganic sulfur (except dithionate). However, the data on some of these compounds must be questioned in view of their known instability; thus, Steinberg (234) found that *Aspergillus niger* grows much better on old than on fresh samples of sodium sulfide and disulfide.

It should be noted that the difference between *Brevilegnia gracilis* and *Saprolegnia delica* in their sulfur nutrition parallels that seen elsewhere (Chapter 3) in their carbon nutrition—the soil-inhabiting *B. gracilis* is more omnivorous than its aquatic relative.

The details of sulfate reduction are not fully known. The available data suggest the following pathway (44):

Sulfate $(SO_4^{--}) \rightarrow$ sulfite $(SO_3^{--}) \rightarrow$ sulfide (S^{--}) or thiosulfate $(S_2O_3^{--}) \rightarrow$ cysteine $\rightarrow$ methionine   (1)

The obviously necessary intermediates are not known, nor is it possible to say at what point in Equation 1 the sulfur becomes attached to an organic molecule, but the scheme is in agreement with nutritional data on genetically different mutants of *Neurospora crassa* (89), *Aspergillus nidulans* (83, 188), and *Venturia inaequalis* (104). Shepherd (219) proposes a dual pathway of cysteine biosynthesis in *A. nidulans*.

The naturally occurring fungi which require reduced sulfur are, we may suppose, unable to carry out one or more of the reactions of Equation 1. Thus *Blastocladiella emersonii* grows with either cysteine or methionine (13) and is presumably blocked prior to cysteine synthesis; *Allomyces arbuscula,* on the other hand, appears unable to use any source of sulfur other than methionine (99). The same considerations apply to other fungi which require cysteine or methionine (131, 254).

Bulk reduction of sulfate with evolution of hydrogen sulfide is not effected by fungi, as it is by some bacteria. *Candida* spp. reduce sulfite (173), many fungi enzymatically reduce elemental sulfur to H_2S (125, 144, 216), and *Neurospora crassa* reduces selenite to selenium (259).

Sulfur and sulfur compounds are oxidized by fungi: elemental sulfur by *Penicillium luteum* (1) sulfur-containing amino acids by *Aspergillus niger* (68, 148), cysteine by *Microsporum gypseum* (224). Cysteine-sulfinic acid has been proposed as an intermediate in cysteine oxidation (224).

A few minor aspects of sulfur metabolism may be mentioned in conclusion. Commercial enzyme preparations from *Aspergillus* spp. contain a phenolsulfatase, hydrolyzing compounds of the type R—OSO_3K (2, 162, 163, 165); other sulfatases have not been reported from fungi (66). *Penicillium notatum* is able to split a carbon-sulfur bond (32). The toxicity of barium to *Aspergillus niger* results from the removal of sulfate, and barium is not toxic if sulfur is supplied in some other form (228, 234). Finally, the reduced sulfur requirement of the yeast phase of *Histoplasma capsulatum* (186, 209) is a requirement for reducing conditions, not for reduced sulfur as such. Transfer of methyl groups to sulfur is summarized in Chapter 6; reductive steps occur in the over-all metabolism of sulfur, selenium, and tellurium.

4. MAGNESIUM

Magnesium, customarily provided as the sulfate at about 0.001 M, probably has as its principal essential function the activation of enzymes necessary to normal metabolism and growth. The optimum is dependent on the concentration of the carbon source (241), the production by the organism of hydroxy acids or other chelate-forming molecules which tend to render magnesium unavailable, and the concentrations of other ions to which magnesium is antagonistic. *Asper-*

gillus terreus in surface culture requires much more magnesium than it does in shaken culture (119, 120).

The enzymes activated by magnesium in *in vitro* systems are often also activated by manganese or other divalent ions, but it is believed that magnesium is the physiologically active metal (115, 126). None of the physiological effects of magnesium deficiency has been conclusively related to enzyme malfunction, but it is reasonable to suppose that, for example, enhancement of riboflavin formation by magnesium deficiency in *Aspergillus niger* (114, 210) reflects an impairment of the normal oxidative system. In bacteria, magnesium accelerates the uptake of phosphate, possibly by reason of the role of the metal in transphosphorylations (3).

The absorption of magnesium is somewhat slower at neutral than at acid reaction, resulting in a slightly higher optimum at neutrality (236). Magnesium is precipitated and rendered virtually unavailable at high pH in the presence of ammonium ion (62).

As suggested above, the apparent magnesium requirement is probably affected by other ions. This is deduced from the very great activity of magnesium in antagonizing the toxicity to fungi of such metals as aluminum, copper, and mercury (120, 122, 136); similar results with other ions have been reported in studies on bacteria (3, 130). The most attractive theory explaining this antagonism is that of MacLeod and Snell (130), that other metals compete with magnesium for enzyme surfaces and that the resulting metal-enzyme complex is inactive or less active than the natural magnesium complex. Competition, however, need not be limited to enzymatic reactions. Marsh (136) showed clearly that magnesium prevents the absorption of copper by conidia of *Sclerotinia fructicola;* this finding suggests a competition of the two elements at the cell membrane.

Beryllium is said to replace magnesium partially and under special circumstances (238).

5. IRON

Fungi and actinomycetes require approximately 0.1–0.3 ppm of iron, more in concentrated media (36, 37, 100, 169, 241). *Aspergillus niger* utilizes either ferrous or ferric iron (168). Iron is lost from solution at neutral or alkaline pH; inclusion in the medium of a chelating agent, e.g., citrate, reduces the loss (62, 88).

The most obvious metabolic role of iron is in the formation of iron-containing metabolites. Those known in the fungi include catalase and the cytochromes (Chapter 7), coprogen and the ferrichromes

(Chapter 10), the heme pigment of *Neurospora crassa* and *Penicillium notatum* (103), and the pigment pulcherrimin of *Torulopsis pulcherrima* (40, 107). Preparations of aspergillin, the spore pigment of the black *Aspergillus* spp., contain 0.26 per cent iron (191).

Aspergillus niger releases into the medium relatively large amounts of a substance or substances, not citrate, which bind ferric iron (67); the possible ecological value is obvious (158).

A few of the metabolic effects of iron may be ascribed to direct use of the element; increases in catalase (257) and in pulcherrimin (201) are of this type. Other metabolic effects of iron concentration, e.g., on organic acid formation (45, 57, 184, 185), on penicillin production (108), on the balance of gentisyl alcohol and patulin (Chapter 6), and on sporulation and spore color (118, 211), are known, but the operative mechanisms are obscure. Only one persistent pattern may be discerned: the maximum formation of certain metabolites—streptomycin (37), penicillin (100), and citrinin (9)—requires more iron than is needed for maximum growth. The data on organic acid accumulation as affected by iron are too much in conflict to allow any generalization (36, 57, 183); as discussed elsewhere (Chapter 6), it is most probable that deficiencies or excesses of iron and other inorganic constituents act positively on acid formation, when they do, by virtue of interference with normal metabolism.

6. ZINC

The essentiality of zinc for growth in fungi has been confirmed many times (35). Reported optima, determined, of course, under different conditions, range from 0.001 to 0.5 ppm; probably 0.5–1.0 ppm is adequate in routine work (5, 36, 37, 76, 241). Higher concentrations of zinc may be toxic, especially at high pH (117, 174); the toxicity is reversed by certain other divalent ions (130). Inhibition of sporulation by zinc is reversed by iron (174, 200). High levels of zinc induce genetically stable variation in *Fusarium* sp. (46) and *Helminthosporium sativum* (145). Partial replacement of zinc by cadmium (101) probably results from contamination of the cadmium with zinc (227).

The metabolic effects of zinc deficiency almost defy enumeration; several reviews consider them in detail (35, 57, 58, 183). The major types of metabolic effects are:

1. Accumulation of organic acids at levels of zinc too low for normal growth. Associated with this is a positive effect of the metal on the

economic coefficient and on carbon dioxide evolution. The effect of zinc on citric acid formation is, in almost all reported instances, to decrease the per cent conversion of carbohydrate to citrate (35). This zinc effect is not specific; citric acid accumulation is favored by other mineral deficiencies (36).

2. Lowering of specific enzyme concentrations in cells grown in low-zinc media. Enzymes affected include pyruvic carboxylase (59, 242) and ethanol dehydrogenase and the tryptophan-synthesizing enzyme (156). Diphosphopyridine nucleotidase, on the other hand, is increased by moderate zinc deficiency (156, 157). It should not be assumed, however, that these effects are specific to zinc.

3. Decrease by zinc of the accumulation of certain antibiotics (141, 245). In *Aspergillus ochraceus,* the specific 6β-hydroxylation of steroids is much retarded by zinc deficiency (51).

4. Increase in cytochrome synthesis in *Ustilago sphaerogena* at high zinc (76), with an accompanying decrease in ferrichrome accumulation (158).

5. Changes in cell composition (127, 189, 214).

6. Stimulation by zinc of the *in vitro* formation of vesicles by *Puccinia coronata* (218).

7. A shift in the proportions of related ring compounds produced by *Penicillium urticae* (52).

8. Effects of zinc supply on sporulation, reviewed by Foster (57).

Zinc is known to activate a few enzymes specifically (126) and others non-specifically (207); ethanol dehydrogenase and glutamic dehydrogenase are zinc proteins (249, 250). The diverse effects of zinc on metabolism suggest in addition that it is concerned with the synthesis of enzyme proteins; this hypothesis applies especially to the second, third, fourth, and seventh effects just listed.

7. COPPER

Copper is required by fungi for normal growth and sporulation at about 0.01–0.1 ppm (36, 37, 100, 241). Higher concentrations are of course toxic, although two fungi make visible growth even in a saturated solution of copper sulfate (226). The uptake of copper is somewhat greater at moderate pH than at low pH (215).

Perhaps the most striking physiological effect of copper deficiency is the reduction in pigmentation of the colored spores of *Aspergillus* spp. (26, 102, 142, 150) and *Trichoderma viride* (27). Although other metal deficiencies also affect spore pigmentation (58), copper is probably the most important, at least for the dark spore pigments.

It has been mentioned earlier (Chapter 6) that copper may play a role in chlorine metabolism of fungi. The possibility that, as in animals (134), copper is essential for normal iron metabolism has not been explored.

8. MANGANESE

The essentiality of manganese in small amounts, about 0.005–0.01 ppm, has been demonstrated for a number of fungi (23, 36, 53, 57, 86, 137, 190, 199, 227, 241); we may assume that fungi in general require it, although the effects of deficiency are not apparent for all. The requirement is more easily shown at low pH than at high (121).

Manganese deficiency has several physiological effects (57, 183), including a pronounced decrease in sporulation. The frequent role of the metal in activation of enzymes, especially those of the citric acid cycle (136), suggests a role for it in metabolism at this point; manganese concentration also affects the concentration of other enzymes in the cell (86).

The biological oxidation of manganese in soil can be demonstrated perhaps best in soil percolation experiments (129). It is probable that fungi as well as other organisms carry out this reaction; the limited evidence is reviewed by Mulder and Gerretsen (153) and by Starkey (225).

9. MOLYBDENUM

The essentiality of molybdenum for *Aspergillus niger* was discovered by Steinberg (229). The requirement is small—estimates range from 0.1 parts per billon (152, 168) to 10 ppb (241)—and *A. niger* responds to as little as 0.02 ppb (152). Vanadium does not replace molybdenum (168).

It has been observed repeatedly that the molybdenum requirement of both *Aspergillus niger* and *Neurospora crassa* is higher if nitrate is used as the source of nitrogen than if ammonium nitrogen is provided (152, 170, 230). The explanation for this phenomenon is the first unequivocal demonstration of a specific enzymatic basis for a deficiency symptom in fungi. Molybdenum participates as electron carrier in the reduction of nitrate by enzymes of *Neurospora crassa, Escherichia coli,* and soybean; the evidence for this conclusion is reviewed by Nason

(155). The valence states of molybdenum which function in electron transport are the +5 and the +6 (171).

Molybdenum must, however, have other functions, inasmuch as a molybdenum deficiency can be demonstrated in media not containing nitrate (152, 168, 170).

10. CALCIUM

The effect of calcium on the growth of fungi has only recently been recognized, although the first report of such an effect was in 1922 (258). Species in 19 genera, including representatives of all the major groups of fungi and of the genus *Streptomyces,* have been found to respond to added calcium by an increase in dry weight (62, 63, 73, 99, 113a, 117, 128, 166, 175, 178, 198, 239, 246, 253). Reported optima range from 0.5 to 20 ppm. Some fungi, it should be noted, cannot be shown to require calcium (198, 239). Figure 3 illustrates the response to calcium.

Strontium partially replaces calcium for *Allomyces arbuscula* (99) and several other fungi (117, 198, 239). Strontium is firmly bound by mycelium of *Rhizopus* sp. (116).

One may still ask, however, whether the so-called calcium require-

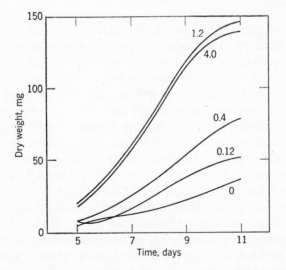

Figure 3. The growth of *Coprinus ephemerus* at different levels of calcium (milligrams per liter). Redrawn from Fries (63), by permission of the *Svensk Botanisk Tidskrift.*

ment of fungi is specific. Calcium in many organisms, including fungi (117), protects against the injurious effects of certain common monovalent cations, especially hydrogen, sodium, and potassium. In bacteria, calcium and related ions also protect against zinc toxicity (127). These non-nutritional effects, the wide range of optima reported, the extent of replacement by strontium, and the fact that some fungi do not respond at all to calcium all argue for some caution in interpretation of the data as reflecting an absolute and specific requirement. It is noticeable that in a casamino acids medium, with high sodium concentration, calcium affects the growth of *Aspergillus oryzae* (222), but the related *A. niger* in the usual low-sodium media does not respond to calcium (239). The crucial experiment would be, of course, to determine whether an apparent calcium requirement can be eliminated by adjusting the concentration of other ions.

It has been found that calcium affects the time required for perithecial formation in *Chaetomium* spp. (14, 15) and the intensity of conidiation in *Trichoderma viride* (27).

Calcium, like magnesium, may be made less available if chelating agents, e.g., citrate, are present in the medium, and is less available, because of precipitation, at high pH than at low.

11. COBALT

In spite of early claims of the essentiality of cobalt for fungi, reviewed by Marston (138), there is at present no conclusive evidence of a cobalt requirement; some more recent data are suggestive, however (11). Cobalt is required by animals but not, apparently, by higher plants (138). As mentioned elsewhere (Chapter 10), vitamin B_{12} is made by *Streptomyces* spp.—and for the synthesis cobalt must be required—but whether the vitamin is produced by true fungi is uncertain. Furthermore, neither the fungi nor the actinomycetes are known to require the vitamin. Although cobalt activates some enzymes, e.g., the dipeptidase of *Aspergillus oryzae* (42), its only known essential function in organisms generally is as a constituent of vitamin B_{12}. In view of the very great technical difficulty in establishing a cobalt requirement if the metal is only needed for B_{12} synthesis (94), it may be more profitable to explore the B_{12} metabolism of fungi than to attack the cobalt problem directly; preliminary results (168) suggest that neither B_{12} nor cobalt is essential to *Aspergillus niger*.

Cobalt is accumulated by *Neurospora crassa* (12), the degree of accumulation—up to 23 times the external concentration—being a function of the amount of cobalt in the medium. Up to 40 per cent of the cobalt so accumulated is bound to a protein. Cobalt accumulation in *N. crassa* is affected indirectly by the iron concentration (11).

Cobalt at appreciable concentrations is toxic to fungi and other organisms. Toxicity is reduced by histidine (181, 182, 212), which presumably forms a complex with the cobalt ion. The uptake of cobalt by *Aspergillus niger* is sharply reduced by the addition of relatively small amounts of magnesium (3). A third complication in cobalt toxicity is the observation that, although iron and cobalt do not simply compete, the enzymatic symptoms of cobalt toxicity in *Neurospora crassa* resemble closely the symptoms of iron deficiency (80).

12. OTHER INORGANIC NUTRIENTS

Aspergillus niger responds slightly to vanadium (17, 18, 19) and fleshy fungi take up vanadium from the soil (20), but satisfactory proof of an essential role is not at hand. Vanadium is essential, however, for the alga *Scenedesmus obliquus* (6).

Steinberg has reported growth increases from addition of gallium (231) and—only with glycerol as carbon source—of scandium (233). Results on gallium have not, however, proved reproducible (237).

Claims of an essential or growth-promoting role of boron (256) and organic compounds of silicon (87) have not as yet been confirmed; Winfield (255) reports negative results with boron. Chlorine appears to have no necessary role in the nutrition of fungi (60) although chlorinated metabolites are not uncommon (Chapter 6), and chlorine is essential to higher plants (28). Other metals, e.g., aluminum and chromium, often exert physiological effects and may even under peculiar circumstances improve growth, but it has not been suggested that they are essential.

13. BIOASSAY OF MINERALS

The response of fungi to nutrients is sensitive enough so that a number of bioassays for inorganic elements in soil have been developed to the point of practical utility. Almost all the work has been with *Aspergillus niger*, although a radial growth assay for phosphorus with *Cunninghamella* spp. was devised in 1934 (139, 140).

Bioassays for minerals are more laborious than chemical determinations and are intrinsically less accurate; precision is especially low in those assays based on visual estimates of growth or spore color (151). The principal advantage of the bioassay method, and the reason for its popularity, is that it may more nearly approximate a determination of

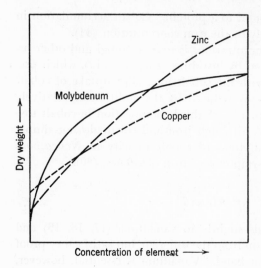

Figure 4. The form of assay curves, employing *Aspergillus niger,* for zinc, molybdenum, and copper. Redrawn from D. J. D. Nicholas, *The Analyst,* Vol. 77, p. 629-642 (1952), by permission of the Society for Analytical Chemistry.

the minerals actually available to a crop plant. The assumption made, therefore, is that the fraction of a given mineral which the plant cannot absorb is equally unavailable to the fungus. Consequently, the major criterion for the practicability of a bioassay must be the degree to which the assay results predict the behavior of crop plants in a given soil; correlation with chemical determinations is of secondary importance. Correlative studies have usually shown at least fair agreement between growth of *Aspergillus niger* and growth of higher plants in soils deficient in phosphorus, potassium, zinc, copper, and molybdenum (47, 73, 147, 150, 168). The fungus is less suitable for manganese determination because metabolic acids make more manganese available to it than is available for higher plants (153).

Typical assay curves are shown, in simplified form, in Figure 4; it is to be noted that the response is not rectilinear. Detailed methods are described by Donald et al. (47), Gerretsen (73), Mulder (151), and Nicholas (168).

14. PROBLEMS IN MINERAL NUTRITION

Two general approaches may be used in determining the essentiality of a given element. One may design a medium free of the element in question and containing all other materials necessary for growth. Essentiality is shown by a quantitatively determined growth response to graded amounts of some soluble compound containing the element. Obviously, the medium must be purified rigorously for the study of micronutrients, and, equally important, the compound added must not contain any growth-promoting substances.

The second approach, little used so far, is to determine that some metabolite which contains the element is essential to growth. For example, if the vitamins B_{12} prove to be essential, then cobalt must be essential.

Details of the methods for purification of media for studies of micronutrient elements lie outside the scope of this work. There is no one best method for all materials, and the choice depends on the particular element under study. The most useful over-all methods involve adsorption on calcium carbonate (240) or aluminum compounds (48, 221). Special methods have been described for copper (151, 167, 168), manganese (168), and molybdenum (81, 168). It appears that the chelating agents (8-hydroxyquinoline, diphenylthiocarbazone, etc.) are not only less efficient for most micronutrient elements but are likely to be toxic to the organism. Detailed comparisons of different methods have been published by Steinberg (240), Donald et al. (48), and Nicholas (168).

Methods of obtaining inorganic salts of maximum purity are discussed by Hutner et al. (94).

The sources of contamination in micronutrient work are well known by now: the inoculum, glassware, distilled water from a metal still, sugars and polyatomic alcohols, hydroxy acids, inorganic salts, and complex extracts of biological origin (92, 168, 229, 230, 232). Amino acids are often so heavily contaminated that they cannot be employed at all (235).

Chelating agents may be used to exaggerate a requirement and make it more readily detectable. Thus, Hutner (93) added citrate to hold calcium and other elements in solution; the calcium requirement in the absence of the complexing anion is estimated by extrapolation.

Work with the major inorganic nutrients is, of course, somewhat simpler inasmuch as deficiencies are not made up by minor amounts of contamination. Methodological problems do, however, arise even here. Thus, the usual practice in working at low or zero potassium is to supply phosphate as the sodium salt; this, of course, ignores the possibility that sodium partially replaces potassium. In this particular instance, the solution is to use an amine in place of the alkali metal to control pH (126).

In reporting results, the concentration permitting half maximal growth is a more useful datum than that at which maximum growth occurs.

Although an optimum amount of a given element may be defined for rigidly specified conditions (236, 237), it must be realized that there is no absolute optimum concentration of an element for even one species. Some of the complicating factors may be mentioned. First, the need for inorganic nutrients is proportional to the carbohydrate supply (241). Second, the need for an element may be increased or decreased by the presence of a second element, the important nutritional factor becoming then the ratio of the two (60, 129); in practice, this means that equally good growth is observed over a range of total salt concentration (43, 77, 128). Third, the nutrients and metabolites which form chelate complexes with minerals are present in continually changing amounts; although a chelating agent may on the one hand solubilize a mineral and so make it more available, on the other hand the cell must compete with the chelate complex for the element. Fourth, the pH of the medium—again a factor not usually constant for the entire life cycle—affects the solubility of most inorganic salts (62, 78, 88, 230), the state of oxidation of manganese (225), and the stability of chelated complexes (25). Finally, changes in the conditions of culture may change the apparent requirement for a mineral, as in the case of the magnesium requirement of *Aspergillus terreus* (119, 120).

The use of metabolically inert chelating agents, particularly ethylenediaminetetraacetic acid (EDTA, versene) solves some of the practical problems of supplying a fungus with minerals; the compound has been used successfully, at 2–5 ppm, for several fungi (194, 209a, 252) and for *Streptomyces nitrificans* (213). However, this and similar agents may prove to be toxic (63, 128, 243). Added citrate or malate, unless utilized by the organism, can be used to keep minerals soluble (92).

The fungi accumulate minerals against a concentration gradient; the data are particularly clear for cobalt (11, 12), silver and cesium (144), and potassium (54). These examples, and the accumulation of rubidium by fleshy basidiomycetes (21), make it clear in addition that accumulation of non-essential elements is common. The energy for accumulation must come, of course, from respiration. The very striking effect of magnesium on the uptake of cobalt by *Aspergillus niger* (3) and of copper by *Sclerotinia fructicola* (132) suggests that reactions at a semi-permeable membrane are of importance in mineral nutrition. In yeast, there is good evidence for carrier systems in the transport of cations across the membrane (61).

The functions of the minerals required by fungi deserve further study. Phosphorus and sulfur occur in known essential compounds, and their major role appears to be constitutive. The other essential mineral elements are today more or less conventionally assigned a "catalytic" function as activators or active centers of enzymes. Reasons exist, of course, for this general belief: the function of molybdenum in nitrate reductase and zinc in ethanol dehydrogenase, the occurrence of copper and iron in purified enzymes, and the known activating effect of magnesium, manganese, and calcium on isolated enzymes. Further study of possible enzymatic roles will undoubtedly be rewarding, but too narrow a dedication to this task may mean neglect of other, as yet unknown, physiological reactions of the metals.

BIBLIOGRAPHY

1. Abbott, E. V. 1923. *Soil Sci.* 16: 207–216.
2. Abbott, L. D., Jr. 1947. *Arch. Biochem.* 15: 205–214.
3. Abelson, P. H. and E. Aldous. 1950. *J. Bacteriol.* 60: 401–413.
4. Allen, M. B. and D. I. Arnon. 1955. *Physiol. Plantarum* 8: 653–660.
5. Anderson-Kottö, I. and G. C. Hevesy. 1949. *Biochem. J. (London)* 44: 407–409.
6. Arnon, D. I. and G. Wessl. 1953. *Nature (London)* 172: 1039–1040.
7. Auhagen, E. and S. Grzycki. 1933. *Biochem. Z.* 265: 217–222.
8. Baba, S. 1943. *Proc. Imp. Acad. (Tokyo)* 19: 70–76.
9. Bailey, J. M. and C. J. Cavallito. 1943. *J. Bacteriol.* 45: 30–31.
10. Bajaj, V., S. P. Damle, and P. S. Krishnan. 1954. *Arch. Biochem. Biophys.* 50: 451–460.
11. Ballantine, R. 1953. *J. Cellular Comp. Physiol.* 42: 415–426.
12. Ballantine, R. and D. G. Stephens. 1951. *J. Cellular Comp. Physiol.* 37: 369–387.
13. Barner, H. D. and E. C. Cantino. 1952. *Am. J. Botany* 39: 746–751.
14. Basu, S. N. 1951. *J. Gen. Microbiol.* 5: 231–238.
15. Basu, S. N. 1952. *J. Gen. Microbiol.* 6: 199–204.
16. Bayliss, M., D. Glick, and R. Siene. 1948. *J. Bacteriol.* 55: 307–316.
17. Bertrand, D. 1941a. *Bull. soc. chim. biol.* 23: 467–471.
18. Bertrand, D. 1941b. *Compt. rend. (Paris)* 213: 254–257.
19. Bertrand, D. 1942. *Ann. inst. Pasteur* 68: 226–244.
20. Bertrand, D. 1943. *Bull. soc. chim. biol.* 25: 194–197.
21. Bertrand, G. and D. Bertrand. 1949. *Ann. inst. Pasteur* 76: 199–202.
22. Bhargava, K. S. 1945. *Proc. Indian Acad. Sci. B*, 21: 344–349.
23. Blank, L. M. 1941. *J. Agr. Research* 62: 129–160.
24. Blumenthal, H. J., A. Hemerline, and S. Roseman. 1956. *Bacteriol. Proc. (Soc. Am. Bacteriologists)* 1956: 109.
25. Bobtelsky, M. and J. Jordan. 1945. *J. Am. Chem. Soc.* 67: 1824–1831.
26. Bortels, H. 1927. *Biochem. Z.* 182: 301–358.
27. Brian, P. W. and H. G. Hemming. 1950. *Trans. Brit. Mycol. Soc.* 33: 132–141.
28. Broyer, T. C., A. B. Carlton, C. M. Johnson, and P. R. Stout. 1954. *Plant Physiol.* 29: 526–532.
29. Butkewitsch, W. S. (Butkevich, V. S.) and A. G. Timofeeva. 1934. *Microbiologiya* 3: 574–584.
30. Cantino, E. C. 1950. *Quart. Rev. Biol.* 25: 269–277.
31. Cantino, E. C. 1955. *Quart. Rev. Biol.* 30: 138–149.
32. Challenger, F. and Y. C. Liu. 1950. *Rec. trav. chim.* 69: 334–342.
33. Chang, S. C. 1940. *Soil Sci.* 49: 197–210.
34. Chattaway, F. W., C. C. Thompson, and A. G. E. Barlow. 1954. *Biochim. et Biophys. Acta* 14: 583–584.
35. Chesters, C. G. C. and G. N. Rolinson. 1951a. *Biol. Revs. Cambridge Phil. Soc.* 26: 239–252.

36. Chesters, C. G. C. and G. N. Rolinson. 1951b. *J. Gen. Microbiol.* 5: 553–558.
37. Chesters, C. G. C. and G. N. Rolinson. 1951c. *J. Gen. Microbiol.* 5: 559–565.
38. Cochrane, V. W. and P. L. Hawley. 1956. *J. Bacteriol.* 71: 308–314.
39. Contardi, A. and A. Ercoli. 1933. *Biochem. Z.* 261: 275–302.
40. Cook, A. H. and C. A. Slater. 1956. *J. Chem. Soc. (London)* 1956: 4130–4133, 4133-4135.
41. Courtois, J. and G. Joseph. 1947. *Bull. soc. chim. biol.* 29: 951–955.
42. Crewther, W. G. and F. G. Lennox. 1953. *Australian J. Biol. Sci.* 6: 410–427.
43. Darby, R. T. and G. R. Mandels. 1954. *Mycologia* 46: 276–288.
44. Davis, B. D. 1955. *Advances in Enzymol.* 16: 247–312.
45. Di Capua, A. 1933. *Gazz. chim. ital.* 63: 296–302.
46. Dimock, A. W. 1936. *Zentr. Bakteriol. Parasitenk. Abt. II,* 95: 341–347.
47. Donald, C., B. I. Passey, and R. J. Swaby. 1952a. *Australian J. Agr. Research* 3: 305–325.
48. Donald, C., B. I. Passey, and R. J. Swaby. 1952b. *J. Gen. Microbiol.* 7: 211–220.
49. Dox, A. W. 1911. *J. Biol. Chem.* 10: 77–80.
50. Dox, A. W. and R. Golden. 1911. *J. Biol. Chem.* 10: 183–186.
51. Dulaney, E. L., E. O. Stapley, and C. Hlavac. 1955. *Mycologia* 47: 464–474.
52. Ehrensvärd, G. 1955. *Exp. Cell. Research,* Suppl. 3: 102–109.
53. English, M. P. and N. H. Barnard. 1955. *Trans. Brit. Mycol. Soc.* 38: 78–82.
54. Eno, C. F. and H. W. Reuzer. 1950. *Soil Sci.* 80: 199–209.
55. Feeney, R. E. and J. A. Garibaldi. 1948. *Arch. Biochem.* 17: 447–458.
56. Forrest, I. S., A. Grauer, and C. Neuberg. 1954. *Enzymologia* 16: 305–310.
57. Foster, J. W. 1939. *Botan. Rev.* 5: 207–239.
58. Foster, J. W. 1949. *Chemical Activities of Fungi.* New York: Academic Press, pp. 648.
59. Foster, J. W. and F. W. Denison, Jr. 1950. *Nature (London)* 166: 833–834.
60. Fothergill, P. G. and R. Ashcroft. 1955. *J. Gen. Microbiol.* 12: 387–395.
61. Foulkes, E. C. 1956. *J. Gen. Physiol.* 39: 687–704.
62. Fries, L. 1945. *Arkiv Botan.* 32 (10): 1–8.
63. Fries, L. 1956. *Svensk Botan. Tidskr.* 50: 47–96.
64. Fries, N. 1945. *Arkiv Botan.* 32 (8): 1–9.
65. Fries, N. 1946. *Svensk Botan. Tidskr.* 40: 127–140.
66. Fromageot, C. 1950. In J. B. Sumner and K. Myrbäck (eds.), *The Enzymes,* Vol. 1 (1), p. 517–526. New York: Academic Press.
67. Garibaldi, J. A. and J. B. Neilands. 1956. *Nature* (London) 177: 526–527.
68. Garreau, Y. 1941. *Compt. rend. soc. biol.* 135: 508–510.
69. Gayet, J. 1948a. *Bull. soc. chim. biol.* 30: 488–496.
70. Gayet, J. 1948b. *Bull. soc. chim. biol.* 30: 542–547.
71. Gayet, J. 1949a. *Bull. soc. chim. biol.* 31: 796–800.
72. Gayet, J. 1949b. *Bull. soc. chim. biol.* 31: 1046–1051.
73. Gerretsen, F. C. 1948. *Anal. Chim. Acta* 2: 782–792.
74. Gollmick, F. 1936. *Zentr. Bakteriol. Parasitenk. Abt. II,* 93: 421–442.
75. Golueke, C. G. 1957. *J. Bacteriol.* 74: 337–344.
76. Grimm, P. W. and P. J. Allen. 1954. Plant Physiol. 29: 369–377.
77. Haenseler, C. M. 1921. *Am. J. Botany* 8: 147–163.
78. Halvorson, H. O. and R. L. Starkey. 1927. *J. Phys. Chem.* 31: 626–631.
79. Harley, J. L., C. C. McCready, and J. K. Brierley. 1953. *New Phytologist* 52: 124–132.
80. Healy, W. B., S. Cheng, and W. D. McElroy. 1955. *Arch. Biochem. Biophys.* 54: 206–214.
81. Hewitt, E. J. and D. G. Hallas. 1951. *Plant and Soil* 3: 366–408.
82. Hockenhull, D. J. D. 1948. *Biochem. J. (London)* 43: 498–504.
83. Hockenhull, D. J. D. 1949. *Biochim. et Biophys. Acta* 3: 326–335.
84. Hockenhull, D. J. D. 1950. *J. Exp. Botany* 1: 194–200.

85. Hofmann, E. and H. Scheck. 1950. *Biochem. Z.* 321: 98–106.
86. Hofmann, E., H. Scheck, and K. Saffert. 1950. *Biochem. Z.* 320: 126–135.
87. Holzapfel, L. and W. Engel. 1954. *Z. Naturforsch.* 9b: 602–606.
88. Hopkins, E. F. and F. B. Wann. 1926. *Botan. Gaz.* 81: 353–376.
89. Horowitz, N. H. 1950. *Advances in Genet.* 3: 33–71.
90. Howell, A., Jr. and R. J. Fitzgerald. 1953. J. *Bacteriol.* 66: 437–442.
91. Hungate, F. P. and T. J. Mannell. 1952. *Genetics* 37: 709–719.
92. Hutner, S. H. 1946. *J. Bacteriol.* 52: 213–221.
93. Hutner, S. H. 1948. *Trans. N. Y. Acad. Sci.* II, 10: 136–141.
94. Hutner, S. H., L Provasoli, A Schatz, and C. P. Haskins. 1950. *Proc. Am. Phil. Soc.* 94: 152–170.
95. Ingelman, B. 1950. In J. B. Sumner and K. Myrbäck (eds.), *The Enzymes,* Vol. 1 (1), p. 511–516. New York: Academic Press.
96. Ingelman, B. and H. Malmgren. 1947. *Acta Chem. Scand.* 1: 422–432.
97. Ingelman, B. and H. Malmgren. 1948. *Acta Chem. Scand.* 2: 365–380.
98. Ingelman, B. and H. Malmgren. 1949. *Acta Chem. Scand.* 3: 157–162.
99. Ingraham, J. L. and R. Emerson. 1954. *Am. J. Botany* 41: 146–152.
100. Jarvis, F. G. and M. J. Johnson. 1950. *J. Bacteriol.* 59: 51–60.
101. Javillier, M. 1913. *Ann. inst. Pasteur* 27: 1021–1038.
102. Javillier, M. 1939. *Ann. fermentations* 5: 371–381.
103. Keilin, D. and A. Tissieres. 1953. *Nature (London)* 172: 393–394.
104. Keitt, G. W. and D. M. Boone. 1954. *Phytopathology* 44: 362–370.
105. Kitasato, T. 1928a. *Biochem. Z.* 197: 257–258.
106. Kitasato, T. 1928b. *Biochem. Z.* 201: 206–211.
107. Kluyver, A. J., J. P. van der Walt, and A. J. van Triet. 1953. *Proc. Natl. Acad. Sci. U. S.* 39: 583–593.
108. Koffler, H., S. G. Knight, and W. C. Frazier. 1947. *J. Bacteriol.* 53: 115–123.
109. Krishnan, P. S. 1951a. *Arch. Biochem.* 32: 230–231.
110. Krishnan, P. S. 1951b. *Nature (London)* 168: 171.
111. Krishnan. P. S. 1952. *Arch. Biochem. Biophys.* 37: 224–234.
112. Krishnan, P. S. and V. Bajaj. 1953a. *Arch. Biochem. Biophys.* 42: 174–184.
113. Krishnan, P. S. and V. Bajaj. 1953b. *Arch. Biochem. Biophys.* 47: 39–55.
113a. Lamprecht, L. 1957. *Arch. Mikrobiol.* 27: 182–218.
114. Lavollay, J. and F. Laborey. 1941. Ann. fermentations 6: 129–142.
115. Lehninger, A. L. 1950. *Physiol. Revs.* 30: 393–429.
116. Lewin, S. Z., P. J. Lucchesi, and J. E. Vance. 1953. *J. Am. Chem. Soc.* 75: 6058.
117. Lindeberg, G. 1944. *Symbolae Botan. Upsalalienses* 8 (2): 1–183.
118. Linossier, G. 1910. *Compt. rend. (Paris)* 151: 1075–1076.
119. Lockwood, L. B. and G. E. N. Nelson. 1946. *Arch. Biochem.* 10: 365–374.
120. Lockwood, L. B. and M. D. Reeves. 1945. *Arch. Biochem.* 6: 455–469.
121. Löhnis, M. P. 1944. *Antonie van Leeuwenhoek J. Microbiol. Serol.* 10: 100–122.
122. Lohrmann, W. 1940. *Arch. Mikrobiol.* 11: 329–367.
123. Lvoff, S. and E. L. Limberg. 1938. *Compt. rend. acad. sci. U. R. S. S.* 21: 194–198.
124. Lwoff, A. and H. Ionesco. 1948. *Ann. inst. Pasteur* 74: 442–450.
125. McCallan, S. E. A. and F. Wilcoxon. 1931. *Contribs. Boyce Thompson Inst.* 3: 13–38.
126. McElroy, W. D. and A. Nason. 1954. *Ann. Rev. Plant Physiol.* 5: 1–30.
127. McHargue, J. S. and R. K. Calfee. 1931. *Botan. Gaz.* 91: 183–193.
128. Machlis, L. 1953. *Am. J. Botany* 40: 450–459.
129. MacLeod, R. A. and E. E. Snell. 1948. *J. Biol. Chem.* 176: 39–52.
130. MacLeod, R. A. and E. E. Snell. 1950. *Ann. N. Y. Acad. Sci.* 52: 1249–1259.
131. McVeigh, I. and E. Bell. 1951. *Bull. Torrey Botan. Club* 78: 134–144.
132. Malmgren, H. 1952. *Acta Chem. Scand.* 6: 16–26.

320   INORGANIC NUTRITION AND METABOLISM

133. Mann, P. J. G. and J. H. Quastel. 1946. *Nature (London)* 158: 154–156.
134. Mann, T. 1944a. *Biochem. J. (London)* 38: 339–345.
135. Mann, T. 1944b. *Biochem. J. (London)* 38: 345–351.
136. Marsh, P. B. 1945. *Phytopathology* 35: 54–61.
137. Marshall, B. H., Jr. 1955. *Phytopathology* 45: 676–680.
138. Marston, H. R. 1952. *Physiol. Revs.* 32: 66–121.
139. Mehlich, A., E. B. Fred, and E. Truog. 1934. *Soil Sci.* 38: 445–458.
140. Mehlich, A., E. B. Fred, and E. Truog. 1935. *J. Am. Soc. Agron.* 27: 826–832.
141. Menzel, A. E. O., O. Wintersteiner, and J. C. Hoogerheide. 1944. *J. Biol. Chem.* 152: 419–429.
142. Metz, O. 1930. *Arch. Mikrobiol.* 1: 197–251.
143. Michel-Durand, E. 1938. *Bull. soc. chim. biol.* 20: 399–412.
144. Miller, L. P., S. E. A. McCallan, and R. M. Weed. 1953. *Contribs. Boyce Thompson Inst.* 17: 151–171, 173–195, 283–298.
145. Millikan, C. R. 1940. *J. Australian Inst. Agr. Sci.* 6: 203–205.
146. Molliard, M. 1920. *Compt. rend. (Paris)* 170: 949–951.
147. Mooers, C. A. 1938. *Soil Sci.* 46: 211–227.
148. Mothes, K. 1939. *Planta* 29: 67–109.
149. Mücke, D. 1954. *Flora* 141: 30–50.
150. Mulder, E. G. 1939. *Arch. Mikrobiol.* 10: 72–96.
151. Mulder, E. G. 1948a. *Anal. Chim. Acta* 2: 793–800.
152. Mulder, E. G. 1948b. *Plant and Soil* 1: 94–119.
153. Mulder, E. G. and F. C. Gerretsen. 1952. *Advances in Agron.* 4: 222–277.
154. Muntz, J. A. 1947. *J. Biol. Chem.* 171: 653–665.
155. Nason, A. 1956. In W. D. McElroy, and B. Glass (eds.), *Symposium on Inorganic Nitrogen Metabolism*, p. 109–136. Baltimore: The Johns Hopkins Press.
156. Nason, A., N. O. Kaplan, and S. P. Colowick. 1951. *J. Biol. Chem.* 188: 397–406.
157. Nason, A., N. O. Kaplan, and H. A. Oldewurtel. 1953. *J. Biol. Chem.* 201: 435–444.
158. Neilands, J. B. 1957. *Bacteriol. Revs.* 73: 101–111.
159. Neuberg, C. and H. A. Fischer. 1938a. *Compt. rend. trav. lab. Carlsberg. Sér. Chim.* 22: 366–374.
160. Neuberg, C. and H. A. Fischer. 1938b. Enzymologia 2: 241–257.
161. Neuberg, C., A. Grauer, and I. Mandl. 1950. *Enzymologia* 14: 157–163.
162. Neuberg, C. and K. Kurono. 1923. *Biochem. Z.* 140: 295–298.
163. Neuberg, C. and J. Wagner. 1925. *Biochem. Z.* 161: 492–505.
164. Neuberg, C. and J. Wagner. 1926a. *Biochem. Z.* 171: 485–500.
165. Neuberg, C. and J. Wagner. 1926b. *Biochem. Z.* 174: 457–463.
166. Newton, W. 1946. *Sci. Agr.* 26: 303–304.
167. Nicholas, D. J. D. 1950. *J. Sci. Food Agr.* 1: 339–344.
168. Nicholas, D. J. D. 1952. *Analyst* 77: 629–642.
169. Nicholas, D. J. D. 1956. *J. Gen. Microbiol.* 15: 470–477.
170. Nicholas, D. J. D., A. Nason, and W. D. McElroy. 1954. *J. Biol. Chem.* 207: 341–351.
171. Nicholas, D. J. D. and H. M. Stevens. 1956. In W. D. McElroy and B. Glass (eds.), *Symposium on Inorganic Nitrogen Metabolism*, p. 178–183. Baltimore: The Johns Hopkins Press.
172. Nickerson, W. J. 1951. *Trans. N. Y. Acad. Sci. II*, 13: 140–145.
173. Nickerson, W. J. 1953. *J. Infectious Diseases* 93: 43–56.
174. Nickerson, W. J. and J. B. Chadwick. 1946. *Arch. Biochem.* 10: 81–100.
175. Norkrans, B. 1950. *Symbolae Botan. Upsalienses* 11 (1): 1–126.
176. Orskov, S. L. 1948. *Acta Pathol. Microbiol. Scand.* 25: 277–283.
177. Ovcharov, K. E. 1937. *Compt. rend. acad. sci. U. R. S. S.* 16: 461–464. (*Chem. Abstr.* 32: 1745. 1938.)
178. Painter, H. A. 1954. *J. Gen. Microbiol.* 10: 177–190.

179. Pathak, M. A. and A. Sreenivasan. 1955. *Arch. Biochem. Biophys.* 59: 366–372.
180. Perkins, D. D. 1949. *Genetics* 34: 607–626.
181. Perlman, D. 1948. *Am. J. Botany* 35: 36–41.
182. Perlman, D. 1949a. *Am. J. Botany* 36: 180–184.
183. Perlman, D. 1949b. *Botan. Rev.* 15: 195–220.
184. Perlman, D. 1951. *Am. J. Botany* 38: 652–658.
185. Perlman, D., W. W. Dorrell, and M. J. Johnson. 1946. *Arch. Biochem.* 11: 130–143.
186. Pine, L. 1954. *J. Bacteriol.* 68: 671–679.
187. Pisano, M. A., B. H. Olson, and C. L. San Clemente. 1954. *J. Bacteriol.* 68: 444–449.
188. Pontecorvo, G. *et al.* 1953. *Advances in Genet.* 5: 141–238.
189. Porges, N. 1932. *Botan. Gaz.* 94: 197–205.
190. Purdy, L. H., Jr. and R. G. Grogan. 1954. *Phytopathology* 44: 36–39.
191. Quilico, A. and A. Di Capua. 1933. *Atti accad. naz. Lincei. Ser.* 6, 17: 177–182.
192. Raistrick, H. and J. M. Vincent. 1948. *Biochem. J. (London)* 43: 90–99.
193. Rautanen, N. and A.-E. Kylä-Siurola. 1954. *Acta Chem. Scand.* 8: 106–111.
194. Reischer, H. S. 1951. *Mycologia* 43: 142–155.
195. Rennerfelt, E. 1934. *Planta* 22: 221–239.
196. Rippel, A. and G. Behr. 1934. *Arch. Mikrobiol.* 5: 561–577.
197. Rippel, A. and G. Behr. 1936. *Arch. Mikrobiol.* 7: 584–589.
198. Rippel, A. and U. Stoess. 1932. *Arch. Mikrobiol.* 3: 492–506.
199. Robbins, W. J. and A. Hervey. 1944. *Bull. Torrey Botan. Club* 71: 258–266.
200. Roberg, M. 1928. *Centr. Bakteriol. Parasitenk. Abt. II*, 74: 333–370.
201. Roberts, C. 1946. *Am. J. Botany* 33: 237–244.
202. Roberts, R. B., I. Z. Roberts, and D. B. Cowie. 1949. *J. Cellular Comp. Physiol.* 34: 259–292.
203. Robertson, H. E. and P. D. Broyer. 1956. *Arch. Biochem. Biophys.* 62: 380–395, 396–401.
204. Roche, J. 1950. In J. B. Sumner and K. Myrbäck (eds.), *The Enzymes*, Vol. 1 (1), p. 473–510. New York: Academic Press.
205. Rothstein, A. and R. Meier. 1949. *J. Cellular Comp. Physiol.* 34: 97–114.
206. Sadasivan, V. 1950. *Arch. Biochem.* 28: 100–110.
207. Sadasivan, V. 1952. *Arch. Biochem. Biophys.* 37: 172–185.
208. Saksena, R. K., S. K. Jain, and S. M. H. Jafri. 1953. *J. Indian Botan. Soc.* 31: 281–286.
209. Salvin, S. B. 1949. *J. Infectious Diseases* 84: 275–283.
209a. Sanwal, B. D. and R. S. Sandhu. 1956. *Experientia* 12: 380–381.
210. Sarasin, A. 1953. *Ber. schweiz. botan. Ges.* 63: 287–316.
211. Sauton, B. 1910. *Compt. Rend. (Paris)* 151: 241–243.
212. Schade, A. L. 1949. *J. Bacteriol.* 58: 811–822.
213. Schatz, A., R. R. Mohan and G. S. Trelawny. 1955. *Antonie van Leeuwenhoek J. Microbiol. Serol.* 21: 225–238.
214. Schulz, G. 1937. *Planta* 27: 196–218.
215. Schwartz, W. and H. Steinhart. 1933. *Arch. Mikrobiol.* 4: 301–325.
216. Sciarini, L. J. and F. F. Nord. 1943. *Arch. Biochem.* 3: 261–267.
217. Semeniuk, G. 1944. *Iowa State Coll. J. Sci.* 18: 325–358.
218. Sharp, E. L. and F. G. Smith. 1952. *Phytopathology* 42: 581–582.
219. Shepherd, C. J. 1956. *J. Gen. Microbiol.* 15: 29–38.
220. Shibata, C. 1927. *Centr. Bakteriol. Parasitenk. Abt. II*, 71: 232–247.
221. Shu, P. and M. J. Johnson. 1948. *J. Bacteriol.* 56: 577–585.
222. Simonart, P. and K. Y. Chow. 1954. *Antonie van Leeuwenhock J. Microbiol. Serol.* 20: 210–216.
223. Smith, V. M. 1949. *Arch. Biochem.* 23: 446–472.
224. Stahl, W. H., B. McQue, G. R. Mandels, and R. G. H. Siu. 1949. *Arch. Biochem.* 20: 422–432.

225. Starkey, R. L. 1955. *Soil Sci.* 79: 1–14.
226. Starkey, R. L. and S. A. Waksman. 1943. *J. Bacteriol.* 45: 509–519.
227. Steinberg, R. A. 1935. *Bull. Torrey Botan. Club* 62: 81–90.
228. Steinberg, R. A. 1936a. *Botan. Gaz.* 97: 666–671.
229. Steinberg, R. A. 1936b. *J. Agr. Research* 52: 439–448.
230. Steinberg, R. A. 1937. *J. Agr. Research* 55: 891–902.
231. Steinberg, R. A. 1938. *J. Agr. Research* 57: 569–574.
232. Steinberg, R. A. 1939a. *J. Agr. Research* 59: 731–748.
233. Steinberg, R. A. 1939b. *J. Agr. Research* 59: 749–764.
234. Steinberg, R. A. 1941. *J. Agr. Research* 63: 109–127.
235. Steinberg, R. A. 1942. *J. Agr. Research* 64: 455–475.
236. Steinberg, R. A. 1945a. *Plant Physiol.* 20: 600–608.
237. Steinberg, R. A. 1945b. *Soil Sci.* 60: 185–189.
238. Steinberg, R. A. 1946. *Am. J. Botany* 33: 210–214.
239. Steinberg, R. A. 1948. *Science* 107: 423.
240. Steinberg, R. A. 1950. *Arch. Biochem.* 28: 111–116.
241. Steinberg, R. A. and J. D. Bowling. 1939. *J. Agr. Research* 58: 717–732.
242. Strauss, B. S. 1953. *Arch. Biochem. Biophys.* 44: 200–210.
243. Sussman, A. S. 1954. *J. Gen. Physiol.* 38: 59–77.
244. Tandon, M. P. 1950. *Proc. Indian Acad. Sci. B,* 32: 7–11.
245. Texera, D. 1948. *Phytopathology* 38: 70–81.
246. Treschow, C. 1944. *Dansk Botan. Arkiv* 11 (6): 1–180.
247. Tsuyuki, H. and R. A. MacLeod. 1951. *J. Biol. Chem.* 190: 711–719.
248. Turian, G. 1956. *Experientia* 12: 24–26.
249. Vallee, B. L., S. J. Adelstein, and J. A. Olson. 1955. *J. Am. Chem. Soc.* 77: 5196.
250. Vallee, B. L. and F. L. Hoch. 1955. *Proc. Natl. Acad. Sci.* U. S. 41: 327–338.
251. Varma, T. N. R. and K. S. Srinivasan. 1954. *Enzymologia* 17: 116–122.
252. Vishniac, H. S. 1955. *J. Gen. Microbiol.* 12: 455–463.
253. Waksman, S. A. 1953. *Neomycin.* New Brunswick: Rutgers Univ. Press. pp. 219.
254. Whiffen, A. J. 1945. *J. Elisha Mitchell Sci. Soc.* 61: 114–123.
255. Winfield, M. E. 1945. *Australian J. Exp. Biol. Med. Sci.* 23: 267–272.
256. Yogeswari, L. 1948. *Proc. Indian Acad. Sci. B,* 28: 177–201.
257. Yoshimura, F. 1939. *Botan. Mag. (Tokyo)* 53: 125–138.
258. Young, H. C. and C. W. Bennett. 1922. *Am. J. Botany* 9: 459–469.
259. Zalokar, M. 1953. *Arch. Biochem. Biophys.* 44: 330–337.

10. Vitamin Requirements of Fungi

Fungi, like all other organisms so far known, require minute amounts of specific organic compounds for growth. The cell may synthesize its own supply of one of these growth factors, or it may be dependent, in whole or in part, on an exogenous supply. Commonly, we refer to the dependence on exogenous supply as a requirement, realizing that the organism which synthesizes its own growth factors is equally "dependent" on them for normal metabolism.

The definition of growth factors may be broad or narrow. We may, for example, include as growth substances all compounds required in small amounts and not used for energy (260). This broader definition includes amino acids, purines, and choline as growth factors. A narrower concept, the one used here, excludes compounds that function as structural materials, even though they are needed in small amounts.

Most of the known vitamins have a catalytic function in the cell as coenzymes or constituent parts of coenzymes. This function is stressed in the definition of vitamins employed in this chapter: organic molecules required in small amounts and not, so far as we know, used as sources of either energy or structural materials of protoplasm. This definition is arbitrary and provisional. Arbitrary, because it separates constituents of coenzymes (e.g., riboflavin) from constituents of enzymes (e.g., amino acids) and cannot separate, for example, the role of adenine in adenosine triphosphate from its role in the structure of nucleic acids. Provisional, because the cofactor role of some of the vitamins, especially inositol, is uncertain.

323

This chapter, then, includes substances, primarily the water-soluble vitamins, which are thought to be catalytic in function; the amino acids and nitrogen bases are considered in Chapter 8, as is the plant growth factor indoleacetic acid.

The history of our knowledge of the vitamin requirements of fungi is reviewed by Janke (117), Robbins and V. Kavanagh (213), Schopfer (239), and Knight (122). Although the work on yeasts and yeastlike fungi really began in the nineteenth century, the vitamin needs of the filamentous fungi have been studied intensively only since 1934, i.e., since the papers of Schopfer (236, 237) on thiamine and the growth of *Phycomyces blakesleeanus*. Most work has been devoted to the requirements of naturally occurring fungi and, more recently, to the requirements of induced mutants; both types of material have provided significant information on the biosynthesis and the function of vitamins in living things generally.

1. PROBLEMS OF METHOD

The central methodological problem in vitamin studies is that of the degree to which the investigator knows the composition of the medium. Almost any natural product, e.g., sucrose or asparagine, is contaminated with significant amounts of some vitamins; procedures for purification will be found in the literature on particular growth factors.

For very limited purposes, e.g., in formulating a medium for routine use, it may be sufficient to use the approximate methods so common in the literature on vitamin nutrition. However, a serious study of vitamin nutrition requires at the least that three methodological criteria be met:

1. The measurement of growth should be objective and quantitative. Although growth on agar has been used fairly successfully in particular problems, it cannot be relied upon, and dry weight or turbidity is to be preferred (Chapter 1). Pyridine-extracted agar (214) may, however, be used for some problems.

2. Over some range of concentration of the vitamin, it should be shown that growth is a function of dose (concentration or total amount of the vitamin).

3. If growth occurs on the basal medium lacking added vitamin, an independent assay of the medium for the vitamin should be made. One very simple test consists of growing on the basal medium an organism known to require the factor absolutely. Other problems of method are summarized by Robbins and V. Kavanagh (213).

Especially with negative results, i.e., the finding that an organism does not need a vitamin, still further precautions may be mentioned. First, the basal medium must be free of the vitamin; even cotton plugs may contribute growth factors (248, 251). Second, it is essential that the organism be serially subcultured in the vitamin-free medium for at least three transfers. In some investigations (131) the inoculum has no effect, but this cannot be assumed. The criterion of serial subculture is the one most frequently disregarded, and in consequence most reports of a lack of need for a vitamin—especially those, e.g., biotin, for which the requirement is always small—are not wholly reliable.

The use of crude extracts of natural products in the preliminary search for vitamin requirements is, of course, helpful and, within limits, valuable. However, the simple observation that such an extract increases growth has no necessary bearing on vitamin nutrition, since so many other materials, known and unknown, are present in these extracts. Thus, the effect of agar on growth of several fungi (132) and the effect of yeast extract on cytochrome synthesis by *Ustilago sphaerogena* (89) are both attributable to the zinc content of the natural product, not at all to organic materials.

The vitamin content of many common constituents of culture media is known (34, 44, 95, 206, 217, 224, 264); occurrence in other natural products is reviewed in general works on the vitamins (225, 249).

2. THE NATURE OF VITAMIN REQUIREMENTS

It is generally assumed that a fungus or other organism which is independent of an externally supplied vitamin is so by virtue of its ability to synthesize the compound: a thiamine-independent fungus synthesizes thiamine, etc. The validity of this assumption is borne out by experimental evidence in all cases so far investigated, and is logically deduced from the premise that the known vitamins have essential functions in all cells. This premise, it should be noted, extends only to the water-soluble or B vitamins.

Further evidence, if such is needed, for the essentiality of vitamins in those fungi which do not require an external supply is found in the fact that deficient mutants can usually be obtained by appropriate techniques; examples, in addition to the classical *Neurospora crassa,* include species of *Penicillium* (17) and *Aspergillus* (115, 195, 199), genera in which naturally occurring vitamin deficiencies are uncommon.

The simplest situation in vitamin studies is that of complete inability of a given fungus to synthesize one or more vitamins. In this circumstance, the cell depends absolutely on an external supply and, at least over a certain range, growth will be proportional to the supply of the required factor or factors. Many natural and induced deficiencies are or appear to be of this type, which is the most easily detectable.

A somewhat more complicated situation arises if a fungus is able to synthesize a vitamin, but so slowly that under the usual conditions of culture the rate of all other processes is potentially faster than vitamin synthesis. Here we find the organism growing slowly in the absence of exogenous vitamin but responding to an external supply by a faster rate of growth. Such partial deficiencies are also common, perhaps more common than complete deficiencies. Examples include the requirements of particular fungi for thiamine (16, 65, 183, 186), biotin (144, 216), pyridoxine (66, 67, 216, 217), nicotinic acid (291), and inositol (238).

It also follows that any growth-regulating process—including vitamin synthesis—may be limiting under some conditions and not under others. A vitamin requirement that is manifest only under certain circumstances is termed a conditioned requirement. The known types of conditioned deficiency in fungi may be classified as follows:

1. The deficiency is apparent or more severe at particular temperatures, pH levels, or salt concentrations.

2. The requirement for a vitamin is reduced or, more rarely, eliminated by provision in the medium of a precursor or of a metabolite for the synthesis of which the vitamin is essential.

3. The deficiency is limited to or more acute at a particular stage of development.

Environmental factors conditioning vitamin deficiencies include temperature, acidity, and salt concentration. A mutant of *Neurospora crassa*, for example, requires riboflavin only at relatively high temperatures (172). *Sclerotinia camelliae* requires more inositol at 26° C than at 18° but is inhibited by inositol at 27° (8); a temperature-dependent inositolless mutant of *N. crassa* is also known (113). *Sordaria fimicola* requires thiamine only if the initial pH of the culture is less than 4.0, possibly because thiamine synthesis is inhibited by hydrogen ion (139). A similar phenomenon in mutants of *Neurospora* spp. which require pyridoxine appears, however, to reflect a requirement for free ammonia rather than a direct effect of acid (268). The influence of pH on the *p*-aminobenzoic acid requirement seems, finally, to be exerted through permeability effects (325). *Pythium butleri* requires exogenous thiamine only in a high-salt medium (211).

The second type of conditioned requirement is more easily explained: a precursor of the vitamin or a metabolite in the synthesis of which the vitamin is essential will obviously reduce the demand for the exogenous vitamin. The replacement of nicotinic acid by large amounts of tryptophan represents replacement by a precursor (20). The replacement of *p*-aminobenzoic acid by methionine (269) may be interpreted as evidence that at least one function of the vitamin is in the biosynthesis of methionine, and a similar mechanism is invoked to explain the partial replacement of biotin by aspartic acid (190).

The third type of conditioned requirement is the most interesting and the least studied: the possibility that fungi change in their synthetic capacity and in their vitamin needs during development. It must be realized that the typical vitamin experiment performed with fungi actually measures in the first instance the capacity of the spores to germinate in the absence of the vitamin in question; if the spore germination process requires the growth factor, the organism as such is recorded as having the requirement. It is entirely possible that spore germination may require factors which mature mycelium can synthesize for itself. Thus, the growth of *Memnoniella echinata* from a spore inoculum requires biotin, which is not replaceable by desthiobiotin. However, if desthiobiotin is added to a growing culture supplied with limiting amounts of biotin, the desthiobiotin elicits a significant growth response (191). Evidently, the mycelium is able to convert desthiobiotin to biotin but the spore cannot. Successful use of the differential germination method for the detection of vitamin-deficient mutants (69, 308) shows that spore germination is affected by growth factor deficiencies.

Several fungi—*Alternaria solani* (138), *Fusarium solani* (285), and *Penicillium digitatum* (61)—are reported to be accelerated in early growth by vitamins the requirements for which are not evident if total growth over a long period is measured. In *Myrothecium verrucaria* a requirement for biotin is detectable only at a stage shortly after spore germination (157).

Among the dimorphic fungi (Chapter 1), a single study (229) suggests that the yeast and the mycelial phases of some forms differ in their biotin requirement.

The onset of reproduction as a phase of growth may, although the data are far from decisive, involve changes in vitamin needs and responses. There is, however, no evidence of a singular association of one vitamin with sporulation *per se,* independent of growth. This problem is considered in Chapter 11.

Multiple requirements are especially common in the yeasts; five or six vitamins may be needed (27, 29, 39). Among the filamentous fungi, there are several instances of a requirement for three different vitamins, e.g., in *Ascoidea rubescens* (67), *Blastocladia pringsheimii* (35), *Ceratostomella microspora* (216), and *Trichophyton discoides* strains (152, 222).

Inhibitory effects of vitamins have been reported occasionally. Thiamine depresses the growth of *Fusarium* spp. (55, 285, 304) and *Rhizopus* spp. (142, 210, 238); biotin may reduce growth or enzyme formation (11, 228, 253, 316). Large amounts of pyridoxine do not, however, appear to depress growth (67). The mechanism of inhibition is not always known; thiamine inhibition has been attributed to ammonia accumulation in *Trichoderma viride* (16) and to ethanol accumulation in *Rhizopus suinus* (247).

3. THE METABOLISM OF VITAMINS

Apart from their catalytic role in metabolism, vitamins are themselves metabolites and are both synthesized and destroyed in the cell. More or less comprehensive surveys of vitamin synthesis have been reported for *Penicillium* spp. (37, 100, 178, 274), and a good deal of information is available on vitamin synthesis by *Aspergillus* spp. (37, 60, 85, 127, 181, 233, 262) and *Streptomyces* spp. (47, 100, 103, 105, 106, 151). The vitamin content of microorganisms is reviewed comprehensively by Van Lanen and Tanner (288). As mentioned earlier, we may assume that a fungus which does not require one of the water-soluble vitamins known to be required by other fungi is able to synthesize it.

Vitamins synthesized by a fungus usually appear in the medium and are detected there by bioassay; however, in *Penicillium chrysogenum* the greater part of the thiamine, riboflavin, and nicotinic acid produced remains in the cell (100), and the same is true of thiamine in some other fungi (133) and of riboflavin in *Aspergillus niger* (60).

The destruction of vitamins by fungi has been less thoroughly studied. *Phycomyces blakesleeanus* and *Sclerotium rolfsii* destroy the thiazole moiety of thiamine (21, 120). A mutant of *Neurospora crassa* destroys pyridoxine, and this destruction is inhibited competitively by thiamine (96).

4. FUNGI IN THE BIOASSAY OF VITAMINS

Analysis for individual vitamins by a biological assay is often, for one reason or another, superior to chemical analysis. This is especially true if a biologically active vitamin exists in more than one chemical form. Bioassays employing filamentous fungi have been devised for thiamine, biotin, pyridoxine, p-aminobenzoic acid, pantothenic acid, and inositol (239, 259, 281). Usually, dry weight is the criterion, although pyruvic acid formation (93), pigment production (289), and rate of growth on agar (10, 277, 282) have all been proposed.

Assays based on the dry weight of vitamin-requiring fungi have in general the advantages and disadvantages of any biological assay (171, 259). However, the relatively more tedious procedures necessary with the fungi have persuaded most investigators to use, whenever possible, bioassays based on yeast or bacterial growth or metabolism. In special cases, fungi may prove more valuable; thus, different fungi able to use either the pyrimidine or the thiazole moiety of thiamine were used by Krampitz and Woolley (124) in a study of the thiaminase of carp.

Bioassays using fungi are critically reviewed by Snell (259); others have been described for biotin (224), pantothenate (290), and thiamine (93, 289). The *Phycomyces* assay for thiamine is reviewed by Ødegård (185). A survey of the response of many fungi to graded doses of water-soluble vitamins (136) brings out some of the difficulties inherent in biological assay procedures.

5. THIAMINE

Thiamine (aneurin, vitamin B_1) is the first vitamin to have been studied as a known entity in the nutrition of fungi, and is the vitamin most frequently required by fungi. Thiamine deficiencies occur in all major taxonomic groups—although the ascomycetes have been less thoroughly investigated than others—and in fungi from many different natural environments.

Reported requirements vary widely (65, 226, 300); time of harvest, temperature, and the composition of the medium can be expected to affect thiamine demand. It seems at least possible that those fungi with very small requirements are able to synthesize thiamine once growth has been initiated. A typical response curve is shown in Figure 1.

The metabolically active form of thiamine is the pyrophosphate, long known as cocarboxylase because of its coenzyme function in the decarboxylation of pyruvic acid. Thiamine pyrophosphate is also the coenzyme for transketolase and for a variety of enzymatic reactions of α-keto acids (118). In the fungi, its role in the metabolism of pyruvic acid is clear from its acceleration of ethanol formation (42, 247) and the accumulation of pyruvate in thiamine-deficient cultures (64, 93, 304). Acceleration of glucose utilization (101) and decrease in oxalate accumulation (175) may operate through the same mechanism.

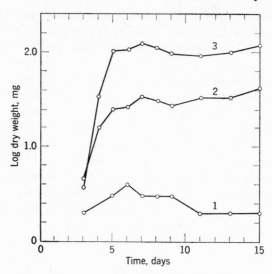

Figure 1. The response of *Phycomyces blakesleeanus* to thiamine. Thiamine at zero (curve 1), 0.2 (curve 2), and 1.0 (curve 3) mμM per 50 ml. From data of Dr. Frederick Kavanagh.

Cocarboxylase itself has been reported to replace thiamine (142, 256), possibly entering the cell without dephosphorylation (231).

Other metabolic functions of thiamine in fungi are suggested by the sparing effect of oxaloacetate (13, 82) and the effect of thiamine in promoting cytochrome synthesis by *Ustilago sphaerogena* (89).

Free thiamine chloride hydrochloride has the structure:

$$\left[H_3C \underset{N}{\overset{N}{\diagdown}} \begin{array}{c} NH_2 \cdot HCl \\ CH_2 \end{array} \underset{N}{\overset{S}{\diagup}} \begin{array}{c} CH_2CH_2OH \\ CH_3 \end{array} \right]^+ \quad Cl^-$$

Thiamine can be synthesized chemically by coupling the two moieties, 2-methyl-5-bromomethyl-6-aminopyridine and 4-methyl-5-β-hydroxyethylthiazole, commonly referred to as pyrimidine and thiazole, respectively. Some microorganisms can use one or the other moiety by itself to fill their thiamine requirement. The different types of fungi, and some examples, are shown in Table 1; the most common requirement is for the pyrimidine moiety, i.e., most thiamine-deficient fungi can synthesize thiazole and couple the two moieties to make the complete molecule. Several studies have established that an organism able

Table 1.   Response of Fungi to Thiamine and Its Moieties*

Minimum Requirement	Examples
Intact thiamine	*Ceratostomella fimbriata, Chalaropsis thielavioides* (220), *Cortinarius glaucopus* (167); *Phytophthora* spp. (188, 204), *Tilletia tritici* (46), *Trichophyton discoides* (222)
Both moieties	*Boletus variegatus* (167); *Ceratostomella* spp. (220), *Marasmius perforans* (145), *Phycomyces* spp. (130, 205, 210), *Piricularia oryzae* (284), *Polyporus versicolor* (220), *Tilletia horrida* (245), *Ustilago* spp. (15)
Thiazole	*Collybia velutipes*† (156), *Endomyces magnusii* (165), *Mucor ramannianus* (173, 174), *Stereum frustulosum* (182)
Pyrimidine	*Allomyces kniepii* (196), *Blakeslea trispora* (130), *Blastocladiella emersonii* (7), *Ceratostomella* spp. (220), *Cercosporella herpotrichoides* (45), *Collybia tuberosa, Coprinus lagopus* (130), *Fomes* spp. (332), *Hypholoma fasciculare* (245), *Marasmius fulvobulbillosus* (145), *Nocardia* spp. (157), *Polyporus* spp. (332), *Sclerotium* spp. (205), *Sphaerulina trifolii* (210), *Stereum murraii* (208), *Trichophyton tonsurans* (273)

* A more inclusive list is given by Robbins and V. Kavanagh (213).
† Not definitely established.

to live with either moiety alone does in fact make the other and synthesize thiamine (14, 21, 133, 220, 239); neither pyrimidine nor thiazole by itself has a vitamin function.

A great deal of attention has been devoted to the specificity of the structures of thiazole and pyrimidine for fungi. In general, the requirements are quite specific (213, 225, 239); most utilizable modifications, e.g., the substitution of an acetyl for a hydroxyl group or of an ethyl for a methyl group, are either minor or are very likely transformed biologically into the natural product. Allithiamine fully replaces thiamine in the nutrition of *Endoconidiophora fimbriata, Mucor ramannianus,* and other fungi and can be converted into thiamine in the cell (141).

It might be assumed *a priori* that biosynthesis of thiamine proceeds via a coupling of the two moieties. However, there are some difficulties with this simple concept as applied to *Neurospora crassa,* and Harris (97, 98), on the basis of indirect evidence from nutritional studies, has proposed that thiamine biosynthesis proceeds in this fashion:

Pyrimidine + unidentified thiazole precursor →
$$\text{thiaminelike intermediate} \rightarrow \text{thiamine} \quad (1)$$

Direct coupling of pyrimidine and thiazole may occur as a minor pathway.

We may assume that synthesis of the pyrimidine moiety follows that of other pyrimidines (Chapter 8). The origin of thiazole in *Neurospora crassa* is apparently related to amino acid metabolism (50).

Two fungi, *Phycomyces blakesleeanus* and *Sclerotium rolfsii,* which can use the two moieties in place of thiamine, also destroy or convert to an inactive form part of the thiazole, whether added as thiamine or as free thiazole. *Phytophthora cinnamomi,* which requires intact thiamine, does not destroy free or combined thiazole. Thus the destruction of thiazole seems to be unrelated to the use of thiamine in the growth processes of the fungi (120). The effect of temperature on the enzyme which destroys thiazole may explain the observation that the efficiency of thiamine for growth increases with decreasing temperature (212).

The compound "pyrithiamine" is inhibitory to those fungi, e.g., *Phytophthora cinnamomi,* which require intact thiamine, and does not inhibit those, e.g., *Neurospora crassa,* which synthesize thiamine; organisms requiring only one moiety of thiamine are intermediate in susceptibility (312, 314). However, the problem needs further study, in view of the fact that thiamineless mutants of *Neurospora crassa* do not respond according to expectations (279). Further, it is believed that "pyrithiamine" is a mixture of different compounds; neopyrithiamine has been synthesized (303) and has the structure, of a pyridine analogue of thiamine, originally assigned to "pyrithiamine." Neopyrithiamine competitively inhibits thiamine metabolism in animals (162). "Pyrithiamine" can be used by pyrimidine-deficient fungi as a source of the pyrimidine ring (207).

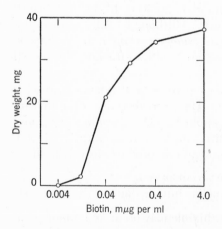

Figure 2. The response of *Stachybotrys* sp. (SN 1) to biotin. From data of Marsh and Bollenbacher (161).

6. BIOTIN

Biotin (vitamin H, coenzyme R) is required by many yeasts and fungi; all the major taxonomic groups of the fungi are represented by biotin-requiring types (5, 35, 67, 128, 161, 214, 219, 240, 241). The absolute requirement is usually less than 5 μg per liter (Figure 2).

The role of biotin is not certain; in bacteria, it or a derivative of it is probably involved in several enzymatic systems (126). Evidence from studies of several fungi (111, 155, 190) implicates biotin in the synthesis of aspartic acid, inasmuch as aspartate partially replaces biotin in nutrition. It seems likely that the reaction affected by biotin is either the carboxylation of pyruvic acid to yield oxalacetic acid or the conversion of oxalacetate to aspartate (92):

$$\text{Pyruvic acid} + CO_2 \rightarrow \text{oxalacetic acid} \rightarrow \text{aspartic acid} \qquad (2)$$

A second probable function of biotin in fungi is in the synthesis of essential fatty acids; oleic acid partially replaces biotin for a *Neurospora crassa* mutant (111) and for *Ophiostoma pini* (163). It must be said that evidence for the essentiality of fatty acids for fungi is incomplete; the possibility is raised by (a) the stimulating effect of oleic acid on growth (12, 84, 332) and (b) the occurrence in *Neurospora crassa* of mutants requiring fatty acids (129).

Less well-defined and probably indirect effects of biotin on fungi include inhibition of growth of a pantothenicless mutant (228), inhibition of enzyme synthesis in one strain of *Neurospora crassa* (11), and change in the growth pattern of the dimorphic *Sporotrichum schencki* (160). *Mitrula paludosa* requires biotin only if ammonium nitrogen is used in the medium (67).

In relation to biosynthesis, the structures of three compounds are of interest:

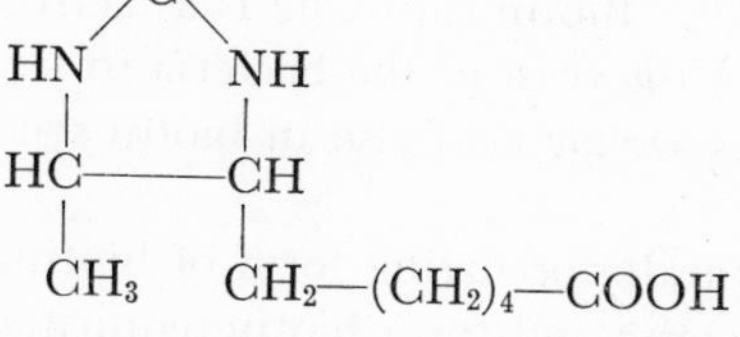

Desthiobiotin

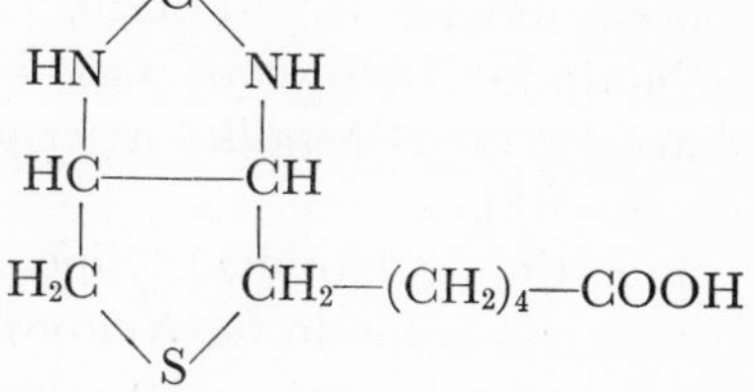

Biotin

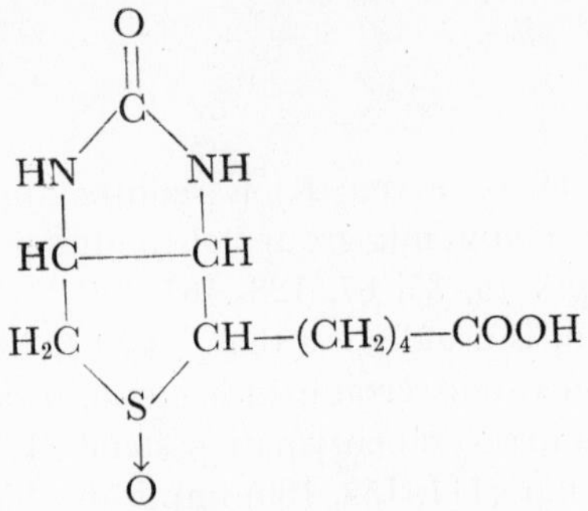

$$O$$
$$\|$$
$$C$$

HN   NH

HC————CH

H_2C $CH—(CH_2)_4—COOH$

S

↓

O

Biotin sulfoxide

Tatum (276) studied the nutrition of biotinless mutants of *Penicillium chrysogenum*. One mutant can use desthiobiotin as well as biotin; a second mutant accumulates desthiobiotin but cannot use it. Production of desthiobiotin in this strain is increased by provision of pimelic acid [$HOOC—(CH_2)_5—COOH$]. Equation 3 therefore summarizes the known steps in biosynthesis:

$$\text{Pimelic acid} \to \text{desthiobiotin} \to \text{biotin} \qquad (3)$$

Biotin-deficient fungi isolated from nature fall into two groups. The first, exemplified by *Ceratostomella ips, Neurospora crassa, Blastomyces dermatitidis,* and yeast (49, 95, 143), can grow, at least to a degree, with desthiobiotin in place of biotin; these fungi are presumably blocked in a step prior to desthiobiotin synthesis. The second group, which includes *Ceratostomella pini* and *Sordaria fimicola,* cannot use desthiobiotin (135, 143) and is therefore blocked in the conversion of desthiobiotin to biotin. Those fungi known only to be unable to use pimelic acid in place of biotin (219) cannot yet be placed in either group. We have noted earlier the different responses of spores and pregrown cultures of *Memnoniella echinata* to desthiobiotin.

Biotin sulfoxide is formed by *Aspergillus niger* in synthetic medium; since pimelic acid and desthiobiotin increase the yield, and since added biotin is quantitatively converted to the sulfoxide, it is concluded that *A. niger* synthesizes biotin as in Equation 3 and then transforms it to biotin sulfoxide (54, 317, 320, 321, 322). Biotin sulfoxide is as active as biotin for *Neurospora crassa* but not for yeast or the bacteria so far tested (321). *Aspergillus niger* utilizes azelaic acid also in biotin synthesis (318).

Biocytin, ε-N-biotinyl-L-lysine, a naturally occurring form of biotin, is as active as biotin for *Neurospora crassa* and for a biotin-requiring mutant of *Penicillium chrysogenum* (319). The oxygen analogue of biotin, *dl*-Oxybiotin (O-heterobiotin), has slight activity for fungi (190), as it does for other organisms (92). Specific anti-biotin activity against fungi is reported for avidin (317), biotin sulfone (321), and γ-(3,4-ureylenecyclohexyl)butyric acid (191).

7. PYRIDOXINE

Pyridoxine (vitamin B_6, adermin) appears to be required by fewer fungi than is biotin or thiamine. Several species of *Ceratostomella* (*Ophiostoma*) require it (67, 215), as do *Ascoidea rubescens* and *Trichophyton discoides* (67, 215, 222). The requirement is highly species-specific within the genus *Ceratostomella*.

Pyridoxineless mutants of *Neurospora crassa* and *N. sitophila* grow better at limiting pyridoxine concentration if thiamine is present (263, 279). This relation between two vitamins has been explained by the postulate that thiamine competitively inhibits the endogenous destruction of pyridoxine (96). Conversely, pyridoxine inhibits the biosynthesis of thiamine, probably by preventing the incorporation of the pyrimidine moiety (98).

As mentioned above, certain mutants of *Neurospora crassa* require pyridoxine only at low pH. The mechanism of this conditioned deficiency is a requirement for free ammonia in the absence of pyridoxine; at low pH, insufficient free ammonia is present and the vitamin is therefore needed for growth (268).

The coenzyme form of pyridoxine is pyridoxal-5-phosphate, known to be the coenzyme for enzymes of amino acid metabolism, specifically decarboxylases, transaminases, and racemases (286). Insofar as these enzymes are present in fungi (Chapter 8), we may assume the involvement of the coenzyme also. In addition, pyridoxal phosphate has been specifically shown to be active in several isolated enzyme systems of *Neurospora crassa* (201, 268, 287, 327). Pyridoxine deficiency in *N. crassa* mutants is accompanied by accumulation of nitrite from nitrate, indicating a role of pyridoxal phosphate in nitrite reduction (255).

Although pyridoxine, pyridoxamine, and pyridoxal are equally usable by fungi (261), other modifications of the basic molecule are usually inactive or toxic (218); the few that are active can easily be guessed to be converted in the cell to pyridoxine (198, 218).

The growth of a pyridoxineless mutant of *Neurospora sitophila* is inhibited by 4-deoxypyridine; the inhibition is competitively reversed by pyridoxine and its derivatives (197, 198).

8. RIBOFLAVIN

Riboflavin (vitamin B_2, lactoflavin) is only rarely required by micro-organisms isolated from nature. Several of the lactic acid bacteria are riboflavin-deficient (192); the yeasts appear not to require it (29). A single report, without data, indicates that *Poria vaillantii* requires riboflavin (119); this is the first such claim for a filamentous fungus. *Dictyostelium* spp. have an absolute requirement (271).

However, riboflavinless mutants can usually be isolated by appropriate techniques (23, 77, 115, 121, 195). Of these, the most interesting is the mutant of *Neurospora crassa* isolated by Mitchell and Houlahan (172). This strain does not require exogenous riboflavin at moderate temperatures, but only if grown at 28° C or higher (Figure 3). Even at the elevated temperature, the mutant synthesizes riboflavin if it is provided initially with some of the vitamin.

Riboflavin has been shown directly to be formed by many yeasts and fungi (60, 91, 100, 137, 172, 189, 288, 302, 335). In two yeastlike fungi, *Eremothecium ashbyii* and *Ashbya gossypii,* yields are high enough so that commercial use is practicable (75); it is believed that up to 6 mg per milliliter of free riboflavin is produced by *A. gossypii* in a complex medium. Although esters of riboflavin, especially flavin adenine dinucleotide, occur in the cell, only free riboflavin is found in the medium (252, 326).

The physiological conditions of riboflavin synthesis in the yeastlike fungi have been of both practical and theoretical interest. Although even relatively small amounts of iron inhibit riboflavin synthesis by *Clostridium acetobutylicum* (109) and *Candida* spp. (275), *Ashbya*

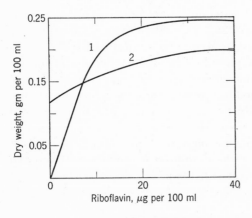

Figure 3. The response of a *Neurospora crassa* mutant to exogenous riboflavin. Curve 1, at 30°C; curve 2, at 25°. Redrawn from Nicholas (180), by permission of the *Journal of General Microbiology.*

gossypii and *Eremothecium ashbyii* are less sensitive to iron (75, 301). Moderate levels of glucose, a slightly acid pH, and aeration all improve the yield of riboflavin (202, 243, 301). Riboflavin formation by *Aspergillus niger* is favored by any of a variety of nutritional factors, all of which somewhat retard growth (230).

The structure of riboflavin is:

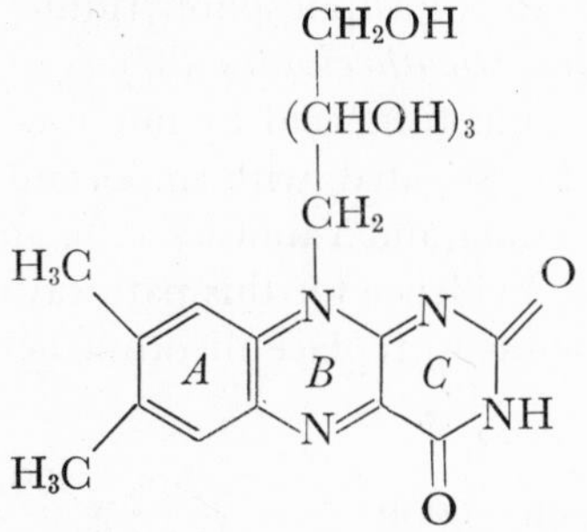

Provision of certain purines, e.g., adenine or guanine, to *Eremothecium ashbyii* increases the yield of riboflavin (26, 153, 155). The entry of isotopic formate, carbon dioxide, and acetate (194) and of labeled adenine (163) into the molecule also suggests that the synthesis of ring *C* is similar to the synthesis of the pyrmidine ring of a purine or that the pyrimidine ring of a purine is incorporated intact (156).

Inhibition studies with 1,2-dichloro-4,5-diaminobenzene led Woolley (310, 311) to suggest that the natural precursor of ring *A*—and of cyanocobalamin (p. 343)—is 1,2-dimethyl-4,5-diaminobenzene.

The cellular function of riboflavin is to provide the prosthetic group of a number of oxidizing enzymes, the flavin enzymes (114). Flavin enzymes known in fungi include glucose aerodehydrogenase and other respiratory enzymes (Chapter 7) and several enzymes of nitrogen metabolism—nitrate reductase, nitrite reductase, hydroxylamine reductase, and the amino acid oxidases (Chapter 8). Evidence from organisms other than the fungi indicates that riboflavin plays a role in the synthesis of nicotinic acid (41).

Zalokar (335) has suggested that a riboflavin-protein complex may be the photoreceptor in the light-activated synthesis of carotene by *Neurospora crassa* (Chapter 6).

9. NICOTINIC ACID

Deficiencies for nicotinic acid—or its amide, which appears from limited evidence to be physiologically equivalent to the free acid in fungi—occur in relatively few fungi: *Microsporum audouini* (5), *Blas-*

tocladia pringsheimii (35), *Venturia inaequalis* (63), *Phlyctorhiza variabilis* (227), and individual isolates of *Trichophyton equinum* (79) and *Glomerella cingulata* (270). Deficiencies may be complete or partial.

The known function of nicotinic acid is as a constituent of the respiratory coenzymes diphosphopyridine nucleotide and triphosphopyridine nucleotide (257). Diphosphopyridine nucleotide has been isolated from *Fusarium tricothecioides* (87).

The biosynthesis of nicotinic acid by mutants of *Neurospora crassa* has been intensively investigated, with important results. These studies are reviewed by Bonner and Yanofsky (20), and a suggested scheme is shown in Figure 4. Evidence for this pathway comes primarily from the ability of compounds to replace nicotinic acid in the nutrition of

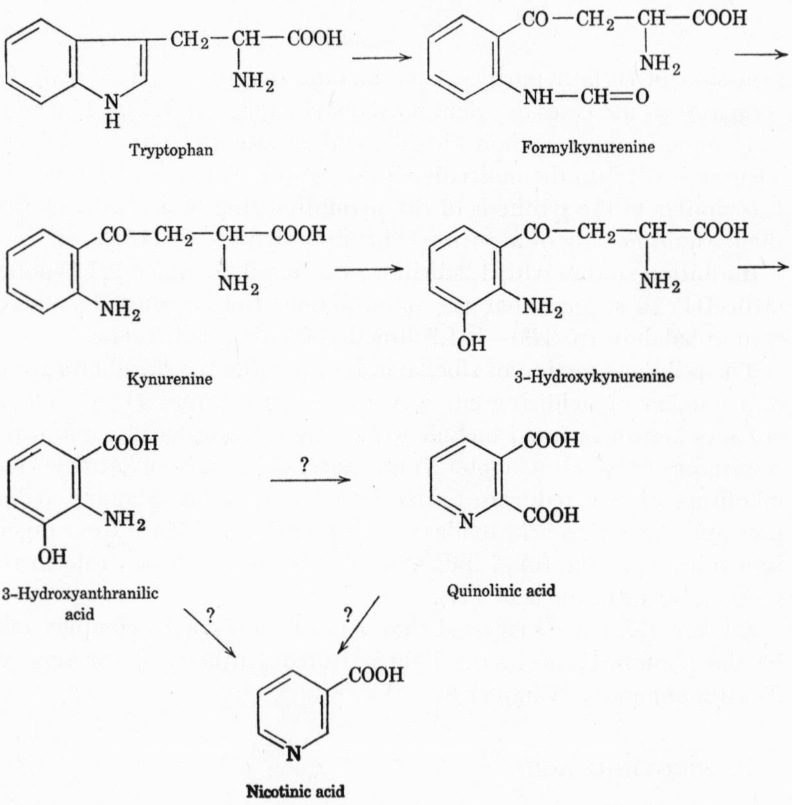

Figure 4. The probable pathway of conversion of tryptophan to nicotinic acid in *Neurospora crassa*. Modified from Greenberg (88), by permission of Academic Press, Inc.

deficient mutants and from the accumulation of intermediates by deficient strains. Thus, one nicotinicless mutant cannot use quinolinic acid and accumulates detectable amounts of this compound, indicating that it is blocked in the conversion of quinolinate to the vitamin (19, 102). Other mutants accumulate 3-hydroxyanthranilic acid (18) or a derivative of kynurenine (328), or convert one intermediate into others (330).

As indicated in Figure 4, the steps from 3-hydroxyanthranilic acid to nicotinic acid are still uncertain and may follow one of the two possibilities shown, via unstable intermediates (88).

Preliminary studies of nicotinicless mutants of *Aspergillus nidulans* (195) suggest that a second and shorter pathway occurs in addition to the reactions of Figure 4; this shorter sequence cannot be detected in *Neurospora crassa* (187).

The *Neurospora* pathway is probably followed also in the rat, for which some direct enzymatic evidence is available (257). In the bacteria so far studied, the pathway does not appear to be applicable (328). Evidence on other fungi is limited to the finding, mentioned earlier, that tryptophan and certain other intermediates of the *Neurospora* pathway replace nicotinic acid for *Trichophyton equinum* (51, 79).

10. INOSITOL

Requirements for inositol (*meso*-inositol, *i*-inositol, *myo*-inositol) are rather rare in fungi; complete or partial deficiencies have been reported in, for example, yeasts (30), *Trichophyton faviforme* (82), *Lophodermium pinastri* (123), *Sclerotinia camelliae* (8), *Rhizopus suinus* (238), *Eremothecium ashbyii* (243, 331), *Diplocarpon rosae* (253), and *Diaporthe phaseolorum* var. *bataticola* (283). Inositolless mutants have been found in *Neurospora crassa* (9) and other fungi (17, 70, 121).

It is doubtful whether inositol should be considered a vitamin as the word is used here. No coenzyme function is known in any organism; rather, the finding that most of the inositol of *Neurospora crassa* mycelium is associated with phospholipid suggests that it is a structural component of the cell (74).

The magnitude of the inositol requirement is much greater than that of the other vitamins (136, 259, 281), again suggesting a structural rather than a catalytic role. The weight of dry cells per gram thiamine needed is about $0.5–2.5 \times 10^6$, and the comparable value for inositol is only 600–900 (65). Figure 5 illustrates the growth response to inositol.

The inositol requirement is highly specific (125, 242). Phytin, the salt of inositol hexaphosphoric acid, replaces inositol for *Eremothecium*

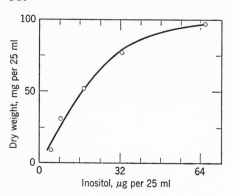

Figure 5. The response of an inositolless mutant of *Neurospora crassa* to inositol. From Leonian and Lilly (136), courtesy of the West Virginia University Agricultural Experiment Station.

ashbyii (170), but neither phytin nor lipositol is utilizable by an inositolless mutant of *Neurospora crassa* (9).

As mentioned earlier, no general function of inositol is known in fungi. Inositol overcomes the inhibition caused by high levels of some other vitamins (238, 253), and has been stated to cause a conidial type of growth in *Ophiostoma multiannulatum* (72). The response of *Sclerotinia camelliae* to inositol is conditioned by temperature (8).

The insecticide γ-hexachlorocyclohexane (gammexane) has been investigated as a possible inhibitory analogue of inositol; it is not, however, structurally an analogue of *meso*-inositol but of *muco*-inositol (125). Gammexane inhibition of *Neurospora crassa* appears to be based on two mechanisms: an interference with the metabolism of exogenous inositol in an inositol-requiring mutant and a second mechanism which is independent of inositol metabolism (93).

11. PARA-AMINOBENZOIC ACID

Only one fungus, *Blastocladia ramosa*, deficient for *p*-aminobenzoic acid (PABA) is known to occur naturally (39a); a yeast, *Rhodotorula aurantiaca*, is reported to show an absolute requirement (221), and several bacteria require the compound (323). Mutants of several filamentous fungi require PABA (17, 68, 83, 115, 195), so it is presumably a normal metabolite. The deficient mutant of *Neurospora crassa* grows maximally with PABA at about 5 μg per liter (281); the requirement is lower at acid pH than at neutral pH, presumably by reason of a faster penetration of the undissociated acid into the cell (325). The requirement of the *N. crassa* mutant is highly specific: of closely related compounds only 2-fluoro-*p*-aminobenzoic acid has appreciable activity (323).

Although the folic acid molecule contains the structure of p-amino-benzoic acid, it seems doubtful that the major function of PABA is in the formation of folic acid; for example, folic acid does not replace PABA for *Neurospora crassa* (1, 333). Several metabolic roles of PABA have been suggested, especially a function in the introduction of 1-carbon intermediates into other compounds (254). The fact that methionine replaces PABA for a mutant of *Neurospora crassa* supports this possibility; the vitamin here probably functions in the methylation of homocysteine (269). Other functions no doubt exist (266), but they have not yet been shown in the fungi.

The biosynthesis of PABA by *Neurospora crassa* is a special case of aromatic synthesis. A single gene mutant is deficient for PABA, trypto-phan, phenylalanine, and tyrosine; shikimic acid replaces all these requirements (280). The probable pathway of the synthesis is considered elsewhere (Chapter 8).

PABA in high concentrations is toxic to fungi (38), but in *Neurospora crassa* it is converted to a pigment of unknown structure and to N-acetyl-p-aminobenzoic acid (200). The acetylation of PABA occurs also in animal tissues (323).

The metabolic importance of PABA was first recognized by Woods (307), who found that the bacteriostatic effect of sulfanilamide is competitively antagonized by PABA. The same antagonism has been observed in fungi (24, 48, 99), and we may assume that the same mechanism prevails.

Emerson and Cushing (58) isolated a sulfonamide-resistant mutant of *Neurospora crassa* and a second mutant requiring sulfonamides for growth. The requirement is absolute at 35°C, partial at lower incubation temperatures (56). Later studies by Zalokar (333) suggest that the sulfa-requiring strain is abnormally sensitive to the PABA which is formed in its own cells; the beneficial effect of sulfonamides is, in this view, based on its antagonism of the toxic effect of PABA. Some of the difficulties of this hypothesis are discussed by Mitchell (171); a relationship to amino acid metabolism is apparently involved (57, 334). The present uncertain status of the sulfonamide requirement reflects the limitations of growth methods used by themselves for the solution of essentially biochemical problems.

12. PANTOTHENIC ACID

Requirements for pantothenic acid, although fairly common in yeasts (27, 29, 134), are rare or unknown in the filamentous fungi. *Penicillium digitatum* is stimulated in the early stages of growth by pantothenate (61, 315), and it has been reported that *Polyporus texanus* requires pantothenate (332). Pantothenicless mutants have been obtained frequently in the fungi (83, 121, 195, 278).

Pantothenic acid functions in metabolism as a constituent of the larger molecule coenzyme A, an essential cofactor in a number of acyl transfer and related reactions (147, 184). The effect of pantothenate on carotenogenesis in *Mucor hiemalis* presumably results from an increase in the rate of acetyl transfer (90).

Presumably all fungi except those needing exogenous pantothenate synthesize the vitamin; this is borne out by analysis of, for example, *Boletus edulis* (40), *Neurospora crassa* (297), and a few other fungi (181). The ultimate step in pantothenate synthesis is known to be the coupling of pantoic acid and β-alanine. This coupling is carried out by growing cells, resting cells, and a cell-free preparation (acetone powder) of *Neurospora crassa* (296). Surprisingly, the enzyme is found also in a pantothenicless mutant, the cells of which do not under the usual conditions of still culture form pantothenate from the two precursors (295). However, it has been found that the coupling reaction above does proceed in "pantothenicless" cells grown under aeration (297). Either we have here in still culture a gene-controlled suppression of an enzyme, or the mutant strain is unable under limited aeration to provide the energy necessary for the formation of the peptide bond of pantothenic acid.

The origin of the pantoic acid moiety in fungi is not known; in bacteria, *p*-aminobenzoic acid is involved, and there is some evidence that α-ketoisovaleric acid is a precursor of pantoic acid (266).

13. PTEROYLGLUTAMIC ACID

Pteroylglutamic acid (vitamin Bc, *Lactobacillus casei* factor, folic acid, folacin) and its relatives are required by microorganisms and higher animals; probably the several active compounds are all converted to the same form (265). *Venturia inaequalis* is reported to be stimulated in its growth by pteroylglutamic acid (63); no fungi or actinomycetes are known to require the factor.

A substance active for *Lactobacillus casei* is produced by several fungi, including species of *Absidia, Aspergillus, Chaetomium, Circinella, Fusarium, Monascus, Mucor, Neurospora, Pencillium,* and *Rhizopus* (30, 164, 178). The identity of this product is uncertain. Citrovorum factor, another member of this group of compounds, is formed by *Streptomyces griseus* (59).

Rhizopterin, N-formylpteroic acid, is formed by *Rhizopus nigricans*

(306) and replaces pteroylglutamic acid for strains of *Streptococcus lactis* (265). Presumably it and the factor active for *L. casei* are both utilized by the fungi producing them in the same biological reactions for which the coenzyme form of pteroylglutamic acid is required in bacteria and animals.

14. THE VITAMINS B$_{12}$

The vitamins B$_{12}$ comprise a family of compounds, the chemical and biological relationships of which are not fully understood. Vitamin B$_{12}$ itself, or cyanocobalamin, was the first discovered, and its structure is now known (22, 110); other cobalamins, e.g., hydroxocobalamin, can be converted to it by cyanide treatment. A second group of compounds differs from the cobalamins in the nucleotide moiety; these are active for some microorganisms only (25, 62). Vitamin B$_{12}$ is believed to function in the cell in the synthesis of 1-carbon fragments, especially the labile methyl group (25).

Vitamin B$_{12}$ and related compounds are required by several bacteria and algal flagellates (62), not, so far as is now known, by actinomycetes or fungi. Higher animals require the vitamin, green plants do not.

The synthesis of cobalamins occurs in certain of the true bacteria and especially in species of *Streptomyces* and *Nocardia,* of the Actinomycetales (32, 43, 53, 94, 116, 203, 209, 232, 267, 305). Commercial supplies of the vitamin can in fact be obtained as byproducts of antibiotic production by *Streptomyces* spp. (324). Cobalt added to the culture medium increases the yield of cyanocobalamin from *Streptomyces griseus* (104).

In addition to cyanocobalamin, species of *Streptomyces* form hydroxocobalamin (vitamin B$_{12a}$, B$_{12b}$), in which the cyanide of cyanocobalamin is replaced by hydroxyl, and vitamin B$_{12c}$, containing a nitrite radical in place of cyanide; all three forms have been isolated from one species, *S. griseus* (43).

Synthesis of vitamin B$_{12}$ in the filamentous fungi has not been demonstrated conclusively. Substances active for *Lactobacillus leichmanii* are formed by *Ashbya gossypii* (258) and *Aspergillus niger* (179). However, the *L. leichmanii* assay is not specific enough to support a final identification (62).

It has been mentioned earlier that inhibition studies point to 1,2-dimethyl-4,5-diaminobenzene as a precursor of riboflavin. These investigations (310, 311) implicate this compound also as a precursor of the cobalamins; the structure is known to be part of the larger cobalamin molecule. Other evidence bears out the suggestion that the biosyntheses of riboflavin and of cobalamins are related (62, 266). *Streptomyces olivaceus* incorporates labeled 5,6-dimethylbenzimidazole without dilution into the cobalamin molecule (299); more recent and still preliminary evidence is in favor of δ-aminolevulinic acid as a precursor (250).

15. VITAMINS K

Vitamins K_1 and K_2 are required by higher animals. Both are derivatives of 2-methyl-1,4-napthoquinone, and it appears that any compound containing this nucleus is active in animals (3).

Many bacteria produce vitamin K_2 (2), and the phthiocol of *Mycobacterium tuberculosis*—chemically 2-methyl-3-hydroxy-1,4-naphthoquinone—has K activity (3). The six fungi that have been tested (2) do not have detectable vitamin K activity. Other 1,4-naphthoquinones are known to be produced by fungi (Chapter 6), but none of these is a 2-methyl derivative.

No requirement for the K vitamins is known in the fungi; Almquist (3) reviews the conflicting evidence for a K requirement in *Mycobacterium paratuberculosis* (313).

Some compounds structurally related to vitamin K, specifically 2-chloro-1,4-naphthoquinone (246) and 2,3-dichloro-1,4-benzoquinone, are fungitoxic (Chapter 14). Menadione (2-methyl-1,4-naphthoquinone) competitively inhibits the action of both of these compounds in certain biological systems (246, 309). However, the fungitoxicity and the reversal by menadione are not adequate evidence for a role of the K vitamins in fungal metabolism; one may equally well consider the antagonists as foreign toxicants competing for the same site of action (309).

16. OTHER GROWTH FACTORS

The only well-characterized growth factor for fungi that has not so far been mentioned is coprogen, required by species of *Pilobolus* and first isolated from manure (107). Bioassays indicate that this factor is manufactured by some other fungi and several actinomycetes (108), and crystalline coprogen has been isolated from *Penicillium* sp. (193).

Coprogen is related chemically and biologically to two other materials, ferrichrome and the *Arthrobacter terregens* factor. Ferrichrome and ferrichrome A are nitrogenous iron-containing pigments of *Ustilago sphaerogena* (76, 176); the effect of zinc on synthesis suggests that ferrichrome is a precursor of cytochrome c (177). The growth factor for *Arthrobacter terregens,* although not identical with either coprogen or ferrichrome, is evidently related to them; thus both ferrichrome and coprogen are active for *A. terregens* (33, 148, 149) and *Pilobolus* spp. (177a).

Sterols are produced by many fungi (Chapter 6); so far only *Labyrinthula vitellina*—of uncertain taxonomic position but possibly a myxomycete—has been shown to have a steroid requirement (293, 294). It has been claimed (4) that anaerobic growth of *Saccharomyces cerevisiae* in a synthetic medium is dependent on ergosterol or other sterols.

Many still unknown factors have been postulated for particular fungi. Mycorrhizal fungi are stimulated by materials from plant roots and forest litter, and the effect cannot be traced to known vitamins or amino acids (166, 167, 168). The myxomycetes apparently require for their growth one or more bacterial proteins (112, 272), not vitamins as we have here used the term. As mentioned earlier, growth-stimulating effects of crude natural materials do not necessarily implicate a vitamin.

Other vitamins—ascorbic acid and vitamins A, D, and E—required by animals do not appear to play any essential role in the fungi (28, 86); ascorbic acid may, however, affect growth through its effect on the oxidation-reduction potential.

17. THE OCCURRENCE OF VITAMIN DEFICIENCIES IN THE FUNGI

It will be clear from the preceding discussion of individual vitamins that some deficiencies occur frequently, others more rarely. The vitamin most often required by fungi from nature is thiamine; usually the deficiency is for the pyrimidine moiety, and we have noted only a few instances of a deficiency for thiazole (Table 1). Biotin is very often required, and deficiencies in pyridoxine or its derivatives are frequently encountered. Pantothenic acid and nicotinic acid requirements are rare in nature, and we have at present only single reports of requirements for riboflavin and *p*-aminobenzoic acid among filamentous fungi.

This lop-sided distribution of vitamin requirements demands an attempt at an explanation. Assuming that spontaneous mutations in nature are like those induced by mutagens, forms deficient for riboflavin of *p*-aminobenzoic acid must arise from time to time. Their failure to survive—if it is real and not an artifact of screening methods —may result from either or both of two conditions, viz.:

1. The required vitamin is not available in the environment.

2. The derangement of metabolism associated with the deficiency is so great that even with the missing factor available in the environment the mutant is at a selective disadvantage and cannot propagate itself.

The second of these hypotheses is the more attractive, inasmuch as even the plant pathogens, living in close contact with higher plant cells, do not seem to develop strains deficient for certain vitamins.

18. VITAMINS, TAXONOMY, AND ECOLOGY

Comparative physiology often affords clues to taxonomic and phylogenetic relationships. Vitamin deficiencies do not, so far as can be determined, offer such clues. From the frequency of induced mutations, one would expect that vitamin deficiencies occur at random within species, genera, and higher categories; this appears to be true. Marked differences between the vitamin demands of strains of a single species are often encountered, e.g., *Trichophyton* spp. and other animal pathogens (5, 80, 81, 152), *Lenzites trabea* (140), *Boletus granulatus* (169), and *Glomerella cingulata* (270). In culture, both *Fusarium avenaceum* (214) and *Ustilago major* (15) give rise to clones which differ in requirements from the parent strain.

Within a genus, again, species differ widely in vitamin demands; examples include the genus *Ophiostoma* and its asexual form *Ceratostomella* (66, 67, 215, 217, 224), *Trichophyton* (31, 80, 222, 223), *Ustilago* (245), *Candida* (241), *Boletus* (169), *Marasmius* (145), and *Absidia* (213).

In the light of this intra- and interspecific variation, it is difficult to imagine that vitamin needs per se can separate taxons or can yield valid evidence of phylogeny.

The theory of Lwoff (150) and Knight (122), that metabolic deficiencies have arisen in the evolution of microorganisms by loss of functions originally present, has been generally accepted. If we grant, in view of the argument just made, that this loss of function has not followed phylogenetic or taxonomic divisions, we may ask if there is any relation of vitamin needs to ecology.

First, it appears that some genera as isolated from nature rarely have vitamin deficiencies. Only a tentative listing can be made at present, in view of the methodological difficulty in establishing the absence of a requirement: *Aspergillus, Chaetomium, Fusarium, Mucor, Penicillium, Rhizopus, Streptomyces,* and *Zygorhynchus* (213). Exceptions occur in most of these genera, i.e., some isolates are deficient or partially deficient for a given vitamin (61, 195, 214), and deficient mutants may be obtained in both *Aspergillus* and *Penicillium* (17, 115, 195). These genera are all vigorous saprophytes, widespread in nature, and frequently isolated from soil. They seem to form, therefore, an ecological type independent of taxonomic boundaries; at present, however, it is fruitless to speculate on the biochemical, genetic, or environmental determinants involved.

Soil-inhabiting fungi are not, however, as a group independent of vitamins, many soil fungi requiring them for maximal growth (6). Soil, especially soil of high organic matter, contains several vitamins (234, 235), probably formed by higher plants (298) or algae (78); it is not surprising, therefore, to find deficient soil fungi.

Certain major ecological groups show no general pattern of vitamin dependence; these include animal pathogens (5, 52, 223), plant pathogens (45, 46, 55, 215, 217, 244, 336), and the aquatic phycomycetes as a group (36). Among the insect pathogens, however, limited data suggest a tendency for species of wide host range, e.g., *Isaria farinosa,* to be independent of growth factors, and more specialized pathogens, e.g., *Hirsutella* spp., to require vitamins and organic nitrogen (154).

The nearest approach to a correlation of a taxonomic group with a vitamin requirement is in the Agaricales; almost all the fungi in this group that have been investigated require thiamine, replaceable for most by the pyrimidine moiety (71, 119, 145, 146, 166, 183, 213, 332). Ecologically, these include wood-destroying, litter-decomposing, and mycorrhizal groups, i.e., groups living in environments in which it is likely that thiamine is present. A similar situation may prevail in some of the orders of the lower phycomycetes (36), but too few species have been investigated, far fewer than among the Agaricales.

BIBLIOGRAPHY

1. Agarwala, S. C. and W. H. Peterson. 1950. *Arch. Biochem.* 27: 304–315.
2. Almquist, H. J. 1941. *Physiol. Revs.* 21: 194–216.
3. Almquist, H. S. 1954. In W. H. Sebrell, Jr. and R. S. Harris (eds.), *The Vitamins,* Vol. 2, p. 389–399, 415–418. New York: Academic Press.
4. Andreasen, A. A. and T. J. B. Stier. 1953. *J. Cellular Comp. Physiol.* 41: 23–36.
5. Arêa Leão, A. E. de and A. Cury. 1950. *Mycopath. et Mycol. Appl.* 5: 65–90.
6. Atkinson, R. G. and J. B. Robinson. 1955. *Can. J. Botany* 33: 281–288.
7. Barner, H. D. and E. C. Cantino. 1952. *Am. J. Botany* 39: 746–751.
8. Barnett, H. L. and V. G. Lilly. 1948. *Am. J. Botany* 35: 297–302.
9. Beadle, G. W. 1944. *J. Biol. Chem.* 156: 683–689.
10. Beadle, G. W. and E. L. Tatum. 1941. *Proc. Natl. Acad. Sci. U. S.* 27: 499–506.
11. Bender, A. E., H. A. Krebs, and N. H. Horowitz. 1949. *Biochem. J. (London)* 45: xxi–xxii.

12. Benham, R. W. 1941. *Proc. Soc. Exp. Biol. Med.* 46: 176–178.
13. Benham, R. W. 1945. *Proc. Soc. Exp. Biol. Med.* 58: 199–201.
14. Bhargava, K. S. 1946. *Lloydia* 9: 13–23.
15. Blumer, S. 1940. *Mitt. naturforsch. Ges. Bern* 1940: 19–36.
16. Blumer, S. 1944. *Ber. schweiz. botan. Ges.* 54: 605–624.
17. Bonner, D. M. 1946. *Am. J. Botany* 33: 788–791.
18. Bonner, D. M. 1948. *Proc. Natl. Acad. Sci. U. S.* 34: 5–9.
19. Bonner, D. M. and C. Yanofsky. 1949. *Proc. Natl. Acad. Sci. U. S.* 35: 576–581.
20. Bonner, D. M. and C. Yanofsky. 1951. *J. Nutrition* 44: 603–616.
21. Bonner, J. and E. R. Buchman. 1939. *Proc. Natl. Acad. Sci. U. S.* 25: 164–171.
22. Bonnet, R. *et al.* 1955. *Nature (London)* 176: 328–330.
23. Bradley, S. G. and J. Lederberg. 1956. *J. Bacteriol.* 72: 219–225.
24. Brian, P. W. 1944. *Nature (London)* 153: 83–84.
25. Briggs, G. M. and F. S. Daft. 1955. *Ann. Rev. Biochem.* 24: 339–392.
26. Brown, E. G., T. W. Goodwin, and S. Pendlington. 1955. *Biochem. J. (London)* 61: 37–46.
27. Burkholder, P. R. 1943. *Am. J. Botany* 30: 206–211.
28. Burkholder, P. R. and I. McVeigh. 1942. *Science* 95: 127–128.
29. Burkholder, P. R., I. McVeigh, and D. Moyer. 1944. *J. Bacteriol.* 48: 385–391.
30. Burkholder, P. R., I. McVeigh, and K. Wilson. 1945. *Arch. Biochem.* 7: 287–303.
31. Burkholder, P. R. and D. Moyer. 1943. *Bull. Torrey Botan. Club* 70: 372–377.
32. Burton, M. O. and A. G. Lochhead. 1951. *Can. J. Botany* 29: 352–359.
33. Burton, M. O., F. J. Sowden, and A. G. Lochhead. 1954. *Can. J. Biochem. and Physiol.* 32: 400–406.
34. Cannon, M. D., R. K. Boutwell, and C. A. Elvehjem. 1945. *Science* 102: 529–530.
35. Cantino, E. C. 1948. *Am. J. Botany* 35: 238–242.
36. Cantino, E. C. 1955. *Quart. Rev. Biol.* 30: 138–149.
37. Carpenter, C. C. and E. W. Friedlander. 1942. *Science* 95: 625.
38. Cavill, G. W. K. and J. M. Vincent. 1945. *Nature (London)* 155: 301.
39. Clark, F. M., N. C. Banister, and W. R. Mitchell. 1948. *Arch. Biochem.* 17: 3–9.
39a. Crasemann, J. M. 1957. *Am. J. Botany* 44: 218–224.
40. Dagys, J. and P. Bluzmanas. 1943. *Ber. deut. botan. Ges.* 61: 49–66.
41. Dalgliesh, C. E. 1955. *Advances in Protein Chem.* 10: 33–150.
42. Dammann, E., O. T. Rotini, and F. F. Nord. 1938. *Biochem. Z.* 297: 185–202.
43. Darken, M. A. 1953. *Botan. Rev.* 19: 99–130.
44. Day, D. 1942. *Bull. Torrey Botan. Club* 69: 11–20.
45. Défago, G. 1939. *Ber. schweiz. botan. Ges.* 49: 413–414.
46. Défago, G. 1940. *Phytopathol. Z.* 13: 293–315.
47. De Vries, W. H. et al. 1950. *J. Am. Chem. Soc.* 72: 4838.
48. Dimond, N. S. 1941. *Science* 94: 420–421.
49. Dittmer, K., D. B. Melville, and V. du Vigneaud. 1944. *Science* 99: 203–205.
50. Doudney, C. O. and R. P. Wagner. 1953. *Proc. Natl. Acad. Sci. U. S.* 39: 1043–1052.
51. Drouhet, E. 1954. *Congr. Intern. Botan., 8ᵉ Congr. Paris, Rapps. Communs. 8, Sect.* 18–20: 112–113.
52. Drouhet, E. and F. Mariat. 1952. *Ann. inst. Pasteur* 82: 337–347.
53. Dulaney, E. L. and P. L. Williams. 1953. *Mycologia* 45: 345–358.
54. Eakin, R. A. and E. A. Eakin. 1942. *Science* 96: 187–188.
55. Elliott, E. S. 1949. *Proc. West Va. Acad. Sci.* 20: 65–68.
56. Emerson, S. 1947. *J. Bacteriol.* 54: 197–207.
57. Emerson, S. 1949. *Cold Spring Harbor Symposia Quant. Biol.* 14: 40–48.
58. Emerson, S. and J. E. Cushing. 1946. *Federation Proc.* 5: 379–389.

59. Emery, W. B., K. A. Lees, and A. D. Walker. 1950. *Biochem. J.* (*London*) 46: 572–574.
60. Emmenegger, T. 1954. *Ber. schweiz. botan. Ges.* 64: 453–486.
61. Fergus, C. L. 1952. *Mycologia* 44: 183–189.
62. Ford, J. E. and S. H. Hutner. 1955. *Vitamins and Hormones* 13: 101–136.
63. Fothergill, P. G. and R. Ashcroft. 1955. *J. Gen. Microbiol.* 12: 387–395.
64. Friend, J. and T. W. Goodwin. 1954. *Biochem. J.* (*London*) 57: 434–437.
65. Fries, N. 1938. *Symbolae Botan. Upsalienses* 3 (2): 1–188.
66. Fries, N. 1942. *Svensk Botan. Tidskr.* 36: 451–466.
67. Fries, N. 1943. *Symbolae Botan. Upsalienses* 7 (2): 5–73.
68. Fries, N. 1945. *Arkiv Botan.* 32 (8): 1–9.
69. Fries, N. 1947. *Nature* (*London*) 159: 199.
70. Fries, N. 1948. *Hereditas* 34: 338–350.
71. Fries, N. 1949. *Svensk Botan. Tidskr.* 43: 316–342.
72. Fries, N. 1950. *Arkiv Botan.*, Ser. 2, 1: 271–287.
73. Fuller, R. C., R. W. Barratt, and E. L. Tatum. 1950. *J. Biol. Chem.* 186: 823–827.
74. Fuller, R. C. and E. L. Tatum. 1956. *Am. J. Botany* 43: 361–365.
75. Gaden, E. L., Jr., D. N. Petsiavas, and J. Winoker. 1954. *J. Agr. Food Chem.* 2: 632–638.
76. Garibaldi, J. A. and J. B. Neilands. 1955. *J. Am. Chem. Soc.* 77: 2429–2430.
77. Garnjobst, L. and E. L. Tatum. 1956. *Am. J. Botany* 43: 149–157.
78. Gäumann, E. and O. Jaag. 1950. *Phytopathol. Z.* 17: 218–228.
79. Georg, L. K. 1949a. *Proc. Soc. Exp. Biol. Med.* 72: 653–655.
80. Georg, L. K. 1949b. *Trans. N. Y. Acad. Sci.* II, 11: 281–286.
81. Georg, L. K. 1950. *Mycologia* 42: 683–692.
82. Georg, L. K. 1951. *Mycologia* 43: 297–309.
83. Giles, N. H. 1946. *J. Bacteriol.* 52: 504.
84. Goldschmidt, M. C. and H. Koffler. 1950. *Ind. Eng. Chem.* 42: 1819–1823.
85. Gorcica, H. J., W. H. Peterson, and H. Steenbock. 1935. *J. Nutrition* 9: 691–699.
86. Gottlieb, D. and G. M. Gilligan. 1946. *Arch. Biochem.* 10: 163–164.
87. Gould, B. S., A. A. Tytell, and H. Jaffe. 1942. *J. Biol. Chem.* 146: 219–224.
88. Greenberg, D. M. 1954. In D. M. Greenberg (ed.), *Chemical Pathways of Metabolism*, Vol. 2, p. 113–147. New York: Academic Press.
89. Grimm, P. W. and P. J. Allen. 1954. *Plant Physiol.* 29: 369–377.
90. Grob, E. C., V. Grundbacher, and W. H. Schopfer. 1954. *Experientia* 10: 378–379.
91. Guilliermond, A., M. Fontaine, and A. Raffy. 1935. *Compt. rend.* (*Paris*) 201: 1077–1080.
92. Gyorgy, P. 1954. In W. H. Sebrell, Jr. and R. S. Harris (eds.), *The Vitamins*, Vol. 1, p. 527–588. New York: Academic Press.
93. Haag, E. 1940. *Compt. rend. soc. phys. et hist. nat. Genève* 57: 136–139.
94. Hall, H. F. et al. 1953. *Appl. Microbiol.* 1: 124–129.
95. Halliday, W. J. and E. McCoy. 1955. *J. Bacteriol.* 70: 464–468.
96. Harris, D. L. 1952. *Arch. Biochem. Biophys.* 41: 294–304.
97. Harris, D. L. 1955. *Arch. Biochem. Biophys.* 57: 240–251.
98. Harris, D. L. 1956. *Arch. Biochem. Biophys.* 60: 35–43.
99. Hartelius, V. and K. Roholt. 1946. *Compt. rend. trav. lab. Carlsberg. Sér. physiol.* 24: 163–171.
100. Hata, T. et al. 1951. *J. Antibiotics* (*Japan*) Ser. 4A: 31–39.
101. Hawker, L. E. 1944. *Ann. Botany* 8: 79–90.
102. Henderson, L. M. 1949. *J. Biol. Chem.* 181: 677–685.
103. Hendlin, D., M. C. Caswell, V. J. Peters, and T. R. Wood. 1950. *J. Biol. Chem.* 186: 647–652.

104. Hendlin, D. and M. L. Ruger. 1950. *Science* 111: 541.
105. Herrick, J. A. and C. J. Alexopoulos. 1942. *Bull. Torrey Botan. Club:* 69: 569–572.
106. Herrick, J. A. and C. J. Alexopoulos. 1943. *Bull. Torrey Botan. Club:* 70: 369–371.
107. Hesseltine, C. W. et al. 1952. *J. Am. Chem. Soc.* 74: 1362.
108. Hesseltine, C. W. et al. 1953. *Mycologia* 45: 7–19.
109. Hickey, R. J. 1945. *Arch. Biochem.* 8: 439–447.
110. Hodgkin, D. C. et al. 1955. *Nature (London)* 176: 325–328.
111. Hodson, A. Z. 1949. *J. Biol. Chem.* 179: 49–52.
112. Hok, K. A. 1954. *Am. J. Botany* 41: 792–799.
113. Horowitz, N. H. 1950. *Advances in Genet.* 3: 33–71.
114. Huennekens, F. M. 1956. *Experientia* 12: 1–6.
115. Iguchi, N. 1952. *J. Agr. Chem. Soc. Japan* 26: 146–151.
116. Janicki, J. et al. 1954. *Acta Microbiol. Polon.* 3: 3–9.
117. Janke, A. 1939. *Zentr. Bakteriol. Parasitenk. Abt. II*, 100: 409–459.
118. Jansen, B. C. P. 1954. In W. H. Sebrell, Jr. and R. S. Harris (eds.), *The Vitamins*, Vol. 3, p. 426–442. New York: Academic Press.
119. Jennison, M. W., M. D. Newcomb, and R. Henderson. 1955. *Mycologia* 47: 275–304.
120. Kavanagh, F. 1942. *Bull. Torrey Botan. Club* 69: 669–692.
121. Keitt, G. W. and D. M. Boone. 1954. *Phytopathology* 44: 362–370.
122. Knight, B. C. J. G. 1945. *Vitamins and Hormones* 3: 108–228.
123. Kögl, F. and N. Fries. 1937. *Z. physiol. Chem. Hoppe-Seyler's* 249: 93–110.
124. Krampitz, L. O. and D. W. Woolley. 1944. *J. Biol. Chem.* 152: 9–17.
125. Lardy, H. A. 1954. In W. H. Sebrell, Jr. and R. S. Harris (eds.), *The Vitamins*, Vol. 2, p. 323–329, 342–351. New York: Academic Press.
126. Lardy, H. A. and H. Peanasky. 1953. *Physiol. Revs.* 33: 560–565.
127. Lavollay, J. and F. Laborey. 1941. *Ann. fermentations* 6: 129–142.
128. Leaver, F. W., J. Leal, and C. R. Brewer. 1947. *J. Bacteriol.* 54: 401–408.
129. Lein, J. S. and P. S. Lein. 1949. *J. Bacteriol.* 58: 595–599.
130. Leonian, L. H. and V. G. Lilly. 1938. *Phytopathology* 28: 531–548.
131. Leonian, L. H. and V. G. Lilly. 1939. *Phytopathology* 29: 592–596.
132. Leonian, L. H. and V. G. Lilly. 1940a. *Am. J. Botany* 27: 18–26.
133. Leonian, L. H. and V. G. Lilly. 1940b. *Plant Physiol.* 15: 515–525.
134. Leonian, L. H. and V. G. Lilly. 1942. *Am. J. Botany* 29: 459–464.
135. Leonian, L. H. and V. G. Lilly. 1945a. *J. Bacteriol.* 49: 291–298.
136. Leonian, L. H. and V. G. Lilly. 1945b. *West Va. Univ. Agr. Exp. Sta. Bull.* 319: 1–35.
137. Levine, H. et al. 1949. *Ind. Eng. Chem.* 41: 1665–1668.
138. Lewis, R. W. 1952. *Phytopathology* 42: 657–659.
139. Lilly, V. G. and H. L. Barnett. 1947. *Am. J. Botany* 34: 131–138.
140. Lilly, V. G. and H. L. Barnett. 1948. *J. Agr. Research* 77: 290–300.
141. Lilly, V. G., H. L. Barnett, and B. G. Anderson. 1953. *Science* 118: 548–549.
142. Lilly, V. G. and L. H. Leonian 1940. *Proc. West Va. Acad. Sci.* 14: 44–49.
143. Lilly, V. G. and L. H. Leonian. 1944. *Science* 99: 205–206.
144. Lindeberg, G. 1939. *Svensk Botan. Tidskr.* 33: 85–90.
145. Lindeberg, G. 1944. *Symbolae Botan. Upsalienses* 8 (2): 1–183.
146. Lindeberg, G. and K. Molin. 1949. *Physiol. Plantarum* 2: 138–144.
147. Lipmann, F. 1954. In W. H. Sebrell, Jr. and R. S. Harris (eds.), *The Vitamins*, Vol. 2, p. 598–625. New York: Academic Press.
148. Lochhead, A. G. and M. O. Burton. 1953a. *Congr. intern. microbiol., 6th Congr.*, 1: 298–301.
149. Lochhead, A. G. and M. O. Burton. 1953b. *Can. J. Botany* 31: 7–22.
150. Lwoff, A. 1936. *Ann. fermentations* 2: 419–427.

151. Mackinnon, J. E. 1942. *Bull. Torrey Botan. Club* 69: 21–26.
152. Mackinnon, J. E. and R. C. Artagaveytia-Allende. 1948. *J. Bacteriol.* 56: 91–96.
153. MacLaren, J. A. 1952. *J. Bacteriol.* 63: 233–241.
154. MacLeod, D. M. 1954. *Ann. N. Y. Acad. Sci.* 60 (1): 58–70.
155. McNutt, W. S., Jr. 1954. *J. Biol. Chem.* 210: 511–519.
156. McNutt, W. S., Jr. 1956. *J. Biol. Chem.* 219: 365–373.
157. Mandels, G. R. 1955. *Am. J. Botany* 42: 921–929.
158. Marczynski, R. 1943. *Am. Midland Naturalist* 30: 164–170.
159. Mariat, F. 1954. *Ann. inst. Pasteur* 87: 233–236.
160. Mariat, F. and E. Drouhet. 1953. *Ann. inst. Pasteur* 84: 659–662.
161. Marsh, P. B. and K. Bollenbacher. 1946. *Am. J. Botany* 33: 245–249.
162. Martin, G. J. 1951. *Biological Antagonism.* New York: The Blakiston Co. pp. 516.
163. Mathiesen, A. 1950. *Physiol. Plantarum* 3: 93–102.
164. Matsuda, T. 1949. *Vitamins (Kyoto)* 2: 121–124, 144–145. (*Chem. Abstr.* 45: 10300. 1951.)
165. Meissel, M. N. 1947. *Nature (London)* 160: 269–270.
166. Melin, E. 1948. *Trans. Brit. Mycol. Soc.* 30: 92–99.
167. Melin, E. 1954. *Svensk Botan. Tidskr.* 48: 86–94.
168. Melin, E. and V. S. R. Das. 1954. *Physiol. Plantarum* 7: 851–858.
169. Melin, E. and B. Nyman. 1941. *Arch. Mikrobiol.* 12: 254–259.
170. Minoura, K. 1950. *J. Fermentation Technol. (Japan)* 28: 125–129. (*Biol. Abstr.* 26: 9227. 1952.)
171. Mitchell, H. K. 1950. *Vitamins and Hormones* 8: 127–150.
172. Mitchell, H. K. and M. B. Houlahan. 1946. *Am. J. Botany* 33: 31–35.
173. Müller, F. W. 1941. *Ber. schweiz. botan. Ges.* 51: 165–256.
174. Müller, W. and W. H. Schopfer. 1937. *Compt. rend. (Paris)* 205: 687–689.
175. Nagata, Y., A. Matuda and M. Hiura. 1954. *Research Bull. Fac. Agr., Gifu Univ. (Japan)* No. 3: 100–101.
176. Neilands, J. B. 1952. *J. Am. Chem. Soc.* 74: 4846–4847.
177. Neilands, J. B. 1953. *J. Biol. Chem.* 205: 647–650.
177a. Neilands, J. B. 1957. *Bacteriol. Revs.* 73: 101–111.
178. Newell, G. W., W. H. Peterson, and C. A. Elvehjem. 1947. *Poultry Sci.* 26: 284–288.
179. Nicholas, D. J. D. 1952. *Analyst* 77: 629–642.
180. Nicholas, D. J. D. 1956. *J. Gen. Microbiol.* 15: 470–477.
181. Nielsen, N. and V. Hartelius. 1945. *Compt. rend. trav. lab. Carlsberg. Sér. physiol.* 24: 117–124.
182. Noecker, N. L. and M. Reed. 1943. *Am. Midland Naturalist* 30: 171–174.
183. Norkrans, B. 1950. *Symbolae Botan. Upsalienses* 11 (1): 1–126.
184. Novelli, G. D. 1953. *Physiol. Revs.* 33: 525–543.
185. Ødegård, K. 1952. *Physiol. Plantarum* 5: 583–608.
186. Otani, Y. 1952. *Ann. Phytopathol. Soc. Japan* 27: 9–15.
187. Partridge, C. W. H., D. M. Bonner, and C. Yanofsky. 1952. *J. Biol. Chem.* 194: 269–278.
188. Payette, A. and C. Perrault. 1944. *Can. J. Research C,* 22: 127–132.
189. Peltier, G. L. and R. Borchers. 1947. *J. Bacteriol.* 54: 519–520.
190. Perlman, D. 1948. *Am. J. Botany* 35: 36–41.
191. Perlman, D. 1951. *Am. J. Botany* 38: 652–658.
192. Peterson, W. H. and M. S. Peterson. 1945. *Bacteriol. Revs.* 9: 49–109.
193. Pidacks, C. et al. 1953. *J. Am. Chem. Soc.* 75: 6064–6065.
194. Plaut, G. W. E. 1954. *J. Biol. Chem.* 208: 513–520.
195. Pontecorvo, G. et al. 1953. *Advances in Genetics* 5: 141–238.
196. Quantz, L. 1943. *Jahrb. wiss. Botan.* 91: 120–168.

197. Rabinowitz, J. C. and E. E. Snell. 1953a. *Arch. Biochem. Biophys.* 43: 399–407.
198. Rabinowitz, J. C. and E. E. Snell. 1953b. *J. Am. Chem. Soc.* 75: 998–999.
199. Raper, K. B., R. D. Coghill, and A Hollaender. 1945. *Am. J. Botany* 32: 165–176.
200. Reid, E. B., E. G. Pritchett, and J. E. Cushing. 1952. *J. Biol. Chem.* 199: 443–450.
201. Reissig, J. L. 1952. *Arch. Biochem. Biophys.* 36: 234–235.
202. Renaud, J. and M. Lachaux. 1945. *Compt. rend. (Paris)* 221: 187–188.
203. Rickes, E. L. et al. 1948. *Science* 108: 634–636.
204. Robbins, W. J. 1938a. *Bull. Torrey Botan. Club* 65: 267–276.
205. Robbins, W. J. 1938b. *Proc. Natl. Acad. Sci. U. S.* 24: 53–56.
206. Robbins, W. J. 1939. *Am. J. Botany* 26: 772–777.
207. Robbins, W. J. 1941. *Proc. Natl. Acad. Sci. U. S.* 27: 419–422.
208. Robbins, W. J. and A. Hervey. 1955. *Mycologia* 47: 155–162.
209. Robbins, W. J., A. Hervey, and M. E. Stebbins. 1950. *Bull. Torrey Botan. Club* 77: 423–441.
210. Robbins, W. J. and F. Kavanagh. 1938a. *Am. J. Botany* 25: 229–236.
211. Robbins, W. J. and F. Kavanagh. 1938b. *Bull. Torrey Botan. Club* 65: 453–461.
212. Robbins, W. J. and F. Kavanagh. 1944. *Bull. Torrey Botan. Club* 71: 1–10.
213. Robbins, W. J. and V. Kavanagh. 1942. *Botan. Rev.* 8: 411–471.
214. Robbins, W. J. and R. Ma. 1941. *Bull. Torrey Botan. Club* 68: 446–462.
215. Robbins, W. J. and R. Ma. 1942a. *Am. J. Botany* 29: 835–842.
216. Robbins, W. J. and R. Ma. 1942b. *Arch. Biochem.* 1: 219–229.
217. Robbins, W. J. and R. Ma. 1942c. *Bull. Torrey Botan. Club* 69: 184–203.
218. Robbins, W. J. and R. Ma. 1942d. *Bull. Torrey Botan. Club* 69: 342–352.
219. Robbins, W. J. and R. Ma. 1942e. *Science* 96: 406–407.
220. Robbins, W. J. and R. Ma. 1943. *Bull. Torrey Botan. Club* 70: 190–197.
221. Robbins, W. J. and R. Ma. 1944. *Science* 100: 85–86.
222. Robbins, W. J. and R. Ma. 1945. *Am. J. Botany* 32: 509–523.
223. Robbins, W. J., J. E. Mackinnon, and R. Ma. 1942. *Bull. Torrey Botan. Club* 69: 509–521.
224. Robbins, W. J. and M. B. Schmidt. 1939. *Bull. Torrey Botan. Club* 66: 139–150.
225. Robinson, F. A. 1951. *The Vitamin B Complex.* New York: John Wiley and Sons, pp. 688.
226. Rother, W. 1954. *Arch. Mikrobiol.* 20: 89–108.
227. Rothwell, F. M. 1956. *Am. J. Botany* 43: 28–32.
228. Ryan, F. J., C. Kunin, R. Ballentine, and W. Maas. 1953. *J. Bacteriol.* 65: 434–439.
229. Salvin, S. B. 1949. *J. Infectious Diseases* 84: 275–283.
230. Sarasin, A. 1953. *Ber. schweiz. botan. Ges.* 63: 287–316.
231. Sarett, H. P. and V. H. Cheldelin. 1944. *J. Biol. Chem.* 156: 91–100.
232. Saunders, A. P., R. H. Otto, and J. C. Sylvester. 1952. *J. Bacteriol.* 64: 725–728.
233. Scheunert, A. and M. Schieblich. 1936. *Biochem. Z.* 286: 66–71.
234. Schmidt, E. L. 1951. *Soil Sci.* 71: 129–140.
235. Schmidt, E. L. and R. L. Starkey. 1951. *Soil Sci.* 71: 221–231.
236. Schopfer, W. H. 1934a. *Arch. Mikrobiol.* 5: 511–549.
237. Schopfer, W. H. 1934b. *Ber. deut. botan. Ges.* 52: 308–312.
238. Schopfer, W. H. 1942. *Compt. rend. soc. phys. et hist. nat. Genève* 59: 101–106.
239. Schopfer, W. H. 1943. *Plants and Vitamins.* Waltham, Mass.: Chronica Botanica Co., pp. 293.

240. Schopfer, W. H. 1944a. *Compt. rend. soc. phys. et hist. nat. Genève* 61: 147–152.
241. Schopfer, W. H. 1944b. *Compt. rend. soc. phys. et hist. nat. Genève* 61: 232–236.
242. Schopfer, W. H. 1944c. *Helv. Chim. Acta* 27: 468–471.
243. Schopfer, W. H. 1944d. *Helv. Chim. Acta* 27: 1017–1032.
244. Schopfer, W. H. and S. Blumer. 1938. *Arch. Mikrobiol.* 9: 305–367.
245. Schopfer, W. H. and S. Blumer. 1940. *Arch. Mikrobiol.* 11: 205–214.
246. Schopfer, W. H. and E. C. Grob. 1949. *Helv. Chim. Acta* 32: 829–838.
247. Schopfer, W. H. and M. Guilloud. 1945. *Z. Vitaminforsch.* 16: 181–296.
248. Schopfer, W. H. and W. Rytz, Jr. 1937. *Arch Mikrobiol.* 8: 244–248.
249. Sebrell, W. H., Jr. and R. S. Harris (eds). 1954. *The Vitamins.* New York: Academic Press, 3 vols.
250. Shemin, D., J. W. Corcoran, C. Rosenblum, and I. M. Miller. 1956. *Science* 124: 272.
251. Sherwood, M. B. and E. D. Singer. 1944. *J. Biol. Chem.* 155: 361–362.
252. Shimizu, S., S. Chara, and K. Minoura. 1952. *J. Fermentation Technol. (Japan)* 30: 13–22. (*Chem. Abstr.* 48: 3449. 1954.)
253. Shirakawa, H. S. 1955. *Am. J. Botany* 42: 379–384.
254. Shive, W. 1951. *Vitamins and Hormones* 9: 75–130.
255. Silver, W. and W. D. McElroy. 1954. *Arch. Biochem. Biophys.* 51: 379–394.
256. Sinclair, H. M. 1937. *Nature (London)* 140: 361.
257. Singer, T. P. and E. B. Kearney. 1954. *Advances in Enzymol.* 15: 79–139.
258. Smiley, K. L. et al. 1951. *Ind. Eng. Chem.* 43: 1380–1384.
259. Snell, E. E. 1948. *Physiol. Revs.* 28: 255–282.
260. Snell, E. E. 1951. In F. Skoog (ed.), *Plant Growth Substances*, p. 431–446. Madison: Univ. of Wisconsin Press.
261. Snell, E. E. and A. N. Rannefeld. 1945. *J. Biol. Chem.* 157: 475–489.
262. Srinivasan, K. S. and C. V. Ramakrishnan. 1952. *Biochim. et Biophys. Acta* 9: 156–160.
263. Stokes, J. L., J. W. Foster, and C. R. Woodward, Jr. 1943. *Arch. Biochem.* 2: 235–245.
264. Stokes, J. L., M. Gunness, and J. W. Foster. 1944. *J. Bacteriol.* 47: 293–299.
265. Stokstad, E. L. R. 1954. In W. H. Sebrell, Jr. and R. S. Harris (eds.), *The Vitamins*, Vol. 3, p. 89–121, 124–216. New York: Academic Press.
266. Stokstad, E. L. R., H. P. Broquist, and N. H. Sloane. 1955. *Ann. Rev. Microbiol.* 9: 111–144.
267. Stokstad, E. L. R., T. H. Jukes, J. Pierce, A. C. Page, Jr., and A. L. Franklin. 1949. *J. Biol. Chem.* 180: 647–654.
268. Strauss, B. S. 1951. *Arch. Biochem.* 30: 292–305.
269. Strehler, B. L. 1950. *J. Bacteriol.* 59: 105–111.
270. Struble, F. B. and G. W. Keitt. 1950. *Am. J. Botany* 37: 565–576.
271. Sussman, M. 1956. *Ann. Rev. Microbiol.* 10: 21–50.
272. Sussman, M. and S. G. Bradley. 1954. *Arch. Biochem. Biophys.* 51: 428–435.
273. Swartz, H. E. and L. K. Georg. 1955. *Mycologia* 47: 475–493.
274. Tanner, F. W., Jr., S. E. Pfeiffer, and J. M. Van Lanen. 1945. *Arch. Biochem.* 8: 29–36.
275. Tanner, F. W., Jr., C. Vojnovich, and J. M. Van Lanen. 1945. *Science* 101: 180–181.
276. Tatum, E. L. 1945. *J. Biol. Chem.* 160: 455–459.
277. Tatum, E. L. and G. W. Beadle. 1942. *Proc. Natl. Acad. Sci. U. S.* 28: 234–243.
278. Tatum, E. L. and G. W. Beadle. 1945. *Ann. Missouri Botan. Garden* 32: 125–129.

279. Tatum, E. L. and T. T. Bell. 1946. *Am. J. Botany* 33: 15–20.
280. Tatum, E. L., S. R. Gross, G. Ehrensvärd, and L. Garnjobst. 1954. *Proc. Natl. Acad. Sci. U. S.* 40: 271–276.
281. Tatum, E. L., M. G. Ritchey, E. V. Cowdry, and L. F. Wicks. 1946. *J. Biol. Chem.* 163: 675–682.
282. Thompson, R. C., E. R. Isbell, and H. K. Mitchell. 1943. *J. Biol. Chem.* 148: 281–287.
283. Timnick, M. B., V. G. Lilly, and H. L. Barnett. 1951. *Phytopathology* 41: 327–336.
284. Tomizawa, C. 1952. *Ann. Phytopathol. Soc. Japan* 27: 113–118.
285. Turel, F. 1952. *Phytopathol. Z.* 19: 307–342.
286. Umbreit, W. W. 1954. In W. H. Sebrell, Jr. and R. S. Harris (eds.), *The Vitamins*, Vol. 3, p. 234–242. New York: Academic Press.
287. Umbreit, W. W., W. A. Wood, and I. C. Gunsalus. 1947. *J. Biol. Chem.* 165: 731–732.
288. Van Lanen, J. M. and F. W. Tanner, Jr. 1948. *Vitamins and Hormones* 6: 163–224.
289. Villaneuva, J. R. 1955. *Nature (London)* 176: 465.
290. Villela, G. G. 1947. *Bull. soc. chim. biol.* 29: 763–767.
291. Villela, G. G. and A. Cury. 1950. *J. Bacteriol.* 59: 1–11.
292. Vinson, L. J., L. R. Cerecedo, R. P. Mull, and F. F. Nord. 1945. *Science* 101: 388–389.
293. Vishniac, H. S. 1955. *J. Gen. Microbiol.* 12: 464–472.
294. Vishniac, H. S. and S. W. Watson. 1953. *J. Gen. Microbiol.* 8: 248–255.
295. Wagner, R. P. 1949. *Proc. Natl. Acad. Sci. U. S.* 35: 185–189.
296. Wagner, R. P. and B. H. Guirard. 1948. *Proc. Natl. Acad. Sci. U. S.* 34: 398–402.
297. Wagner, R. P. and C. H. Haddox. 1951. *Am. Naturalist* 85: 319–330.
298. West, P. M. 1939. *Nature (London)* 144: 1050–1051.
299. Weygand, F., H. Klebe, and A. Trebst. 1954. *Z. Naturforsch.* 9b: 449–450.
300. White, N. H. 1941. *J. Australian Council Sci. Ind. Research* 14: 137–146.
301. Wickerham, L. J., M. H. Flickinger, and R. M. Johnston. 1946. *Arch. Biochem.* 9: 95–98.
302. Willstaedt, H. 1935. *Ber. deut. chem. Ges.* 68B: 333–340.
303. Wilson, A. N. and S. A. Harris. 1949. *J. Am. Chem. Soc.* 71: 2231–2233.
304. Wirth, J. C. and F. F. Nord. 1942. *Arch. Biochem.* 1: 143–163.
305. Witkus, E. R., F. Gentile, L. Kelly, and L. Murphy. 1954. *Can. J. Botany* 32: 503–505.
306. Wolf, D. E. et al. 1947. *J. Am. Chem. Soc.* 69: 2753–2759.
307. Woods, D. D. 1940. *Brit. J. Exp. Pathol.* 21: 74–89.
308. Woodward, V. W., J. R. DeZeeuw, and A. M. Srb. 1954. *Proc. Natl. Acad. Sci. U. S.* 40: 192–200.
309. Woolley, D. W. 1945. *Proc. Soc. Exp. Biol. Med.* 60: 225–228.
310. Woolley, D. W. 1950. *Proc. Soc. Exp. Biol. Med.* 75: 745–746.
311. Woolley, D. W. 1951. *J. Exp. Med.* 93: 13–24.
312. Woolley, D. W. 1952. *A Study of Antimetabolites.* New York: John Wiley and Sons, pp. 269.
313. Woolley, D. W. and J. R. McCarter. 1940. *Proc. Soc. Exp. Biol. Med.* 45: 357–360.
314. Woolley, D. W. and A. G. C. White. 1943. *J. Exp. Med.* 78: 489–497.
315. Wooster, R. C. and V. H. Cheldelin. 1945. *Arch. Biochem.* 8: 311–320.
316. Worley, C. L. 1942. *Plant Physiol.* 17: 278–288.
317. Wright, L. D. and E. L. Cresson. 1954. *J. Am. Chem. Soc.* 76: 4156–4160.
318. Wright, L. D., E. L. Cresson, and C. A. Driscoll. 1955. *Proc. Soc. Exp. Biol. Med.* 89: 234–236.

319. Wright, L. D., E. L. Cresson, K. V. Liebert, and H. R. Skeggs. 1952. *J. Am. Chem. Soc.* 74: 2004–2006.
320. Wright, L. D., E. L. Cresson, J. Valiant, D. E. Wolf, and K. Folkers. 1954a. *J. Am. Chem. Soc.* 76: 4160–4163.
321. Wright, L. D., E. L. Cresson, J. Valiant, D. E. Wolf, and K. Folkers. 1954b. *J. Am. Chem. Soc.* 76: 4163–4166.
322. Wright, L. D. and C. A. Driscoll. 1954. *J. Am. Chem. Soc.* 76: 4999–5000.
323. Wright, L. D. and P. A. Tavormina. 1954. In W. H. Sebrell, Jr. and R. S. Harris (eds.), *The Vitamins*, Vol. 3, p. 13–52. New York: Academic Press.
324. Wuest, H. M. 1954. In W. H. Sebrell, Jr. and R. S. Harris (eds.), *The Vitamins*, Vol. 1, p. 417–421. New York: Academic Press.
325. Wyss, O., V. G. Lilly, and L. H. Leonian. 1944. *Science* 99: 18–19.
326. Yagi, K., Y. Matsuoka, S. Kuyama, and M. Tada. 1956. *J. Biochem. (Tokyo)* 43: 93–100.
327. Yanofsky, C. 1952. *J. Biol. Chem.* 198: 343–352.
328. Yanofsky, C. 1954. *J. Bacteriol.* 68: 577–584.
329. Yanofsky, C. and D. M. Bonner. 1950. *Proc. Natl. Acad. Sci. U. S.* 36: 167–176.
330. Yanofsky, C. and D. M. Bonner. 1951. *J. Biol. Chem.* 190: 211–218.
331. Yaw, K. E. 1952. *Mycologia* 44: 307–317.
332. Yusef, H. 1953. *Bull. Torrey Botan. Club* 80: 43–64.
333. Zalokar, M. 1948. *Proc. Natl. Acad. Sci. U. S.* 34: 32–36.
334. Zalokar, M. 1950. *J. Bacteriol.* 60: 191–203.
335. Zalokar, M. 1955. *Arch. Biochem. Biophys.* 56: 318–325.
336. Zscheile, F. P. 1951. *Phytopathology* 41: 1115–1124.

11. Reproduction

$$T$$he attention of those interested in physiological aspects of the reproductive process in fungi has been focused almost exclusively on the problem of the initiation of sporulation, and these studies occupy the bulk of this chapter. The further development of the reproductive structures has in the main been treated as a problem in morphology, and, with some exceptions, its physiological and biochemical determinants are unknown.

Naturally enough, any physiological study tends to emphasize the one or two factors in reproduction which are manipulated by the experimenter. It should, of course, be obvious that reproduction requires that all genetic and environmental factors be favorable. This complexity is particularly apparent in ecological studies of the higher fungi (115).

Although some tentative conclusions on fungi in general have been proposed, it should be emphasized that any organism must be studied individually; there is no one "formula" for sporulation.

It is fair to say that most of our knowledge of reproduction in the fungi comes from essentially qualitative data. Sporulation occurs under some conditions, but not under others, and data may be reported in simple "yes" or "no" categories. No objection can be made to this procedure in general; however, it is becoming clear that some problems require quantitative data on the intensity of sporulation. This is particularly true of nutritional studies, in which the response is likely to be quantitative rather than all-or-none.

It has not been possible, with present information, to consider the physiology of resting structures, e.g., chlamydospores and sclerotia, separately or in detail. Chlamydospore formation is probably a response to unfavorable environmental conditions (214, 215, 231, 266).

356

Sclerotium development is, of course, often a prelude to sexual reproduction and may be expected to be influenced by the same factors,
allowing for a higher nutritional level entailed by the larger mass (1,
249, 252, 290). The "sclerotia" of myxomycetes are purely resting
structures and appear to develop primarily as a response to desiccation (110, 154, 166).

The geotropism of large sporophores is an established fact of observation (27, 49, 50, 278), but its physiological correlates have not yet
been uncovered.

Finally, in the list of omissions, purely genetic problems are not here
considered. These are, of course, most important to a thorough understanding of reproduction, but they lie outside the field of physiology.

1. LIGHT

The reactions of fungi to visible and ultraviolet light are of three
principal types: inductive effects, inhibition, and trophic responses.
Inductive effects include both absolute light requirements for initiation
or maturation of reproductive structures and quantitative responses,
i.e., an increase in the number of reproductive structures upon illumination.

Light is absolutely required for the formation of various types of
reproductive organs in certain species. As examples we may cite the
requirement of light for the formation of sporophores in the Agaricales (226, 253), of perithecia (264), of apothecia (248, 283, 319), of
basidiocarps in the Gasteromycetes (298), of pycnidia (105, 183, 185),
of sporangia in the Mucorales (221), of conidia in the Mucorales (18)
and Fungi Imperfecti (97, 159), and of Myxomycete sporangia (117).
Smith (263) reviews still other examples.

As might be expected, the effect of light is not always exerted at the
same point in these diverse fungi: to take two extremes, light is required for the first steps in sexual reproduction in *Pyronema confluens* (248) and for all stages in *Polyporus arcularius* (110a), but only
for pileus development in some Agaricales (27, 106). Whether all
developmental stages of the *Coprinus lagopus* sporophore require light
is in dispute (196, 294).

Light of the visible range often has the effect of increasing the number of reproductive structures formed (82, 89, 120, 124, 130, 264).
More striking effects of this type are induced by ultraviolet light in
certain ascomycetes and Fungi Imperfecti; both sexual and asexual
structures are affected (11, 66, 160, 198, 232, 262, 271, 272, 273, 274).
Ultraviolet effects are exerted in the cell, not in the medium (74, 271),

and cannot be ascribed to temperature effects (262). The effective wavelength is still in doubt (88, 232), but it is probably longer than the well-known "germicidal" wavelength of 254 mμ. Ultraviolet light, of course, in high doses represses both sporulation and growth.

Most of the work on induction and stimulation by visible light has been at best semi-quantitative. The available data on the action spectrum indicate fairly consistently that the effective wavelengths are in the blue region of the spectrum (37, 83, 117, 198, 248, 250a, 263, 277, 319). Morphogenetic action on *Coprinus lagopus* is maximal at 440–460 mμ (255), close to the peak of the action spectrum of phototropism.

The amount of light needed for inductive response is similarly uncertain; it is much less than normal daylight exposure (105, 168). The maximal effect of light on fruiting in *Coprinus lagopus* is exerted by exposure for 5 seconds at 0.1 foot-candles intensity (196).

So much attention has been focused on the positive effects of light that the possibly more important inhibitory action may be overlooked. Induction of conidiation in *Choanephora cucubitarum* requires a dark as well as a light period (18), and light of wavelength below 580 mμ appears to be inhibitory (80). Dark periods are required for maximum production of ascospores by *Diaporthe phaseolorum* (286) and of conidiophores by *Alternaria brassicae* (312). For the Myxomycete *Didymium eunigripes*, Leith (189, 190) presents evidence for both induction and inhibition of sporangial formation by different wavelengths. Finally, the type of zonation in which spore production is greater during dark periods (see below) is most easily interpreted as resulting from a light inhibition of sporulation.

The diurnal cycle of *Pseudoperonospora humuli* and other downy mildew fungi in nature involves both light inhibition and light stimulation, although effects on the host metabolism cannot be excluded (315). Other diurnal cycles in nature (314, 316) and the frequently observed nocturnal production of conidia (161, 162) may also result from light inhibition, although the dominant factor in noctural formation of spores by *Sclerospora* spp. has been thought to be water (306, 307).

Zonation—the formation of fruiting structures in concentric rings on an agar surface or on the host plant—is a common phenomenon and may best be considered at this point, since light is usually the primary environmental factor. The occurrence of light-induced zonation is reviewed by Hall (214) and by Hafiz (123). A simple explanation is rendered difficult by the observation that two extreme types of response to an alternation of light and dark periods are known, viz.:

Type 1. The fungus sporulates well in darkness, much less or not at all during the light period. Examples are *Cephalothecium roseum* (145) and *Sclerotinia fructicola* (124).

Type 2. The organism, e.g., *Fusarium* spp. (29, 124, 320), sporulates poorly in the dark and forms a zone of spores after even a brief exposure to light.

It seems necessary to explain Type 1 reactions as the result of light inhibition of sporulation. Type 2 responses are more difficult; we may propose, however, that light inhibits mycelial growth—reports of such inhibition are reviewed in Chapter 13—and that stimulation to sporulation results from the check upon vegetative growth. The light effect in these fungi is exerted only upon actively growing hyphal tips (29, 45, 264).

Temperature alternations also induce the formation of zones of reproductive structures (94, 123, 131, 250a, 320); it appears, especially from the data of Ellis (94) and Hafiz (123), that the immediate stimulus for sporulation is a check in growth.

Zonation of reproductive structures in some fungi is dependent neither upon light nor upon temperature fluctuations (40, 75, 146, 206); presumably nutritional factors are involved here, but they are not understood. The pH of the medium has an effect (212, 240).

Any unitary hypothesis to explain the action of light on sporulation will have to take account of several facts, viz.:

1. The indifference of many fungi to light stimuli.
2. The high specificity of the response. Thus, the formation of conidia of *Choanephora cucurbitarum* is governed by light, but the development of the sporangia is independent of light (18), and the formation of zygospores is inhibited by light at low temperature (20).
3. The fact that light may either stimulate or inhibit sporulation.
4. The partial replacement of the light effect by high temperature (29, 37, 185, 212), by periodic exposure to air (206), by treatment with oxidizing agents (82), or by mechanical agitation (37, 275).
5. The observation of Houston and Oswald (159) that *Helminthosporium gramineum* forms spores in the dark if growing on host tissue but requires light for sporulation on agar media.
6. The extreme sensitivity of the response (29, 168), which suggests that an enzymatic mechanism is triggered by the stimulus.
7. The frequent efficacy of ultraviolet radiation, known to be injurious to all organisms in sufficient dose. Sporulation of *Alternaria solani* is induced by either ultraviolet or mechanical damage (74).

A unified theory should take as its principal postulate that light is inhibitory to one or more regulatory systems which in the normal culture prevent or retard reproduction and favor continued vegetative growth. That is to say, there is in truth no such thing as stimulation by light in the induction of reproductive activity; instead, growth is checked and the chain of events so initiated leads to reproduction if other factors are not limiting. Alternative explanations are possible, and several have held specifically that stimuli for reproduction do not check growth; nevertheless, the weight of the evidence favors the hypothesis presented. Confirmation must wait upon studies which determine accurately and quantitatively the effects of light on both reproduction and growth simultaneously.

Phototropic responses are common in fungi; examples include the orientation of basidiomycete sporophores (37, 278, 298) and of asci or ascocarps (8, 41, 53). Gametic phototaxis has been reported (180). The most dramatic and the most thoroughly investigated phototropic reaction is that of the sporangiophores of *Phycomyces* spp. and *Pilobolus* spp., observed also in others of the Mucorales (96).

Consideration of phototropism in *Phycomyces* spp. should begin with the observation of Blaauw (32), confirmed by Castle (68), that a sporangiophore illuminated equally from two sides exhibits a measurable temporary acceleration in vertical growth, the "light growth reaction." A more recent study of this phenomenon (86) brings out several important aspects: (1) the response probably involves no net increase in total growth; (2) the effect of the light stimulus depends in a predictable fashion on the level of illumination prior to the application of the stimulus; (3) there is a latent period of about 2.5 seconds; and (4) the magnitude of the increased growth is proportional to the strength of the stimulus. This last observation is important in showing that the light growth reaction is not an all-or-none, or threshold, reaction.

Granted that illumination can increase growth, the fact of phototropism—unequal growth—requires some mechanism whereby the sporangiophore wall distal to the light grows more rapidly than the proximal wall. Castle (71, 72) argues that the size, shape, and refractive index of the sporangiophore combine in the "lens effect" to concentrate unilateral illumination in such a way that the distal region of the protoplasm receives more light than the proximal. This is consistent with the observation that sporangiophores immersed in paraffin oil become negatively phototropic (14, 48), with the effect of ultraviolet light (66a), and with the demonstration by Banbury (14) that illumination of only one edge of the sporangiophore causes localized extension of that side and consequent curvature.

This theory, and others of the same general type (32), fail, as Delbrück and Reichardt (86) point out, to account for the extreme localization of the receptor which is implied by the unidirectionality of the phototropic curvature; if the entire growing zone were affected, unilateral illumination and the known spiral habit of growth would combine to generate a helical shape of the sporangiophore.

The action spectrum of phototropism in *Phycomyces blakesleeanus* (Figure 1) and *Pilobolus kleinii* has a maximum at about 430–500 mμ (54, 55, 69, 99). This has often been taken as evidence for a carotenoid receptor pigment, carotenoids being present in these fungi and absorbing maximally in the same region of the spectrum (297). However, as Galston (107) points out, riboflavin or a derivative of it could with equal probability be the receptor. Carotenogenesis in *Phycomyces* sp. can be suppressed, at least below detectable levels, without impairment of the phototropic response (241).

Nor are there any solid data on chemical mediators between the light absorbing system and the growth (or wall extension) response. In higher plants it has been suggested that auxin (indoleacetic acid) is involved, but its role is not yet entirely certain (107). Fungi do produce auxin (Chapter 8), and it is found in fact in the sporangiophore of *Phycomyces nitens* (151), but there is at present no reason to accept—and there is considerable evidence against—an auxin theory of phototropism in the fungi (14).

Phototropism in *Pilobus kleinii* has been investigated especially by Buller (53), who reviews the earlier literature. In this species a pig-

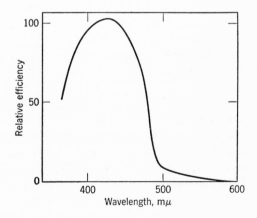

Figure 1. The action spectrum of phototropism in *Phycomyces blakesleeanus.* Redrawn from Castle (69), by permission of The Rockefeller Institute for Medical Research.

mented "ocellus" at the base of the subsporangium is believed to be the photosensitive area, but it should be noted that photosensitivity is apparent before the formation of the subsporangium (222) and that other phototropic forms do not have an "ocellus."

Other light responses of *Pilobolus* spp. may be briefly noted. Light induces the formation of the trophocyst, or sporangial primordium, of some isolates; Page (221) raises the possibility of a flavin receptor in this reaction. Second, alternations of light and dark, or of temperature, set up a periodic rhythm in the development of sporangia (175, 196). This rhythm, once established, persists for two or three 24-hour cycles after the removal of the stimulus (254, 291). Finally, the forcible discharge of the sporangium is hastened by light (55).

Light has other effects on the reproductive apparatus, notably a positive effect on the size and septation of macrospores of *Fusarium* spp. (130, 264). Pigment production is also enhanced by light (189, 264), but attempts to connect this phenomenon with induction of sporangia in *Didymium eunigripes* were unsuccessful (189).

Exposure to light, unless appropriate filters and cooling devices are used, means an increase in temperature. Thus, the apparent attraction of myxomycete pseudoplasmodia to light is a temperature effect; the plasmodium moves toward a source of heat along a temperature gradient as small as 0.05°C per centimeter (35). Similarly, a negative phototropic response of *Phycomyces* sp. to intense light was shown by Castle (70) to be a heat effect. Many reports on light effects have not included quantitative determinations of the ambient temperature; possibly some of the apparent complexities may disappear when such data become available.

2. TEMPERATURE

Only two generalizations can be formulated with respect to temperature and sporulation. First, the temperature range permitting reproduction is usually narrower than that permitting growth. Second, each spore form has its own temperature optimum, which may or may not coincide with that of vegetative growth or of other spore forms of the same species.

The relative narrowness of the temperature limits of reproduction is virtually universal in the fungi. Examples include both sexual and asexual spores in the phycomycetes (174) and ascomycetes (148, 194, 281), sporophores of basidiomycetes (5, 182), and spores of the Fungi Imperfecti (2, 204, 287). Usually the differences in range are not

great; *Phoma apiicola* is an extreme with mycelial growth on agar at
5–28°C but pycnidium formation only at 13–26° (25).

The optimum temperature for sporulation of a given species may
be either close to the growth optimum, as in *Piricularia oryzae* (149)
and *Rhizopus* spp. (303), or rather different, lower in *Fusarium con-
glutinans* (287) and higher in *Sphaerotheca pannosa* (194).

Different spore forms of a given species often differ in their temperature requirements. Thus, the zygotes of *Sporodinia grandis* and of
Saprolegnia mixta form at lower temperatures than do the corresponding asexual sporangia (172, 173). Perithecia of *Aspergillus* spp. (171,
256) and of *Ceratostomella* (*Ophiostoma*) *fimbriata* (17) are produced
in abundance at relatively high temperature and are replaced by conidia at lower. *Pseudopeziza ribis* forms conidia at 20–24°C, microconidia at lower temperatures (33).

It must be borne in mind that most of these data are only semi-
quantitative, and that the same uncertainties are involved in the definition of an optimum for reproduction as in the definition of a growth
optimum (Chapter 1). One such complication is illustrated by the
findings of Robbins and Schmitt (245) on *Phycomyces blakesleeanus:*
the failure of progametes to form at 26°C is the result of the accumulation of acid in the medium before the two strains meet. Presumably,
progametes would form at 26° if the pH were controlled.

One may speculate that sexual stages adapted to survive a cold winter are formed prefentially at low temperature, and that fungi which
must live through a hot and dry season will tend to form their dormant
spores at higher temperature. However, there is as yet no ecological
or physiological data bearing on this possibility, and the failure of
sexual reproduction in *Neurospora crassa* at high temperature (305)
speaks against the idea. The asci of *Erysiphe graminis* mature somewhat more rapidly if chilled briefly, but they do mature without cold
treatment (114). The apothecia of *Claviceps purpurea* appear, from
limited data, to develop only if the sclerotia bearing them are exposed
to low temperature (170). Zygospore formation in *Thamnidium* spp.
is also best at low temperature (150).

Temperature-induced zonation has been considered elsewhere
with the conclusion that the positive effect of high or low temperature on spore formation is probably effected by retardation of
mycelial growth.

Morphological effects of temperature are easily observed; as examples we may cite the finding that the conidia of *Cercospora sesami* are
larger at an intermediate temperature than at higher or lower tem-

peratures (79), and the effect of temperature on the morphology of the conidial fructification in *Aspergillus janus* (239).

3. WATER RELATIONS

Satisfactorily quantitative determinations of the moisture requirements of sporulation are rare. Indications are, however, that specific fungi have specific requirements. At one extreme, *Colletotrichum lindemuthianum* and other anthracnose fungi sporulate much more profusely at high than at low humidity (318). Conidiation in *Sclerospora* spp. (306, 307) and in *Peronospora destructor* (317) is also favored by high humidity. The formation of sexual structures in ascomycetes and basidiomycetes (10, 111, 283) and sporangium formation in *Sporodinia grandis* (147) are believed to proceed more rapidly at high than at low moisture levels.

Somewhat lower humidities are tolerated, but are not necessarily required, by some of the rust fungi (318), by *Botrytis cinerea* (140), and by *Bremia lactucae* (228). Species of *Alternaria* in culture sporulate rather better if the culture is allowed to dry out (90, 233). Finally, the powdery mildew fungi appear to be relatively independent of humidity or possibly favored in both sexual and asexual reproduction by lower atmospheric moisture (47, 125, 318). Asci of *Erysiphe graminis* are reported to form only if the perithecium is alternately wetted and dried (76), but it seems doubtful that this is a general requirement among the powdery mildew fungi.

The weight of evidence favors the generalization that reproductive processes, in most fungi at least, are favored by moderate rather than high atmospheric humidity. However, one may see from even a superficial glance at the original work that accurate control of the environment and quantitative determination of the intensity of sporulation have not usually been achieved.

Different spore forms of a single species occasionally show different humidity responses; examples include the two asexual spore forms of *Choanephora cucurbitarum* (19) and the zygote and sporangium of *Sporodinia grandis* (13, 172, 247).

Miscellaneous reported effects of atmospheric humidity include negative hydrotropism of sporangiophores (172, 300), transitory acceleration of the growth of sporangiophores of *Phycomyces nitens* at high humidity (300), and changes in the size or morphology of conidia (98, 119) and sporophores (39).

Spore discharge in fungi has been studied in some detail; the summary of Ingold (162) has been supplemented more recently by investigations of spore discharge in rust fungi (220) and *Nigrospora sphaerica* (302). With the possible exception of "drop-excretion" discharge in basidiomycetes (50, 51, 52, 229), all these discharge mechanisms rely in some way on either substrate or atmospheric water. We infer that osmotic forces are at work. In immature asci (162) and in the immature active layer of *Sphaerobolus* spp. (299) glycogen is abundant; its disappearance at maturity suggests that the uptake of water is mediated by enzymatic conversion of the osmotically inactive polysaccharide to osmotically active sugars. Such a mechanism, if suitably quantified, might be extended to cover all discharge mechanisms which depend on increasing turgor of a cell or cell layer.

The elevation of the receptaculum in the Phallales is accompanied by disappearance of glycogen, but in this instance the increase in size may be true growth (58, 95). Elongation of the *Agaricus campestris* sporophore has been shown to be a growth process rather than simple water uptake (36).

4. OXYGEN, CARBON DIOXIDE, AND VOLATILE SUBSTANCES

It is a common observation that sporulation is reduced in closed containers (82, 126, 185) and that submerged mycelium fails to develop spores (84, 201, 321). Although this is usually ascribed to an oxygen deficit, it seems more likely that the accumulation of carbon dioxide is the critical factor. *Pyronema confluens*, for example, does not fruit in a closed tube, but if alkali is present to absorb carbon dioxide, perithecia develop (248). Carbon dioxide accumulation inhibits the asexual reproduction of *Choanephora cucurbitarum* (19) and sporophore development in *Agaricus campestris* (181) and *Collybia velutipes* (227).

In large culture containers the sporulation of *Piricularia oryzae* is dependent upon aeration of the vessel; Henry and Anderson (149) suggest that metabolically produced ammonia is the inhibitory factor. An unidentified volatile substance, probably of microbial origin, inhibits sporophore development in *Psalliota campestris* (199).

The best available data on the oxygen requirement for sporulation are those of Denny (87). Any reduction of oxygen below atmospheric pressure delays the appearance of perithecia. Further, visually estimated mycelial growth appeared to be normal at oxygen pressures too low for reproduction. The same phenomenon—a higher oxygen requirement for fruiting than for growth—is reported by Ternetz (283).

Plant pathogenic fungi usually, and with an obvious ecological advantage, form their reproductive structures on the surface of the host. It is reasonable to speculate that either the higher oxygen requirement or the lower carbon dioxide tolerance of sporulation is the mechanism that ensures extramatrical sporulation; it is significant that active anaerobic respiratory mechanisms are common in the lower phycomycetes and the genus *Fusarium,* forms in which resting spores or conidia often occur within host tissues (93).

Several *Penicillium* spp. sporulate in shaken cultures, but the determinants are not known (102, 122). In our laboratory we have observed that *Fusarium solani* forms abundant macrospores in shake culture, particularly in certain media. Conidia of *Streptomyces griseus* appear in aerated cultures at the time of autolysis (67).

In a very brief note, Richards (242) reported that ozone appears to stimulate sporulation in *Alternaria* spp.; *Mycosphaerella citrullina* forms more pycnidia if exposed to ozone, but the spores are non-viable.

The striking effect of carbon dioxide and bicarbonate on sporangial development in *Blastocladia* and *Blastocladiella* spp. is considered later in this chapter.

5. ACIDITY

Although pH has definite effects on reproduction, no unitary hypothesis or generalization is possible; as mentioned elsewhere (Chapter 1), pH effects are exerted in a variety of ways. Furthermore, the common failure to determine the final pH casts doubt on much of the available data. In general, it appears that the pH range for sporulation is somewhat narrower than that for growth (5, 20, 23, 192, 193, 276). Within the physiological range, an acid reaction is often less favorable than a neutral or mildly alkaline reaction (170, 245, 276), but exceptions to this rule have been reported (5, 156).

Lockwood (192) showed that in several fungi perithecia form over a wide range of pH values, but asci mature only at neutral or slightly alkaline reaction. This finding is of particular importance because often the only data submitted in pH studies concern macroscopically visible fruit bodies.

In *Mycosphaerella pinodes* pycnidia, pseudothecia, and chlamydospores are reported to have different pH optima (266), but other data on the same species are not easily reconciled with this claim (23). The pH range for sporangium formation by *Physarum polycephalum* is narrowed by high temperature cultivation (116).

6. CARBON NUTRITION

The classical work on the influence of nutrition, and for that matter of all environmental factors, on reproduction in fungi is that of Klebs (172, 173, 174). In relation to nutrition, his major points may be formulated briefly:

1. Sexual and asexual reproduction are most likely to occur when a vigorous mycelium exhausts its nutrients or is transferred to a medium low in nutrients.

2. Formation of fruiting structures therefore occurs over a narrower range of nutrient concentrations than does vegetative growth.

3. Fruiting structures of different fungi, or different spore forms of the same fungus, have specific requirements for nutrient concentration. In *Saprolegnia mixta* and *Sporodinia grandis* the sexual spore stage requires a higher nutrient level than the asexual stages.

With minor modifications—most importantly that the concentration of the carbon source is usually more decisive than that of other nutrients—these generalizations still stand. It would be tedious indeed to list all the fungi that conform to Klebs' predictions; some of the more significant modern results with pure cultures deserve, however, some attention.

Suppression, relative or absolute, of reproductive stages at higher concentrations of carbohydrate—concentrations that permit heavy vegetative growth—has been found in studies of ascomycetes (59, 137, 141), phycomycetes (267), and imperfect fungi (44, 45, 82). More extensive reviews of the literature on this topic are available (140, 185).

The same phenomenon can be demonstrated more neatly by transfer experiments, in which a mycelium growing in a concentrated medium is transferred to or allowed to grow into a more dilute medium. Such experiments almost always confirm the first principle of Klebs (6, 81, 82, 142, 185, 219, 296). In general, transfer to water is less successful than transfer to a dilute medium.

Finally, it follows from the first principle that spore formation should occur at the point in the culture cycle at which the carbon source is substantially exhausted; studies on myxomycetes (62, 238) demonstrate this principle clearly. The same response has been shown in *Melanconium fuligineum* in a different manner: heavy inoculation of an agar surface accelerates sporulation because of the more rapid utilization of nutrients (285).

It has often, of course, been found in studies of particular fungi that Klebs' first principle does not hold or is overridden by other factors (78, 184, 185); this is best documented in studies on fleshy basidiomycetes (185, 226), in which the relatively greater mass of the fruit body might be expected a priori to change the usual relation.

The mechanism by which high nutrient concentrations inhibit sporulation is not definitely established. One cause which must be operative in some cultures is simply the accumulation of toxic metabolites; effects of culture age and of concentration have been attributed to this phenomenon (104, 251). It seems, however, unlikely that such accumulation can be a general explanation of the concentration effect. For the present, we may posit, no doubt oversimplifying the picture, that a limitation of growth per se is the stimulus to reproduction, and that the effect of high nutrient levels is merely to postpone the onset of starvation.

The second principle of Klebs is a corollary of the first. Granted that some minimum amount of growth must precede fruiting, and that too high concentrations delay or inhibit fruiting, then the range of concentration suitable for reproduction must necessarily be narrower than that suitable for vegetative growth.

The third principle, of specificity of requirements, is obvious insofar as different species are concerned. Even within a species, however, different spore forms have different requirements; examples include the sexual and asexual stages of Sporodinia grandis (13, 96) and the alternative asexual stages of Blakeslea trispora (112).

The concentration of the carbon source affects the type of asexual spore formed in Cytosporina ludibunda and related fungi (218) and the septation of macrospores of Fusarium sp. (157).

The type of carbon source used strongly influences the formation of reproductive structures, both sexual and asexual. In general, it is found that oligosaccharides and polysaccharides support more fruiting than do the simple hexoses; cellulose, a very slowly available compound for most fungi, is the best carbon source for sporulation of some forms (85, 319).

The mechanism of specific carbon source effects has been thoroughly investigated by Hawker and her collaborators (133, 137, 141) and by Bretzloff (42). There seems little doubt that the primary mechanism is actually a concentration effect, i.e., it exemplifies Klebs' first principle. Essentially, provision of a slowly utilizable carbon compound is the same as use of a low concentration of a more available sugar. That is, the fungus hydrolyzes (or phosphorylates) the complex carbohydrate slowly, the result being a steady maintenance of a low con-

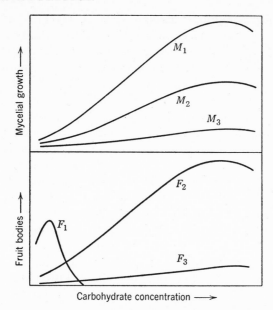

Figure 2. The response of growth and fruiting to carbohydrate concentration. M_1 and F_1, mycelial growth and fruiting, respectively, with a readily available carbohydrate; M_2 and F_2, the same with a more slowly available carbohydrate; M_3 and F_3, the same with a very slowly utilizable carbohydrate. From Hawker (140), by permission of the University of London Press, Ltd.

centration of hexose. This point is shown admirably in Figure 2, from Hawker (140).

This principle explains many of the effects of particular carbon sources on reproductive activity. Thus, the optimum sucrose concentration for fruiting in *Melanospora destruens* is ten times that in *M. zamiae,* indicating—and this is borne out by sucrase assays—that the latter species utilizes sucrose much more rapidly than the former (141).

Hawker (137, 138) has suggested that the favorable effect of sucrose is in part to be attributed to the formation of phosphorylated hexoses from it by the fungus. This, it must be admitted, seems unlikely and is certainly not established by data available at present; phosphorylated compounds have, however, been tentatively implicated in studies on stimulation by contaminating organisms (p. 372).

7. NITROGEN NUTRITION

The concentration of the nitrogen source in the medium is important for fruiting, i.e., an optimum concentration can be determined under specified conditions; account must be taken, however, of the carbon source and its concentration (257, 305). In general, high concentrations of nitrogen suppress sporulation (109, 153, 250).

Specific effects of particular compounds are often reported but cannot be combined in a general theory; pH effects and contamination of organic nitrogen sources with growth factors unduly complicate interpretation of experimental data. Asparagine, so often a favorable source of nitrogen for growth, generally represses sporulation (5, 28, 208, 226, 257). The asparagine effect may arise from ammonia accumulation or may be another example of the competition between vegetative growth and reproductive activity. It should also be noted that asparagine, of the sources of nitrogen tested, is the best for perithecium formation in *Diaporthe phaseolorum* (286).

The effect of hypoxanthine (or guanine) on zygospore formation in *Phycomyces blakesleeanus* is probably not specifically a reproductive phenomenon and is considered elsewhere (Chapter 12). The very striking positive effect of low concentrations of histamine on zygospore formation in *P. blakesleeanus* (250) merits reinvestigation.

8. MINERAL NUTRITION

Numerous observations, some of which have been mentioned in Chapter 9, attest to the influence of mineral nutrition on sporulation; these are reviewed in more detail by Foster (101). As expected, either deficiencies or excesses of particular elements reduce or inhibit sporulation; these reactions require no further comment. The important question is whether the mineral requirements for sporulation differ qualitatively or quantitatively from those for growth.

There is no evidence for a qualitative difference, i.e., sporulation never requires an element which is non-essential to growth. Quantitatively, however, there are differences, most of which are subsumed in the generalization that sporulation is reduced by partial deficiencies in certain elements much more than growth is reduced by the same deficiency. Experiments with copper almost invariably show that sporulation of *Aspergillus niger* is reduced drastically by a deficiency which has a small or even no effect on dry weight (205, 211, 246, 269, 270, 313). This copper effect is found also in work with *Penicillium* spp. and *Phoma betae* (205). The effect of copper deficiency on spore pigment has been noted earlier (Chapter 9).

The same phenomenon—sharp reduction in sporulation with only a small decrease in growth—occurs with partial deficiencies of iron (246) or manganese (26, 155, 193, 269, 270). It is a general rule, even with a major element like potassium (209) or magnesium (230), that sporulation is prevented by deficiencies which do not completely inhibit growth. That is, sporulation requires more of a mineral than the minimum necessary for measurable growth.

Much has been made of the repressive effect of added zinc on sporulation (38, 113, 152, 165, 246). Toxicity, of course, is possible, but it seems more likely that in the concentrated media used, provision of zinc simply postpones sporulation by allowing more luxuriant vegetative growth.

The response of *Chaetomium globosum* to calcium (21, 22) is an apparent contradiction to the principle that sporulation and growth have qualitatively the same mineral requirements: calcium does not affect dry weight but does increase perithecium formation. The fact that many fungi, including other *Chaetomium* spp., do respond in growth to calcium and the possibility that calcium is an antagonist rather than a nutrient (Chapter 9) are arguments against immediate revision of the principle. It may be noted that sporulation in *Aspergillus niger* is inhibited by high levels of NaCl without any apparent effect on growth (201).

One rather serious reservation attaches to most of the results mentioned in this section—sporulation is estimated visually rather than measured quantitatively. A second limitation is that most of the work has been with *Aspergillus niger;* study of other organisms might cause us to modify some of the conclusions now accepted.

9. VITAMINS AND UNIDENTIFIED FACTORS

Under this head, we consider only substances which exert a nonspecific effect; hormones and hormone-like substances are taken up in the next section.

The data available show that most fungi which require biotin or thiamine need more of the vitamin for adequate sporulation than they do for measurable vegetative growth (17, 134). Thus, *Sordaria fimicola* in a medium without biotin makes about one-third maximal growth but does not form perithecia unless the vitamin is supplied; in this species biotin deficiency results in abortion or failure to mature of ascospores (16).

However, one cannot specify an "optimum" level of a vitamin without reference to other constituents of the medium. *Ceratostomella fimbriata*, for example, requires thiamine in proportion to the total concentration of the medium (17). Conversely, it is well established, for numerous fungi, that provision of thiamine raises the level of carbohydrate optimal for fruiting (59, 132, 133, 134, 135, 140). The simplest explanation of this phenomenon is based on the fact that thiamine accelerates glucose utilization (136); this is in accord with our previous conclusion that exhaustion of the carbon source is required for the initiation of reproduction.

There is no conclusive evidence that any fungus requires a known vitamin specifically for the reproductive process and independently of growth effects. The available data can more or less satisfactorily be explained on the basis of the two generalizations just stated: that fruiting may require more of a vitamin than measurable growth, and that vitamins may accelerate sugar utilization and so hasten the onset of reproduction. However, at least the possibility of a more direct relation is raised by the work of Barnett and Lilly (17) on *Ceratostomella fimbriata;* a thiamine-starved mycelium begins to fruit if transferred to a thiamine solution containing no other nutrients.

Unidentified materials in crude plant and microbial extracts often increase fruiting. Examples include both sexual reproduction (164, 186, 226, 259, 322) and asexual reproduction (121, 144, 169).

It is often found, usually as a result of accidental contamination of cultures, that other fungi and bacteria encourage fungal reproduction. Many such cases are reviewed by Asthana and Hawker (6) and by Raper (236); other instances may also be cited here (24, 143, 243, 258). However, there is no assurance that these are vitamin effects— pH, for example, or nutrient concentration could be the decisive factor. Stimulation of conjugation of *Zygosaccharomyces* spp. by *Aspergillus niger* has been described; the effect of the fungus is replaced by a mixture of riboflavin and an organic acid (216, 217). The association in nature of *Gonatorrhodiella highlei* with *Nectria coccinea* may be explained by some chemical influence of the latter on the reproduction of *G. highlei* (7).

Another series of investigations, reviewed by Buston and Khan (60), suggests that the effect of contaminating organisms on perithecium formation in *Melanospora destruens* and *Chaetomium globosum* is to be attributed to organic phosphorus compounds, particularly 3-phosphoglyceric acid, liberated by the inducing fungus. Whether this is a direct effect is, however, not yet clear. In *C. globosum,* perithecial production is associated with a high level of organic phosphate esters (61).

Several apparently unrelated synthetic organic compounds are reported to increase sporulation without a corresponding increase in growth; possibly the effect is an antagonism of inhibitors present in the growth medium (158, 295).

10. SPECIFIC REPRODUCTIVE HORMONES

Hormones—endogenous chemical substances which influence or determine reproductive processes—have been unequivocally demonstrated in certain of the Oomycetes, notably *Achlya* spp., by J. R. Raper, who reviewed the entire field in 1952 (236).

Certain strains of *Achlya bisexualis* and *A. ambisexualis* are "heterothallic," i.e., the male and female sex organs—antheridia and oogonia, respectively—are borne on different thalli. This type of heterothallism is perhaps more clearly described as haplodioecism. When thalli of opposite sex are in the same medium, the development of the sex organs is under hormonal control. The hormones whose existence and action must be inferred from convincing physiological and morphogenetic evidence are summarized in Table 1. It is apparent that the

Table 1. The Sexual Hormones of *Achlya* Spp.

Hormone	Produced by	Action
A, A^2	Female vegetative plant	Induces antheridial hyphae on male plant
A^1	Male vegetative plant	Augments A and A^2
A^3	Male vegetative plant	Depresses action of A and A^2
B	Antheridial hyphae	Induces oogonial initials on female plant
C	Oogonial initials	(a) Induces antheridial hyphae to grow along a concentration gradient toward the oogonium; (b) induces the formation and delimitation of the antheridium in the male plant
D	Antheridia	Induces (a) delimitation of the oogonium and (b) differentiation of oospheres

* From Raper (236).

entire sequence of events leading up to fertilization is under specific and sequential hormonal control. The hormones are produced in extremely small amounts, so small that only a start has been made toward chemical fractionation (237). Biological activities indicate that the battery of hormones produced by *A. bisexualis* is not fully identical with that of *A. ambisexualis* (234).

Others of the Saprolegniacae—*Thraustotheca clavata* and the "homothallic" *Achlya americana*—are governed in reproduction by similar but not identical hormone systems (235, 236). Preliminary evidence of a hormonal system in *Sapromyces reinschii* has also been obtained (30).

Burgeff (56) studied *Mucor mucedo,* a heterothallic Zygomycete which copulates by the fusion of identical gametangia when two strains of opposite mating type are brought together. The two morphologically identical types are called for convenience plus (+) and minus (−); historically, at least, the term heterothallism is appropriately applied to this situation. Burgeff showed that at least two of the steps in reproduction are initiated by a chemical, diffusible stimulus. Zygophore development in each strain is begun only when the opposite strain is close enough for the stimulus to reach receptive hyphae. The somewhat clumsy term "telemorphosis" has been used for this reaction. A second reaction, also initiated by a diffusible metabolite, has been called "zygotropism": zygophores of each strain bend toward those of the opposite strain, preparatory to contact and fusion.

These reactions in *Mucor mucedo* have been confirmed (167, 176, 225) and found also to prevail in *Pilobolus crystallinus* (177, 178). Limited evidence suggests that the zygotropic reaction is effected by a volatile product (15, 167). Such a material would have to be of very high activity to induce a differential growth response in an organ as small as the zygophore.

Banbury (14) reports evidence that zygophores of the same strain in *Mucor mucedo* exert a mutual repulsion, also by a volatile substance. This recalls the numerous examples of "aversion" or "barrage": a zone of inhibition develops between certain colonies of the same or of different species and not between others. This phenomenon is reviewed by Cayley (73) and by Takemaru (282); little physiological work has been done, although it has been suggested that a volatile material is responsible (293).

A final type of interstrain chemical influence is shown by a slight increase in oxygen uptake when (+) and (−) mycelia occupy the same respirometric vessel (57).

None of the hormonal activities of the Zygomycetes has been separated physiologically or biochemically from the others; it is not yet possible, therefore, to describe any such elegant sequential mechanism as that of *Achlya* spp.

At this point we may briefly mention the numerous attempts to find physiological or biochemical differences between (+) and (−) strains of species of the Mucorales. Various workers have claimed that the strains differ in growth rate on certain sugars, sucrase or catalase formation, lipid or carotenoid content, sugar content, reductive capacity, susceptibility to poisons, and so on. Most of these are reviewed by Ronsdorf (250) and by Raper (236). Study of the original papers and of the divergent results obtained leaves one skeptical of all this work.

The most recent claimed difference, a color reaction with strong alkali (292), was found invalid almost immediately (46). Enzyme differences between opposite mating types in *Neurospora crassa* (103) and growth differences between (+) and (−) strains of *Ustilago* spp. (284) are exposed, until confirmed, to a similar skepticism.

The long debate over the existence of perithecium-inducing hormones in *Neurospora sitophila* is reviewed by Raper (236); the work of Aronescu (3, 4) in particular seems conclusively negative. This conclusion must stand unless challenged by new evidence. However, in *Glomerella cingulata*, like *Neurospora* a member of the Sphaeriales, there is preliminary evidence for a diffusible metabolite which induces the formation of perithecia (92, 200). Since the various steps of sexual reproduction in *G. cingulata* are gene-controlled (308), it is perhaps not too fanciful to envision a one gene–one hormone relation.

In *Ascobolus stercorarius* the induction of ascogonia and other early steps in sexual reproduction are controlled by diffusible materials, presumably hormones (31). The branching of the trichogyne in *Neurospora sitophila* (9) and the suppression of conidiation in *Glomerella cingulata* by filtrates from perithecial cultures (309) are also very probably hormone effects. There is no evidence as yet for hormonal mechanisms in basidiomycetes.

The literature on the chemical stimulus for the aggregation of myxamoebae in the Acrasiae has been thoroughly reviewed by K. B. Raper (238) and by Sussman (279). The substance responsible has been termed acrasin (34) and has now been separated from the cells; it was found to consist of two components and to be destroyed by some system, probably an enzyme, of the cell (260, 280). It is especially interesting that acrasin not only attracts scattered myxamoebae but also stimulates them in turn to produce acrasin; the effect is that of a chain reaction which extends the range of the chemotactic system much beyond any possible range based only on diffusion from a single point.

11. METABOLISM AND REPRODUCTION

Throughout this chapter we have stressed the concept that the major stimulus to reproduction is exhaustion of the medium. However, many different metabolic changes occur at the same time in a culture, and the possibility must be kept in mind that one or more of these changes is the primary stimulus to spore formation. In particular, the mycelium begins to autolyze (Chapter 1). In yeast colonies on agar, ascospores appear in that part of the colony which is undergoing autolysis (191). Now, it is possible that some factor in normal cells is released by their death and reaches a threshold concentration high enough to induce sporulation. This possibility also relates to the stimulation of reproduction by ultraviolet radiation; it has been suggested (286) that cells killed by the radiation release into the medium substances which favor perithecial development. This line of investigation deserves more attention than it has so far received.

Other metabolic changes are often coincident with the onset of reproduction, e.g., changes in respiratory rate (118), appearance of tyrosinase (153) or other enzymes (100), and formation of carotenoids (57a, 150a, 288, 289). The correlation between tyrosinase formation and protoperithecium development in *Neurospora crassa* is the most striking, in that a wide variety of environmental factors suppress both enzyme activity and reproductive capacity, but it cannot yet be said that the relationship is causal (304).

One obvious physiological necessity in sporulation is the transport of materials—presumably in a soluble form—from the mycelium to the developing spores. In *Aspergillus flavus* the appearance of conidia is coincident with a marked fall in mycelial nitrogen, easily interpreted as resulting from transport (224). Phosphate transfer is even more dramatic in *A. niger;* during spore formation mycelial phosphorus declines as much as 80 per cent, and at least some of this phosphorus appears in the spores (12).

The transport of materials into fruiting structures may be more complete than it is usually thought to be. Thus, microscopic observation of *Ascochyta pisi* in an infected leaf shows the mycelium apparently devoid of protoplasm at the time of formation of pycnidia (43).

Blastocladia pringsheimii in its natural habitat forms two types of sporangia: thin-walled zoosporangia and thick-walled resting sporangia. In pure culture, resting sporangia form only at very high carbon dioxide pressure, specifically in 99.5 per cent CO_2 at pH 5.5 (63). This discovery initiated an important series of investigations by Cantino and collaborators of members of the related genus *Blastocladiella*. These investigations have been reviewed by Cantino (64), and a brief summary is in order at this point.

Blastocladiella emersonii zoospores develop into a two-celled thallus consisting of a basal rhizoidal cell and an apical sporangium. The sporangium is either a thin-walled papillate zoosporangium or a thick-walled resistant sporangium. In pure culture the type of sporangium formed is controlled by bicarbonate; virtually all thalli develop resistant sporangia if 0.01 M bicarbonate is supplied to the medium. The problem, thus, is not that of initiation of reproduction but of the type of reproduction which occurs. The explanation proposed by Cantino for the effect of bicarbonate is that the ion in some way interferes with the oxidative decarboxylation of α-ketoglutaric acid. Concurrently, several other enzyme activities of the plant disappear and a new polyphenol oxidase becomes evident. The upshot of these changes is a reorientation of metabolism resulting in the formation of the resistant sporangium; this involves necessarily the synthesis of the chitin, melanin, and γ-carotene characteristic of the resistant sporangium.

These conclusions have been buttressed by study of a mutant strain of *B. emersonii* which does not, even with bicarbonate, form resistant sporangia. Crude cell-free extracts from the mutant strain are devoid of aconitase and of the enzyme system oxidizing α-ketoglutarate via the cytochromes (65). Precisely these enzymes are postulated to be required in the normal strain for the expression of the bicarbonate effect.

The rather elaborate metabolic hypotheses which have been erected in the course of this study of reproduction in *Blastocladiella* are somewhat provisional and speculative; further investigation is clearly necessary. But, however the hypothesis may have to be modified later, it should be recognized as a bold and imaginative attempt to correlate biochemical events and patterns of morphogenesis.

12. THE SPORULATION OF PLANT PATHOGENS

Reproductive processes in fungi pathogenic to or deriving their food from higher plants are difficult to study but pose at least two interesting questions: the influence of the host on sporulation in general, and specific relations between the host and particular stages in the life cycle of the pathogen.

It is a commonplace that plant pathogens often lose their capacity to sporulate during continuous artificial culture. Of course, this may only be an example of the very common phenomenon, not at all restricted to plant pathogens, of the selection in culture of non-sporulating variants (77, 127, 128, 138, 207, 213, 223, 244, 310, 311). However, there is still the question of how contact with the host—often only in a single passage—acts to select for restoration of reproductive capacity.

It seems probable that specific features of the food plant promote sporulation over and above any selective process. We have already noted the important observation that the host tissue replaces a light requirement for the sporulation of *Helminthosporium gramineum*. Experiments with autoclaved plant extracts are of little real help in working out the problem, since labile materials are probably involved. Cold sterilization of natural substrates by, for example, propylene oxide appears much more promising as a technique (129, 265). Analogously, the insect pathogen *Cordyceps militaris* forms perithecia on dead pupae but not on autoclaved pupae (261).

The relation of the host to sporulation has one other dimension, the influence of the host on the intensity and on the type of sporulation. This has been most thoroughly studied in relation to the appearance of the telial stage of rust fungi. From the work of Morgenthaler (210) and Waters (301) we may list factors that encourage or hasten the development of the telial stage:

1. Exposure of the host to low temperature or to slow drying.
2. Starvation of the host by dark incubation.
3. Growth of the fungus on a partially resistant host.
4. Wounding of the inoculated leaf.
5. Transfer of detached leaves from sucrose to water.

Obviously, effects of this type must be indirect for the obligate parasites, but the pattern seems clear that telia form under conditions of privation; the analogy to Klebs' conclusions is close. The factor that is dominant in nature is not known; it is most probable that drying out in autumn is dominant (91, 108), but simple starvation cannot be dismissed.

Perithecial formation in *Erysiphe graminis*—also an obligate parasite —is more rapid if the relatively resistant older leaves of the host are infected (114). Here again, we may speculate that resistance of the host accelerates the reproduction of the pathogen by depriving it of some essential factor.

Host influences on spore size merit brief mention. Uredospores of rust fungi are smaller on a resistant host than on a susceptible one, and they are smaller if the host is held under conditions unfavorable to its growth (187, 188, 268). Similar findings on other fungi have been summarized by Fischer and Gäumann (98).

13. CONCLUSIONS

The major barrier to generalizing about reproduction in the fungi is the repeated failure of experimental work to discriminate adequately between growth and sporulation; too often, only one is measured quantitatively. Consequently, many of our hypotheses on reproduction must leave open the possibility that the factor concerned may act on growth rather than specifically on the formation of spores.

The most inclusive generalization is that reproduction is initiated by factors which check the growth of an established mycelium without too drastically poisoning its metabolism. Studies on the effect of light, especially ultraviolet light, are the most important evidence, in view of the well-established lethal action of radiation. Gross mutilation by scraping or cutting induces sporulation in a few fungi (195, 206, 233); in scraped cultures of *Alternaria solani* Kunkel (179) observed that conidiophores arise from broken hyphae. Initiation of sporulation as the result of temperature changes, exhaustion of nutrients, and various treatments of the host plant of a pathogen are all consistent with the injury hypothesis.

Granted that a check in growth initiates sporulation, we can only speculate on the intimate mechanism. Perhaps the most promising suggestion is that injured or moribund cells release substances which act on surviving cells and divert them into a new developmental path.

It must be noted that a contrary hypothesis, that sporulation requires specific positive stimuli rather than the negative stimulation of injury, could easily be built up. In particular, the ready sporulation of many fungi on the living host plant or on cold-sterilized plant materials argues for nutritional factors which must be present in some threshold amount to permit sporulation or which must be synthesized by the fungus before reproductive activity can begin.

Less inclusive, but important and more firmly based, generalizations may be listed briefly in conclusion:

1. Reproduction occurs, in general, over a narrower range of environmental conditions than does growth; this is especially clear in findings on temperature, acidity, mineral, and oxygen requirements. The optimum for reproduction may be the same as or different from that of mycelial growth.

2. Klebs' principle, that reproduction is favored by depriving an established mycelium of one or more nutrients, is valid in general, especially for carbon and nitrogen sources. It must be qualified only to take account of the fact that for some nutrients—certain vitamins and minerals—the absolute amount required for sporulation is higher than that which supports growth. This qualification essentially only changes the definition of the "established mycelium" to indicate that it must have certain materials in high concentration.

3. There is no conclusive evidence for a specific nutritional factor required for sporulation and not required at all for growth. Specific endogenous hormones are, however, established as vital to reproductive activity, or at least to the orderly development of reproductive structures once these are initiated.

4. The requirements for sexual and asexual reproduction in a given

species are usually not alike, so that in a sense the two types compete. Apart from the relatively trivial generalization that the larger sexual structures must require more energy for their formation than the (usually) smaller asexual organs, there is as yet no good evidence for a universal difference between sexual and asexual reproduction; this possibility, however, should surely be explored. A few instances have been noted in which two different asexual structures have different requirements.

BIBLIOGRAPHY

1. Allington, W. B. 1936. *Phytopathology* 26: 831–844.
2. Ames, A. 1915. *Phytopathology* 5: 11–19.
3. Aronescu, A. 1933. *Mycologia* 25: 43–54.
4. Aronescu, A. 1934. *Mycologia* 26: 244–252.
5. Aschan, K. 1954. *Physiol. Plantarum* 7: 571–591.
6. Asthana, R. P. and L. E. Hawker. 1936. *Ann. Botany* 50: 325–343.
7. Ayres, T. T. 1941. *Mycologia* 33: 178–187.
8. Backus, M. P. 1937. *Mycologia* 29: 383–386.
9. Backus, M. P. 1939. *Bull. Torrey Botan. Club* 66: 63–76.
10. Badcock, E. C. 1943. *Trans. Brit. Mycol. Soc.* 26: 127–132.
11. Bailey, A. A. 1932. *Botan. Gaz.* 94: 225–271.
12. Bajaj, V., S. P. Damle, and P. S. Krishnan. 1954. *Arch. Biochem. Biophys.* 50: 451–460.
13. Baker, R. E. D. 1931. *New Phytologist* 30: 303–316.
14. Banbury, G. H. 1952. *J. Exp. Botany* 3: 77–85, 86–94.
15. Banbury, G. H. 1955. *J. Exp. Botany* 6: 235–244.
16. Barnett, H. L. and V. G. Lilly. 1947a. *Am. J. Botany* 34: 196–204.
17. Barnett, H. L. and V. G. Lilly. 1947b. *Mycologia* 39: 699–708.
18. Barnett, H. L. and V. G. Lilly. 1950. *Phytopathology* 40: 80–89.
19. Barnett, H. L. and V. G. Lilly. 1955. *Mycologia* 47: 26–29.
20. Barnett, H. L. and V. G. Lilly. 1956. *Mycologia* 48: 617–627.
21. Basu, S. N. 1951. *J. Gen. Microbiol.* 5: 231–238.
22. Basu, S. N. 1952. *J. Gen. Microbiol.* 6: 199–204.
23. Baumann, G. 1953. *Kühn-Arch.* 67: 305–383.
24. Benedek, T. 1943. *Mycologia* 35: 222–242.
25. Bennett, C. W. 1921. *Mich. State Univ. Agr. Exp. Sta. Tech. Bull.* 53: 1–40.
26. Bertrand, D. and A. De Wolf. 1955. *Compt. rend. (Paris)* 241: 1877–1880.
27. Biffen, R. H. 1898. *J. Linnean Soc. London, Botany* 34: 147–172.
28. Bille-Hansen, E. 1953. *Physiol. Plantarum* 6: 523–528.
29. Bisby, G. R. 1925. *Mycologia* 17: 89–97.
30. Bishop, H. 1940. *Mycologia* 32: 505–529.
31. Bistis, G. 1956. *Am. J. Botany* 43: 389–394.
32. Blaauw, A. H. 1914. *Z. Botan.* 6: 641–703.
33. Blodgett, E. W. 1936. *Phytopathology* 26: 115–152.
34. Bonner, J. T. 1947. *J. Exp. Zool.* 106: 1–26.
35. Bonner, J. T., W. W. Clarke, Jr., C. L. Neely, Jr., and M. K. Slifkin. 1950. *J. Cellular Comp. Physiol.* 36: 149–158.
36. Bonner, J. T., K. K. Kane, and R. H. Levey. 1956. *Mycologia* 48: 13–19.
37. Borriss, H. 1934. *Planta* 22: 644–684.

38. Bortels, H. 1927. *Biochem. Z.* 182: 301–358.
39. Bose, S. R. 1943. *Mycologia* 35: 33–46.
40. Brandt, W. H. 1953. *Mycologia* 45: 194–208.
41. Brefeld, O. 1877. *Botan. Ztg.* 35: 386.
42. Bretzloff, C. W., Jr. 1954. *Am. J. Botany* 41: 58–67.
43. Brewer, D. and B. H. MacNeill. 1953. *Can. J. Botany* 31: 739–744.
44. Brian, P. W. and H. G. Hemming. 1950. *Trans. Brit. Mycol. Soc.* 33: 132–141.
45. Brown, W. 1925. *Ann. Botany* 39: 373–408.
46. Brucker, W. 1955. *Arch. Protistenk.* 100: 339–350.
47. Buchheim, A. 1928. *Ber. deut. botan. Ges.* 46: 167–180.
48. Buder, J. 1918. *Ber. deut. botan. Ges.* 36: 103–105.
49. Buller, A. H. R. 1909 *Researches on Fungi,* Vol. 1. London: Longmans, Green and Co., pp. 287.
50. Buller, A. H. R. 1922. *Researches on Fungi,* Vol. 2. London: Longmans, Green and Co., pp. 492.
51. Buller, A. H. R. 1924. *Researches on Fungi,* Vol. 3. London: Longmans, Green and Co., pp. 611.
52. Buller, A. H. R. 1933. *Researches on Fungi,* Vol. 5. London: Longmans, Green and Co., pp. 416.
53. Buller, A. H. R. 1934. *Researches on Fungi,* Vol. 6. London: Longmans, Green and Co., pp. 513.
54. Bünning, E. 1937a. *Planta* 26: 719–736.
55. Bünning, E. 1937b. *Planta* 27: 583–610.
56. Burgeff, H. 1924. *Botan. Abh., Heft* 4: 3–135.
57. Burnet, J. H. 1953. *New Phytologist* 52: 58–64, 86–88.
57a. Burnet, J. H. 1956. *New Phytologist* 55: 45–49.
58. Burt, E. A. 1897. *Botan. Gaz.* 24: 73–92.
59. Buston, H. W. and S. N. Basu. 1948. *J. Gen. Microbiol.* 2: 162–172.
60. Buston, H. W. and A. H. Khan. 1956. *J. Gen. Microbiol.* 14: 655–660.
61. Buston, H. W. and B. Rickard. 1956. *J. Gen. Microbiol.* 15: 194–197.
62. Camp, W. G. 1937. *Am. J. Botany* 24: 300–303.
63. Cantino, E. C. 1949. *Am. J. Botany* 36: 95–112.
64. Cantino, E. C. 1956. *Mycologia* 48: 225–240.
65. Cantino, E. C. and M. T. Hyatt. 1953. *J. Bacteriol.* 66: 712–720.
66. Carlile, M. J. 1956. *J. Gen. Microbiol.* 14: 643–654.
66a. Carlile, M. J. 1957. *Nature (London)* 180: 202.
67. Carvajal, F. 1947. *Mycologia* 39: 426–440.
68. Castle, E. S. 1929. *J. Gen. Physiol.* 12: 391–400.
69. Castle, E. S. 1931. *J. Gen. Physiol.* 14: 703–711.
70. Castle, E. S. 1932. *J. Gen. Physiol.* 15: 487–489.
71. Castle, E. S. 1933. *J. Gen. Physiol.* 17: 41–62.
72. Castle, E. S. 1935. *Cold Spring Harbor Symposia Quant. Biol.* 3: 224–229.
73. Cayley, D. M. 1931. *J. Genet.* 24: 1–63.
74. Charlton, K. M. 1953. *Trans. Brit. Mycol. Soc.* 36: 348–355.
75. Chaudhuri, H. 1923. *Ann. Botany* 37: 519–539.
76. Cherewick, W. J. 1944. *Can. J. Research C,* 22: 52–86.
77. Chilton, S. J. P. 1943. *Mycologia* 35: 13–20.
78. Chona, B. L. 1932. *Trans. Brit. Mycol. Soc.* 17: 221–228.
79. Chowdhury, S. 1944. *J. Indian Botan. Soc.* 23: 91–106.
80. Christenberry, G. A. 1938. *J. Elisha Mitchell Sci. Soc.* 54: 297–310.
81. Claussen, P. 1912. *Z. Botan.* 4: 1–64.
82. Coons, G. H. 1916. *J. Agr. Research* 5: 713–769.
83. Cooper, D. C. and C. L. Porter. 1928. *Phytopathology* 18: 881–899.
84. Couch, J. N. 1939. *Am. J. Botany* 26: 119–130.
85. Darby, R. T. and G. R. Mandels. 1955. *Plant Physiol.* 30: 360–366.

86. Delbrück, M. and W. Reichardt. 1956. In D. Rudnick (ed.), *Cellular Mechanisms in Differentiation and Growth*, p. 3–44. Princeton: Princeton Univ. Press.
87. Denny, F. E. 1933. *Contribs. Boyce Thompson Inst.* 5: 95–102.
88. Diener, U. L. 1955. *Phytopathology* 45: 141–143.
89. Dillon Weston, W. A. R. 1936. *Trans. Brit. Mycol. Soc.* 20: 112–115.
90. Dimock, A. W. and J. H. Osborn. 1943. *Phytopathology* 33: 372–381.
91. Doran, W. L. 1921. *Mass. Agr. Exp. Sta. Bull.* 202: 39–66.
92. Driver, C. H. and H. E. Wheeler. 1955. *Mycologia* 47: 311–316.
93. Elarosi, H. 1956. *Nature (London)* 177: 665–666.
94. Ellis, M. 1931. *Trans. Brit. Mycol. Soc.* 16: 102–114.
95. Errera, L. 1885. *Mem. Cour. Acad. Roy. Belg.* 37 (3): 1–50.
96. Falck, R. 1901. *Beitr. Biol. Pflanz.* 8: 213–306.
97. Fikry, A. 1932. *Ann. Botany (London)* 46: 29–70.
98. Fischer, E. and E. Gäumann. 1929. *Biologie der pflanzenbewohndenen parasitischen Pilze.* Jena: Gustav Fischer, pp. 428.
99. Flint, L. A. 1942. *Am. J. Botany* 29: 672–674.
100. Flügge, H. 1939. *Vorratspflege u Lebensmittelforsch.* 2: 237–256. (*Zentr. Bakteriol. Parasitenk. Abt. II*, 102: 401. 1940.)
101. Foster, J. W. 1939. *Botan. Rev.* 5: 207–239.
102. Foster, J. W., L. E. McDaniel, H. B. Woodruff, and J. L. Stokes. 1945. *J. Bacteriol.* 50: 365–368.
103. Fox, A. S. and W. O. Gray. 1950. *Proc. Natl. Acad. U. S.* 36: 538–546.
104. Frank, M. C., C. T. Calam, and P. H. Gregory. 1948. *J. Gen. Microbiol.* 2:70–79.
105. Fulkerson, J. F. 1955. *Phytopathology* 45: 22–25.
106. Galleymore, H. B. 1949. *Trans. Brit. Mycol. Soc.* 32: 315–317.
107. Galston, A. W. 1950. *Botan. Rev.* 16: 361–378.
108. Gassner, G. and W. Franke. 1938. *Phytopathol. Z.* 11: 517–570.
109. Geach, W. L. 1936. *J. Council Sci. Ind. Research (Australia)* 9: 77–87.
110. Gehenio, P. M. 1944. *Biodynamica* 4: 359–368.
110a. Gibson, I. A. S. and J. Trapnell. 1957. *Trans. Brit. Mycol. Soc.* 40: 213–220.
111. Girbardt, M. 1952. *Flora, N. F.* 39: 477–525.
112. Goldring, D. 1936. *Ann. Missouri Botan. Garden* 23: 527–541.
113. Gollmick, F. 1936. *Zentr. Bakteriol. Parasitenk. Abt. II*, 93: 421–442.
114. Graf-Marin, A. 1934. *Cornell Univ. Agr. Exp. Sta. Mem.* 157: 1–48.
115. Grainger, J. 1946. *Trans. Brit. Mycol. Soc.* 29: 52–64.
116. Gray, W. D. 1939. *Am. J. Botany* 26: 709–714.
117. Gray, W. D. 1953. *Mycologia* 45: 817–824.
118. Gregg, J. H. 1950. *J. Exp. Zool.* 114: 173–196.
119. Gregory, P. H. 1939. *Trans. Brit. Mycol. Soc.* 23: 24–54.
120. Greis, H. 1937. *Botan. Arch.* 38: 113–151.
121. Grossbard, E. 1954. *Phytopathology* 44: 110–111.
122. Grosser, A., H. Kundtner-Schwarzkopf, and K. Bernhauer. 1950. *Arch. Mikrobiol.* 15: 247–252.
123. Hafiz, A. 1951. *Trans. Brit. Mycol. Soc.* 34: 259–269.
124. Hall, M. P. 1933. *Ann. Botany* 47: 543–578.
125. Hammarlund, J. C. 1925. *Hereditas* 6: 1–126.
126. Hampson, C. R. 1954. *J. Bacteriol.* 67: 739–740.
127. Hansen, H. N. 1938. *Mycologia* 30: 442–455.
128. Hansen, H. N. and W. C. Snyder. 1944. *Science* 99: 264–265.
129. Hansen, H. N. and W. C. Snyder. 1947. *Phytopathology* 37: 369–371.
130. Harter, L. L. 1939. *Am. J. Botany* 26: 234–243.
131. Hatch, W. R. 1936. *Mycologia* 28: 439–444.
132. Hawker, L. E. 1936. *Ann. Botany* 50: 699–717.
133. Hawker, L. E. 1939a. *Ann. Botany* 3: 455–468.

134. Hawker, L. E. 1939b. *Ann. Botany* 3: 657–675.
135. Hawker, L. E. 1942. *Ann. Botany* 6: 631–636.
136. Hawker, L. E. 1944. *Ann. Botany* 8: 79–90.
137. Hawker, L. E. 1947a. *Ann. Botany* 11: 245–260.
138. Hawker, L. E. 1947b. *Nature (London)* 159: 136.
139. Hawker, L. E. 1948. *Ann. Botany* 12: 77–79.
140. Hawker, L. E. 1950. *Physiology of Fungi.* London: University of London Press, Ltd., pp. 360.
141. Hawker, L. E. and S. D. Chaudhuri. 1946. *Ann. Botany* 10: 185–194.
142. Hawn, E. J. and T. C. Vanterpool. 1953. *Can. J. Botany* 31: 699–710.
143. Hazen, E. L. 1947. *Mycologia* 39: 200–209.
144. Hazen, E. L. 1951. *Mycologia* 43: 284–296.
145. Hedgecock, G. C. 1906. *Ann. Rept. Missouri Botan. Garden* 17: 115–117.
146. Hein, I. 1930. *Am. J. Botany* 17: 143–151.
147. Heintzeler, I. 1939. *Arch. Mikrobiol.* 10: 92–132.
148. Henriksson, L. E. and J. F. Morgan-Jones. 1951. *Svensk Botan. Tidskr.* 45: 648–657.
149. Henry, B. W. and A. L. Anderson. 1948. *Phytopathology* 38: 265–278.
150. Hesseltine, C. W. and P. Anderson. 1956. *Am. J. Botany* 43: 696–703.
150a. Hesseltine, C. W. and R. F. Anderson. 1957. *Mycologia* 49: 449–452.
151. Heyn, A. N. J. 1935. *Proc. Koninkl. Akad. Wetenschap. Amsterdam* 38: 1074–1081.
152. Hickey, R. J. and H. D. Tresner. 1952. *J. Bacteriol.* 64: 891–892.
153. Hirsch, H. M. 1954. *Physiol. Plantarum* 7: 72–97.
154. Hodapp, E. L. 1942. *Biodynamica* 4: 33–46.
155. Hofmann, E., H. Scheck, and K. Saffert. 1950. *Biochem. Z.* 320: 126–135.
156. Hopkins, E. F. 1922. *Phytopathology* 12: 390–393.
157. Horne, A. S. and J. H. Mitter. 1927. *Ann. Botany* 41: 519–547.
158. Horsfall, J. G. and S. Rich. 1955. *Trans. N. Y. Acad. Sci.* II, 18: 69–80.
159. Houston, B. R. and J. W. Oswald. 1946. *Phytopathology* 36: 1049–1055.
160. Hutchinson, A. H. and M. R. Ashton. 1930. *Can. J. Research* 3: 187–198.
161. Ingold, C. T. 1933. *New Phytologist* 32: 178–196.
162. Ingold, C. T. 1946. *Trans. Brit. Mycol. Soc.* 29: 43–51.
163. Ingold, C. T. 1953. *Dispersal in Fungi.* Oxford: Clarendon Press, pp. 197.
164. Jacobs, S. E. and A. W. Marsden. 1948. *Ann. Appl. Biol.* 35: 18–24.
165. Javillier, M. 1913. *Ann. inst. Pasteur* 27: 1021–1038.
166. Jump, J. A. 1954. *Am. J. Botany* 41: 561–567.
167. Kehl, H. 1937. *Arch. Mikrobiol.* 8: 379–406.
168. Kerl, I. 1937. *Z. Botan.* 31: 129–174.
169. Kilpatrick, R. A. and H. W. Johnson. 1956. *Phytopathology* 46: 180–181.
170. Kirchhoff, H. 1929. *Centr. Bakteriol. Parasitenk. Abt. II,* 77: 310–369.
171. Klebs, G. 1896. *Ueber die Fortpflanzungs-Physiologie der niederen Organismen, der Protobionten. Die Bedingungen der Fortpflanzung bie einigen Algen und Pilzen.* Jena: Gustav Fischer. pp. 543.
172. Klebs, G. 1898. *Jahrb. wiss. Botan.* 32: 1–70.
173. Klebs, G. 1899. *Jahrb. wiss. Botan.* 33: 513–593.
174. Klebs, G. 1900. *Jahrb. wiss. Botan.* 35: 80–203.
175. Klein, D. T. 1948. *Botan. Gaz.* 110: 139–147.
176. Kohler, F. 1935. *Planta* 23: 358–377.
177. Krafczyk, H. 1931. *Ber. deut. botan. Ges.* 49: 141–146.
178. Krafczyk, H. 1935. *Beitr. Biol. Pflanz.* 23: 349–396.
179. Kunkel, L. O. 1918. *Brooklyn Botan. Garden Mem.* 1: 306–312.
180. Kusano, S. 1930. *Japan. J. Botany* 5: 35–132.
181. Lambert, E. B. 1933. *J. Agr. Research* 47: 599–608.
182. Lambert, E. B. 1938. *Botan. Rev.* 4: 397–426.

183. Lehman, S. G. 1923. *Ann. Missouri Botan. Garden* 10: 111–178.
184. Leonian, L. H. 1923. *Phytopathology* 13: 257–272.
185. Leonian, L. H. 1924. *Am. J. Botany* 11: 19–50.
186. Leonian, L. H. and V. G. Lilly. 1937. *Am. J. Botany* 24: 700–702.
187. Levine, M. N. 1923. *J. Agr. Research* 24: 539–567.
188. Levine, M. N. 1928. *Phytopathology* 18: 7–123.
189. Lieth, H. 1954. *Ber. deut. botan. Ges.* 67: 323–325.
190. Lieth, H. 1956. *Arch. Mikrobiol.* 24: 91–104.
191. Lindegren, C. C. and E. Hamilton. 1944. *Botan. Gaz.* 105: 316–321.
192. Lockwood, L. B. 1937. *Mycologia* 29: 289–290.
193. Löhnis, M. P. 1944. *Antonie van Leeuwenhoek J. Microbiol. Serol.* 10: 100–122.
194. Longrée, K. 1939. *Cornell Univ. Agr. Exp. Sta. Mem.* 223: 1–43.
195. McCallan, S. E. A. and S. Y. Chan. 1944. *Contribs. Boyce Thompson Inst.* 13: 323–335.
196. McVickar, D. L. 1942. *Am. J. Botany* 29: 372–380.
197. Madelin, M. F. 1956a. *Ann. Botany* 20: 307–330.
198. Madelin, M. F. 1956b. *Ann. Botany* 20: 467–480.
199. Mader, E. O. 1943. *Phytopathology* 33: 1134–1145.
200. Magie, R. O. 1935. *Phytopathology* 25: 131–159.
201. Mann, M. L. 1932. *Bull. Torrey Botan. Club* 59: 443–490.
202. Markert, C. L. 1949. *Am. Naturalist* 83: 227–231.
203. Marsh, P. B. and K. Bollenbacher. 1946. *Am. J. Botany* 33: 245–249.
204. Mathur, R. S., H. L. Barnett, and V. G. Lilly. 1950. *Phytopathology* 40: 104–114.
205. Metz, O. 1930. *Arch. Mikrobiol.* 1: 197–251.
206. Milburn, T. 1904. *Centr. Bakteriol. Parasitenk. Abt. II*, 13: 129–138, 257–276.
207. Miller, J. J. 1945. *Can. J. Research C*, 23: 16–43.
208. Mix, A. J. 1933. *Phytopathology* 23: 503–524.
209. Molliard, M. 1920. *Compt. rend. (Paris)* 170: 949–951.
210. Morgenthaler, O. 1910. *Centr. Bakteriol. Parasitenk. Abt. II*, 27: 73–92.
211. Mulder, E. G. 1939. *Arch. Mikrobiol.* 10: 72–96.
212. Munk, M. 1912. *Centr. Bakteriol. Parasitenk. Abt. II*, 32: 353–375.
213. Nagel, C. M. 1934. *Phytopathology* 24: 1101–1110.
214. Nickerson, W. J. and Z. Mankowski. 1953a. *Am. J. Botany* 40: 584–591.
215. Nickerson, W. J. and Z. Mankowski. 1953b. *J. Infectious Diseases* 92: 20–25.
216. Nickerson, W. J. and K. V. Thimann. 1941. *Am. J. Botany* 28: 617–621.
217. Nickerson, W. J. and K. V. Thimann. 1943. *Am. J. Botany* 30: 94–101.
218. Nittimargi, N. M. 1937. *Ann. Botany* 49: 19–40.
219. Obel, P. 1910. *Ann. Mycol.* 8: 421–443.
220. Pady, S. M. 1948. *Mycologia* 40: 21–33.
221. Page, R. M. 1956. *Mycologia* 48: 206–224.
222. Parr, R. 1918. *Ann. Botany* 32: 177–205.
223. Perlman, D., R. B. Greenfield, Jr., and E. O'Brien. 1954. *Appl. Microbiol.* 2: 199–202.
224. Pillai, N. C. and K. S. Srinivasan. 1956. *J. Gen. Microbiol.* 14: 248–255.
225. Plempel, M. 1957. *Arch. Mikrobiol.* 26: 151–174.
226. Plunkett, B. E. 1953. *Ann. Botany* 17: 193–217.
227. Plunkett, B. E. 1956. *Ann. Botany* 20: 563–586.
228. Powlesland, R. 1954. *Trans. Brit. Mycol. Soc.* 37: 362–371.
229. Prince, A. E. 1943. *Farlowia* 1: 79–93.
230. Rabinowitz-Sereni, D. 1933. *Bol. R. Staz. Veg.* 13: 203–226. (*Biol. Abstr.* 10: 17992. 1936.)
231. Ram, C. S. V. 1952. *Nature (London)* 170: 889.
232. Ramsey, G. B. and A. A. Bailey. 1930. *Botan. Gaz.* 89: 113–136.

BIBLIOGRAPHY

385

233. Rands, R. D. 1917. *Phytopathology* 7: 316–317.
234. Raper, J. R. 1939. *Am. J. Botany* 26: 639–650.
235. Raper, J. R. 1950. *Botan. Gaz.* 112: 1–24.
236. Raper, J. R. 1952. *Botan. Rev.* 18: 447–545.
237. Raper, J. R. and A. J. Haagen-Smit. 1942. *J. Biol. Chem.* 143: 311–320.
238. Raper, K. B. 1956. *Mycologia* 48: 169–205.
239. Raper, K. B. and C. Thom. 1944. *Mycologia* 36: 555–575.
240. Reidemeister, W. 1909. *Ann. Mycol.* 7: 19–44.
241. Reinert, J. 1952. *Naturwiss.* 39: 47–48.
242. Richards, M. C. 1949. *Phytopathology* 39: 20.
243. Robak, H. 1941. *Nyt Mag. Naturv.* 81: 105–116. (*Rev. Appl. Mycol.* 25: 331. 1946.)
244. Robbins, W. J. and I. McVeigh. 1949. *Mycologia* 41: 141–170.
245. Robbins, W. J. and M. B. Schmitt. 1945. *Am. J. Botany* 32: 320–326.
246. Roberg, M. 1928. *Centr. Bakt. Parasitenk. Abt. II*, 74: 333–370.
247. Robinson, R. 1926. *Trans. Brit. Mycol. Soc.* 10: 307–314.
248. Robinson, W. 1926. *Ann. Botany* 40: 245–272.
249. Rogers, C. H. 1939. *J. Agr. Research* 58: 701–709.
250. Ronsdorf, L. 1931. *Planta* 14: 482–514.
250a. Sagromsky, M. 1952. *Flora, N. F.* 39: 300–313, 560–564.
251. Salvin, S. B. 1942. *Am. J. Botany* 29: 97–104.
252. Sanford, G. B. 1956. *Phytopathology* 46: 281–284.
253. Schenck, E. 1919. *Beih. Botan. Centr.* 36, Abt. I: 355–413.
254. Schmidle, A. 1951. *Arch. Mikrobiol.* 16: 80–100.
255. Schneiderhöhn, G. 1955. *Arch. Mikrobiol.* 21: 230–236.
256. Schönborn, W. 1955. *Arch. Mikrobiol.* 22: 408–431.
257. Schopfer, W. H. 1928. *Bull soc. botan. Genève* 20: 149–323.
258. Schopfer, W. H. 1935. *Compt. rend. soc. phys. et hist. nat. Genève* 50: 152–154.
259. Schopfer, W. H. and S. Blumer. 1940. *Protoplasma* 34: 524–532.
260. Shaffer, B. M. 1956. *Science* 123: 1172–1173.
261. Shanor, L. 1936. *J. Elisha Mitchell Sci. Soc.* 52: 99–104.
262. Smith, E. C. 1935. *Bull. Torrey Botan. Club* 62: 151–164.
263. Smith, E. C. 1936. In B. M. Duggar (ed.), *Biological Effects of Radiation*, Vol. 2, p. 889–918. New York: McGraw-Hill Book Co.
264. Snyder, W. C. and H. N. Hansen. 1941. *Mycologia* 33: 580–591.
265. Snyder, W. C. and H. N. Hansen. 1947. *Phytopathology* 37: 420–421.
266. Sörgel, G. 1953. *Arch. Mikrobiol.* 19: 372–397.
267. Sost, H. 1955. *Arch. Protistenk.* 100: 541–564.
268. Stakman, E. C. and M. N. Levine. 1919. *J. Agr. Research* 16: 43–77.
269. Steinberg, R. A. 1935. *Bull. Torrey Botan. Club* 62: 81–90.
270. Steinberg, R. A. 1936. *Am. J. Botany* 23: 227–231.
271. Stevens, F. L. 1928. *Botan. Gaz.* 86: 210–225.
272. Stevens, F. L. 1930a. *Am. J. Botany* 17: 870–881.
273. Stevens, F. L. 1930b. *Zentr. Bakteriol. Parasitenk. Abt. II*, 82: 161–174.
274. Stevens, F. L. 1931. *Mycologia* 23: 134–139.
275. Stiefel, S. 1952. *Planta* 40: 301–312.
276. Stockdale, P. M. 1953. *J. Gen. Mikrobiol.* 8: 434–441.
277. Stoll, K. 1936. *Zentr. Bakteriol. Parasitenk. Abt. II*, 93: 296–298.
278. Streeter, S. G. 1909. *Botan. Gaz.* 48: 415–426.
279. Sussman, M. 1956. *Ann. Rev. Microbiol.* 10: 21–50.
280. Sussman, M., F. Lee, and N. S. Kerr. 1956. *Science* 123: 1171–1172.
281. Sweet, H. R. 1941. *Am. J. Botany* 28: 150–161.
282. Takemaru, T. 1954. *Botan. Mag. (Tokyo)* 67: 82–86.
283. Ternetz, C. 1900. *Jahrb. wiss. Botan.* 35: 273–312.

284. Thren, R. 1937. *Z. Botan.* 31: 337–391.
285. Timnick, M. B., H. L. Barnett, and V. G. Lilly. 1952. *Mycologia* 44: 141–149.
286. Timnick, M. B., V. G. Lilly, and H. L. Barnett. 1951. *Phytopathology* 41: 327–336.
287. Tisdale, W. B. 1923. *J. Agr. Research* 24: 55–86.
288. Turian, G. 1952. *Experientia* 8: 302.
289. Turian, G. and F. T. Haxo. 1954. *Botan. Gaz.* 115: 254–260.
290. Tyner, L. E. and G. B. Sanford. 1935. *Sci. Agr.* 16: 197–207.
291. Uebelmesser, E.-R. 1954. *Arch. Mikrobiol.* 20: 1–33.
292. Utiger, H. 1953. *Naturwiss.* 40: 292–293.
293. Vandendries, R. 1934. *Compt. rend. (Paris)* 198: 193–195.
294. Voderberg, K. 1950. *Planta* 37: 612–625.
295. Wagner, F. 1955. *Arch. Mikrobiol.* 22: 313–323.
296. Wakefield, E. M. 1910. *Naturw. Z. Land.-u. Forstwirtschaft* 7: 521–551.
297. Wald, G. 1943. *Vitamins and Hormones* 1: 195–227.
298. Walker, L. B. 1927. *J. Elisha Mitchell Sci. Soc.* 42: 151–178.
299. Walker, L. B. and E. N. Andersen. 1925. *Mycologia* 17: 154–159.
300. Walter, H. 1921. *Z. Botan.* 13: 673–718.
301. Waters, C. W. 1928. *Phytopathology* 18: 157–213.
302. Webster, J. 1952. *New Phytologist* 51: 229–235.
303. Weimer, J. L. and L. L. Harter. 1923. *J. Agr. Research* 24: 1–40.
304. Westergaard, M. and H. M. Hirsch. 1954. *Proc. Symposium Colston Research Soc.*, 7, p. 171–181. New York: Academic Press.
305. Westergaard, M. and H. K. Mitchell. 1947. *Am. J. Botany* 34: 573–577.
306. Weston, W. H., Jr. 1923. *J. Agr. Research* 23: 239–278.
307. Weston, W. H., Jr. 1924. *J. Agr. Research* 27: 771–784.
308. Wheeler, H. E. 1954. *Phytopathology* 44: 342–345.
309. Wheeler, H. E. 1956. *Mycologia* 48: 349–354.
310. Wilhelm, S. 1947. *Mycologia* 39: 716–724.
311. Williams, A. M. and E. McCoy. 1953. *Appl. Microbiol.* 1: 307–313.
312. Witsch, H. von, and F. Wagner. 1955. *Arch. Mikrobiol.* 22: 307–312.
313. Wolff, L. K. and A. Emmerie. 1930. *Biochem. Z.* 228: 443–450.
314. Yarwood, C. E. 1936. *J. Agr. Research* 52: 645–657.
315. Yarwood, C. E. 1937. *J. Agr. Research* 54: 365–373.
316. Yarwood, C. E. 1941. *Am. J. Botany* 28: 355–357.
317. Yarwood, C. E. 1943. *Hilgardia* 14: 595–691.
318. Yarwood, C. E. 1956. *Plant Disease Reptr.* 40: 318–321.
319. Yu, C. C. 1954. *Am. J. Botany* 41: 21–30.
320. Zachariah, A. T., H. N. Hansen, and W. C. Snyder. 1956. *Mycologia* 48: 459–467.
321. Zalokar, M. 1954. *Arch. Biochem. Biophys.* 50: 71–80.
322. Zentmyer, G. A. 1952. *Phytopathology* 42: 24.

12. Spore Germination

Spores—specialized, self-contained, microscopic structures capable of initiating new growth—are the principal agent of dispersal of fungi. Consequently, any consideration of ecology or of the spread of economically important fungi must take spore germination into account. The control of plant diseases by protectant fungicides is in essence the problem of inhibiting the germination of spores. And, the transformation of a relatively inactive structure into an actively growing thallus poses some fundamental problems of interest to biology as a whole.

In this chapter, the several cytological and morphological types of spore have been distinguished in the discussion only if some important physiological aspect is specific to the type. In the long run, we may suppose, such a practice—treating the rust fungus teliospore and the myxomycete swarmspore alike—will prove indefensible. For the present, however, the available information does not permit separate treatment of the different spore forms, except in such special cases as the dormant "resting" spores.

It will be seen that, as usual in the fungi, the corpus of knowledge is seriously out of balance. We find literally hundreds of studies of temperature and water relations of the economically important fungi, but such groups as the aquatic fungi, the fleshy basidiomycetes, and the actinomycetes are virtually unknown in this dimension. More serious still, concentration on well-known and easily determined environmental factors has meant relative neglect of the fundamental metabolic processes which control germination and of the physiological and bio-chemical changes consequent upon germination. It is reasonable to expect that investigations into these and related topics would in turn throw light on some of the more obscure environmental and ecological problems in spore physiology.

1. MEASUREMENT

The most commonly used criterion of spore germination is the frac-tion of spores that in a given time forms a germ tube; the time period is usually chosen so as to allow all viable spores to germinate. Spores are sown on water, on agar, or on nutrient media, incubated under controlled conditions, and counted microscopically; or, the spores may be germinated in an aerated or shaken liquid medium (65). Self-in-hibition and other associative effects (p. 413) make it imperative that the concentration of spores be held constant and be known. It is usu-ally convenient to bring the spore suspension to a known turbidity, measured optically and previously standardized against a direct micro-scopic count (240). Spore concentration can also be estimated by capillary volume (192, 289). Clumping of spores introduces error and must therefore be minimized (130).

The rate of germination may be determined by periodic counts dur-ing the experiment and often provides valuable supplementary infor-mation.

A second major criterion is the latent period of germination, the time required for germination to begin or to reach some specified low value (25, 118, 287). Limited evidence suggests that this is fundamen-tally different from total germination, in that temperature affects it differently (p. 410) and toxicants may exert greater or less effect on the latent period than on total germination (287).

The rate of increase in the length of the germ tube is again a differ-ent criterion of spore activity. In general, it is more sensitive to tem-perature than is total germination, responding more like mycelial growth; similarly, the pH range for optimum germ tube growth in *Alternaria solani* is rather narrower than that for best total germina-tion (159). The rate of elongation can be expressed as a velocity con-stant (126).

No one of these criteria can be said to be "best." The method used must take account of the problem which is under investigation. Fun-damental studies on the germination process, for example, might make use of the rate of germination and the total germination. On the other hand, an ecological or epidemiological problem might be served better by measurements of germ tube growth. Infection of a plant by a pathogen is dependent usually on at least some extension of the germ tube; if this process is more sensitive to unfavorable conditions than is total germination, a false picture of the potentialities of the organism will be deduced from observations on total germination alone. Unfortunately, germ tube measurements are rather more laborious and are perhaps avoided for that reason; a rapid, semi-automatic method of determining germ tube lengths should not be beyond the capacity of modern instrumentation and would be a real contribution to the study of fungi.

2. THE GERMINATION PROCESS

Just as we have had to lump together the various morphological types of fungus spore, it is also necessary, with some exceptions, to consider the several germination types as if they were all alike. Of these, the most common and the most frequently studied is formation of one or more germ tubes which grow indeterminately and develop into a mycelium in culture or in a parasitized plant or animal. Among the phycomycetes several types of spore germinate by the formation of smaller endogenous spores, i.e., the parent structure is functionally a sporangium. In *Phytophthora infestans* the same structure—perhaps best called a conidiosporangium—germinates either by a tube or by formation of swarmspores, depending upon the environment, particularly temperature, and perhaps on the age and previous history of the structure (19, 63, 279, 291). The chlamydospores of the smut fungi germinate somewhat differently under different external conditions of temperature (140), concentration (132), and nutrients (264). Basidiospores of *Rhizoctonia solani* form secondary spores on water agar, germ tubes on a nutrient agar (131). The macroconidium of *Thielaviopsis paradoxa* similarly germinates very differently on water and on nutrient agar (149).

Multicellular spores often germinate by the simultaneous formation of two or more germ tubes (179); in *Pestalotia* spp., however, the basal cell normally gives rise to the germ tube (300), and germination in *Helminthosporium sativum* may be either polar or bipolar (137).

Conidia of the higher fungi may have one, two, or several nuclei at the time of their formation; a few examples may be cited:

1. Predominantly uninucleate: *Aspergillus* spp. (8, 12), *Colletotrichum destructivum* (49), *Trichoderma viride* (12), *Verticillium alboatrum* (128).

2. Predominantly multinucleate: *Aspergillus echinulatus* (8), *Botrytis cinerea* (128), *Helminthosporium sativum* (54, 137). Sporangiospores of *Rhizopus nigricans* are uninucleate (12), those of *Mucor dispersus* multinucleate (68).

Nuclear condition is of particular importance in genetic studies, since a heterokaryotic mycelium which produces uninucleate conidia—more accurately, conidia from uninucleate conidiophores—essentially regenerates the parent types in the absence of gene exchange (112). By extension of this principle, it is possible to infer from genetic evidence in *Streptomyces* spp. that the conidia are uninucleate or arise from uninucleate cells (28).

The number of nuclei in macroconidia of *Neurospora crassa* is reduced by cultivation in a minimal medium (138) or in a sorbose medium (5). The nuclei of the higher fungi are, of course, normally haploid; Roper (236) has, however, succeeded in inducing the formation of diploid conidia in *Aspergillus nidulans*, and camphor treatment of *Neurospora crassa* induces the formation of possibly diploid cells (243).

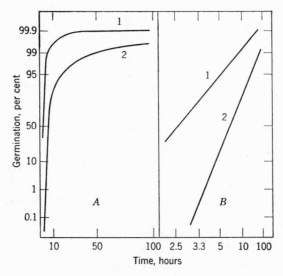

Figure 1. The time course of spore germination (probit scale) in *Monilinia fructicola* (curves 1) and *Alternaria solani* (curves 2). Arithmic function of time plotted in *A*, reciprocal function in *B*. Redrawn from Wellman and McCallan (299), by permission of the Boyce Thompson Institute for Plant Research, Inc.

A given population of spores germinates over a period of time; if the population is standardized as to age, there is good evidence that random variability is the cause of the spread in time of germination. As shown in Figure 1, a plot of per cent germination on a probit scale against the reciprocal of time is linear (provided a correction is made for non-viable spores); i.e., time of germination is normally distributed. Similar data have been reported in studies of *Neurospora crassa* (240). The over-all rapidity of germination is a species characteristic: *Melampsora lini* begins germination in less than one hour (129), but *Phoma apiicola* spores require 24–48 hours (13). Other data on rapidity of germination are reviewed by Gottlieb (113) and by Doran (73).

The three distinguishing morphological events of typical spore germination are: nuclear division (8, 12), swelling of the spore, and emergence of the germ tube. Swelling, with one significant exception, appears to be universal in fungi and actinomycetes, having been described in sporangiospores (41), ascospores (121), basidiospores (32, 135), and conidia (25, 114, 125, 192, 255, 260a, 306). The exception— apart from the fact that observations on *Sclerotinia fructicola* conflict (192, 306)—is found among the powdery mildew fungi; conidia of these do not swell prior to germination (306). The significance of swelling in relation to water requirements will be considered later.

There is scattered evidence that physiological changes also occur during the germination process, although the data cannot be generalized to all fungi. Anion toxicity is more marked in the early stage of germination of the resistant sporangium of *Blastocladiella* sp. (45) than in a later stage; oxygen uptake by ascospores of *Neurospora tetrasperma* becomes more sensitive to iodoacetamide after appearance of the germ tube (109); and in the same material cation permeability appears to change at the beginning of germination (274). Other evidence of separable physiological states during the germination process appears in studies of oxygen uptake and of temperature responses.

Germ tube growth presumably follows the same rules as any other mycelial growth. Extension occurs at the tip only (259, 263). For at least some time, growth is exponential, i.e., the logarithm of germ tube length increases linearly with time (220, 259); germ tube growth in *Ustulina vulgaris*, however, is reported to follow a different course (301).

Germ tube tropisms toward water and toward nutrients have been reported, but the evidence is conflicting and inconclusive (9, 55, 100, 117, 203). It is not, in particular, necessary to postulate a chemotropic reaction in the penetration of plant pathogens into host tissue (39, 40,

62). Here an unspecified contact stimulus, "thigmotropism," is supposed to operate. The possibility of chemotropism has been reopened more recently in studies on *Saprolegnia ferax* (87).

One type of germ tube tropism is well documented—the negative tropism of germ tubes toward each other (55, 100, 117). As described by Stadler (263), germ tubes of *Rhizopus nigricans* form on the side of the spore distant from other spores and, in addition, actually bend away from other germ tubes during their growth. The stimulus is almost certainly chemical, and it is tempting to consider an auxinlike growth factor in explanation of the bending phenomenon. This possibility is also suggested by the finding that germ tubes of rust fungi are longer when germinating spores are crowded than when they are more disperse (83, 314). However, Stadler (263) presents some evidence against an explanation based on growth factors; instead, he postulates an unstable inhibitor which has the effect of thickening or strengthening the wall of the spore or germ tube. The last word on this problem has clearly not been spoken.

Germ tubes of sporidia and of uredospores of *Puccinia* spp. react negatively to strong light; studies with filters indicate that the active wavelength is in the blue region of the visible spectrum (90, 98, 235, 266). It will be recalled from Chapter 11 that it is these shorter wavelengths which are most active in phototropic and inductive effects on reproductive structures. Negative phototropism is also shown by conidia of powdery mildew fungi (204, 305).

3. SPORE METABOLISM

Water, minerals, carbohydrates, and other constituents of fungus spores have been mentioned incidentally in Chapter 2. In relation to spore germination the important materials are water—considered elsewhere in this chapter—and, probably, lipids. It should also be recalled that spores of *Aspergillus niger* are relatively high in total phosphorus, a part of which is in organic combination (7, 154):

Although the fat content of most spores is not unusually high (248, 271), three bits of evidence suggest that fats provide energy for the germination of spores which do not require an exogenous source of carbon. First, microscopic observation shows that stainable lipids disappear during germination (82, 150). Second, the respiratory quotient of *Neurospora sitophila* macroconidia is about 0.7 (208), a value characteristic of, but of course not sufficient evidence for, fat oxidation. Finally, the data of Table 1 show that, at least in high-fat spores, the principal organic material disappearing during germination is the

Table 1. Chemical Changes during Germination of Uredospores
of *Puccinia graminis tritici**

Amount, Per Cent of Dry Weight

Fraction	Before Germination	After Germination
Carbohydrate	21.9	22.4
Chitin	1.4	3.4
Protein	25.9	22.3
Lipid	19.7	7.8

* From Shu, Tanner, and Ledingham (254), by permission of the *Canadian Journal of Botany*.

lipid fraction. The conidia of *Erysiphe graminis,* like the rust spores of Table 1, appear to be relatively high in fat (310).

During the germination of spores of *Aspergillus nidulans,* the most pronounced changes which occur in the first few hours are: decline in polymetaphosphate and in organically bound phosphate, disappearance of part of the free amino acids of the spore, and a progressive fall in total lipid (253).

Several hydrolytic enzymes—acting on starch, oligosaccharides, glucosides, pectic substances, proteins, and urea—occur in crude spore preparations; the early literature is reviewed by Mandels and Norton (195). Spores of *Myrothecium verrucaria* have been found to possess an enzymatic system acting on ascorbic acid (185, 186), another system oxidizing sulfhydryl compounds to disulfides (191), and one or possibly two enzymes acting on sucrose (184, 187, 188). The invertase of *M. verrucaria* is synthesized rapidly during germination and appears in the medium almost immediately (190). These enzymes are inactivated by an acid treatment which does not kill the spore or damage its respiration; from this fact it has been proposed that they are located at or near the spore surface (184, 185). The diphosphopyridine nucleotidase of *Neurospora crassa* is produced primarily or entirely by the conidia and is so easily washed out of the cell that it, too, may have a surface location (309).

Although there is as yet no reason to think that spore respiration differs fundamentally from that of mycelium, studies of the general problem should contribute to our understanding of both spore germination and fungicidal action. Data available at present are too fragmentary to support any firm theoretical structure or even generalized description; the work summarized here should not therefore be taken as necessarily applying to all fungi.

The endogenous respiration of ascospores of *Neurospora tetrasperma* is shown in Figure 2. The curve has an upward break coincident with

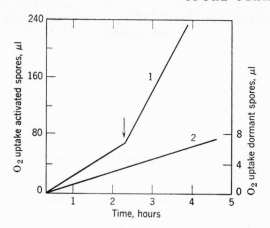

Figure 2. Oxygen consumption of activated (curve 1) and dormant (curve 2) ascospores of *Neurospora tetrasperma*. The arrow marks the time of appearance of germ tubes. Redrawn from Goddard and Smith (110), by permission of *Plant Physiology*.

the appearance of the germ tube; this particular type of curve is not universal in the fungi and would not necessarily occur under different conditions of nutrient or oxygen supply. Endogenous respiration in *Memnoniella echinata* and *Aspergillus luchuensis* is affected by ammonium ion and by the previous cultural history of the spore population (64). Oxygen pressure also affects the endogenous rate (110, 194).

Spores generally, but not always, respond to added substrates by an increase in respiratory rate; increases may also be induced by provision of nitrogen or of complex nutrients in addition to a carbon source (173, 193, 254, 255). The data of Table 2 are fairly typical in that the range of response is from zero to high; since, however, the substrate was sucrose, the results reflect hydrolytic as well as respiratory capacities.

Just as mature mycelium, spores of a given species may or may not ferment glucose anaerobically. Uredospores of *Puccinia graminis tritici* do not form carbon dioxide anaerobically (254); at the other extreme, both activated ascospores and conidia of *Neurospora* spp. ferment vigorously and have demonstrable glycolytic enzymes (59, 110, 209).

Not much can be said at this time of detailed respiratory pathways in spores. Acids of the tricarboxylic cycle are oxidized by conidia of *Neurospora sitophila*, are found in conidial homogenates, and appear in the medium during germination (174, 208, 293). Poisons which affect glycolysis and the cytochrome system usually inhibit spore respiration, but several anomalies in the results make interpretation dif-

Table 2. Endogenous and Exogenous Oxygen Uptake
by Conidia of Fungi*

Oxygen Uptake†

Species	No Substrate (endogenous)	Sucrose, 1 per cent	Exogenous‡ Endogenous
Neurospora sitophila	8.6	68.6	7.0
Monilinia fructicola	5.1	54.2	9.6
Cephalosporium acremonium	2.7	42.8	14.8
Myrothecium verrucaria	8.8	22.1	1.5
Stemphylium sarcinaeforme	2.0	21.7	9.8
Alternaria oleracea	7.1	17.4	1.5
Aspergillus niger	12.8	17.7	0.4
Rhizopus nigricans	8.5	9.2	0.1

* Drawn from more extensive data of McCallan, Miller, and Weed (173), by permission of the Boyce Thompson Institute for Plant Research, Inc.
† In μl/5 hr/mg fresh spores.
‡ Exogenous = uptake with sucrose less endogenous uptake.

ficult (64, 110, 254). In general, but with some exceptions, germination is more sensitive than spore respiration to both inorganic and organic fungicides (Chapter 14).

4. MATURATION AND DORMANCY

It is a common observation that morphologically normal and apparently fully developed spores often do not germinate until after a period of time. If this period is relatively short, we speak of maturation; if it is on the contrary a matter of weeks or months, the spore is said to have a dormant stage or resting period. There is as yet no evidence which enables us to say whether these two phenomena are different or the same.

The failure of newly formed spores to germinate normally is best documented in studies on the uredospores of the rust fungi (73, 200, 245, 322), the behavior of which is exemplified by the data of Figure 3. As shown, immature spores have both a slower rate of germination and lower total germination than have mature spores. In addition, immature spores are more sensitive to unfavorable temperatures (57, 73). It appears from most work that immature uredospores can ripen after removal from the sorus (11, 57, 178). The very long period of poor germinability of aeciospores of Gymnosporangium spp. has been noted repeatedly but has not as yet been analyzed (20, 99, 178, 222, 282).

Both asexual and sexual spores of ascomycetes germinate poorly

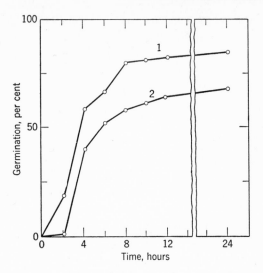

Figure 3. The rate of germination of mature (curve 1) and immature (curve 2) uredospores of *Phragmidium mucronatum*. Redrawn from Cochrane (57), by permission of the Cornell University Agricultural Experiment Station.

when newly formed (42, 145, 240). Conidia of powdery mildew fungi do not germinate until detached from the chain in which they are formed, possibly because they are impermeable to gases until exposed (33), or because the parent mycelium forms a diffusible germination inhibitor (70); this is not, therefore, comparable to immaturity.

Many phycomycetes form thick-walled resting spores; these are probably always the site of meiosis, and at least part of their apparent resting period represents the time required for cytological processes (81). Whether there is in addition a further period of purely physiological dormancy is still uncertain. There can be no doubt that the environment, especially temperature, influences the length of the resting period in some members of the Saprolegniales (246) and Peronosporales (3, 17, 18). However, it is not yet possible to define the locus of this effect. Many oospores, it should be noted, germinate immediately after their formation (157, 321), as do also the resistant sporangia of *Blastocladiella* sp. (45).

The rest period of resistant sporangia of *Allomyces* spp. is shortened dramatically by certain cultural conditions and by indoleacetic acid (176, 177). In this and related genera the strength of the sporangium wall may be one of the decisive factors in germination (176, 270)— sporangia grown under conditions in which the wall is thin germinate without a rest period.

The ascospores of many ascomycetes, particularly but not exclusively coprophilic forms, exhibit a pronounced dormancy which is broken by brief exposure to high temperature (69, 120, 121, 122, 123, 139, 251). Rather intensive study of ascospore dormancy in *Neurospora* spp. has revealed several features of the phenomenon:

1. Activation—breaking of dormancy—is reversible, i.e., activated ascospores become dormant again if prevented from germinating (107).

2. Activated ascospores decarboxylate pyruvic acid and respire vigorously; dormant spores respire slowly (Figure 2) and do not decarboxylate pyruvate (108, 110).

3. Furfural and related unsaturated heterocyclic compounds activate fresh ascospores (79, 272, 273). Aged dormant spores are activated by furfural only if they are first heated (275).

Emerson (80) proposes that furfural duplicates the action of a natural catalyst which is normally induced to form or to become active by the heat treatment. It is of course equally possible that a natural inhibitor is present in fresh spores and is inactivated by heat or by those chemicals which induce germination.

Neither permeability to water nor to gases can be invoked as a factor in ascospore dormancy in *Neurospora tetrasperma* (107, 170). However, the activating effect of alkali on ascospores of *Ascobolus* spp. (318) may implicate permeability to water, and dormant ascospores of *N. tetrasperma* are relatively impermeable to cations (169a).

Sporangiospores of *Phycomyces blakesleeanus* are activated by a heat treatment, e.g., 15 minutes at 50°C (232). The effect is duplicated by hypoxanthine.

Teliospores of the rust fungi normally do not germinate until several months after their formation. Although chemical and moisture treatments have been reported to hasten germination (142, 181, 196, 221, 280), the same treatments fail in other studies (129, 156). Until systematic analysis has been accomplished, we must assume a long obligate rest period as characteristic in these spores.

In the life cycle of the smut fungi the chlamydospore is analogous to the teliospore of the rust fungi. Periods of 200 days or more are required for germination to begin in certain races of *Ustilago striaeformis* (66, 152). The germination of these spores is often much accelerated by chemical treatments (47, 66, 165, 205, 206), by low-temperature soaking (136), by high-temperature cultivation of the infected host (152), or by variations in moisture (281). Mechanical abrasion also shortens the dormant period in *Ustilago striaeformis* (153).

It is not yet possible to envision a single explanation for all types of long obligatory rest periods. If we define dormancy as a rest period after the spore has completed both its morphological and its cytological development, and if we assume that at least part of the rest period in the phycomycete and basidiomycete spores just considered is such true dormancy, then the most promising hypothesis is that some factor associated with the heavy spore wall—possibly impermeability, possibly simple mechanical strength—is determinative. It is not likely that the same explanation will fit ascospore dormancy in *Neurospora,* in which an internal, biochemical mechanism seems more probable. However, ascospore dormancy in *Onygena equina* develops only after the heavy spore wall is laid down—the immature spore germinates without a dormant period (30).

5. SPORE LONGEVITY

Several fungi form asexual spores whose survival under the most favorable conditions is measured in days only; examples include the conidia of the powdery mildew fungi (317), the sporangium of *Peronospora tabacina* (302), and the sporidia (basidiospores) of some rust fungi (178, 222, 262). The short life of the powdery mildew conidia is probably related to the high water content of the spores (317).

Aeciospores and uredospores of the rust fungi are intermediate in longevity. Although in a few species these spores may under exceptionally favorable conditions survive for as long as a year (57, 77, 89, 214), their lives under most conditions of storage are weeks or months only (6, 20, 72, 73, 74, 221) and are even less under uncontrolled natural conditions (57, 237). Early work on spore survival in the rust fungi is reviewed by Maneval (193) and by Zimmerman (322).

Types of spore characterized by a long or very long life include the chlamydospores of the Ustilaginales (88, 171, 278), basidiospores of Hymenomycetes (95, 127), and at least some ascospores (46, 127). Spores with long periods of inability to germinate—resting spores of phycomycetes, teliospores of the rust fungi, and certain ascospores—are *ipso facto* long-lived.

Although the rule in the fungi is that asexual spores are relatively short-lived, the conidia of certain imperfect fungi and of actinomycetes may survive very long periods (15, 175, 212, 234, 297). Ecologically, it appears that the survival function typical of sexual spores is taken over in these forms, which lack a sexual stage, by the conidia. Dried swarmspores of the Myxomycetes similarly are reported to survive many years (78, 258).

Techniques of preservation of spores are briefly reviewed in Chapter 1.

Temperature is one of the major factors in the longevity of spores. Almost without exception, survival is greatest at low temperature, i.e., near 0°C. This is particularly well documented for uredospores of rust fungi (57, 77, 214, 215, 237) and conidia of powdery mildew fungi (317). Presumably, spore metabolism is accelerated at high temperature, reserves are exhausted, and death (inability to germinate) ensues. The effect of subzero temperatures on survival is considered later (Chapter 13).

Relative humidity is the second major factor in spore longevity and, in nature, is probably more often limiting than is temperature. Here, however, the relation is not so simple, and we must for the present at least distinguish three types of response to atmospheric moisture. Conidia of *Sphaerotheca pannosa* (167), sporidia of rust fungi (222, 262), and conidiosporangia of *Phytophthora* spp. (63, 141) survive longest at saturation and are less viable at any relative humidity less than 100 per cent. Typical data appear in Figure 4. It should be noted that precisely these spores have just been described as short-lived in general; their susceptibility to desiccation is almost certainly the reason for their failure to survive.

Uredospores of the rust fungi exhibit a different and characteristic response to humidity. Virtually all studies agree that survival is great-

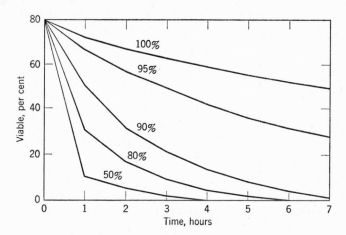

Figure 4. The survival of sporangia of *Phytophthora infestans* at different relative humidities. Redrawn from Crosier (63), by permission of the Cornell University Agricultural Experiment Station.

est at intermediate relative humidity and is less at either extreme (6, 57, 129, 214, 215, 221, 237). Chlamydospores of *Urocystis tritici* respond in the same way (206). Damage at low moisture levels is probably simple water loss; consideration of the possible effects of high humidity leads us to the third and final category of humidity response.

This last type of response is exemplified by both ascospores and endoconidia of *Endoconidiophora fagacearum* (201) and by conidia of *Helminthosporium oryzae* (211); these remain viable longest at low humidity, especially if the temperature is unfavorably high for survival. It has been suggested that at high humidity the metabolism of this type of spore is accelerated, with a consequent reduction in longevity (201); the mechanism of such an effect is obscure, but this is at present the most attractive hypothesis and may be extended to the problem of uredospore survival at high humidity.

Spores in nature are often protected from rapid loss of water by a gelatinous matrix, by the structure in which they are formed, or by host plant tissues; several such phenomena are reviewed by Gottlieb (113).

Spores of *Myrothecium verrucaria* are strongly affected by the history of the culture, in particular by the composition of the medium (64). Spores from a mycelium grown on filter paper survive more than twice as long as those from any of three agar media; this greater viability is not, however, correlated with the rate of loss of dry weight. The growth medium also exerts a significant effect on the dry weight, nitrogen content, and respiratory behavior of spores of *M. verrucaria*. Conidia of nutritionally deficient mutants of *Ophiostoma multiannulatum* die less rapidly in a starvation medium than do conidia of the parent non-deficient stock; it has been suggested that the deficient spores metabolize less and hence survive longer (96).

Physiologically, senescent spores are characterized by poor germinability, by a slower rate of germination (36, 57, 194), and by lower respiratory activity (64).

In *Streptomyces* sp., ageing of the spore population at low temperature increases the recovery of mutant types; the mechanism is obscure (294).

6. NUTRITION AND GERMINATION

Germination may be considered as a growth process in which some or all the necessary nutrients are present in the spore *ab initio*. We may therefore expect two extreme types of relation to external nutrients—complete independence in some fungi and complete dependence on one or more nutrients in others—and various degrees of partial dependence on the environment.

Experimentally, nutritional independence of the spore is difficult to prove; it is essential that washed spores, free of materials carried over from the growth medium, be used, or that spores be collected in such a way as to prevent contamination with nutrient materials (163). Washing, of course, must be as brief as possible in order to minimize any loss of materials from the interior of the spore. Washed ascospores of *Neurospora tetrasperma* germinate in distilled water (274) and are therefore to be classed as nutritionally independent. The uniformly good germination of rust uredospores and aeciospores which have been collected by shaking from the host plant suggests that these, too, are independent of the environment; it has been noted earlier (Table 1) that uredospores are unusually high in reserve lipids. Although it is perhaps justifiable to assume that the larger resting spores of fungi are nutritionally independent, critical evidence is lacking. Conidia of the powdery mildew fungi, collected, like the rust spores, by shaking, germinate well on water, although sugars and several natural materials improve germination (167, 307, 309, 317).

Nutritional dependence is more easily demonstrated and is probably more common than independence. Many fungus spores germinate very poorly or not at all without added nutrients; examples include basidiospores of *Psalliota bispora* and other Hymenomycetes (94, 95, 105), ascospores of *Sordaria fimicola* (29, 43), and conidia of several imperfect fungi (75, 194). Other fungi, too numerous to mention individually, germinate fairly well in water but do so more completely or more rapidly in nutrient media (52, 53, 75, 85, 124, 202) or in contact with complex biological products (35, 36, 38, 60, 101, 113, 147, 151, 158). Since unwashed spores have been used in many of these studies, nutritional deficiencies are probably more acute than they appear to be.

The simplest view is that the three reactions just described—complete independence, partial dependence, and complete dependence—reflect the adequacy or availability of the reserve substances of the spore. Critical studies on washed spores show that requirements may be simple or complex. Washed spores of *Sclerotinia fructicola* require a carbon source (163), those of *Fusarium roseum* need both carbon and nitrogen (255), and spores of *Glomerella cingulata* must be supplied carbon, nitrogen, phosphorus, and sulfur (164). Responses to minerals, e.g., magnesium (163), are not necessarily nutritional. Spores are so sensitive to ions that minerals such as magnesium may act primarily as antidoting agents.

Mutants of *Neurospora crassa* which are deficient for amino acids

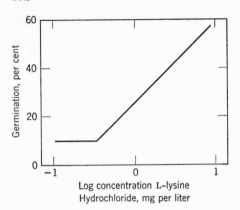

Figure 5. The response to graded doses of lysine of macroconidia of a lysine-requiring mutant of *Neurospora crassa.* Redrawn from Ryan (240), by permission of the *American Journal of Botany.*

produce macroconidia which require the amino acid for prompt germination, although the spores will germinate in time without the compound (239, 240). The response of one such mutant to lysine is shown in Figure 5. The assay is complicated by the fact that amino acids are somewhat inhibitory to spore germination in both mutant and normal *Neurospora crassa.* Parathiotrophic mutants of *Aspergillus nidulans* respond in the same way to sulfur compounds (252).

Hypoxanthine, partially replaced by guanine, accelerates both spore germination and early growth of *Phycomyces blakesleeanus* (226, 227, 228, 229, 230, 231, 233, 238). The effect of organic acids and of various physical and chemical treatments in increasing spore germination in this species has tentatively been ascribed to their influence on the availability of hypoxanthine (232).

Although, as mentioned above, complex biological materials improve germination in many species, relatively few vitamin requirements for spore germination have been worked out: *Memnoniella echinata* requires biotin (216), *Myrothecium verrucaria* also needs biotin but only in the phase following germ tube emergence (189), and *Colletotrichum gloeosporioides* is reported, without data, to respond to riboflavin and other vitamins (61). As discussed briefly in Chapter 10, successful use of the differential germination method for the detection of vitamin-deficient mutants implies that these mutants require the factor for spore germination as well as for growth. Promotion of basidiospore germination by co-culture with *Torulopsis sanguinea* is at least suggestive of a vitamin effect (94, 95), as is also the observation that the parent mycelium itself stimulates spore germination in *Psalliota campestris* (76).

Germination of uredospores of *Melampsora lini* is increased by methyl-*p*-hydroxybenzoate and by aureomycin (288); there is, however, no evidence of a nutritional mechanism in this as yet unexplained phenomenon.

Conidia of *Erysiphe graminis* respond slightly to nutrients, but the response is strongly conditioned by temperature and by the time of collection of the spores, i.e., by their previous history (316, 317).

Ammonium salts, often a utilizable nutrient, are toxic to some species of *Mycena,* but not to all; mycelial growth is much less sensitive, or possibly insensitive, to concentrations of ammonium tartrate which completely inhibit basidiospore germination (97). Chlamydospore germination in *Tilletia* spp. has repeatedly been found to be inhibited by complex biological products which are nutritive for other organisms (171).

Ecologically, a nutritional requirement for spore germination may be an advantage, helping to insure that germination will not occur in environments devoid of the materials needed for continued growth.

7. pH AND GERMINATION

It has been mentioned earlier, in Chapter 1, that spore germination usually has a narrower pH range than growth, presumably because there is less time for metabolic products to modify an unfavorable medium. In the same chapter, some of the ambiguities of acidity data were considered; the same ambiguities attach to germination experiments, in particular to the finding that several fungi show a double pH optimum under some conditions (90, 283, 295).

Analysis of spore germination data reveals several complicating factors: (1) strains of a given species differ in response (43), (2) the type of buffer—and a buffer is essential in pH studies—affects the shape and limits of the curve (274), (3) nutrient materials often modify the pH response profoundly (43, 295), and (4) the previous history of the spore population influences its behavior (2). These considerations suggest a certain caution in the interpretation of the rather extensive literature on pH-response curves, to which we now turn.

Spores of most fungi germinate best at pH 4.5–6.5, with limits at about pH 3 and pH 8. These rough figures apply to, for example, uredospores of several rust fungi (2, 90, 266), ascospores (14, 43, 301), chlamydospores of *Urocystis tritici* (206), and spores of myxomycetes (257).

Variations from this general pattern are several: a few fungi have more acid optima (283, 295), some have optimum zones extending to about pH 8 (60, 146, 160, 161, 295), and many germinate over a somewhat wider range than the typical (53, 198, 257, 295, 301).

It is probable that only in rather unusual environments, e.g., very acid soils, is pH a natural limiting factor for spore germination. Insofar as acidity and alkalinity are ecological influences, their effects on mycelial growth and spore formation are likely to be more decisive.

8. WATER AND GERMINATION

Available water is one of the primary determinants of spore germination. Consequently, a considerable body of evidence has accumulated on the moisture responses of economically important fungi; several reviews of these data have been published (56, 71, 113, 256). The effect of humidity on spore survival has already been considered.

Certain problems of method have received less attention than they deserve. Most investigators have reported data in terms of relative humidity; although this practice is justifiable, a clearer picture of water relations emerges when the vapor pressure deficit is taken as the criterion (67, 262). The absolute humidity is not a useful value (224). The importance of accurate temperature control, especially in attempts to discriminate between free water and a saturated atmosphere with no free water, has not always been realized. Both static and moving-air systems for the simultaneous control of temperature and humidity have been described (56, 57, 67); the static principle—incubation in a closed system over a humidity-regulating solution—is both simpler and more accurate.

When germination is measured on solid substrates which take up water—agar, grain, textiles, etc.—the minimum humidity permitting germination is often lower than that in the absence of substrate (4, 22, 118). This, we may reasonably infer, means that the water-absorbing capacity of these substrates is greater than that of the spore, but this explanation begs the question of how the spore is able to draw water from the substrate.

The response to moisture is usually conditioned by temperature. Thus, conidia of *Uncinula necator* are adversely affected by low humidity at 28°C or above, not at 25° or 20° (67). The optimum humidity for germination of *Aspergillus niger* conidia is substantially higher at 40° than at 30°C (25). In *Alternaria citri,* both germination time and germ tube length are less affected by relative humidity at the temperature optimum for germination than at non-optimal temperatures (286).

Excluding the powdery mildew and the rust fungi, to be taken up later, the fungi can be classified according to the minimum relative humidity at which detectable germination occurs. Several, including species of *Aspergillus, Penicillium,* and a few other genera, form spores which germinate at relative humidities near 80 per cent (4, 25, 118, 132, 162, 244, 250, 320). A somewhat larger group of species germinate at humidities of 90–95 per cent and do not require liquid water; examples include *Alternaria brassicae, Colletotrichum* spp. (51), *Ustilago* spp. (56), *Cladosporium* spp. (51, 119, 224), *Botrytis cinerea* (224), *Fomes annosus* (225), *Septoria apii, Fusarium* spp., and *Verticillium albo-atrum* (247). Still higher humidity is required by such fungi as *Venturia inaequalis* (56) and *Magnusia brachytricha* (277). Most of or all the fungi mentioned in this paragraph germinate better at high humidity than at low, regardless of the minimum value.

Finally, the spores of many fungi are found to germinate only in liquid water; in this group we may mention conidia and ascospores of *Endoconidiophora fagacearum* (60), asexual spores of the Peronosporales (73, 141, 302, 308), and conidia of *Sclerotinia* spp. (56, 73).

Almost all studies of uredospore germination in rust fungi agree that liquid water is required and that germination is nil even at 100 per cent humidity in the absence of free water (1, 10, 57, 111, 129, 133, 134, 267, 308, 322). It is not always realized that temperature control must be extremely accurate if a humidity of 100 per cent is to be maintained without condensation of liquid water. For this reason, we must reject those reports in which accurate temperature control is not specified and germination in the absence of free water is claimed. This stricture does not, however, apply to the work of Clayton (56), who found that uredospores of *Puccinia coronata* and *P. graminis* germinate at 100 per cent relative humidity, albeit less well than in the presence of free water.

Aeciospores, teliospores, and sporidia of *Gymnosporangium globosum* all require liquid water for germination (174).

Alone among the fungi, the powdery mildew fungi form conidia which in the experience of most workers germinate at very low relative humidity, even over desiccants (33, 34, 48, 56, 67, 306). Exposure to liquid water, in fact, inhibits germination and may cause death of the spore by plasmoptysis (67, 167). As a result of these water relations, the powdery mildew diseases are favored in nature by relatively dry conditions (26, 48, 311).

Yarwood has in a series of papers (306, 310, 312) provided evidence that the ability of these spores to germinate at low humidity is a function of their high water content. Two different methods of determining water content agree in assigning a value of about 70 per cent water to the conidia of *Erysiphe polygoni*. This is much higher than the water content of other fungus spores. Correspondingly, although difficulties of measurement exist, the density of the spores of powdery mildew conidia is less than that of most other spores. Finally, it has been shown that spore volume decreases during germination in dry air. Although somewhat conflicting data and a theory based on the hypothetical conversion of bound to free water have been reported (33, 34), it seems that the high water content of conidia of the powdery mildew fungi explains their ability to germinate at low humidity. The occurrence of plasmoptysis in pure water argues for a rapid entrance into the spore; this is still to be reconciled with the observation that the loss of water from ungerminated spores is very slow—approximately 0.08 per cent of the loss from an equivalent free water surface (312).

These studies on the powdery mildews have been generalized by Yarwood (310) in the proposition that fungus spores of the usual type, i.e., those with a low water content, must absorb water to about the level of that in the powdery mildew conidia (70 per cent) before they can germinate. This hypothesis explains the swelling of these spores so frequently reported (p. 391), and in fact demands that all spores of low water content swell on germination. This appears to be the most promising general explanation of humidity relations.

As is to be expected, fungi tolerant of low humidity are also in general tolerant of high osmotic pressure in the germination medium. This relation is brought out in Figure 6.

Conidia of *Erysiphe graminis* germinate in concentrations of deuterium oxide up to 100 per cent, but the heavy water is markedly inhibitory to germ tube elongation (220); *Macrosporium sarcinaeforme* is unable to germinate in 60 per cent deuterium oxide (213).

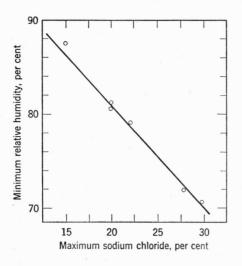

Figure 6. The relation of the minimum relative humidity to the maximum tolerated concentration of sodium chloride for spore germination in several fungi (*Aspergillus* spp., *Penicillium* spp., *Fusarium moniliforme*). Each plotted point refers to one species. Drawn from data of Armolik and Dickson (4).

9. TEMPERATURE AND GERMINATION

The so-called cardinal temperatures for spore germination—the minimum, optimum, and maximum—have been determined for very many fungi; most data on plant pathogens reported prior to 1936 are summarized by Togashi (285), other results by Wolf and Wolf (303). The student is immediately struck by the frequent and pronounced disagreements in this literature; some of these are probably inherent in the nature of the material, whereas others are traceable to inadequate methods of study.

Some examples of reported cardinal temperatures are shown in Table 3. The total range of temperatures permitting at least some germina-

Table 3.   Cardinal Temperatures of Spore Germination

Species	Minimum, °C	Optimum, °C	Maximum, °C
Albugo candida (199)	0	~10	25
Peronospora effusa (102)	~4	9	~27
Mastigosporium album (24)	—	10	20–25
Cronartium ribicola uredospores (71)	8	14	25
Puccinia malvacearum teliospores (71)	3	14	30
Phragmidium mucronatum aeciospores (57)	3–6	15–21	27–30
Phytophthora infestans, direct (63)	6	24	27–30
P. infestans, indirect (63)	1.5	12	21–24
Phoma apiicola (13)	10	16–18	23
Tranzschelia punctata uredospores (111)	8	13–26	38
Herpobasidium deformans (115)	1	18–26	33
Endoconidiophora fagacearum (85)	3	21–32	33–36
Colletotrichum indicum (166)	16	20–32	—
Erysiphe polygoni (317)	5	25	35
Allomyces arbuscula, meiosporangia (261)	14–16	20–26	32–34
Glomerella cingulata (299)	15	27	35+
Magnusia nitida (276)	1.5	~32	43
Ustilago zeae (144)	8	26–34	36–38
Rhizopus nigricans (298)	1.5	26–28	33
R. chinensis (298)	10	43–45	51

tion varies in these data from 13 centigrade degrees, in *Phoma apiicola,* to 40, in *Rhizopus chinensis* and *Magnusia nitida*. Optima range from a low of 9°C in *Peronospora effusa* to a high of 43–45° in *Rhizopus chinensis*. In general, it appears from these and other data, and is to be expected on theoretical grounds, that fungi with a high optimum have a broader total range than those with a low optimum; that is, fungi with a high optimum have in a sense solved the problem of developing at high temperature without losing their capacity to germinate at low temperature. Spore germination in the truly thermophilic fungi and actinomycetes has not been studied quantitatively.

Primarily from the data collected by Togashi (285), we can estimate that the "average" optimum for plant pathogenic fungi is about 25°. No similar estimate can be made for saprophytic fungi; probably the figure is somewhat higher.

Certain groups of fungi can be roughly characterized as a whole by their temperature preferences. Thus, species of *Aspergillus* tend to have high optima (21, 25), those of *Peronospora* to prefer rather low temperatures (84, 285). Uredospores of most rust fungi germinate best at 22° or lower (44, 57, 72, 183, 266, 268, 285, 322), although exceptions to this rule have been reported (111). Limited data on *Coprinus* spp. suggest a rather high optimum, 30–35° (146).

Conidia of the powdery mildew fungi as a rule germinate best at a moderately low temperature, about 21°. However, reported optima for different species range from 6° to 28°, and within one species, *Erysiphe cichoracearum,* strains with optima of 15° and 28° occur (317). Similarly, physiologic races of other parasitic fungi, e.g., *Puccinia glumarum* (268) and *Tilletia* spp. (171), may differ considerably in their responses to temperature. Intrageneric variations in response are exemplified in *Rhizopus:* individual species have optima as low as 27° and as high as 44° (298).

Figure 7 depicts representative types of curves of total spore germination versus temperature. The most frequent shape of curve is roughly symmetrical—or is slightly skewed to the right—with a wide optimum zone; this curve is usually found in studies of the rust fungi (44, 57, 266, 268, 269) and has been reported for such divergent types as *Fusarium lini* (31), *Ustilago* spp. (16), *Coccomyces hiemalis* (148), and several Hymenomycetes (260). An extreme example is found in the response of conidia of *Magnusia* spp. (276).

No one type of curve can, however, be said to characterize all fungi. The two most common modifications are (1) curves which are skewed to the right, like most mycelial growth curves (53, 115, 167, 317, 318), and (2) curves with a sharp optimum rather than a broad optimal zone (71, 93, 129, 143, 296). More rarely, a curve skewed to the left has been reported (48, 84) from studies of fungi with low optimum temperatures.

The diversity of types of curve becomes less surprising when one considers the number of factors that have been shown to affect the shape of the curve. Of these, time of observation is the most impor-

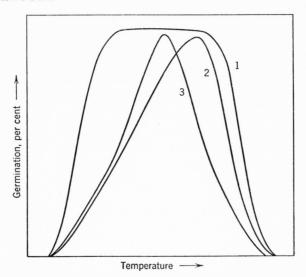

Figure 7. Idealized types of temperature-response curves of spore germination. The distinctive features are exaggerated for emphasis. Curve 1, symmetrical with a broad optimum; curve 2, skewed to the right; curve 3, symmetrical with a sharp optimum.

tant: early observation yields a curve with a sharply defined optimum, but in time the germination at less favorable temperatures catches up and the optimum becomes much broader. This phenomenon appears to be general (13, 23, 84, 166, 219, 241, 260, 299).

Second in importance to the time effect as a factor in determining the shape of the temperature curve is the general principle that the limits of germination are narrower if some other factor is non-optimal. Thus, conidia of *Sclerotinia fructicola* at an unfavorably acid pH germinate only at 13–29°C and the curve is sharply peaked at 21°; at a more favorable reaction, pH 2.4, both the total range and the optimum are much broader (283). The depressant effect of low temperature on *Erysiphe graminis* germination is virtually abolished in the presence of nutrients (317), and the minimum temperature of germination in *Colletotrichum lagenarium* is lower in a nutrient medium than in water (101). The principle applies also to relative humidity, i.e., the temperature curve becomes narrower and sharper as the humidity becomes more unfavorable to germination (118, 286).

Although different spore forms of the same species usually have at least similar temperature responses (148, 178, 285), the endoconidia and macroconidia of *Chalaropsis thielavioides* show optima at 9–30°

and 12°, respectively; in this organism the age of endoconidia has a pronounced effect on the shape of the temperature-germination curve (168).

So far, we have considered the response of germination, i.e., initiation of the germ tube, to temperature. The further growth of the germ tube may be plotted against temperature. When such curves are compared to germination curves, there is often, perhaps usually, a close correspondence (42, 86, 93, 103, 146, 241). With many fungi, the optimum is rather narrower than that for germination; examples include *Erysiphe graminis* (317), *Physalospora obtusa* (92), *Clasterosporium carpophilum* (103), and several rust fungi (57, 20, 266). In still other fungi, the shape of the curve or the position of the optimum, or both, are different (84, 102, 116, 148, 260). In general, it appears that germ tube growth is closer in its temperature response to mycelial growth than it is to spore germination; the data of Snell (260) on *Lenzites sepiaria* are especially instructive in this connection. For this reason, there are many problems, especially in plant pathology, in which the temperature characteristics of germ tube growth are more illuminating than those of germination.

The preceding discussion emphasizes the limitations of the conventional temperature study of spore germination. Results often depend upon the criterion used, and upon such sometimes uncontrolled variables as age of spore, humidity, and pH. The studies are not, however, to be dismissed as useless; thus, it is often possible to correlate the ecological niche of a parasitic fungus with the response of its spores to temperature (44, 57, 317).

In this discussion we have tacitly assumed that temperature affects all processes up to the appearance of the germ tube in the same way. There is indirect evidence, from two types of temperature reaction, that this assumption is not valid, that the processes which initiate spore germination have a different sensitivity from later stages.

Although it might be expected *a priori* that at lower temperatures the rate of all processes is slower, the data of Figure 8 show a more complex situation: to be sure, the rate of germination at suboptimal temperatures is somewhat less than the rate at the optimum (18°), but the principal effect of low temperature is to delay the onset of germination, i.e., to increase the latent period. Once germination has begun, it is almost as rapid at low temperature as at high. Similar data may be found in studies of *Fusarium moniliforme* (241), *Sclerotinia fructicola* (299), and *Magnusia* spp. (276). Both rate and latent period are strongly affected by low temperature in *Phytophthora infestans* (63) and *Uncinula necator* (67). The latent period, and by inference the metabolic

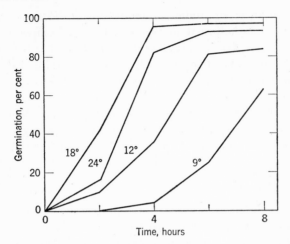

Figure 8. Temperature and the rate of germination of uredospores of *Phragmidium mucronatum*. Redrawn from Cochrane (57), by permission of the Cornell University Agricultural Experiment Station.

reactions occurring in the very earliest phases of germination, is uniformly extremely sensitive to low temperature. At supraoptimal temperatures there is again evident a differential sensitivity of these early reactions (284).

Sensitivity to low temperature of the processes concerned in the initiation of germination is paralleled by sensitivity of the same processes to a favorable temperature. The germination of uredospores of *Phragmidium mucronatum* at non-optimal temperatures is markedly accelerated by exposure for a short time to a moderate temperature; for example, germination at 9°C is increased about 160 per cent by a preexposure for one hour at 18°, during which exposure there is no visible sign of germination (58). The same phenomenon in *Puccinia chrysanthemi* is suggested by the data of Campbell and Dimock (44). Similarly, direct germination, by germ tube formation, of the conidiosporangia of *Phytophthora infestans* at 20° is greatly increased by prior exposure for 5–10 minutes to 40° (279).

It can be suggested, therefore, that early metabolic reactions in germination have a different and more sensitive response to temperature than do the later stages. Obviously, the evidence is far from complete. It is perhaps analogous that the cracking of the sporangium wall in *Blastocladiella* sp. responds somewhat differently to temperature than do the later stages of germination (45).

Parenthetically, it may be noted that these results have a methodological significance: in studies of temperature, the medium and its container must be adjusted to the experimental temperature before spores are sown. We may assume that this precaution has often been overlooked and deduce that many temperature-germination curves are in error, in that they exaggerate the extent of germination at sub- and supraoptimal temperatures.

As noted in Chapter 1, a given fungus usually has about the same temperature response whether mycelial growth or spore germination is the criterion (24, 86); a few exceptions have been reported (84, 298).

10. OXYGEN AND GERMINATION

It will be recalled that mycelial growth in fungi is often possible at very low oxygen pressures but that truly anaerobic growth is unlikely (Chapter 1). Virtually the same applies to spore germination in general, with a few exceptions to be noted here.

Failure of submerged spores to germinate or to germinate normally has often been observed and credited, without proof, to oxygen deficit. As pointed out by Gottlieb (113), too many other factors are affected by submergence for this simple evidence to be aceptable.

Ideally, experimental studies on the oxygen requirements for spore germination should include, first, demonstration of the response to graded oxygen pressures which are accurately measured and, second, proof that the spores which fail to germinate at a given pO_2 are still viable. Relatively few experiments meet this ideal standard. Uredospores of *Puccinia graminis tritici* (2) and chlamydospores of *Ustilago zeae* (217) fail to germinate at zero oxygen pressure and reach maximum or near-maximum germination at 30–38 mm of oxygen. Conidia of *Botrytis cinerea* germinate as well in 5 per cent oxygen as in air (37), but spores of *Synchytrium endobioticum* are severely inhibited at 3 per cent oxygen (292).

Removal of oxygen by pyrogallol prevents germination in, for example, uredospores of rust fungi (6, 129) and chlamydospores of *Ustilago avenae* (143). Although conidia of *Erysiphe graminis* are reported to germinate at a low level in an atmosphere of nitrogen (70), other studies on powdery mildew fungi indicate that germination is prevented by anaerobiosis (34, 167). Ascospores of *Neurospora tetrasperma* also fail to germinate anaerobically (107).

Conidiosporangia of three species of *Phytophthora* can germinate by swarmspore formation—but not by germ tube—under anaerobiosis, although other members of the Peronosporales fail completely to germinate without oxygen (291). In the Mucorales, it appears that spores of strongly fermentative species have a very low oxygen requirement and those of less strongly fermentative species a higher one; all, however, probably require some oxygen. In this study of the Mucorales (304), it was also found that the swelling of the spore of *Mucor* spp. can occur without oxygen, i.e., oxygen is required only at a later stage in development.

Pure oxygen is at least slowly toxic to spores of *Streptomyces scabies* (242); in short-term experiments inhibition of germination in *Botrytis cinerea* by high oxygen pressure is measurable but small (37).

It appears, to conclude, that spore germination usually requires at least some oxygen, but that the atmospheric level is more than adequate. In nature, it seems unlikely that spore germination is prevented by oxygen deficits except under such extreme conditions as flooded soil or heavily polluted water.

11. CARBON DIOXIDE AND GERMINATION

From the observations cited in Chapter 7, that carbon dioxide often accelerates the early growth of fungi, we might guess that spore germination is accelerated by carbon dioxide. This proves to be true in *Aspergillus niger* (223). Effects of high levels of carbon dioxide in increasing chlamydospore germination have been interpreted, however, as arising primarily from the effect of the dissolved gas on the acidity of the medium (218).

At high concentrations, carbon dioxide is partially or even completely inhibitory to spore germination. Brown (37) determined that the spores of seven different fungi, if sown in water, are completely inhibited by an atmosphere of 20–30 per cent carbon dioxide; sensitivity is markedly less if the spores are sown in a plant decoction. Other reports agree that carbon dioxide is inhibitory and that the level at which germination is affected may be low (180, 266) or high (139, 169). Inhibition at concentrations of 1 per cent or so is probably specific; effects of the higher concentrations could be indirect, e.g., on acidity or on oxygen supply.

12. BIOLOGICAL EFFECTS ON SPORE GERMINATION

It is commonly observed that excessive crowding of spores on a surface results in reduced germination; the phenomenon is known in many fungi (27, 37, 70, 73, 148, 160, 172) and may be described by the general term self-inhibition. In *Neurospora crassa,* crowding of conidia reduces the germination rate, but not total germination (240). These interactions of spore populations are formally analogous to the self-inhibition of growth reported in species of actinomycetes (207, 290) and inhibition of spore germination in *Phycomyces blakesleeanus* by products of mycelial growth (249). However, we may anticipate that these reactions of growing mycelium are more complex and more dependent on the environment than is self-inhibition in spores. *Bacillus globigii* endospores produce a substance, antagonized by alanine, which inhibits germination of fresh endospores of the same species (265).

Self-inhibition has been most clearly demonstrated in studies of rusts, *Uromyces phaseoli* (313, 314), *Puccinia graminis tritici* (2), and *P. helianthi* (315). The inhibitory effect of a dense concentration has been demonstrated *in vivo,* on the host plant, as well as *in vitro* (Figure 9); most of our information indicates that the active material is volatile.

Allen (2) has determined several characteristics of the substance—possibly substances—responsible for self-inhibition of *Puccinia graminis tritici* uredospores. The active material is stable to heat, is inactivated or removed from solution by glass surfaces, and is more effective at high pH than at low. The inhibitor is a spore metabolite produced under aerobic conditions. This differs somewhat from the situation

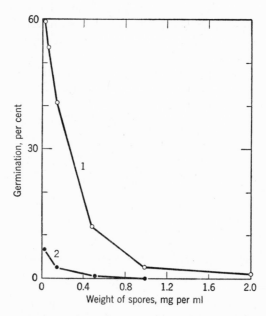

Figure 9. The effect of uredospore concentration on germination in *Puccinia graminis tritici.* Curve 1, spores in open vessels; curve 2, spores in sealed vessels. Redrawn from Allen (2), by permission of *Phytopathology.*

in *Aspergillus niger* (155) and *Coccomyces hiemalis* (148), in both of which limited evidence suggests than an inhibitor is present in the spore at the time of its formation and can be removed by washing.

Preliminary evidence has been reported by Forsyth (91) that *Puccinia graminis tritici* uredospores produce 2-methyl-butene-2 (trimethylethylene), and that this compound inhibits spore germination. Whether this is the effective substance remains to be seen.

Self-inhibition has at least one obvious ecological function, that germination of spores within the fructification is minimized. The ungerminated spore is much more resistant to the environment than the germinated and is, of course, the effective agent of dispersal. Although germination *in situ* has occasionally been reported, it appears to be the exception; this suggests that self-inhibition is a general principle in spore physiology, and that it is not limited to the few fungi so far studied.

At the other extreme from self-inhibition is the situation in *Ophiobolus graminis* (210); ascospores germinate slowly if isolated singly, more rapidly if many spores are present. Still a different effect occurs in certain myxomycetes (257), in which spore germination is promoted by the medium upon which a culture has grown.

Plant materials, besides increasing spore germination through nutrient effects or carbon dioxide evolution, in some cases inhibit germination, e.g., of *Botrytis cinerea* (36, 38) and *Venturia inaequalis* (106). The mechanism of these effects, as that of the inhibition of spore germination in soil (50), is still unknown. Microbial products may also inhibit germination; these include, besides the fungitoxic antibiotics, the compound fusaric acid (Chapter 8), produced by several *Fusarium* spp. and active against *Ustilago zeae* (104).

BIBLIOGRAPHY

1. Abe, T. 1933. *Ann. Phytopathol. Soc. Japan* 2: 502–512.
2. Allen, P. J. 1955. *Phytopathology* 45: 259–266.
3. Arens, K. 1929. *Jahrb. wiss. Botan.* 70: 57–92.
4. Armolik, N. and J. G. Dickson. 1956. *Phytopathology* 46: 462–465.
5. Atwood, K. C. and F. Mukai. 1955. *Genetics* 40: 438–443.
6. Bailey, L. D. 1923. *Minn. Univ. Agr. Exp. Sta. Tech. Bull.* 16: 1–31.
7. Bajaj, V., S. P. Damle, and P. S. Krishnan. 1954. *Arch. Biochem. Biophys.* 50: 451–460.
8. Baker, G. E. 1945. *Mycologia* 37: 582–600.
9. Balls, W. L. 1905. *New Phytologist* 4: 18–19.
10. Beauverie, J. 1924. *Compt. rend. (Paris)* 179: 993–996.
11. Becker, J. 1929. *Kühn-Arch.* 19: 353–411.
12. Bellinger, H. 1956. *Zentr. Bakteriol. Parasitenk. Abt. II,* 109: 13–16.

13. Bennett, C. W. 1921. *Mich. State Univ. Agr. Exp. Sta. Tech. Bull.* 53: 1–40.
14. Bennett, F. T. 1937. *Ann. Appl. Biol.* 24: 236–257.
15. Berestneff, N. M. 1907. *Gentr. Bakteriol. Parasitenk. Abt. I Ref.* 40: 298.
16. Bever, W. M. 1945. *J. Agr. Research* 71: 41–59.
17. Blackwell, E. 1940. *Trans. Brit. Mycol. Soc.* 24: 68–86.
18. Blackwell, E. 1943. *Trans. Brit. Mycol. Soc.* 26: 93–103.
19. Blackwell, E. and G. M. Waterhouse. 1931. *Trans. Brit. Mycol. Soc.* 15: 294–310.
20. Bliss, D. E. 1933. *Iowa State Coll. Agr. Exp. Sta. Research Bull.* 166: 339–392.
21. Blochwitz, A. 1933. *Ann. Mycol.* 31: 73–83.
22. Block, S. S. 1953. *Appl. Microbiol.* 1: 287–293.
23. Blodgett, E. C. 1936. *Phytopathology* 26: 115–152.
24. Bollard, E. G. 1950. *Trans. Brit. Mycol. Soc.* 33: 250–264.
25. Bonner, J. T. 1948. *Mycologia* 40: 728–738.
26. Boughey, A. S. 1949. *Trans. Brit. Mycol. Soc.* 32: 179–187.
27. Boyd, A. E. W. 1952. *Ann. Appl. Biol.* 39: 322–329.
28. Bradley, S. G. and J. Lederberg. 1956. *J. Bacteriol.* 72: 219–225.
29. Bretzloff, C. W., Jr. 1954. *Am. J. Botany* 41: 58–67.
30. Brierley, W. B. 1917. *Ann. Botany* 31: 127–132.
31. Broadfoot, W. C. 1926. *Phytopathology* 16: 951–978.
32. Brodie, H. J. 1936. *Am. J. Botany* 23: 309–327.
33. Brodie, H. J. 1945. *Can. J. Research C,* 23: 198–211.
34. Brodie, H. J. and C. C. Neufeld. 1942. *Can. J. Research C,* 20: 41–61.
35. Brown, R. 1946. *Nature (London)* 157: 64–69.
36. Brown, W. 1922a. *Ann. Botany* 36: 101–119.
37. Brown, W. 1922b. *Ann. Botany* 36: 257–283.
38. Brown, W. 1922c. *Ann. Botany* 36: 285–300.
39. Brown, W. 1936. *Botan. Rev.* 2: 236–283.
40. Brown, W. and C. C. Harvey. 1927. *Ann. Botany* 41: 643–662.
41. Buller, A. H. R. 1934. *Researches on Fungi,* Vol. 6. London: Longmans, Green and Co., pp. 513.
42. Burgert, I. A. 1934. *Phytopathology* 24: 384–396.
43. Butler, E. E. 1956. *Mycologia* 48: 345–348.
44. Campbell, C. E. and A. W. Dimock. 1955. *Phytopathology* 45: 644–648.
45. Cantino, E. C. 1951. *Antonie van Leeuwenhoek J. Microbiol. Serol.* 17: 59–96.
46. Chamberlain, D. W. and J. L. Allison. 1945. *Phytophathology* 35: 241–248.
47. Cheo, P.-C. and J. G. Leach. 1950. *Phytopathology* 40: 584–589.
48. Cherewick, W. J. 1944. *Can. J. Research C,* 22: 52–86.
49. Chilton, S. J. P. 1943. *Mycologia* 35: 13–20.
50. Chinn, S. H. F. 1953. *Can. J. Botany* 31: 718–724.
51. Chowdhury, S. 1937. *Indian J. Agr. Sci.* 7: 653–657.
52. Chowdhury, S. 1944. *J. Indian Botan. Soc.* 23: 91–106.
53. Chowdhury, S. 1946. *J. Indian Botan. Soc.* 25: 123–130.
54. Christensen, J. J. and F. R. Davies. 1937. *Mycologia* 29: 85–99.
55. Clark, J. F. 1902. *Botan. Gaz.* 33: 26–48.
56. Clayton, C. N. 1942. *Phytopathology* 32: 921–943.
57. Cochrane, V. W. 1945a. *Cornell Univ. Agr. Exp. Sta. Mem.* 268: 1–39.
58. Cochrane, V. W. 1945b. *Phytopathology* 35: 361–366.
59. Cochrane, V. W. 1956. Unpublished data.
60. Cole, H., Jr. and C. L. Fergus. 1956. *Phytopathology* 46: 159–163.
61. Cooper, W. C. 1939. *Botan. Gaz.* 100: 844–852.
62. Corner, E. J. H. 1935. *New Phytologist* 34: 180–200.
63. Crosier, W. 1934. *Cornell Univ. Agr. Exp. Sta. Mem.* 155: 1–40.
64. Darby, R. T. and G. R. Mandels. 1955. *Plant Physiol.* 30: 360–366.

65. Davies, O. L., R. B. Duckworth, and G. C. M. Harris. 1948. *Nature (London)* 161: 642.
66. Davis, W. H. 1924. *Phytopathology* 14: 251–267.
67. Delp, C. J. 1954. *Phytopathology* 44: 615–626.
68. Dimond, A. E. and B. M. Duggar. 1941. *Proc. Natl. Acad. Sci. U. S.* 27: 459–468.
69. Dodge, B. O. 1912. *Bull. Torrey Botan. Club* 39: 139–197.
70. Domsch, K. H. 1954. *Arch. Mikrobiol.* 20: 163–175.
71. Doran, W. L. 1919. *Phytopathology* 9: 391–402.
72. Doran, W. L. 1921. *Mass. Agr. Exp. Sta. Bull.* 202: 39–66.
73. Doran, W. L. 1922. *Bull. Torrey Botan. Club* 49: 313–340.
74. Duff, G. H. 1918. *Phytopathology* 8: 289–292.
75. Duggar, B. M. 1901. *Botan. Gaz.* 31: 38–66.
76. Duggar, B. M. 1905. *U. S. Dept. Agr. Bur. Plant Ind. Bull.* 85: 1–60.
77. Dunegan, J. C. and C. O. Smith. 1941. *Phytopathology* 31: 189–191.
78. Elliott, E. W. 1949. *Mycologia* 41: 141–170.
79. Emerson, M. R. 1948. *J. Bacteriol.* 55: 327–330.
80. Emerson, M. R. 1954. *Plant Physiol.* 29: 418–428.
81. Emerson, R. 1950. *Ann. Rev. Microbiol.* 4: 169–200.
82. Evans, M. M. and G. Harrar. 1930. *Phytopathology* 20: 993–997.
83. Ezekiel, W. N. 1930. *Minn. Univ. Agr. Exp. Sta. Tech. Bull.* 67: 1–62.
84. Felton, M. W. and J. C. Walker. 1946. *J. Agr. Research* 72: 69–81.
85. Fergus, C. L. 1954. *Mycologia* 46: 435–441.
86. Fischer, E. and E. Gäumann. 1929. *Biologie der Pflanzenbewohndenen Parasitischen Pilze.* Jena: Gustav Fischer, pp. 428.
87. Fischer, F. G. and G. Werner. 1955. *Z. Physiol. Chem. Hoppe-Seyler's.* 300: 211–236.
88. Fischer, G. W. 1936. *Phytopathology* 26: 1118–1127.
89. Flor, H. H. 1954. *Phytopathology* 44: 469–471.
90. Forbes, I. L. 1939. *Phytopathology* 29: 659–684.
91. Forsyth, F. R. 1955. *Can. J. Botany* 33: 363–373.
92. Foster, H. H. 1937. *Phytopathology* 27: 803–823.
93. Frick, L. 1943. *Phytopathol. Z.* 14: 525–591.
94. Fries, N. 1941. *Arch. Mikrobiol.* 12: 266–284.
95. Fries, N. 1943. *Symbolae Botan. Upsalienses* 6 (4): 6–81.
96. Fries, N. 1948. *Hereditas* 34: 338–350.
97. Fries, N. 1949. *Svensk Botan. Tidskr.* 43: 316–342.
98. Fromme, F. D. 1915. *Am. J. Botany* 2: 82–85.
99. Fukushi, T. 1925. *J. Coll. Agr. Hokkaido Imp. Univ. (Japan)* 15: 269–307.
100. Fulton, H. R. 1906. *Botan. Gaz.* 41: 81–108.
101. Gardner, M. W. 1918. *U. S. Dept. Agr. Bull.* 727: 1–68.
102. Gardner, M. W. 1924. *Proc. Indiana Acad. Sci.* 33: 163–201.
103. Gäumann, E. 1946. *Pflanzliche Infektionslehre.* Basel: Verlag Birkhäuser, pp. 611.
104. Gäumann, E., S. Naef-Roth, and H. Kobel. 1953. *Phytopathol. Z.* 20: 1–38.
105. Gehring, F. 1953. *Angew. Botan.* 27: 97–105.
106. Gilliver, K. 1947. *Ann. Appl. Biol.* 34: 136–143.
107. Goddard, D. R. 1935. *J. Gen. Physiol.* 19: 45–60.
108. Goddard, D. R. 1939. *Cold Spring Harbor Symposia Quant. Biol.* 7: 362–376.
109. Goddard, D. R. 1948. *Growth* 12 (Suppl.): 17–45.
110. Goddard, D. R. and P. E. Smith. 1938. *Plant Physiol.* 13: 241–264.
111. Goldsworthy, M. C. and R. E. Smith. 1931. *Phytopathology* 21: 133–168.
112. Gossop, G. H., E. Yuill, and J. L. Yuill. 1940. *Trans. Brit. Mycol. Soc.* 24: 337–344.
113. Gottlieb, D. 1950. *Botan. Rev.* 16: 229–257.

114. Gottlieb, D. 1953. *Intern. Congr. Microbiol., 6th Congr.,* 5: 122–136.
115. Gould, C. J., Jr. 1945. *Iowa State Coll. J. Sci.* 19: 301–331.
116. Graf-Marin, A. 1934. *Cornell Univ. Agr. Exp. Sta. Mem.* 157: 1–48.
117. Graves, A. H. 1916. *Botan. Gaz.* 62: 337–369.
118. Groom, P. and T. Panisset. 1933. *Ann. Appl. Biol.* 20: 633–660.
119. Guba, E. F. 1938. *Mass. Agr. Exp. Sta. Bull.* 350: 1–24.
120. Gwynne-Vaughan, H. C. I. 1937. *Ann. Botany* 1: 99–105.
121. Gwynne-Vaughan, H. C. I. and H. S. Williamson. 1927. *Ann. Botany* 41: 489–495.
122. Gwynne-Vaughan, H. C. I. and H. S. Williamson. 1933. *Trans. Brit. Mycol. Soc.* 18: 127–134.
123. Gwynne-Vaughan, H. C. I. and H. S. Williamson. 1934. *Ann. Botany* 48: 261–272.
124. Hahne, J. 1925. *Kühn-Arch.* 9: 157–263.
125. Haines, R. B. 1930. *J. Exp. Biol.* 8: 379–388.
126. Haines, R. B. 1931. *J. Exp. Biol.* 9: 45–60.
127. Hansen, E. C. 1897. *Botan. Ztg.* 55, Abt. I: 111–131.
128. Hansen, H. N. 1938. *Mycologia* 30: 442–455.
129. Hart, H. 1926. *Phytopathology* 16: 185–205.
130. Hart, M. P. and D. M. MacLeod. 1955. *Can. J. Botany* 33: 289–292.
131. Hawn, E. J. and T. C. Vanterpool. 1953. *Can. J. Botany* 31: 699–710.
132. Heintzeler, I. 1939. *Arch. Mikrobiol.* 10: 92–132.
133. Hemmi, T. 1934. *Proc. Pacific Sci. Congr. Pac. Sci. Assoc., 5th Congr.* 1933, 4: 3185–3194.
134. Hemmi, T. and T. Abe. 1933. *Forsch. Gebiet Pflanzenkrankheiten (Kyoto)* 2: 1–9.
135. Hesse, R. 1876. *Jahrb. wiss. Botan.* 10: 199–203.
136. Holton, C. S. 1943. *Phytopathology* 33: 732–735.
137. Hrushovetz, S. B. 1956. *Can. J. Botany* 34: 321–327.
138. Huebschman, C. 1952. *Mycologia* 44: 599–604.
139. Hull, R. 1939. *Ann. Appl. Biol.* 26: 800–822.
140. Hüttig, W. 1931. *Z. Botan.* 24: 529–577.
141. Hyre, R. A. and R. S. Cox. 1953. *Phytopathology* 43: 419–425.
142. Johnson, T. 1941. *Phytopathology* 31: 197–198.
143. Jones, E. S. 1923a. *J. Agr. Research* 24: 577–591.
144. Jones, E. S. 1923b. *J. Agr. Research* 24: 593–597.
145. Jones, F. R. 1919. *U. S. Dept. Agr. Bull.* 759: 1–58.
146. Kaufmann, F. H. O. 1934. *Botan. Gaz.* 96: 282–297.
147. Kehl, H. 1943. *Planta* 33: 731–732.
148. Keitt, G. W., E. C. Blodgett, E. E. Wilson, and R. O. Magie. 1937. *Wisconsin Univ. Agr. Exp. Sta. Research Bull.* 132: 1–117.
149. Klotz, L. J. and H. S. Fawcett. 1932. *J. Agr. Research* 44: 155–166.
150. Kordes, H. 1923. *Botan. Arch.* 3: 282–311.
151. Kovacs, A. and E. Szeöke. 1956. *Phytopathol. Z.* 27: 335–349.
152. Kreitlow, K. W. 1943. *Phytopathology* 33: 707–712, 1055–1063.
153. Kreitlow, K. W. 1945. *Phytopathology* 35: 152–158.
154. Krishnan, P. S. and V. Bajaj. 1953. *Arch. Biochem. Biophys.* 47: 39–55.
155. Krishnan, P. S., V. Bajaj, and S. P. Damle. 1954. *Appl. Microbiol.* 2: 303–308.
156. Lambert, E. B. 1929. *Phytopathology* 19: 1–71.
157. Latham, D. H. 1935. *J. Elisha Mitchell Sci. Soc.* 51: 183–188.
158. Leach, J. G. 1923. *Minn. Univ. Agr. Exp. Sta. Tech. Bull.* 14: 1–41.
159. Leben, C. 1954. *Phytopathology* 44: 101–106.
160. Lehman, S. G. 1923. *Ann. Missouri Botan. Garden* 10: 111–178.
161. Le Roux, P. M. and J. G. Dickson. 1957. *Phytopathology* 47: 101–107.

162. Lesage, P. 1895. *Ann. sci. nat. Botan. Sér. 8*, 1: 309–322.
163. Lin, C.-K. 1940. *Cornell Univ. Agr. Exp. Sta. Mem.* 233: 1–33.
164. Lin, C.-K. 1945. *Am. J. Botany* 32: 296–298.
165. Ling, L. 1940. *Phytopathology* 30: 579–591.
166. Ling, L. and J. Y. Yang. 1944. *Ann. Botany* 8: 91–104.
167. Longrée, K. 1939. *Cornell Univ. Agr. Exp. Sta. Mem.* 223: 1–43.
168. Longrée, K. 1940. *Phytopathology* 30: 793–807.
169. Lopriore, G. 1895. *Jahrb. wiss. Botan.* 28: 531–626.
169a. Lowry, R. J., A. S. Sussman, and B. von Böventer. 1957. *Mycologia* 49: 609–622.
170. Lowry, R. J., A. S. Sussman, and B. Heidenhain. 1956. *Mycologia* 48: 241–252.
171. Lowther, C. V. 1950. *Phytopathology* 40: 590–603.
172. McCallan, S. E. A. 1930. *Cornell Univ. Agr. Exp. Sta. Mem.* 130: 25–79.
173. McCallan, S. E. A., L. P. Miller, and R. M. Weed. 1954. *Contribs. Boyce Thompson Inst.* 18: 39–68.
174. McCallan, S. E. A. and F. Wilcoxon. 1936. *Contribs. Boyce Thompson Inst.* 8: 151–165.
175. McCrea, A. 1923. *Science* 58: 426.
176. Machlis, L. and E. Ossia. 1953a. *Am. J. Botany* 40: 358–365.
177. Machlis, L. and E. Ossia. 1953b. *Am. J. Botany* 40: 465–468.
178. MacLachlan, J. D. 1936. *J. Arnold Arboretum (Harvard Univ.)* 17: 1–25.
179. MacMillan, H. G. and O. A. Plunkett. 1942. *J. Agr. Research* 64: 547–559.
180. Magie, R. O. 1935. *Phytopathology* 25: 131–159.
181. Mains, E. B. 1915. *Ann. Rept. Mich. Acad. Sci.* 17: 136–140.
182. Mains, E. B. and H. S. Jackson. 1926. *Phytopathology* 16: 89–120.
183. Mains, E. B. and D. Thompson. 1928. *Phytopathology* 18: 150.
184. Mandels, G. R. 1951. *Am. J. Botany* 38: 213–221.
185. Mandels, G. R. 1953a. *Arch. Biochem. Biophys.* 42: 164–173.
186. Mandels, G. R. 1953b. *Arch. Biochem. Biophys.* 44: 362–377.
187. Mandels, G. R. 1953c. *Exp. Cell Research* 5: 48–55.
188. Mandels, G. R. 1954. *Plant Physiol.* 29: 18–26.
189. Mandels, G. R. 1955. *Am. J. Botany* 42: 921–929.
190. Mandels, G. R. 1956a. *J. Bacteriol.* 71: 684–688.
191. Mandels, G. R. 1956b. *J. Bacteriol.* 72: 230–234.
192. Mandels, G. R. and R. T. Darby. 1953. *J. Bacteriol.* 65: 16–26.
193. Mandels, G. R., H. S. Levinson, and M. T. Hyatt. 1956. *J. Gen. Physiol.* 39: 301–309.
194. Mandels, G. R. and A. B. Norton. 1948. *Research Rept. Quartermaster Gen. Lab., Microbiol. Ser.* 11: 1–50.
195. Mandels, G. R. and A. B. Norton. 1949. *Research Rept. Quartermaster Gen. Lab., Microbiol. Ser.* 12: 1–35.
196. Maneval, W. E. 1922. *Phytopathology* 12: 471–487.
197. Maneval, W. E. 1924. *Phytopathology* 14: 403–407.
198. Marloth, R. H. 1931. *Phytopathology* 21: 169–198.
199. Melhus, I. E. 1911. *Wisconsin Univ. Agr. Exp. Sta. Research Bull.* 15: 25–91.
200. Melhus, I. E. and L. W. Durrell. 1919. *Iowa State Coll. Agr. Exp. Sta. Research Bull.* 49: 115–144.
201. Merek, E. L. and C. L. Fergus. 1954. *Phytopathology* 44: 61–64.
202. Miller, H. J. 1949. *Phytopathology* 39: 245–259.
203. Miyoshi, M. 1895. *Jahrb. wiss. Botan.* 28: 269–289.
204. Neger, F. W. 1902. *Flora* 90: 221–272.
205. Noble, R. J. 1923. *Phytopathology* 13: 127–129.
206. Noble, R. J. 1924. *J. Agr. Research* 27: 451–489.
207. Oki, N. and T. Hata. 1952. *J. Antibiotics (Japan)* 5: 16–23.

208. Owens, R. G. 1955a. *Contribs. Boyce Thompson Inst.* 18: 125–144.
209. Owens, R. G. 1955b. *Contribs. Boyce Thompson Inst.* 18: 145–152.
210. Padwick, G. W. 1939. *Ann. Appl. Biol.* 26: 823–825.
211. Page, R. M., A. F. Sherf, and T. L. Morgan. 1947. *Mycologia* 39: 158–164.
212. Paley, T. 1936. *Arch. Mikrobiol.* 7: 206–209.
213. Parker-Rhodes, A. F. 1943. *Ann. Appl. Biol.* 30: 372–379.
214. Peltier, G. L. 1922. *Nebraska Univ. Agr. Exp. Sta. Research Bull.* 22: 1–15.
215. Peltier, G. L. 1925. *Nebraska Univ. Agr. Exp. Sta. Research Bull.* 34: 1–12.
216. Perlman, D. 1951. *Am. J. Botany* 38: 652–658.
217. Platz, G. A. 1928. *Iowa State Coll. J. Sci.* 2: 137–143.
218. Platz, G. A., L. W. Durrell, and M. F. Howe. 1927. *J. Agr. Research* 34: 137–147.
219. Powlesland, R. 1954. *Trans. Brit. Mycol. Soc.* 37: 362–371.
220. Pratt, R. 1936. *Am. J. Botany* 23: 422–431.
221. Raeder, J. M. and W. M. Bever. 1931. *Phytopathology* 21: 767–789.
222. Reed, H. S. and C. H. Crabill. 1915. *Virginia Agr. Exp. Sta. Tech. Bull.* 9: 1–106.
223. Rippel, A. and H. Bortels. 1927. *Biochem. Z.* 184: 237–244.
224. Rippel, K. 1933. *Arch. Mikrobiol.* 4: 530–542.
225. Rishbeth, H. 1951. *Ann. Botany* 15: 1–21.
226. Robbins, W. J. 1940. *Am. J. Botany* 27: 559–564.
227. Robbins, W. J. 1941. *Botan. Gaz.* 102: 520–535.
228. Robbins, W. J. 1943. *Proc. Natl. Acad. Sci. U. S.* 29: 201–202.
229. Robbins, W. J. and K. C. Hamner. 1940. *Botan. Gaz.* 101: 912–927.
230. Robbins, W. J. and F. Kavanagh. 1942a. *Proc. Natl. Acad. Sci. U. S.* 28: 4–8.
231. Robbins, W. J. and F. Kavanagh. 1942b. *Proc. Natl. Acad. Sci. U. S.* 28: 65–69.
232. Robbins, W. J., V. W. Kavanagh, and F. Kavanagh. 1942. *Botan. Gaz.* 104: 224–242.
233. Robbins, W. J. and M. B. Schmitt. 1945. *Bull. Torrey Botan. Club* 72: 76–85.
234. Roberg, M. 1948. *Arch. Mikrobiol.* 14: 1–11.
235. Robinson, W. 1914. *Ann. Botany* 28: 331–340.
236. Roper, J. A. 1952. *Experientia* 8: 14–15.
237. Rosen, H. R. and L. M. Weetman. 1940. *Arkansas Univ. Agr. Exp. Sta. Bull.* 391: 1–20.
238. Rother, W. 1954. *Arch. Mikrobiol.* 20: 89–108.
239. Ryan, F. J. 1946. *Federation Proc.* 5: 366–369.
240. Ryan, F. J. 1948. *Am. J. Botany* 35: 497–503.
241. Saccas, A. 1951. *Rev. path. végétale et d'entomol. agr. France* 30: 65–96.
242. Sanford, G. B. 1926. *Phytopathology* 16: 525–547.
243. Sansome, E. 1956. *Trans. Brit. Mycol. Soc.* 39: 67–78.
244. Sawyer, W. H., Jr. 1929. *Am. J. Botany* 16: 87–121.
245. Schaffnit, E. 1909. *Ann. Mycol.* 7: 509–523.
246. Schlösser, L. A. 1929. *Planta* 8: 529–570.
247. Schneider, R. 1954. *Phytopathol. Z.* 21: 63–78.
248. Schönborn, W. 1955. *Arch. Mikrobiol.* 22: 408–431.
249. Schopfer, W. H. 1935. *Compt. rend. soc. phys. et hist. nat. Genève* 50: 152–154.
250. Semeniuk, G., C. M. Nagel, and J. C. Gilman. 1947. *Iowa State Coll. Agr. Exp. Sta. Bull.* 349: 225–284.
251. Shear, C. L. and B. O. Dodge. 1927. *J. Agr. Research* 34: 1019–1042.
252. Shepherd, C. J. 1956. *J. Gen. Microbiol.* 15: 29–38.
253. Shepherd, C. J. 1957. *J. Gen. Microbiol.* 16 (1): i.

254. Shu, P., K. G. Tanner, and G. A. Ledingham. 1954. *Can. J. Botany* 32: 16–23.
255. Sisler, H. D. and C. E. Cox. 1954. *Am. J. Botany* 41: 338–345.
256. Siu, R. G. H. 1951. *Microbial Decomposition of Cellulose.* New York: Reinhold Publ. Corp., pp. 531.
257. Smart, R. F. 1937. *Am. J. Botany* 24: 145–159.
258. Smith, E. C. 1929. *Mycologia* 21: 321–323.
259. Smith, J. H. 1924. *New Phytologist* 23: 65–78.
260. Snell, W. H. 1922. *U. S. Dept. Agr. Bull.* 1053: 1–47.
260a. Sörgel, G. 1956. *Phytopathol. Z.* 28: 187–204.
261. Sost, H. 1955. *Arch. Protistenk.* 100: 541–564.
262. Spaulding, P. and A. Rathbun-Gravatt. 1926. *J. Agr. Research* 33: 397–433.
263. Stadler, D. R. 1952. *J. Cellular Comp. Physiol.* 39: 449–474.
264. Stakman, E. C. 1913. *Minn. Univ. Agr. Exp. Sta. Bull.* 133: 1–52.
265. Stedtman, R. L., E. Kravitz, M. Anmuth, and J. Harding. 1956. *Science* 124: 403–405.
266. Stock, F. 1931. *Phytopathol. Z.* 3: 231–279.
267. Straib, W. 1940a. *Zentr. Bakteriol. Parasitenk. Abt. II*, 102: 154–188.
268. Straib, W. 1940b. *Z. Pflanzenkrankh.* 50: 529–552.
269. Stroede, W. 1933. *Phytopathol. Z.* 5: 613–624.
270. Stüben, H. 1939. *Planta* 30: 353–383.
271. Sumi, M. 1928. *Biochem. Z.* 195: 161–174.
272. Sussman, A. S. 1953a. *Am. J. Botany* 40: 401–404.
273. Sussman, A. S. 1953b. *J. Gen. Microbiol.* 8: 211–216.
274. Sussman, A. S. 1954a. *J. Gen. Physiol.* 38: 59–77.
275. Sussman, A. S. 1954b. *Mycologia* 46: 143–150.
276. Sweet, H. R. 1941. *Am. J. Botany* 28: 150–161.
277. Sweet, H. R. 1942. *Am. J. Botany* 29: 436–441.
278. Tapke, V. F. 1955. *Phytopathology* 45: 73–78.
279. Taylor, C. F., et al. 1955. *Phytopathology* 45: 673–676.
280. Thiel, A. F. and F. Weiss. 1920. *Phytopathology* 10: 448–452.
281. Thirumulachar, M. J. and J. G. Dickson. 1949. *Phytopathology* 39: 333–339.
282. Thomas, H. E. and W. D. Mills. 1929. *Cornell Univ. Agr. Exp. Sta. Mem.* 123: 1–21.
283. Tilford, P. E. 1936. *Ohio Agr. Exp. Sta. Bull.* 567: 1–27.
284. Tisdale, W. B. 1920. *Phytopathology* 10: 148–163.
285. Togashi, K. 1949. *Biological Characters of Plant Pathogens. Temperature Relations.* Tokyo: Meibundo, pp. 478.
286. Tomkins, R. G. 1929. *Proc. Roy. Soc. (London) B* 105: 375–401.
287. Tomkins, R. G. 1932. *Trans. Brit. Mycol. Soc.* 17: 147–149.
288. Turel, F. L. M. 1955. *Can. J. Microbiol.* 1: 293–298.
289. Turner, J. N. 1953. *Trans. Brit. Mycol. Soc.* 36: 159–162.
290. Uesaka, I. and Y. Ito. 1951. *J. Antibiotics (Japan)* 4: 418–424.
291. Uppal, B. N. 1926. *Phytopathology* 16: 285–292.
292. Vladimirskaya, N. N. 1954. *Mikrobiologiya* 23: 72–75.
293. Wain, R. L. and E. H. Wilkinson. 1946. *Ann. Appl. Biol.* 33: 401–405.
294. Wainwright, L. K. 1956. *J. Gen. Microbiol.* 14: 533–544.
295. Webb, R. 1921. *Ann. Missouri Botan. Garden* 8: 283–341.
296. Weber, G. F. 1922. *Phytopathology* 12: 89–97.
297. Wehmer, C. 1904. *Ber. deut. botan. Ges.* 22: 476–478.
298. Weimer, J. L. and L. L. Harter. 1923. *J. Agr. Research* 24: 1–40.
299. Wellman, R. H. and S. E. A. McCallan. 1942. *Contribs. Boyce Thompson Inst.* 12: 431–450.
300. Weston, W. H., Jr. 1951. *Trans N. Y. Acad. Sci. II*, 13: 305–308.

301. Wilkins, W. H. 1938. *Trans. Brit. Mycol. Soc.* 22: 47–93.
302. Wolf, F. A., L. F. Dixon, R. McLean, and F. R. Darkis. 1934. *Phytopathology* 24: 337–363.
303. Wolf, F. A. and F. T. Wolf. 1947. *The Fungi, Vol.* 2. New York: John Wiley and Sons, pp. 538.
304. Wood-Baker, A. 1955. *Trans. Brit. Mycol. Soc.* 38: 291–297.
305. Yarwood, C. E. 1932. *Phytopathology* 22: 31.
306. Yarwood, C. E. 1936. *Phytopathology* 26: 845–859.
307. Yarwood, C. E. 1939a. *Phytopathology* 29: 828–829.
308. Yarwood, C. E. 1939b. *Phytopathology* 29: 933–945.
309. Yarwood, C. E. 1941. *Phytopathology* 31: 865.
310. Yarwood, C. E. 1950a. *Am. J. Botany* 37: 636–639.
311. Yarwood, C. E. 1950b. *Calif. Agr.* 4: 7, 12.
312. Yarwood, C. E. 1952. *Mycologia* 44: 506–522.
313. Yarwood, C. E. 1954. *Proc. Natl. Acad. Sci. U. S.* 40: 374–377.
314. Yarwood, C. E. 1956a. *Mycologia* 48: 20–24.
315. Yarwood, C. E. 1956b. *Phytopathology* 46: 540–544.
316. Yarwood, C. E. and M. Cohen. 1949. *Science* 110: 477–478.
317. Yarwood, C. E., S. Sidky, M. Cohen, and V. Santilli. 1954. *Hilgardia* 22: 603–622.
318. Yu, C. C. 1954. *Am. J. Botany* 41: 21–30.
319. Zalokar, M. and V. W. Cochrane. 1956. *Am. J. Botany* 43: 107–110.
320. Zeller, S. M. 1920. *Ann. Missouri Botan. Garden* 7: 51–74.
321. Ziegler, A. W. 1948. *J. Elisha Mitchell Sci. Soc.* 64: 13–40.
322. Zimmerman, A. 1925. *Centr. Bakteriol. Parasitenk. Abt. II,* 65: 311–418.

13. The Action of Physical Agents

I t is convenient, although probably not defensible in the final analysis, to separate the physical and chemical agents that adversely affect fungi. Of the several agents of the first type, attention must be focused upon temperature and radiation. Osmotic pressure has been touched upon earlier, in Chapters 1 and 12. Hydrostatic pressure has hardly been studied in relation to the fungi; very young infections by plant pathogens are prevented from developing by the application of pressure (156), and reduced pressure somewhat facilitates germination in *Erysiphe graminis,* perhaps by accelerating carbon dioxide loss (12). It may be expected that studies of cellular reactions and of the action of fungicides under high pressures will contribute to our understanding of the fungi, as similar studies have contributed to the knowledge of bacteria (76).

1. HIGH TEMPERATURE

The practical problem of heat sterilization is primarily that of killing bacterial endospores; fungal structures, with some exceptions, are less resistant. Consequently, there has been little interest in fundamental studies on the death of fungi at high temperature. However, destruction of fungi within host tissues has proved practicable for a few pathogens which are present as mycelium in seeds or cuttings (148).

The thermal death point, defined as the least temperature at which all cells are killed in 10 minutes, has been determined for spores of several fungi as 40–60°C, a value close to that usually reported for vegetative cells of mesophilic bacteria (1, 19, 21, 24, 88, 128). However, spores of some species are much more resistant; known examples are the conidia of *Nocardia sebivorans* (38) and ascospores of *Byssochlamys fulva* (70), *Neurospora crassa* (40), and *Penicillium* sp. (153), Conidia of thermophilic actinomycetes appear to be heat-resistant (37).

Ascospores are more resistant than conidia in *Neurospora crassa* (40, 125) but are equally susceptible in *Endoconidiophora fagacearum* (24). Data on mycelium are too scanty for generalization; *Fusarium lini* is killed in 10 minutes at 55°, but *Colletotrichum lini* survives 3 or 4 hours at this temperature (139). A culture of *Nocardia sebivorans* withstands 10 minutes at 90° (38), and suspended sclerotia of *Penicillium* sp. are completely killed at 82° only in about 16 hours (153). Spores of *Erysiphe* spp. are somewhat more resistant to heat than mycelium (157), but comparative studies of spores and mycelium in other fungi have not been made.

Neither the thermal death point nor the related thermal death time has proved adequate in studies of bacteria (124), and there is no reason to hope that they will prove to be any more satisfactory for work with fungi. Development of a better index will, however, have to wait until we have more knowledge of the order of death. Characteristically, the killing of vegetative cells of bacteria is exponential, i.e., a plot of the logarithm of survivors against time is linear (118, 124), although non-exponential orders of death by heat are known (77, 119). Data on the killing of fungi by heat are few in number; Figure 1 shows a non-exponential order of heat killing of ascospores of *Byssochlamys fulva;* ascospores of *Penicillium* sp. respond similarly (153). At lower temperatures the curve becomes distinctly sigmoid, i.e., short exposures have proportionately less effect (128). These few statements refer to studies of spores; sclerotia of *Penicillium* sp. respond to heat as one would expect in a multicellular structure (153).

Tentatively, we may propose that the non-exponential order of death of fungus spores reflects genetic heterogeneity of the material, but the data are too limited at present to justify a firm conclusion, and in particular the occurrence of bi- or multinucleate cells may influence the reaction.

Death by heat is most drastically affected by moisture. Cells die much more rapidly at high temperatures if they are wet (22, 37, 74) or if the relative humidity is high (24, 53). Heat resistance in *Byssochlamys fulva* is affected by the pH of the menstruum (70).

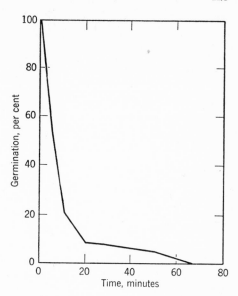

Figure 1. The order of killing of ascospores of *Byssochlamys fulva* by moist heat (85°C). Replotted from Hull (70), by permission of the Cambridge University Press.

The mechanism of death at high temperature is usually thought to be denaturation of proteins; the high Q_{10} of thermal death (128) is consistent with this explanation. Whatever the validity of the denaturation theory at high temperatures, some other explanation must be invoked to explain death at temperatures which are just above the maximum for development. Thus, mitosporangia and sporophytic mycelium of *Allomyces* sp. die within 24 hours at 30° (98), and uredospores of *Phragmidium mucronatum* survive only 12 hours at 27° (22). Presumably some fraction of metabolism continues under these conditions, and either endogenous reserves of essential materials are depleted or essential cofactors decay and cannot be resynthesized. Less likely, but possible, is the accumulation of one or more metabolites in toxic concentrations.

2. LOW TEMPERATURE

No systematic study of damage to fungi by low temperature has been reported. Even more important, the scattered data have been obtained under such different experimental conditions that comparison and generalization must be very tentative indeed. Too often we are not informed of essential factors, particularly (1) the type of cells present, (2) the quantitative degree of injury, (3) the rate of freezing, and (4) the rate of thawing. It must be realized that survival can only be assayed after thawing the material, and, as shown later (Figure 2), the rate of subzero warming is critical.

Exposure to very low temperatures, e.g., that of liquid air, does not completely kill mycelium, fruiting bodies, or dry spores of most fungi (8, 16, 79, 89). The mycelium of some fungi does not survive this treatment (89), and wet conidia of *Neurospora crassa* are killed almost immediately at −170° to −190°C (40).

Exposure to moderately low temperatures—from 0 to −40°C—is of immediate ecological interest and has frequently been investigated. The results, however, defy any neat generalization; either fungi differ very widely in their tolerance or, as suggested above, methods of investigation are so different that comparison is not legitimate. Mycelium of *Phycomyces nitens* and *Botrytis cinerea* is killed by exposure to −15 to −22° (6), and neither mycelium nor sclerotia of *Phymatotrichum omnivorum* survives 24 hours at −13° (39). But mycelium of *Phacidium infestans* and *Collybia velutipes* is still viable after 138 days at −21° (114), and fruit bodies of *Schizophyllum commune* withstand exposure to −15 to −40° (17).

Similar differences are reported in the survival of spores at these moderately low temperatures. Uredospores of the rust fungi are usually found to survive no more than 2 months or so at −15° to −40° (22, 42, 104, 149), but at least some uredospores of *Melampsora lini* are still viable after 1295 days at −10° (41), and uredospores of *Uromyces phaseoli* live as long as 2 years at −20° (59). Both spore forms of *Endoconidiophora fagacearum* are germinable after 83 days at −10° (24).

From these reports and from the partial list compiled by Luyet and Gehenio (91), it appears that spores are in general less damaged by low temperature than mycelium, dry spores less than wet.

Most of the reported experiments on the true fungi are probably examples of relatively slow freezing, in which the primary injurious factor is dehydration; crystals of ice form extracellularly and withdraw water from the cell (105). Damage to dry cells is less than to wet (14, 40), as would be expected. Furthermore, it was early found that solutes protect the mycelium against freezing injury (6); hydrogen bonding substances—sugars, glycols, etc.—essentially lower the amount of water lost to the crystallization process (105). Visual observation suggests that hyphal tips are more susceptible than basal mycelial cells and that aerial hyphae are more resistant than submerged (87); the water content may be a factor in these differences.

Rapid freezing, in which crystal formation occurs throughout both cells and medium, must obviously be so rapid as to limit the size of

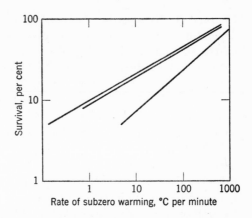

Figure 2. The influence of the rate of warming on viability (germinability) of conidia of *Aspergillus flavus* frozen at —70°C. Each curve represents a separate experiment. Redrawn from Mazur (103), by permission of the Rockefeller Institute for Medical Research.

the individual crystals (105). It follows that thawing must be equally rapid, in order to prevent crystal growth. This is shown especially well by the data of Mazur (103), part of which is reproduced in Figure 2. The lethal effects of slow, as compared to rapid, warming were particularly evident in the range —20 to 0°C; i.e., the rate of subzero warming, not the rate of thawing of ice, is the critical factor.

The possibility of freezing material so rapidly as to prevent crystal formation entirely has been considered at length by Luyet and Gehenio (91). The experimental difficulties are formidable, and there is some problem in determining whether or not success has been achieved (105). In any event, it is clear that prevention of crystal formation is not essential to survival at low temperature.

We may conclude that fungi, especially vegetative mycelium and certain types of spores, are relatively susceptible to freezing injury, particularly to the slow freezing which occurs in nature; repeated freezing and thawing are even more damaging (115). The principal factor is almost certainly the moisture content of the material; it follows that preservation in the frozen state will be most successful if applied to dry spores or other cells which can withstand a preliminary desiccation. Although it is unlikely that freezing can eliminate all cells of a given species, cold injury must be an important ecological factor at least for soil fungi and plant pathogens (22, 39).

3. VISIBLE LIGHT

Light of the visible range, 400–800 mμ, exerts undoubted, but so far ill-defined, influences on mycelial growth, spore germination, and other phenomena; effects on reproduction have been discussed in

Chapter 11. It must be recalled that exposure to "white light" may, depending on the source, involve exposure to some ultraviolet; heating effects, too, cannot de disregarded unless specifically excluded.

Several early observations, reviewed by Smith (127), and later data (20, 58, 75, 113, 129) agree that light retards mycelial growth; dry weight measurements confirm this for *Sclerotinia fructigena* (55) and *Karlingia rosea* (60). The growth of *Botrytis squamosus* on agar is completely inhibited by light (112).

Light stimulation of growth, infrequently reported (60, 127), has been most carefully analyzed in *Blastocladiella emersonii* (18). In this organism dry weight increases of up to 141 per cent, at constant temperature, are induced by illumination. It is observed further that fixation of carbon dioxide is increased by light, and it is proposed that light acts in some way to accelerate the reductive carboxylation of succinic acid and α-ketoglutaric acid.

Vegetative mycelium, like reproductive structures, may be phototropic (122) and may show zonation in response to light and dark periods (25). Pigmentation is frequently dependent upon or enhanced by light (127); *Centrospora acerina* forms its red pigment after a very short exposure (107). Melanogenesis in *Neurospora crassa* is somewhat reduced by illumination (123). The effect of light on carotene formation has been mentioned elsewhere (Chapter 6).

It has been recognized at least since 1860 (61) that strong light inhibits spore germination. Whether spores are more or less sensitive than mycelium is in doubt (127). Obviously, any ultraviolet contamination is especially serious, and there is no doubt that many of the lethal effects of light can be credited to a short wavelength component. However, in both *Erysiphe graminis* (117) and *Puccinia graminis* (30, 31) experiments with filters implicate the longer wavelengths, in the yellow-red region, and exclude ultraviolet. Moist spores are more susceptible than dry (23).

A number of reports—too many to disregard—suggest that spore germination is increased by light or even requires light (47, 48, 71, 106, 130, 155, 160). The mechanism of such an effect is difficult to imagine, and it can only be said at this time that further quantitative work under accurately controlled conditions is necessary.

Photodynamic action has been demonstrated by Kaplan (78) in *Penicillium notatum:* conidia vitally stained with erythrosin are sensitized so that visible light, normally innocuous, becomes mutagenic. Eosin-stained cells of *Neurospora crassa* appear from limited data to respond similarly (34). Methylene blue intensifies the zonation response of *Penicillium notatum* to light (120a).

4. ULTRAVIOLET RADIATION

The lethality and mutagenicity of ultraviolet radiation are problems of general biological interest; studies on fungi have made significant contributions toward their solution. The early, and now largely obsolete, literature is reviewed by Smith (127), more recent work by Pomper and Atwood (116). Techniques for the irradiation of spores and isolation of radiation-induced mutants are well developed (7, 120, 138, 152).

Virtually all studies of the action spectrum of killing and of mutagenesis in fungi, as in other organisms, agree that the most effective wavelength is in the region 260–265 mμ. The action spectrum of lethality to *Trichophyton mentagrophytes* is shown in Figure 3; similar spectra prevail in *Neurospora crassa* (67, 109), *Penicillium notatum* (69), *Ustilago zeae* (85), and *Aspergillus oryzae* (102). The primary peak is generally accepted to be consequent upon the specific absorption of this wavelength by nucleoproteins.

McAulay and associates (92, 93, 94) have reported that biological activity for *Chaetomium globosum* is greatest at 280 mμ, in the region of absorption by proteins. These observations cannot be reconciled with any other data and merit re-examination.

Aspergillus terreus conidia mutate after exposure to higher wavelengths (297 and 313 mμ) or to sunlight (65). Efficiency, however, is

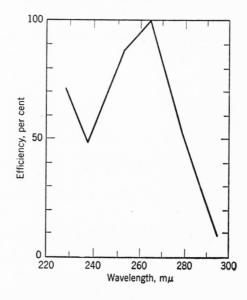

Figure 3. The action spectrum of killing of spores of *Trichophyton mentagrophytes*. Redrawn from original of Figure 4, A. Hollaender and C. W. Emmons, *Journal of Cellular and Comparative Physiology*, Vol. 13, p. 391-402 (1938), by permission of the Wistar Institute of Anatomy and Biology.

very low, and at still longer wavelengths most organisms survive very large doses (50), although bactericidal action can be detected at high intensity (62). The requirement for high intensity poses serious methodological problems in attempts to demonstrate the mutagenicity of the long ultraviolet (43). Very short ultraviolet—the Schumann region, below 200 mμ—has not been studied, primarily for technical reasons; indications are that lethal action at least is very great (85, 111, 159).

The lethality of ultraviolet radiation is most easily expressed by the fraction of irradiated spores which fail to germinate. Doses that are not lethal delay germination or induce abnormalities (33, 64, 67, 85). Different fungi vary widely in susceptibility; thus, spores of *Mucor dispersus* require almost 20 times the energy per spore that is sufficient for an equivalent degree of inactivation of *Aspergillus melleus* spores (32, 33). In surveys of fungal susceptibility it is often noted that

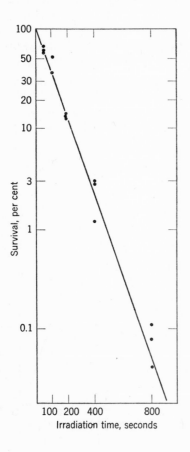

Figure 4. The survival of microconidia of three mutant strains (inositolless) of *Neurospora crassa* as a function of ultraviolet dosage. Redrawn from Giles (51), by permission of the Long Island Biological Association.

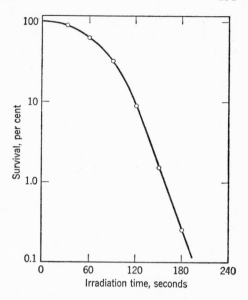

Figure 5. The survival of macroconidia (average number of nuclei 2.67 per conidium) of *Neurospora crassa* as a function of ultraviolet dosage. Redrawn from Atwood and Norman (5), by permission of the National Academy of Sciences.

species with dark spores tend to be more resistant (36, 46), and a protective action of wall pigments in *Puccinia graminis* uredospores has been claimed (29). Pigmentation alone, however, cannot explain specific differences in sensitivity.

The curve generated by a plot of survival against dose is usually one of two types:

1. The exponential curve, in which the logarithm of the fraction surviving is a linear or approximately linear function of dosage. This curve is characteristic of microconidia of *Neurospora crassa* (Figure 4) and spores of *Penicillium* spp. (2, 46), *Aspergillus melleus* (33), and *Streptomyces flaveolus* (80).

2. The sigmoidal curve (Figure 5), which is the more common type, reported in studies of *Aspergillus* spp. (73, 158), *Mucor dispersus* and *Rhizopus suinus* (33), *Ustilago zeae* (85), *Glomerella cingulata* (95), *Fusarium eumartii* (126), *Trichophyton mentagrophytes* (64), and *Streptomyces griseus* (121).

The significance of these curve shapes has been debated vigorously, and it may be too early for a categorical explanation. By itself, the sigmoidal curve could be interpreted as expressive of variability in the spore population, and Markert (95) has shown such variability in sensitivity in *Glomerella cingulata*. However, this interpretation applied to the exponential curve requires a highly improbable distribution of sensitivity within the population. Studies on *Neurospora crassa*

(5, 109, 110) suggest instead that the shape of the dose-response curve is a function of the number of nuclei per cell: exponential for uninucleate spores, sigmoidal for bi- and multinucleate spores. Death in a multinucleate spore requires that several targets must absorb radiation; the sigmoidal curve follows from this requirement.

Two mechanisms of lethality have been proposed (109): induction of recessive lethal mutations and non-genetic damage to nuclei. Obviously, the first of these cannot be of much significance in the death of conidia having more than one nucleus.

The induction of morphological and biochemical mutations by ultraviolet radiation responds rather differently as dosage is increased. As shown in Figure 6, mutation frequency increases with dosage only to a point, then levels off or declines at higher dosage. Dose-response curves of this general type have been reported from several studies in which all morphologically visible mutations are scored (63, 66, 67, 73, 100, 135). However, in one instance in which a known mutation at a single locus was scored, the response curve was strikingly different (51), and the mutation frequency in *Streptomyces flaveolus* does not drop at high dosage (80).

Ultraviolet-induced mutagenesis is affected by several modifying environmental factors. Pretreatment before irradiation with infrared radiation, 2,4-dinitrophenol, or nitrogen mustard increases mutagenesis (133, 134, 135, 136). Survival and mutation rate in *Streptomyces* sp. are modified by treatments applied after irradiation (143, 145, 146). Respiratory poisons and anaerobiosis decrease both the lethal and the mutagenic effects of ultraviolet radiation on *Penicillium chrysogenum*

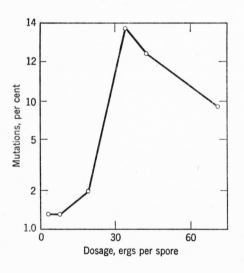

Figure 6. Morphological mutations in *Penicillium notatum* as a function of ultraviolet dosage. Plotted from data of Hollaender (63).

(152). Most important, perhaps, is the observation of McElroy (102) that postirradiation treatment with high hydrostatic pressure reduces the recovery of morphological mutants in *Neurospora crassa* and *Aspergillus terreus*. This observation suggests that the primary action of ultraviolet (and chemical mutagens) is to cause the formation of a semi-stable intermediate which may decay to a new, mutant, state or may revert to its original, normal, state (103). The hypothetical intermediate may be the gene itself or a metabolite or metabolic system (143, 146).

Peroxides and unknown products in irradiated media are mutagenic to *Neurospora crassa* (27, 142). However, results published so far fail to implicate products formed by ultraviolet irradiation of the medium, at the wavelengths employed in mutation studies, as important factors in the induction of mutations.

Photoreactivation was discovered in *Streptomyces griseus* (82) and has been observed in several of the true fungi (13, 17a, 52, 81, 109). As usually studied, photoreactivation means that lethal effects of ultraviolet radiation are counteracted in part by subsequent exposure to light of longer wavelength, 330 to 480 mμ; however, other changes induced by ultraviolet are also counteracted. The action spectrum of photoreactivation in *S. griseus* has a pronounced peak at 436 mμ, differing significantly from the action spectrum of the same process in *Escherichia coli* (83). The theories and problems of photoreactivation are reviewed by Dulbecco (35). Wainwright and Nevill (144) present evidence that photoreactivation exerts independent effects on survival and mutagenesis in *Streptomyces* sp.

5. IONIZING RADIATIONS

Ionizing radiations, as the name implies, are radiations whose passage through a material causes the production of ion-pairs. Most studies on fungi have employed X-rays or the equivalent γ-rays emitted by radium and other radioactive materials; a few data are available on α-rays (from polonium, but also produced by the cyclotron), β-rays (from radioactive materials or from an ion source), and cyclotron-produced neutrons. All these types of radiation, we assume, have the same mode of action but differ, of course, in energy, ionization per unit path length, and ability to penetrate (86). Consequently, physically equivalent doses of different types of ionizing radiation are not biologically equivalent. However, it is not yet clear how such differences in biological effect are to be explained. Thus, in the killing of spores of *Aspergillus terreus,* the densely ionizing radiations (protons and α-rays) are more effective than the less densely ionizing X-rays and γ-rays, but the order of effectiveness is reversed if mutagenesis in *A. terreus* is the criterion (132). The killing of *A. niger* spores by α-irradiation is similarly most effective at high ionization density (161). On the other hand, lethality to vegetative cells of *Escherichia coli* is greatest with radiation of low ionization density (159).

Lethal and mutagenic effects of types of radiation other than X-rays have been reported, viz., neutrons (4, 56, 99), α-particles from polonium and radium (9, 10, 11), γ-rays from radioactive elements (26, 137), and β-particles from carbon-14 or an ion source (84, 150, 151). Earlier studies are reviewed by Smith (127).

The lethal effect of X-irradiation on spores of fungi and actinomycetes can usually be expressed as an exponential or approximately exponential dose-response curve (3, 72, 80, 121). Sigmoid survival curves have only occasionally been reported (45, 90). It seems probable, especially from preliminary work on yeasts, that the form of the curve may be primarily determined by the number of nuclei per cell (116). This consideration cannot apply to the striking response of dry spores of *Aspergillus terreus*: X-irradiation follows the sigmoidal pattern but survival after irradiation with α-particles is exponential (132, 162).

Mutation frequency is linear with dose over a range; as shown in Figure 7, some material shows a plateau in the curve at high dosage (54, 80, 108). Presumably this plateau will be reached with any organism provided the dose is high enough. Theoretical models for this saturation effect are considered by Harm and Stein (57).

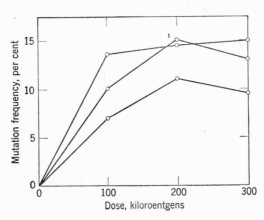

Figure 7. Mutation frequency in *Streptomyces flaveolus* as a function of X-ray dosage. Each curve represents a separate experiment. Redrawn from Kelner (80), by permission of the Williams and Wilkins Company.

Lethality and mutagenic action are not the only effect of irradiation. In particular, irradiated spores may germinate but fail to make continued growth; this phenomenon, reported in several fungi (11, 28, 90, 141) is analogous to the delayed effect of X-irradiation on yeast (116) and to the "microscopic mutant" induced in *Chaetomium globosum* by ultraviolet or ionizing radiation (44, 93). The irradiation of *Aspergillus niger* spores with low (non-lethal) intensities of α-particles results in the development of asporogenous colonies in an unspecified number (11). These delayed effects are perhaps best described as lethal mutations, but something more than a descriptive analysis would surely be of interest.

Stimulation of spore germination by ionizing radiation has been reported (15, 154). Other less well-defined stimulatory effects claimed by earlier workers are reviewed by Smith (127).

The environmental factor most significant in modifying responses of fungi and bacteria to X-irradiation is the ambient oxygen pressure (68, 131): both lethality and mutagenesis are less at low oxygen tension. Sensitivity of *Aspergillus terreus* to X-irradiation is also increased by previous exposure to infrared radiation (133, 135) and by high spore moisture content (131). The lethality of X-irradiation to *Streptomyces* sp. is decreased by various postirradiation treatments (147).

Radiation biology is undergoing rapid advances at this time, and it is to be expected that generalizations will have a short life. In the fungi it appears that the primary effect of radiation is on the nucleus, and this effect—which may be itself complex—is best visualized on the basis of the target theory so strongly urged by Lea (86). However, there is good evidence—especially in the influence of environmental factors on response—that significant secondary reactions, possibly in the cytoplasm, must be postulated both for ultraviolet and for ionizing radiation (116, 159).

6. ELECTROMAGNETIC RADIATION OF LONG WAVELENGTH

Irradiation in the "radio" part of the electromagnetic spectrum may be inhibitory to fungi. Inhibition is, however, a heating effect and does not occur if the temperature is held constant (49, 97, 101, 140).

BIBLIOGRAPHY

1. Ames, A. 1915. *Phytopathology* 5: 11–19.
2. Arima, K. 1951a. *J. Antibiotics (Japan)* 4: 232–237.
3. Arima, K. 1951b. *J. Antibiotics (Japan)* 4: 277–280.

4. Atwood, K. C. and F. Mukai. 1954. *Am. Naturalist* 88: 295–314.
5. Atwood, K. C. and A. Norman. 1949. *Proc. Natl. Acad. Sci. U. S.* 35: 696–709.
6. Bartetzko, H. 1910. *Jahrb. wiss. Botan.* 47: 57–98.
7. Beadle, G. W. and E. L. Tatum. 1945. *Am. J. Botany* 32: 678–686.
8. Becquerel, C. 1910. *Compt. rend. (Paris)* 150: 1437–1439.
9. Berk, S. 1952a. *Mycologia* 44: 587–598.
10. Berk, S. 1952b. *Mycologia* 44: 723–735.
11. Berk, S. 1953. *Mycologia* 45: 488–506.
12. Brodie, H. J. and J. F. Jones. 1946. *Can. J. Research C,* 24: 318–329.
13. Brown, J. S. 1951. *J. Bacteriol.* 62: 163–167.
14. de Bruyn, H. L. G. 1926. *Phytopathology* 16: 121–140.
15. Buchwald, C. E. and R. M. Whelden. 1939. *Am. J. Botany* 26: 778–784.
16. Buller, A. H. R. 1912. *Trans. Brit. Mycol. Soc.* 4: 106–112.
17. Buller, A. H. R. and A. T. Cameron. 1912. *Trans. Roy. Soc. Can.* 6, IV: 73–78.
17a. Buxton, E. W., F. T. Last, and M. A. Nour. 1957. *J. Gen. Microbiol.* 16: 764–773.
18. Cantino, E. C. and E. A. Horenstein. 1956. *Mycologia* 48: 777–799.
19. Chaudhuri, M. 1923. *Ann. Botany* 37: 519–539.
20. Chowdhury, S. 1944. *J. Indian Botan. Soc.* 23: 91–106.
21. Cochran, L. C. 1932. *Phytopathology* 22: 791–812.
22. Cochrane, V. W. 1945a. *Cornell Univ. Agr. Exp. Sta. Mem.* 268: 1–39.
23. Cochrane, V. W. 1945b. *Phytopathology* 35: 458–462.
24. Cole, H., Jr. and C. L. Fergus. 1956. *Phytopathology* 46: 159–163.
25. Coons, G. H. and F. G. Larmer. 1930. *Papers Mich. Acad. Sci.* 11: 75–104.
26. Davis, R. J., V. L. Sheldon, and S. I. Auerbach. 1956. *J. Bacteriol.* 72: 505–510.
27. Dickey, F. H., G. H. Cleland, and C. Lotz. 1949. *Proc. Natl. Acad. Sci. U. S.* 35: 581–586.
28. Dickson, H. 1932. *Ann. Botany* 46: 389–405.
29. Dillon Weston, W. A. R. 1931. *Sci. Agr.* 12: 81–87.
30. Dillon Weston, W. A. R. 1932a. *Phytopathol. Z.* 4: 229–246.
31. Dillon Weston, W. A. R. 1932b. *Sci. Agr.* 12: 352–356.
32. Dimond, A. E. and B. M. Duggar. 1940. *J. Cellular Comp. Physiol.* 16: 55–61.
33. Dimond, A. E. and B. M. Duggar. 1941. *Proc. Natl. Acad. Sci. U. S.* 27: 459–468.
34. Döring, H. 1938. *Naturwiss.* 26: 819–820.
35. Dulbecco, R. 1955. In A. Hollaender (ed.), *Radiation Biology,* Vol. 2, p. 455–486. New York: McGraw-Hill Book Co.
36. English, H. and F. Gerhardt. 1946. *Phytopathology* 36: 100–111.
37. Erikson, D. 1952. *J. Gen. Microbiol.* 6: 286–294.
38. Erikson, D. 1955. *J. Gen. Microbiol.* 13: 127–135.
39. Ezekiel, W. N. 1945. *Phytopathology* 35: 296–301.
40. Faull, A. F. 1930. *Mycologia* 22: 288–303.
41. Flor, H. H. 1954. *Phytopathology* 44: 469–471.
42. Forbes, I. L. 1939. *Phytopathology* 29: 659–684.
43. Ford, J. M. 1947. *J. Gen. Physiol.* 30: 211–216.
44. Ford, J. M. 1948. *Australian J. Exp. Biol. Med. Sci.* 26: 245–251.
45. Ford, J. M. and D. P. Kirwan. 1949. *J. Gen. Physiol.* 32: 647–653.
46. Fulton, H. R. and W. W. Coblentz. 1929. *J. Agr. Research* 38: 159–168.
47. Gassner, G. and E. Niemann. 1954. *Phytopathol. Z.* 21: 367–394.
48. Gassner-Hoechst, G. G. 1954. *Phytopathol. Z.* 21: 53–62.
49. Gier, L. J. 1938. *Trans. Kansas Acad. Sci.* 40: 55–57.
50. Giese, A. C. 1945. *Physiol. Zool.* 18: 223–250.

BIBLIOGRAPHY   437

51. Giles, N. H., Jr. 1951. *Cold Spring Harbor Symposia Quant. Biol.* 16: 283–313.
52. Goodgal, S. H. 1949. *Anat. Rec.* 105: 496.
53. Groom, P. and T. Panisset. 1933. *Ann. Appl. Biol.* 20: 633–660.
54. Gwatkin, R. B. and D. Gottlieb. 1956. *J. Bacteriol.* 71: 328–332.
55. Hall, M. P. 1933. *Ann. Botany* 47: 543–578.
56. Hanson, H. J., W. G. Myers, G. L. Stahly, and J. M. Birkeland. 1946. *J. Bacteriol.* 51: 9–18.
57. Harm, W. and W. Stein. 1956. *Z. Naturforsch.* 11b: 89–105.
58. Harter, L. L. 1939. *Am. J. Botany* 26: 234–243.
59. Harter, L. L. and W. J. Zaumeyer. 1941. *J. Agr. Research* 62: 717–731.
60. Haskins, R. H. and W. H. Weston, Jr. 1950. *Am. J. Botany* 37: 739–750.
61. Hoffman, H. 1860. *Jahrb. wiss. Botan.* 2: 267–337.
62. Hollaender, A. 1943. *J. Bacteriol.* 46: 531–541.
63. Hollaender, A. 1945. *Ann. Missouri Botan. Garden* 32: 165–178.
64. Hollaender, A. and C. W. Emmons. 1939. *J. Cellular Comp. Physiol.* 13: 391–402.
65. Hollaender, A. and C. W. Emmons. 1946. *Cold Spring Harbor Symposia Quant. Biol.* 11: 78–84.
66. Hollaender, A., K. B. Raper, and R. D. Coghill. 1945. *Am. J. Botany* 32: 160–165.
67. Hollaender, A., E. R. Sansome, E. Zimmer, and M. Demerec. 1945. *Am. J. Botany* 32: 226–235.
68. Hollaender, A. and G. E. Stapleton. 1953. *Physiol. Revs.* 33: 77–84.
69. Hollaender, A. and E. Zimmer. 1945. *Genetics* 30: 8.
70. Hull, R. 1939. *Ann. Appl. Biol.* 26: 800–822.
71. Hutchinson, A. H. and M. R. Ashton. 1930. *Can. J. Research* 3: 187–198.
72. Iguchi, N. 1951. *J. Agr. Chem. Soc. Japan* 24: 81–84.
73. Iizuka, H. and T. Yamaguchi. 1952. *J. Agr. Chem. Soc. Japan* 26: 71–74.
74. Jensen, H. 1948. *Physiol. Plantarum* 1: 255–264.
75. Jensen, H. L. 1941. *Proc. Linnean Soc. N. S. Wales* 66: 276–286.
76. Johnson, F. H., H. Eyring, and M. J. Polissar. 1954. *The Kinetic Basis of Molecular Biology.* New York: John Wiley and Sons, pp. 874.
77. Jordan, R. C., S. E. Jacobs, and H. E. F. Davis. 1947. *J. Hyg.* 45: 136–143.
78. Kaplan, R. 1950. *Planta* 38: 1–11.
79. Kärcher, H. 1931. *Planta* 14: 515–516.
80. Kelner, A. 1948. *J. Bacteriol.* 56: 457–465.
81. Kelner, A. 1949a. *J. Bacteriol.* 58: 511–522.
82. Kelner, A. 1949b. *Proc. Natl. Acad. Sci. U. S.* 35: 73–79.
83. Kelner, A. 1951. *J. Gen. Physiol.* 34: 835–852.
84. Kern, H. and B. D. Sanwal. 1954. *Phytopathol. Z.* 22: 449–453.
85. Landen, E. W. 1939. *J. Cellular Comp. Physiol.* 14: 217–226.
86. Lea, D. C. 1955. *Actions of Radiation on Living Cells,* 2nd ed. Cambridge: Cambridge Univ. Press, pp. 416.
87. Lindner, J. 1915. *Jahrb. wiss. Botan.* 55: 1–52.
88. Ling, L. and E. H. Yu. 1941. *Phytopathology* 31: 264–270.
89. Lipman, C. B. 1937. *Bull. Torrey Botan. Club* 64: 537–546.
90. Luyet, B. J. 1932. *Radiology* 18: 1019–1022.
91. Luyet, B. J. and P. M. Gehenio. 1940. *Life and Death at Low Temperatures.* Normandy, Missouri: Biodynamica, pp. 341.
92. McAulay, A. L. and J. M. Ford. 1947. *Heredity (London)* 1: 247–257.
93. McAulay, A. L., J. M. Ford, and D. L. Dobie. 1949. *Heredity (London)* 3: 109–120.
94. McAulay, A. L. and M. C. Taylor. 1939. *J. Exp. Biol.* 16: 474–482.
95. McElroy, W. D. 1952. *Science* 115: 623–626.

96. McElroy, W. D. and C. P. Swanson. 1951. *Quart. Rev. Biol.* 26: 348–363.
97. Macdonald, J. A. 1947. *Ann. Appl. Biol.* 34: 430–434.
98. Machlis, L. and J. M. Crasemann. 1956. *Am. J. Botany* 43: 601–611.
99. Markert, C. L. 1952. *Genetics* 37: 339–352.
100. Markert, C. L. 1953. *Exp. Cell Research* 5: 427–435.
101. Matuo, T. and T. Shioiri. 1951. *Research Repts. Fac. Textile Seric. Shinshu Univ. (Japan)* 1: 47–52. (*Rev. Appl. Mycol.* 34: 234. 1955.)
102. Maxwell, M. E. 1952. *Australian J. Sci. Research* B, 5: 56–63.
103. Mazur, P. 1956. *J. Gen. Physiol.* 39: 869–888.
104. Melander, L. W. 1935. *J. Agr. Research* 50: 861–880.
105. Meryman, H. T. 1956. *Science* 124: 515–521.
106. Neergaard, P. 1941. *Gartner-Tidende* 57: 319–322.
107. Neergaard, P. and A. G. Newhall. 1951. *Phytopathology* 41: 1021–1033.
108. Newcombe, H. B. and J. F. McGregor. 1954. *Genetics* 39: 619–627.
109. Norman, A. 1951. *Exp. Cell Research* 2: 454–473.
110. Norman, A. 1954. *J. Cellular Comp. Physiol.* 44: 1–10.
111. Oster, R. 1934. *J. Gen. Physiol.* 18: 71–88, 243–250, 251–254.
112. Page, O. T. 1956. *Can. J. Botany* 34: 881–890.
113. Page, R. M. 1952. *Am. J. Botany* 39: 731–739.
114. Pehrson, S. O. 1948. *Physiol. Plantarum* 1: 38–56.
115. Piemeisel, F. J. 1917. *Phytopathology* 7: 294–307.
116. Pomper, S. and K. C. Atwood. 1955. In A. Hollaender, (ed.), *Radiation Biology*, Vol. 2, p. 431–453. New York: McGraw-Hill Book Co.
117. Pratt, R. 1944. *Bull. Torrey Botan. Club* 71: 134–143.
118. Rahn, O. 1929. *J. Gen. Physiol.* 13: 179–205.
119. Rahn, O. 1930. *J. Gen. Physiol.* 13: 395–407.
120. Raper, K. B. and D. I. Fennell. 1946. *J. Bacteriol.* 51: 761–777.
120a. Sagromsky, H. 1956. *Biol. Zentr.* 75: 385–397.
121. Savage, G. M. 1949. *J. Bacteriol.* 57: 429–441.
122. Sawyer, W. H., Jr. 1929. *Am. J. Botany* 16: 87–121.
123. Schaeffer, P. 1953. *Arch. Biochem. Biophys.* 47: 359–379.
124. Schmidt, C. F. 1954. In G. F. Reddish (ed.), *Antiseptics, Disinfectants, Fungicides, and Chemical and Physical Sterilization*, p. 720–759. Philadelphia: Lea and Febiger.
125. Shear, C. L. and B. O. Dodge. 1927. *J. Agr. Research* 34: 1019–1042.
126. Smith, E. C. 1935. *Bull. Torrey Botan. Club* 62: 45–58.
127. Smith, E. C. 1936. In B. M. Duggar (ed.), *Biological Effects of Radiation*, p. 889–918. New York: McGraw-Hill Book Co.
128. Smith, J. H. 1923. *Ann. Appl. Biol.* 10: 335–347.
129. Snyder, W. C. and H. N. Hansen. 1941. *Mycologia* 33: 580–591.
130. Sorokine, N. 1876. *Ann. sci. nat. Botan. Sér.* 6, 3: 46–52.
131. Stapleton, G. E. and A. Hollaender. 1952. *J. Cellular Comp. Physiol.* 39, Suppl. 1: 101–113.
132. Stapleton, G. E., A. Hollaender, and F. L. Martin. 1952. *J. Cellular Comp. Physiol.* 39, Suppl. 1: 87–100.
133. Swanson, C. P. 1952. *J. Cellular Comp. Physiol.* 39, Suppl. 1: 27–38.
134. Swanson, C. P. and S. H. Goodgal. 1950. *Genetics* 35: 695–696.
135. Swanson, C. P., A. Hollaender, and B. N. Kaufmann. 1948. *Genetics* 33: 429–437.
136. Swanson, C. P., W. D. McElroy, and H. Miller. 1949. *Proc. Natl. Acad. Sci. U. S.* 35: 513–518.
137. Tarpley, W., J. Ilarsky, B. Manowitz, and R. Horrigan. 1953. *J. Bacteriol.* 65: 305–309.
138. Tatum, E. L., R. W. Barratt, N. Fries, and D. Bonner. 1950. *Am. J. Botany* 37: 38–46.

139. Tochinai, Y. 1926. *J. Coll. Agr. Hokkaido Imp. Univ. (Japan)* 14: 171–236.
140. Tverskay, D. L. 1937. *Plant Protect. (U.S.S.R.)* 1937 (13): 3–28. (*Rev. Appl. Mycol.* 17: 127–128. 1938.)
141. Uber, F. M. and D. R. Goddard. 1934. *J. Gen. Physiol.* 17: 577–590.
142. Wagner, R. P., C. H. Haddox, R. Fuerst, and W. S. Stone. 1950. *Genetics* 35: 237–248.
143. Wainwright, S. D. and A. Nevill. 1955a. *Can. J. Microbiol.* 1: 416–426.
144. Wainwright, S. D. and A. Nevill. 1955b. *Can. J. Microbiol.* 1: 427–439.
145. Wainwright, S. D. and A. Nevill. 1955c. *J. Gen. Microbiol.* 12: 1–12.
146. Wainwright, S. D. and A. Nevill. 1955d. *J. Gen. Microbiol.* 12: 13–24.
147. Wainwright, S. D. and A. Nevill. 1955e. *J. Bacteriol.* 70: 547–551.
148. Walker, J. C. 1950. *Plant Pathology.* New York: McGraw-Hill Book Co., Inc. pp. 699.
149. Ward, H. M. 1902. *Ann. Botany* 16: 233–315.
150. Wheeler, H. E. 1952. *Phytopathology* 42: 431–435.
151. Whelden, R. M. 1940. *Mycologia* 32: 630–643.
152. Whittingham, W. F. and J. F. Stauffer. 1956. *Am. J. Botany* 43: 54–60.
153. Williams, C. C., E. J. Cameron, and O. B. Williams. 1941. *Food Research* 6: 69–73.
154. Woodward, V. W. and C. M. Clark. 1955. *Science* 121: 641–642.
155. Yarwood, C. E. 1939. *Phytopathology* 29: 828–829.
156. Yarwood, C. E. 1953. *Phytopathology* 43: 70–72.
157. Yarwood, C. E., S. Sidky, M. Cohen, and V. Santilli. 1954. *Hilgardia* 22: 603–622.
158. Zahl, P. A., L. R. Koller, and C. P. Haskins. 1939. *J. Gen. Physiol.* 22: 689–698.
159. Zelle, M. R. and A. Hollaender. 1955. In A. Hollaender (ed.), *Radiation Biology*, Vol. 2, p. 365–430. New York: McGraw-Hill Book Co.
160. Ziegler, A. W. 1948. *J. Elisha Mitchell Sci. Soc.* 64: 13–40.
161. Zirkle, R. E. 1940. *J. Cellular Comp. Physiol.* 16: 221–235.
162. Zirkle, R. E., D. F. Marchbank, and K. D. Kuck. 1952. *J. Cellular Comp. Physiol.* 39, Suppl. 1: 75–85.

14. The Action
of
Chemical Agents

Inhibition by chemical agents has probably been the single most active field of investigation of the fungi. Of necessity, however, much of this work has been directed to the practical problem of controlling the fungi pathogenic to plants and to man and other animals and the fungi that destroy economically valuable commodities. Theoretical problems have, of course, not been neglected; the important work has been summarized by Martin (278) and more recently by Horsfall (172, 174).

In a study of the physiology of fungi, such as this, it seems appropriate to concentrate attention upon those materials, regardless of their practical importance, about which we have some information as to mode of action. This approach neglects many fascinating problems in the chemical inhibition of fungi: the role of antibiotic substances in soil (152, 425) and the use of purified antibiotics (218, 337, 396, 430), the expanding field of chemotherapy of plants (90, 175, 176, 402), and many of the developments in the use of organic compounds as fungistatic or fungicidal agents. It is to be hoped that sufficient attention will be devoted to mode of action so that these topics can be treated theoretically in the near future.

The chapter has been organized so as first to consider some general problems and then to give detailed attention to a few types of compounds—heavy metals, sulfur, quinones, and the chelating agents—which have been most actively investigated.

1. THE RESPONSE TO TOXICANTS AND ITS MEASUREMENT

For practical reasons most of our information on the response of fungi to toxic agents relates to the inhibition of spore germination or of mycelial growth. However, other effects are occasionally observed and may be briefly described. The most important aspect of response is, of course, its measurement, since any investigation of mode of action presupposes an accurate, reproducible assay of the biological effect of a fungicidal or fungistatic agent.

Morphological Responses. Morphological abnormalities of growing hyphae are caused by many toxicants, including such diverse agents as diphenyl (340), dyes (363), benzothiazole (142), solanin (2), and sodium tungstate (256). Other instances, as well as data on abnormal development of germ tubes, are tabulated by Horsfall (174). Thymol and carvacrol cause swelling of conidia of *Aspergillus niger* (450), as does phenol (420).

Griseofulvin, an antibiotic produced by *Penicillium* spp. (Chapter 6), causes stunting, branching, distortion, and other abnormalities of growth in virtually all chitin-walled fungi tested, not in the yeasts or Oomycetes, which have non-chitinous walls (Chapter 2). Brian (42) suggests that griseofulvin either acts as a growth regulator or interferes with a growth regulator controlling wall extension; spore germination of *Botrytis allii* is not prevented by a concentration 500 times that which affects germ tube growth (43). Griseofulvin is taken up by green plants (74, 403) and protects to a considerable degree against infection by *Alternaria solani* (44). A few fungi which probably have chitin walls are nonetheless insensitive (304).

Camphor causes the formation of large, possibly diploid, conidia (361, 362). Cholic acid and sodium taurocholate induce the formation of uninucleate cells in the dikaryon of several basidiomycetes, probably converting a clamp initial to a separate branch (286).

Mitotic Poisons. Many fungitoxic substances are known to inhibit mitosis in other organisms (137, 174). Exposure of basidia of *Gymnosporangium clavipes* to penicillin or streptomycin results in abnormal development and interference with meiosis (27). In yeast, penicillin inhibits cell division without inhibiting growth, so that filaments are formed; reversal experiments suggest that sulfhydryl groups essential to cell division are blocked by the antibiotic (310).

The Response of Developmental Stages. Specific inhibition of sporulation has both theoretical and practical importance. Simultaneous

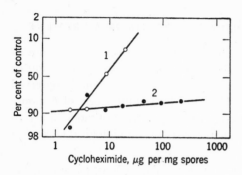

Figure 1. The response of germination (curve 1) and oxygen uptake (curve 2) of *Neurospora sitophila* conidia as a function of the concentration of cycloheximide. Respiration was measured in the presence of sucrose, germination after removal of the toxicant. Redrawn from McCallan, Miller, and Weed (247), by permission of the Boyce Thompson Institute for Plant Research, Inc.

and fully quantitative determinations of both growth and sporulation are difficult; preliminary data suggest that the high metal requirements of sporulation (Chapter 11) make the process especially sensitive to chelating agents, e.g., dimethylglyoxime, but many other types of toxicant also reduce reproductive activity (179, 332, 333, 340, 342, 399, 428, 448, 457).

It is generally believed that mycelial cells are less sensitive to toxicants than are spores; this is borne out by direct comparisons for sulfanilamide (125, 147) and cycloheximide (430a, 431). The difference may, however, be related to uptake (246a).

Inhibition of Respiration. Inhibition of respiratory activity as measured by oxygen uptake is often parallel to growth inhibition (106, 269, 309, 334), and it has even been tentatively suggested that the principal activity of Captan[1] is on pyruvic carboxylase (160). However, most studies, on very different compounds, show that in general endogenous and substrate respiration is much less sensitive to a wide range of fungicides than is spore germination or growth (83, 125, 127, 132, 203, 224).

Figure 1 is drawn from an extensive study of fungicidal activity, judged by killing of spores, and spore respiration; the figure shows that a compound, in this case cycloheximide, kills at concentrations which do not measurably reduce oxygen uptake. The data of Klöpping (203) show a similar relation between fungistatic action and inhibition of respiration; 8-hydroxquinoline has no effect on respiration at a concentration 100 times the fungistatic concentration.

Low concentrations of toxicants often stimulate respiration (247). It seems likely that membrane permeability to substrate is increased

---

[1] N-(trichloromethylthio)-4-cyclohexene-1,2-dicarboximide.

under these conditions, although other explanations are possible (20). Increase in oxygen consumption is also caused by poisons, e.g., 2,4-dinitrophenol, which interfere with the utilization of respiratory energy (380).

We may conclude that in general the activity of fungicides against respiration does not parallel their effects on growth, and infer that effective fungicides usually act on systems much more sensitive than is the gross oxygen uptake. We may speculate that a compound which acts on respiration and growth at approximately the same concentration—mercuric chloride is an example (247)—is a general enzyme poison. It should also be clear that, although a respiratory system may be inhibited by a fungistatic agent, this fact alone is not sufficient evidence that the inhibition observed is the primary locus of toxicity.

Sclerotinia laxa grown in contact with partially inhibitory concentrations of several fungicides is affected physiologically in its formation of respiratory enzymes, some being increased and others decreased in amount by specific compounds (55).

Mutagenic Effects of Chemical Agents. Cultural variants of undetermined genetic status are induced by high levels of zinc (89) and nitrite (Chapter 8). Mutation in fungi, verified by genetic studies, is caused by a wide variety of chemicals, e.g., nitrogen and sulfur mustards and related compounds (16, 286a, 400, 409), peroxides (87, 188), epoxides (208), diazomethane (189), and caffeine (115). Some of these are sulfhydryl reagents, others possibly generate free radicals, but no single mode of action can be proposed at present.

Fungistatic Action of Chemical Agents. Both practically and theoretically, the most important effect of toxicants on fungi is the inhibition of growth.

This fungistatic action is the most frequently measured and should not be confused with killing, fungicidal action *sensu stricto*. We may distinguish two classes of fungistatic assay: (1) determination of mycelial growth on a natural or artificial medium, and (2) determination of spore germination. In both methods, the test fungus and the toxicant are in contact throughout the period of incubation.

The early development of agar plate methods is described by Bateman (22), who established a satisfactory quantitative treatment of the data obtained with *Fomes annosus*. This treatment has since been extended to other fungi (330, 426). After a more or less protracted lag period, which is itself an index of toxicity, the rate of growth across the agar surface is linear with time. Comparison with a control inoculation on toxicant-free agar yields the basic datum, degree of inhibition.

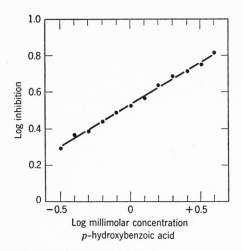

Figure 2. The inhibition of *Aspergillus niger* by *p*-hydroxybenzoic acid in an agar medium. Drawn from data of Vincent (426).

This is related to toxicant concentration by the equation:

$$y = ax^b \qquad (1)$$

where y stands for degree of inhibition, x for concentration of the fungicide, and a and b are constants. A plot of the logarithm of the degree of inhibition against the logarithm of the concentration yields curves of the type shown in Figure 2. Not all curves are as clearly linear as this one (426).

A variety of special methods are essentially similar to the assay of Bateman just described (26, 102, 108, 109, 114, 151, 203, 271, 283, 296, 297, 317, 318, 359). Criteria used include the least concentration preventing all growth, the colony diameter at a fixed time, or the dry weight in liquid culture. A rather different approach is found in the use of filter paper discs impregnated with the toxicant (218, 415); here, of course, diffusion becomes an important factor.

These methods all have particular and limited value; thus, the medical mycologist has a practical interest in the inhibition of established infections rather than in prevention of spore germination. Fungi which do not sporulate in culture may have to be studied as mycelium. For theoretical work on mode of action, however, the presence of nutrients and, in agar media, of undetermined contaminating substances, severely restricts their value. It is almost always found that nutrient materials reduce the apparent toxicity of fungitoxic agents (214, 352, 404). In a qualitative way, it is usually true that the agar plate method and the spore germination method agree, but they may give divergent results for particular compounds (174). As a rule, fungitoxic materials are more active against spore germination and spore respiration than they are against the growth or metabolism of mycelium (125, 147, 271, 341, 430a, 431).

Fungistatic methods adapted for the assay of wood preservatives are reviewed by Cartwright and Findlay (61). The type of assay chosen has marked effects on the apparent efficacy of test compounds (110, 223, 348). Usually, loss in weight of treated wood blocks is the best criterion of protection against decay; a somewhat more rapid assay based on the static bending strength of a treated wood block has been introduced (126).

Special methods for fabric treatments are described by Siu (386). Soil fumigants are usually of interest insofar as they kill organisms, but a fungistatic method of bioassay has been devised (101). For the practical testing of plant protectants, assays employing living inoculated plants are well worked out (243, 245, 251, 280).

The most progress has been made by the use of bioassays which are based on inhibition of spore germination. This fundamental technique has been developed both practically and theoretically by McCallan and by Horsfall, whose papers must be read for a thorough understanding of the method (172, 173, 174, 241, 242, 243, 252, 254, 258, 259, 436, 445). More or less standard procedures have been agreed upon (71, 72).

A standardized spore suspension of a test fungus—*Monilinia fructicola* (=*Sclerotinia fructicola*) and *Stemphylium sarcinaeforme* (=*Macrosporium sarcinaeforme*) are the most often used, but other sporulating fungi are suitable—is allowed to germinate in contact with the toxicant, which may be either mixed with the spore suspension or sprayed on the slide (33). If washed or vacuum-collected spores are used, it is usually necessary to add nutrients, and these materials, especially complex plant products such as orange juice, must be taken into account in any consideration of the mode of action; orange juice, possibly by reason of its content of citric acid, which can complex metals, reduces both the fungicidal and the fungistatic effect of copper on at least many fungi (91, 250, 287).

In the spore germination assay, a simple plot of per cent inhibition (or germination) against toxicant concentration or the logarithm of toxicant concentration yields a sigmoid curve. This can be converted to a straight line in the so-called logarithmic-probability system of coordinates. The abscissa of this curve used in most studies is the logarithm of the dose, the ordinate a calculated "probit" or "normal equivalent deviation." Use of this coordinate system is based on the general phenomenon that resistance in a population to a toxic agent is distributed normally with respect to the logarithm of the dose (30,

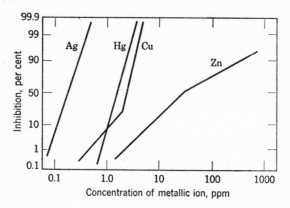

Figure 3. Dosage-response curves for the action of heavy metals on *Stemphylium sarcinaeforme*. Ordinate is probit of per cent inhibition of germination, abscissa is logarithm of concentration. Redrawn from more extensive data of McCallan, Wellman, and Wilcoxon (252) and selected to show different types of curve. Reproduced by permission of the Boyce Thompson Institute for Plant Research, Inc.

174, 244, 446). Representative curves of this type appear in Figure 3. Three characteristics of the log-probit curve are of greatest interest: position, shape, and slope. Lateral position is, of course, indicative of absolute toxicity; either the ED_{50} or the ED_{95}—the concentration required to inhibit germination by, respectively, 50 and 95 per cent—may be determined from the curve and used in the rating of fungicides. Position is affected by several factors in the assay—the presence of nutrients, the age of spores, the concentration of spores, extremes of temperature, the germination time, and the physical or chemical form in which a toxicant is supplied (49, 91, 144, 174, 252, 260, 265, 436).

Non-linear curves are not, however, uncommon; thus, a detailed study of the action of copper sulfate on *Monilinia fructicola* and *Alternaria oleracea* shows for both fungi a J-shaped curve, concave upward (242). Parker-Rhodes (323) proposed that this curvature represents the cumulative effect of more than one chemical or physical process in the inhibition reaction and also detailed an exponential transformation of the independent variable which converts the J curve to a linear form. Use of the transformation does not require acceptance of the multiprocess theory of fungistatic action, some of the difficulties of which are discussed by McCallan (244). Non-linear curves of other types are frequently encountered (242, 244, 252).

The slope of the log-probit curve is its most interesting feature. Since the ordinate is based on the distribution of sensitivity in the population of spores, a steep slope means that there is relatively little difference between the concentration which inhibits the most sensitive spore and that required to prevent germination of the most resistant spore. Conversely, a low slope, or flat dosage-response curve, indicates that the difference in dose required for inhibition of the two extremes of resistance is large (446). Slope is most conveniently measured as the reciprocal of the difference between ED_{84} and ED_{50}.

Although several factors of the assay influence slope, the compound itself is the most significant (252). From this it has been argued that the slope is an indication of the fundamental mode of action (174, 241, 279, 346, 416). That is, compounds with the same mode of action should generate dosage-response curves of the same slope. Rich and Horsfall (346) show that homologues of 2-imidazoline yield curves of similar slope and different position; the ED_{50} varied from 0.0037 to 3.57 μM per square centimeter, but the slopes were essentially alike— 9.37, 11.01, and 9.97. From this and other experience, it is argued that position measures ability of the compound to reach its site of action, and that slope indicates the mode of action once the site has been reached.

Attractive as this hypothesis is, there are other factors that must give us pause. First, as has been mentioned, non-linear curves are not uncommon. Second, there is as yet no measure of mode of action which is truly independent and which could serve as a check on the hypothesis. Finally, virtually all the available data are dosage-response curves in which external concentration is the independent variable. The discovery that fungi accumulate very large amounts of toxicant (p. 450) does not by itself defeat the hypothesis, but this fact does necessitate a re-evaluation of the whole problem (246).

Spores of many fungi increase markedly in size during the first stages of germination (Chapter 12); inhibition of this growth process in *Myrothecium verrucaria* has been adapted to the bioassay of fungistatic agents (268).

Fungicidal Action. Fungicidal action, the killing of fungi by a toxicant, requires an assay method in which cells are exposed to a compound for a known period of time and are then removed from contact with the toxic agent and tested for viability. Such assays have been worked out for a variety of theoretical and practical problems (26, 69, 120, 128, 151, 246a, 250, 360, 463).

The plot of probit of per cent germination against logarithm of time is linear for the action of copper, silver, arsenate, and crystal violet (250). The same plot of the data of Müller and Biedermann (302) shows, however, that the strict exponential relation is evident only at

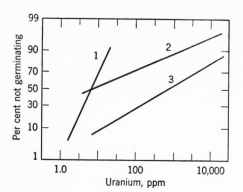

Figure 4. Dosage response curves for the action of uranium acetate on spores of *Alternaria solani*. Curve 1, fungistatic action; curve 2, fungicidal action at 20 hours; curve 3, fungicidal action at 10 minutes. Redrawn from McCallan and Wellman (250), by permission of the Boyce Thompson Institute for Plant Research, Inc.

relatively high concentrations of copper—at lower concentrations there is no perceptible damage for a considerable period of time, after which the exponential form of curve appears. Similarly, the shape of the time-inhibition curve for the action of phenol is affected by the concentration of the toxicant (391).

Killing is also a function of temperature; the fungicidal action of a number of relatively mild materials is sharply and non-linearly increased as the temperature is raised, with an especially sharp break as the temperature approaches its lethal value for spores in the absence of toxicant (183).

Although a strongly fungicidal agent is fungistatic, the reverse is not necessarily true. In particular, several compounds of high fungistatic activity—potassium dichromate, uranyl acetate, imidazolines, and 8-hydroxyquinoline are examples—have only very weak fungicidal activity (250, 437). In general, dosage-response curves for fungicidal action are much flatter than those for fungistatic, i.e., the range in resistance of the population is greater (Figure 4).

2. TOLERANCE AND RESISTANCE

Species of fungi differ widely in their sensitivity to toxicants. This has been especially noticed since the introduction of antibiotics and organic fungicides; differences in sensitivity of 50- to 100-fold are common (203, 270, 349, 440). However, strains tolerant to more general poisons are also encountered in studies on mercury (124, 232, 423), fluoride (227, 423), arsenate (303), and creosote (65). Copper tolerance is often associated with tolerance to hydrogen ion or other cations (195, 387, 397). This suggests that the mechanism of copper tolerance is a general exclusion of cations from the cell. As Horsfall (174) points out, an organism producing metabolic acids may be less sensitive to a toxicant which must compete with hydrogen ion for its site of action.

Fungi may also be "trained," by serial culture in media containing low doses of a toxicant, to tolerate a normally inhibitory concentration. Such adaptation has been demonstrated to arsenite (157), borax (205), fluoride (222), and copper (186, 195); other reports are cited by Leben et al. (217) and Horsfall (174). Such adapted strains and strains which appear spontaneously in culture are usually unstable and lose their resistance on subculture in toxicant-free media (158, 195). Spontaneously arising sectors of Fusarium caeruleum appear in plates exposed to the vapor of 2,3,5,6-tetrachloronitrobenzene, and these variants are somewhat less sensitive to the poison than is the parent strain (263); they are, however, almost equally sensitive—by rather inexact criteria—to 2,3,4,5-tetrachloronitrobenzene (47).

Genetic analysis has been performed only infrequently on resistant strains of fungi. Resistance to indole toxicity in Neurospora crassa (77) and to acriflavine in Aspergillus nidulans (355) is genetically controlled. This is in line with the usual experience in studies on bacteria and yeast (85, 216, 371). Copper-adapted yeast is reported to contain a ribonucleic acid which can be transmitted to, and which confers copper resistance on, normal unadapted yeast cells (293).

Physiological mechanisms of acquired tolerance are possibly of diverse types. Work on the resistance of trypanosomes to arsenicals suggests that resistant strains are less permeable to the drug (38), possibly by virtue of an altered distribution of surface charges (366). Fluoride tolerance in clones of Propionibacterium pentosaceum appears also to be a permeability phenomenon (427). Other mechanisms are, however, possible: an antimycin-resistant variant of Venturia inaequalis probably lacks the normal respiratory system sensitive to the antibiotic (219).

Detoxification of fungicidal agents has been observed and is, of course, a potential mechanism of resistance. Methylation of selenium, tellurium, and arsenic (Chapter 6) conceivably fits in this category. The effects of cycloheximide on both spore germination and respiration decline with time, indicating an inactivation (431, 440). Oxidative processes have been suggested as the basis for resistance to phenols and quinones (200, 347); β-oxidation of a fatty acid side chain or hydroxylation of a ring in some instances causes detoxification (54, 57). Other possible detoxification mechanisms are reviewed by Gottlieb (134); it seems likely that the most common is the complexing of toxic metals by chelate-forming metabolites such as amino acids and hydroxy acids.

3. SELECTIVE ACCUMULATION

We have customarily thought of the inhibiting of an unwanted organism as a problem in selective toxicity, to find materials which are inherently more toxic to one form of life than to others. It has been assumed that the ultimate basis for such a selective action must be the existence of some sensitive protoplasmic reaction in the undesirable organism which does not exist, or is dispensable, in other species. This approach has, of course, had its successes, notably in explaining the chemotherapeutic value of the sulfonamide drugs, but the major effort of modern biology has been to show how similar are all forms of life in fundamental biochemical aspects and thus to render less and less likely the prospect of finding truly selective agents at the protoplasmic level of action.

It now appears that another selective principle may be equally important: the differential accumulation of a toxicant by the unwanted organism. The term selective accumulation has been used by Yarwood (460) to describe the finding that spores of *Uromyces phaseoli* accumulate more sulfur from a fungicidal treatment with the vapor phase than do the leaves of the host plant. That is, we may hope that some materials which are perhaps equally toxic to all organisms may be accumulated selectively by a fungus; the result, of course, is equivalent to selective toxicity and is a form of it, but does not depend on an inherent protoplasmic or enzymatic sensitivity. Selective accumulation does, of course, require that the sensitive organism differ physiologically from the insensitive, but it does not require us to postulate, for example, that protein synthesis or energy metabolism of the susceptible species differs from that of the resistant. The problem becomes narrower and more manageable: by what mechanism does the sensitive organism accumulate, or the insensitive exclude, the toxicant?

In the previous section, some evidence has been cited that resistant strains of microorganisms owe their resistance to the failure of the toxicant to reach sensitive sites. This is in a sense the reverse of selective accumulation, to be considered provisionally as selective exclusion.

The idea of selective accumulation is not, of course, new; it has been known for some time that the lethal action of heavy metals on bacteria follows upon accumulation of the toxicant by cells in amounts far in excess of their concentration in the external medium (455). It is apparent that fungus spores can similarly remove from the medium very large amounts of many different toxicants. Marsh (273) found that spores of *Monilinia fructicola* exposed to copper accumulate the metal to a concentration 2000–4000 times its external concentration. Even more striking results are reported by Miller, McCallan, and Weed (290, 291), using different fungi and such diverse materials as silver, cerium, 2-heptadecyl-2-imidazoline, and ferric dimethyldithiocarbamate. Several features of these data warrant emphasis:

1. Uptake is extremely rapid; spores of *Neurospora sitophila* take up their limit of the imidazoline within 15 seconds from a dilute solution, within 5 minutes from a more concentrated solution. Uptake of dithiocarbamates by yeast is similarly rapid (127).

2. Fungicidal action is a linear function of the amount of toxicant taken up.

3. Some toxicants are concentrated as much as 10,000-fold.

4. A material which has low inherent toxicity on a spore weight basis may be so extensively concentrated by spores as to be an effective inhibitor. The application to bioassay is obvious—external concentration is not necessarily a measure of effective dose. Valko (419) distinguishes "apparent toxicity," a function of external concentration, from "specific toxicity," a function of the amount of toxicant absorbed by the cell.

5. Species differ in the amount taken up of a given toxicant.

6. Unrelated toxicants are taken up independently, i.e., previous ex-

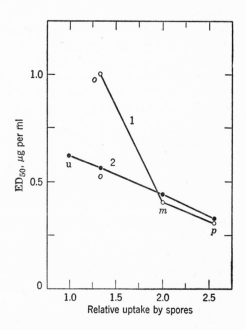

Figure 5. The relation between uptake and antifungal activity (test organism *Neurospora sitophila*) in chlorine derivatives of 2,4-dichloro-6-anilino-*s*-triazine. Curve 1, fungicidal action; curve 2, fungistatic action. Compounds: u = unsubstituted, *o* = ortho-chloro, *m* = metachloro, *p* = para-chloro derivative. Drawn from data of Burchfield and Storrs 51).

posure to one material does not materially change the results with another. Closely related chemicals appear, however, to compete for a common receptor (246, 288).

7. Absorbed toxicants of some types are held firmly in or on the spore and can be released in quantity only by rather drastic treatment. Silver, by contrast, is easily removed by exchange (292).

The relation of uptake to effectiveness is shown in Figure 5 for a series of related *s*-triazines. Fungitoxic action is seen to be correlated with the capacity of the spore to remove the toxicant from solution.

In general, two mechanisms suggest themselves as alternative explanations of the phenomenon of rapid uptake against a concentration gradient. First, it is, of course, known that "active transport" of nutrient materials into cells occurs commonly and results in accumulation against a gradient, and Pramer (336) has shown that streptomycin is so accumulated by *Nitella clavata*. However, to suggest active transport as the mechanism of entrance of a variety of toxicants raises the difficulty that active transport as usually understood necessarily involves the expenditure of metabolic energy and is prevented by many inhibitors. As discussed later in connection with the heavy metals, it seems at present more promising to look toward a second mechanism, the adsorption of the toxicant by a solid phase in or on the cell. For both these alternative mechanisms, it should be noted, the same general relation between uptake and external concentration holds; in both there is some saturation value of the external concentration. Consequently, whether or not the concentration-uptake relation is described by the adsorption isotherm does not distinguish between active transport and adsorption. More important results will come from studies of the effect of metabolic state upon uptake.

Drawing primarily from studies on the action of heavy metals (see below), we may suggest that a toxic material which does not move freely across the semi-permeable membrane undergoes a two-stage process. In the first phase there is a rapid sorption of the toxicant outside the permeability barrier, or perhaps both outside it and on it. In the second phase, the material is released at a slower rate to the interior of the cell from the saturated peripheral sites; only in this phase, for most materials, does interference with growth occur.

This hypothesis has many difficulties which are, however, better considered in connection with heavy metal toxicity. It ignores, for convenience, the possibility that the sorbed toxicant may exert specific effects before it enters the cell at all; this possibility is treated as a separate topic.

4. SURFACE ACTION

It has been suggested immediately above that the first phase of toxicant action is an accumulation of the active material in a peripheral layer or zone outside the semi-permeable membrane. We have further argued that, for most toxicants, the primary inhibitory effect is not at this stage but later, after some of the toxicant has desorbed from the outer zone and penetrated the protoplasm proper. However, such a sharp separation of phases is only a convenience, since accumulation of a foreign material is very likely to have some effects on the cell membrane. Hypothetically we may set up three possible classes: (1) effects of the sorbed toxicant are themselves lethal; (2) sorption contributes to lethality by damaging the osmotic barrier and thereby facilitating or making possible entrance of the toxicant into the protoplast; and (3) sorption has only minor effects.

A number of surface agents are known to be lethal to bacteria, at least in part, as the result of destruction of the semi-permeable membrane (118, 181). The antibiotic polymyxin has the same effect—disruption of the osmotic barrier—in bacteria (307). The contribution of lysis to lethality has, however, been questioned (398).

Surface toxicity need not, in principle at least, be confined to effects on permeability. If surface anabolic reactions are essential to growth, for example, inhibition of them by a non-penetrating toxicant would be sufficient. Finholt et al. (110) interpret the different toxicity of aliphatic amines in malt agar culture vis-a-vis wood block tests as indicating that a toxicant could act externally by preventing the action of an extracellular hydrolytic enzyme essential to survival. This suggestion deserves further exploration; perhaps the most promising possibility is that the extracellular enzymes are actually synthesized exteriorly to the osmotic barrier and that a toxicant might interfere with the synthesis. Such an effect would be missed completely in the usual assay which provides diffusible nutrients and thereby renders the fungus independent of extracellular enzymes.

The second possibility, that sorption of a toxicant might contribute to lethality without being the primary event, comes to mind particularly in relation to a few findings that toxicants at sublethal concentrations alter cell permeability. Cellular phosphorus is lost from spores treated with subfungistatic doses of silver (288) or of substituted s-triazines (51). Lysozyme treatment causes an increase in permeability to water and, probably, to furfural (235). In bacteria, phenol increases permeability to glucose; it is probable that "one-way" effects on permeability occur, a compound increasing the loss of cellular nitrogen and phosphorus but not increasing the entrance of substrates (182).

Finally, we may expect relatively minor effects of sorbed materials, especially on permeability and accumulation. We have referred earlier (Chapter 8) to the possibility that amino acid toxicity is exerted by the exclusion of one acid by another. Among other metabolic effects of β-propiolactone on *Blastomyces dermatitidis* is the inhibition of amino acid uptake (119), although this could be secondary.

Reduction of the rate of solute movement is shown especially well by the studies of Rothstein (356) on the poisoning of yeast respiration by uranium. This appears to be a specific interference with the up-take of hexoses; endogenous respiration and the utilization of pyruvic acid or ethanol are very little affected. Rothstein suggests that uranyl ion complexes with groups at or near the cell surface which are es-sential to sugar uptake, and suggests further that these groups are cellular polyphosphates which are also capable of binding other ions (357). Similar responses to uranium have been found in animal ma-terial (315).

5. HYDROGEN-ION CONCENTRATION

In any survey of the literature on fungicides, one is forcibly struck by the common failure to determine or to report the pH of the test solution. For practical purposes this may not be important, at least if the pH is that of the projected use situation, but conclusions on mode of action of ionizable materials are difficult indeed to draw if the acidity is unknown.

Some effects of pH are obvious: a fungicide may break down more or less rapidly and in so doing yield products of greater or less toxicity; thus, thiosulfate forms a more toxic product (162), and dithiocarba-mates form less toxic materials (432). A second possibility is that the toxicant itself changes the pH to a value unfavorable for growth or spore germination; this can of course be compensated for by specific controls. The chelating agents, as mentioned later, become less effec-tive in binding metals as the pH is lowered; uranyl ion forms complexes with hydroxyl ion at pH values above 4.5 and becomes therefore una-vailable (356). Competition between hydrogen ion and toxic cations is considered in connection with the heavy metals.

When weak acids or bases are dissolved in water, the degree of ioniza-tion is pH-dependent. This is evident by inspection of the equation for the dissociation of an acid:

$$HA \rightleftharpoons H^+ + A^- \tag{2}$$

The negative logarithm of the ionization constant of Equation 2, signified by pK_a, is numerically equal to the pH at which the acid is 50 per cent dissociated. The pK_a is characteristic of the molecule, and one of the commonly overlooked effects of addition of substituents to an organic molecule is that the substituent may change pK_a. Exactly the same considerations, of course, apply to weak bases.

Acidic toxicants almost invariably are more effective at low pH than at high; as discussed later, the effect of pH is most noticeable near pK_a, so that data on very strong and very weak acids will not normally show an effect of hydrogen-ion concentration under the usual experimental conditions. Data on inhibition of fungi which fit the rule of greater activity at low pH are extremely numerous, although they do not include spore germination results. As examples, we may cite the action of fatty acids (161, 350, 354, 456), aromatic acids (75, 76, 78, 162, 339, 390), acid dyes (205), substituted phenols (41, 187, 383), and nitrous acid (Chapter 8).

The usual explanation for the effect of dissociation on toxicity is that only the undissociated molecule enters the cell. This reflects the general experience that ions penetrate the cell at least much more slowly than do neutral molecules (84). Several experiments with fungi have shown that the ester of a toxic acid is more effective than the free acid (24, 62, 140, 178, 301). The ester almost certainly penetrates the cell more rapidly than the partially ionized acid and is then split by esterases. More direct evidence would, however, be desirable, since esterification of an acid may have other effects, for example on reactivity of groups near to the carbonyl carbon.

It is often stated that one can conclude from these pH-activity studies that it is only the undissociated molecule which is toxic, i.e., action within the cell is visualized as caused solely by some combination of the neutral molecule of the acid or base with a sensitive element. For this conclusion to hold, the biologically effective dose in terms of neutral molecules must be invariant with pH; Simon and Blackman (383) review several studies on echinoderm eggs in which this relation prevails for both weak acids and weak bases.

However, studies on a wide variety of compounds—phenols, cresols, fluoride, azide, cyanide, etc.—show quite conclusively that the ion must also play a role in toxicity within the sensitive volume of the cell (382, 383). Figure 6 exemplifies the data: it is seen that as the ionization increases with increasing pH the equi-effective concentration of undissociated molecules actually declines. The total drug—ions plus neutral molecules—rises of course, but it is the fall in undissociated toxicant which is decisive.

Two conclusions flow from this analysis. First, inhibition of the sensitive cell element must be effected by both neutral molecules and ions, although they need not be equally effective. A chemical model for this behavior is analyzed by Briggs (45). Second, the pH at the site of action must be affected by changes in the external pH, in order for the equieffective concentration of the penetrating species to decline as found (these are long-time experiments in which we can assume equilibrium conditions). As mentioned in Chapter 1, the effect of external pH upon cytoplasmic pH is not known with any certainty or precision.

The significance of pK_a can now be assessed (Figure 7). The rise in required concentration for an equal effect begins at about pK_a; at lower pH (higher for a base) there is much less effect of acidity (383). It follows that in theoretical or comparative studies on weak acids or weak bases the effect of ionization can be minimized by assaying activity at a pH at least two units below pK_a (for an acid) or above pK_a (for a base). There are exceptions to this rule, the sulfonamide antibacterials being the outstanding and best-known example (6, 382).

The acridine antibacterials exemplify a rather different relation of toxicity to dissociation and pH (4, 6), one which has so far not come to light among organic fungitoxic materials. In this series only the cation is biologically effective. This fact, and observations on the

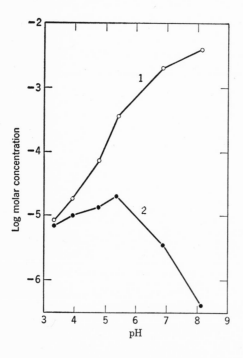

Figure 6. The effect of pH on the concentration of 2,4-dinitrophenol ($pK_a = 4.0$) required to effect a 50 per cent reduction in the growth rate on agar of *Trichoderma viride*. Curve 1, total concentration; curve 2, concentration of undissociated molecules. Redrawn from Simon and Blackman (383), by permission of the Cambridge University Press.

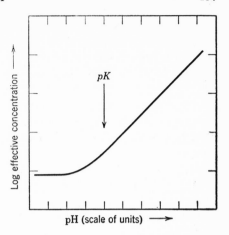

Figure 7. The general form of the relation between pH and the toxicity of a weak acid. Redrawn from Simon and Beevers (381), by permission of the American Association for the Advancement of Science.

effect of structural changes on toxicity, indicates that the acridines act at the surface and that they compete with other cations. Competition between toxicant ions and other cations is considered elsewhere, in connection with the action of copper. It should only be mentioned here that this competition, insofar as hydrogen ion is involved, represents still another effect of pH on fungitoxicity.

Finally, as suggested by Burchfield and Storrs (50), the internal pH of the cell could affect fungicidal action by its influence upon the ionization of cellular compounds which react with the toxicant. Thus, reaction of amino groups with 2,4-dichloro-6-(*o*-chloroanilino)-*s*-triazine probably occurs only if they are unionized, but sulfhydryl groups react only if ionized.

6. STRUCTURE AND ACTIVITY

Structurally Non-Specific Inhibitors. Specific chemical structure as a determinant of toxicity may be approached by considering first the structurally non-specific poisons, the narcotics. These are compounds, the effect of which is freely reversible, e.g., hydrocarbons, chlorinated hydrocarbons, aliphatic alcohols, and phenols. The data on these are, with few exceptions, derived from studies on animal systems.

Probably no compound is absolutely without structural specificity. The structurally non-specific inhibitors are, however, characterized by a relatively low specificity, in the sense that changes in structure cause no apparent change in the mode of action. Historically, the concept of structural non-specificity arose from consideration of the effect of homologous series; in general, toxicity on a molar basis rises with molecular weight as the series is ascended, but at some point the trend is reversed, and higher members of the series are less toxic. All compounds of the series, however, appear to act in the same way on cells.

Early explanations of this homologous series effect were centered on permeability of the cell to toxicants. It was found that toxicity is correlated in such a series with an oil-water partition coefficient. Since the plasma membrane is in general more permeable to non-polar compounds than to polar compounds (84), it was natural to hypothesize that the more lipoid-soluble compounds are more toxic simply because they enter the cell more rapidly.

The classical paper of Ferguson (104) corrects and expands this limited hypothesis by introducing chemical potential as the index. Essentially, Ferguson's principle states that the biological effectiveness of non-specific poisons is a function of proportional concentration at the site of action. At equilibrium any compound is at the same proportional saturation in all phases of the system. Consequently, toxicity is a function, not of bulk concentration in the external phase but of relative concentration or chemical potential. It follows that a substance only sparsely soluble in water will be more active, mole for mole, than a more soluble related compound. Consider compound A, soluble in water to the extent of 1.0 M, and compound B, soluble only to 0.1 M. Ideally, if an 0.05 M solution of B (all phases 50 per cent saturated) exerts a given non-specific effect, compound A will exert the same effect only at 0.5 M, i.e., at 50 per cent of saturation.

Concrete experimental results are not, of course, so neat. It is a matter of some doubt, for example, whether the chemical activity required for a given biological response is constant or rises slowly as a homologous series is ascended (18, 46).

Figure 8, taken directly from Ferguson (104), illustrates the principle for the series of aliphatic primary alcohols. As the series is ascended, all the properties—solubility, surface tension lowering, vapor pressure, and oil-water partition coefficient—which depend on chemical potential change simultaneously. So does toxicity.

It must be emphasized that these considerations do not give specific information as to the site of action. All the constants of Figure 8 are distribution functions. From this we argue that toxicity depends upon a distribution between heterogeneous phases. We can not argue for any one distribution, e.g., that between external solution and protoplasm. The governing partition could, for example, be that between the medium and the cell surface or that between the non-polar portions of a protein chain and the ambient intracellular medium. Acceptance of Ferguson's principle does not of itself commit us to any particular

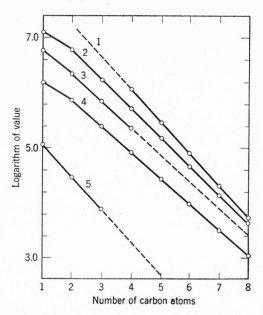

Figure 8. Distribution functions and toxicity in the aliphatic primary alcohols. Curve 1, solubility (μM per liter); curve 2, equitoxic concentration (μM per liter) for *Eberthella typhosa;* curve 3, concentration (μM per liter) reducing the surface tension of water to 50 dynes per centimeter; curve 4, vapor pressure at 25° (mm x 10^4); curve 5, partition coefficient (x 10^3) between water and cottonseed oil. Redrawn from Ferguson (104), by permission of the Cambridge University Press.

critical distribution or site of action. Nor do studies of this type offer the hope of determining the actual site of the toxic action.

It is true, however, that at present the distribution function most susceptible of experimental attack is permeability. That is, changes in toxicity coincident upon changes in thermodynamic activity must be investigated first to see whether the answer lies in the greater rate of entrance of the less water-soluble compounds into the cell. In the aliphatic alcohols, permeability is almost certainly not the answer: toxicity increases rapidly as the molecular weight increases, but all members of the series penetrate very rapidly, and differences in rate of entrance do not explain differences in toxicity (79).

Toxicity does not, of course, increase indefinitely in a homologous series. Above a certain chain length, the exact point depending on the series and on the test organism, toxicity falls off sharply. This cutoff is a reflection, probably, of insolubility of and micelle formation by the higher members of the series (18, 53, 417).

The non-specific poisons are often referred to as "physical" toxicants, apparently because such factors as solubility are of more predictive value for gross biological action than are specific reactive groupings. The dichotomy does not seem justified either on theoretical or experimental grounds. Separation in theory of physical and chemical activities of molecules is artificial; the covalent bond and, for example, van der Waals' forces may both be involved in the reactivity of the same molecule. Experimentally, it is found that such narcotics as urethane, chloral hydrate, and ethyl ether have specific measurable effects on some cell activities at concentrations which do not affect other activities (138, 193, 194, 207, 261, 285). It has been proposed (190, 261) that the ultimate action of structurally non-specific poisons is the denaturation of one or more proteins of the cell. As Danielli (79) points out, this is not in conflict with the more general theory that these poisons act by virtue of their concentration in or on a lipoid phase or non-polar structure of the cell.

The distinguishing feature of the structurally non-specific poisons from a chemical viewpoint is that they must form weak bonds with receptors of the cell. This follows from the fact that inhibition is, within limits, easily reversible by dilution alone. This also explains why activity is associated with chemical potential—a relatively high proportional concentration is necessary if such weak bonds are to occupy receptor sites enough of the time for perceptible inhibition to occur.

Most fungicides are not narcotics, i.e., structural specificity is the rule. The importance of the narcotics to the problem of structure and activity in the fungitoxic materials is that they may explain the effect of modifications of a basic toxicant molecule. Specifically, and following Horsfall (174), we may theorize that for an effective toxicant two requirements must be met. First, there must be one (possibly more) reactive atomic configuration that can combine with and inactivate essential materials of the cell. Second, the total structure of the toxicant molecule must allow concentration at the site of action. This second property includes, but emphatically is not restricted to, entrance into the cell. If, for example, the union between an enzyme and the combining region of a toxicant molecule is ionic or partially ionic, the formation of hydrogen or other weak bonds between the rest of the inhibitor and areas on the enzyme protein adjacent to the point of union would tend to stabilize the enzyme-inhibitor complex (6).

Homologous Series and Fungicidal Action. A selection of recent data on the homologous series effect is embodied in Table 1. Some of these compounds, e.g., the alcohols, are esentially narcotics as described in the previous section. The imidazolines, on the other hand, are prob-

Table 1. Homologous Series and Fungistatic Activity

Series	Organism(s)	Chain Length of Maximum Activity
Saturated aliphatic alcohols (99)	*Penicillium glaucum*	10–11
Saturated aliphatic alcohols (110)	*Lentinus lepideus*	10–11
N-alkylpyridines (230)	Four fungi	14
N-alkyl-α-bromoacetamides (221)	*Aspergillus niger*	6–10
Fatty acids (295)	*Ophiobolus miyabeanus*	10–12
Fatty acids (350)	*Phymatotrichum omnivorum*	11
Fatty acids (456)	Two fungi	11
Aliphatic amines (110)	*Lentinus lepideus*	10–12
Nicotinic acid esters (177)	Two fungi	6–8
2-Alkyl-1-hydroxyethylimidazolines (437)	Four fungi	13–17
Omega-(2-naphthyloxy)-n-alkyl-carboxylic acids (55)	*Aspergillus niger*	2–3

ably more specific in their action. But in both types—specific and non-specific—the homologous series effect is evident. Gross activity, therefore, depends in part on chemical potential, and again we are dealing with a distribution function of some kind. Whether this distribution is between cell and environment, i.e., is a function of permeability, or whether some more subtle partition is decisive, cannot at present be determined.

In general, compounds of this type with branched chains are less toxic than would be anticipated from their molecular weight alone. Evidence for this generalization is reviewed by Horsfall (174).

Data on bacteria illustrate a "quasi-specificity" (202): the carbon chain length for optimum toxicity depends to a considerable extent on the test organism.

Competitive Inhibition. At the other extreme from structurally non-specific inhibitors lies a group of poisons of extreme specificity. These may be detected operationally by the fact that over some range of concentration they compete with a cell metabolite. The theory and known examples have been considered extensively in the literature (277, 353, 454, 455). Of the chemotherapeutic agents, the sulfonamides are the classical example (450). Some at least of the sulfonamides are toxic to certain fungi (393, 449), and the available data (40, 92, 98, 147–149, 365, 393, 410, 449) indicate that, as in bacteria, sulfanilamide competes with *p*-aminobenzoic acid for an essential cell reaction. Sulfanilamide is, however, not strongly fungitoxic (203).

Competitive inhibition in fungi is also demonstrable with metabolite analogues of vitamins (Chapter 10) and amino acids (Chapter 8). Horsfall (174) lists in convenient form a number of examples.

A few of the more active fungicides are conceivably metabolite analogues competing with normal substrates or coenzymes, but in no instance has the action of such a fungicide been explained on this basis. Inhibition by 2,3-dichloro-1,4-napthoquinone is reversed by vitamin K (453), but there is no evidence that the vitamin is essential to fungi. Simple reversal experiments, inconclusive in themselves, have been the bases of suggestions that 2-heptadecyl-2-imidazoline interferes competitively with purine biosynthesis (438), that ascosin is a fatty acid antimetabolite (154), and that propionic acid interferes with acetate metabolism (155, 156, 326).

Inhibition of Enzymes. Present-day biology relies in perhaps too great measure on the findings of enzymology. Toxicants to which no specific role can be assigned are often stated to affect some, unspecified, enzyme or enzymes; such a statement is more an article of faith than an hypothesis.

However, there is no doubt that toxicants do affect enzymes, and we may distinguish three classes in relation to fungi: (1) agents which act specifically by inhibition of one essential enzyme system; (2) agents which act on sulfhydryl enzymes as a group; and (3) agents whose demonstrable reactivity with proteins suggests that they act on enzymes in general. This classification may be considered either as based on decreasing specificity of the fungicide or on our increasing ignorance.

The first group—compounds which owe their toxicity to inhibition of a single enzyme system—is exemplified by the antimycins, antibiotics produced by *Streptomyces* sp. (96, 231). These interfere specifically with electron transport in the cytochrome system (63, 335, 343, 421). Antimycin may affect other electron-transport systems also (305). Obviously, the specifically antifungal activity of the antimycins cannot be explained on this basis alone, since most organisms depend on the cytochrome system.

The action of the so-called uncoupling agents—2,4-dinitrophenol and 3,5-dinitro-*o*-cresol are examples—cannot be specified so narrowly as that of the antimycins. It appears that they prevent the oxidative phosphorylations which are associated with the transfer of electrons from substrate to oxygen (233, 379, 380, 412). The effect is to liberate respiration from the control normally imposed upon it by phosphate storage compounds of the cell, and at the same time inhibit reactions which are driven by the hydrolysis of phosphorylated intermediates. Operationally, it is found that oxidative assimilation is suppressed or endogenous respiration increased; both processes generate an increase in oxygen uptake (52, 67, 145, 331, 446). In view of the generally non-specific action of the phenols as a group (29), nitrophenols probably exert still other effects on cells.

The reagents which inactivate sulfhydryl enzymes form a second category, in which the specificity is toward the group of enzymes rather than toward any one, although differences in sensitivity are common. Free sulfhydryl groups on an enzyme or other protein can be inactivated by any of several reactions (21, 94, 95, 306, 316, 455):

1. Alkylation by, e.g., iodoacetic acid. The product may be visualized as a thioether structure on the enzyme surface.

2. Oxidation of two nearby sulfhydryl groups to a disulfide. Ferricyanide, iodosobenzoic acid and, presumably, almost any mild oxidizing agent can effect this type of inactivation. Thiols protect against this reaction.

3. Mercaptide formation. The characteristic agents of this reaction are heavy metals and trivalent arsenicals; one of the most specific poisons of this type is p-chloromercuribenzoic acid (316). Thiols protect also against these agents.

4. Addition reactions. These have been postulated particularly to explain enzyme inactivation by quinones and other α,β-unsaturated compounds.

Although none of these four types of reaction is certainly known to be responsible for the action of fungitoxicants, it will be seen later that mercaptide formation can be invoked as a possible mechanism for the action of heavy metals against fungi, and that the fungistatic quinones may act either by oxidation or by addition reactions to sulfhydryl groups.

The third group is the most amorphous of all—compounds which are so generally reactive that they may be expected to inactivate a variety of enzymes, possibly by more than one reaction. As mentioned later, the quinones may belong to this group rather than to the class of toxicants affecting sulfhydryl enzymes only. The action of 2,4-dichloro-6-(o-chloroanilino)-s-triazine and its relatives (447) is presumably of this type. Amino acids and peptides are alkylated by an exchange reaction for which the chlorine atoms attached to the heterocyclic ring are responsible, and both sulfhydryl and amino groups are alkylated (50).

As discussed in the section on selective accumulation, many fungicides are active only after a large amount of the toxicant is bound by the cell. This suggests, as McCallan (246) points out, that most fungistatic agents now in use are general poisons rather than inhibitors of specific enzymes. The same conclusion arises from the finding (319) that several very different enzymes are inhibited by fungicides and is supported by the usual failure to obtain mutants resistant to organic fungicides (217).

Structural Modification and Fungitoxicity. The possibility of obtaining new fungicides or more useful modifications of older materials has motivated considerable research on the relation between structure and activity. Unfortunately, much of this work is of little help in determining mode of action, since such essential factors as dissociation of the toxicant, permeability of the cell, and the extent of accumulation are usually unknown.

Horsfall (174) and Sexton (372) review the general field of structure and activity; some especially important recent work has been published on the *s*-triazines (51, 367), derivatives of acetanilide (66), triphenylmethanes and other dyes (93), substituted pyrazoles (267), unsaturated hydrocarbons (262), ethylene oxide derivatives (329), and nitrophenols (374).

The phenols have been the most extensively investigated from this aspect. Phenol itself and many of its derivatives have been regarded as structurally non-specific, i.e., as narcotics (29), but activity toward fungi and bacteria is markedly influenced by the number and type of substituents (372, 408). As a rule, alkylation increases activity and, within limits, the longer the alkyl side chain the greater the toxicity (29, 141, 377). This follows the rule for homologous series, i.e., there is an optimum chain length for activity against a given organism (372). Halogenation also increases the toxicity of phenols (29, 282, 376), but the position of the halogen is important (29, 375, 408). The nitrophenols have already been mentioned as respiratory inhibitors.

The bisphenols—not necessarily resembling the phenols in their action—provide another example of the effect of structure on activity. In general both antifungal and antibacterial activities require that the compound be halogenated, that the linkage between the two rings be *ortho* to hydroxyl groups, and that the two rings be not too far apart (58, 274). Hexachlorophene, or 2,2'-methylenebis(3,4,6-trichlorophenol), illustrates these features:

Replacement of the methylene bridging group by sulfur yields active materials (328), and still other linkages are compatible with activity (73, 295). Bisphenols have proved especially effective in the protection of textiles from fungal decay (386) and against fungi pathogenic to animals (58). The mode of action is not known; hexachlorophene is inhibitory at high dilution to several respiratory enzymes (135, 136).

In considering the effect of substitution on fungitoxicity, data cannot be evaluated properly on the basis solely of the usual two-dimensional visualization of an organic molecule. Some of the often neglected factors may be listed very briefly:

1. A substituent may alter the reactivity of nearby groups or of as large a component as an entire ring. Substituents may be electron-attracting or electron-repelling, may encourage or discourage hydrogen bonding and chelation.

2. A change in structure may either reduce or facilitate stabilization by resonance.

3. The addition of substituents may change the pK_a. This is especially marked in the phenols (29); phenol itself has a pK_a of 10.0, p-nitrophenol of 7.2, 2,4-dinitrophenol of 4.0 (383). Thus, at pH 7 phenol is less than 1 per cent ionized and 2,4-dinitrophenol is over 99 per cent ionized.

4. The oxidation-reduction potential of, for example, the naphthoquinones may be either raised or lowered by substituent groups.

5. The shape of the molecule, considered three-dimensionally, may be altered by substitution; this has been especially thoroughly explored in the acridines, the antibacterial action of which requires a minimum planar area (6).

6. Alterations in a molecule may make it more or less susceptible to biochemical attack by enzymes of the test organism, as suggested by Owens (319) for substituted phenols.

7. Lastly, as previously discussed, changes in the physical properties of a compound may render it more or less able to enter the cell or to accumulate at its site of action.

7. THE ACTION OF HEAVY METALS

The major share of our information on the fungistatic activity of the heavy metals comes from studies on copper, the active ingredient, at least until the advent of organic fungicides, of some of the most important plant and textile protectants. Mercury compounds have been used less for fungi but more as bacteriostatic agents. Silver is of little practical importance because of its cost, although it is an effective toxicant (256, 311, 312). Very little information is available on heavy metals other than these three; chromate complexes have been studied recently (146, 439).

Horsfall (174) summarizes the action of metallic cations, measured by external concentration, against fungi in the order: Ag > Hg > Cu > Cd > Cr > Ni > Pb > Co > Zn > Fe > Ca. For any one organism the order may differ slightly (23, 256, 300). Roughly the same order of effectiveness is found in experiments on animals (373).

Because of the reactivity of the heavy metals, growth experiments in complete media are of dubious value; the spore germination technique is to be preferred. Proteins and peptones are especially active in decreasing fungitoxicity (153, 214, 458), but other materials present in culture media have the same effect (247).

Present information allows us to consider the three most toxic heavy metals—silver, mercury, and copper—together, i.e., to assume provisionally that all have the same general mode of action; silver may, however, differ. We can also, but perhaps with less justification, consider that the final toxic effect of heavy metal compounds is to be ascribed to the metal itself. However, some problems are raised by this second assumption. Different inorganic salts of copper, for example, are not always of equal toxicity (28, 279); when copper is supplied as cupric ammonium sulfate, it is more firmly bound by spores than copper supplied as the sulfate (34). These differences cannot be explained as yet in detail, but we may guess that the form in which copper is supplied affects its uptake by the spore. Provision of silver as the iodide sharply reduces both uptake and toxicity as compared to those of other silver halides (288).

The toxicity of coordination complexes of copper deserves special attention. For years the effectiveness of Bordeaux mixture as a plant protectant was a mystery, inasmuch as the copper is present on the leaf in an insoluble complex. A number of investigations, reviewed by Martin (278) and by McCallan (244), established firmly the proposition that materials from the spore solubilize the copper. The most important of these substances are the amino and hydroxy acids, compounds which form soluble chelate complexes with copper. Monomethylamine liberation by spores of *Tilletia caries* also results in solubilization of copper (327), and seeds of higher plants liberate copper from Bordeaux mixture (429).

This hypothesis requires that soluble copper complexes be toxic. Some data show that, under specified conditions, the glycine and malate action may not be so great (130). Concentration factors are critical: complexes are as fungistatic as copper sulfate itself (257); fungicidal if the ratio of complexing agent to metal is high—five to ten—toxicity disappears (28). This is consistent with the concept that cell and complex compete for copper; it is significant that ethylenediaminetetraacetate (EDTA), which forms very stable metal complexes, abolishes toxicity at a 1:1 molar ratio to copper (28, 302). Unfortunately, these same observations are consistent also with a second explanation, that the malate and glycine complexes enter the cell whereas the EDTA complex does not.

Organic mercurials are generally more toxic than inorganic, both to bacteria (39) and to fungi (174, 372). Part of the answer to their practical effectiveness lies in the appreciable volatility of some of them (17, 88, 220). There is some evidence, however, that the effective organic mercurials penetrate the cell as such, i.e., that they are more readily taken up than mercuric ions (35, 324). Against this may be cited limited evidence from pH studies in a complete growth medium (187) that phenylmercuric acetate is more toxic as the ion. In general, both inorganic and organic mercurials affect the same enzymes and are equally antagonized by thiols, although occasional secondary effects complicate the picture, as in the case of pancreatic amylase (319).

The extreme case of increase in toxicity by provision of a metal in an organic molecule is found in a study of the fungitoxicity of tin compounds (199). Stannous and stannic chlorides are essentially non-toxic, but tri-n-butyltin acetate prevents the growth of fungi at 0.1–0.5 ppm.

McCallan and Wellman (267) find that copper, silver, and mercury are both fungistatic and fungicidal. Fungicidal action is, of course, a function of time of exposure and of the method by which the spores are washed free of toxicant.

The action of heavy metals on fungi may be conveniently divided into two topics: the uptake of metals by spores and the metabolic or other effects of the metal once it has reached a sensitive site.

We have already mentioned that metals, in common with other fungistatic materials, are accumulated by fungus spores in very high concentration and very rapidly (288, 290, 291). Some further light is cast on this by earlier and technically less satisfactory studies on the effect of copper and mercury on *Tilletia tritici* (34, 35, 36). Copper uptake was found to follow the Freundlich adsorption isotherm, i.e., to be non-linearly related to external copper concentration. Copper supplied as an ionizable salt is removable by acid, but the copper of cupric ammonium sulfate, a coordination complex, is not so removed. Finally, ionic copper disappearing from solution is almost quantitatively accounted for by other cations—H^+, Fe^{++}, Mg^{++}, etc.—liberated from the spore.

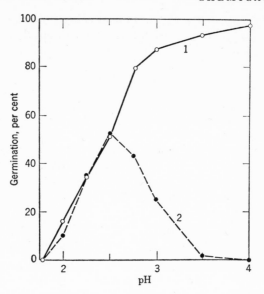

Figure 9. The effect of pH on the toxicity of copper chloride to spores of *Alternaria tenuis*. Curve 1 (solid line), control; curve 2 (broken line), 0.0001 M $CuCl_2$. Drawn from data of Biedermann and Müller (28).

Divalent cations generally reduce both uptake and toxicity of the heavy metals (1, 28, 150, 226, 232, 273, 308). The uptake of silver by spores is reduced by copper and, more completely, by mercury (288). Competition by hydrogen ion is equally important; this is shown in Figure 9 and also by the fact that absorbed copper is removed from spores by acid (3, 34, 174, 291).

There are at present two ways in which to interpret the data on uptake of metals by spores. First, we may assume that the entire volume of the spore protoplasm accumulates the metal. This assumption requires, in view of the rapidity of the uptake, that the metal move relatively freely across the semi-permeable membrane; such a rapid movement is suggested by the speed with which cellular zinc of *Aspergillus niger* exchanges with extracellular zinc (288), and by some data on the loss of potassium from bacteria (209). Staining methods show that copper does enter spores (129, 418), but this approach has not been developed sufficiently to be of critical importance.

The second mode of interpretation is to consider metal uptake as an adsorption, defined as a process that concentrates one component of a system at an interface, and to limit the locus of this adsorption to peripheral regions of the cell, i.e., outside the permeability barrier.

This approach has the advantage that we need not postulate that ions are able to penetrate the cell rapidly; although, as just mentioned, there is some evidence for rapid passage of metals through the membrane, it is generally true, considering all the organisms studied, that cations, especially di- and trivalent cations, do not move easily into cells by diffusion (84). The concept that the initial uptake is an adsorption, or ion exchange, process has the additional advantage of explaining both ion competition effects and the fact that uptake of copper is accompanied by roughly equal extrusion of other ions. Nor does a surface adsorption require that the cell be living or even metabolizing normally; it has been noted (291) that uptake of several materials continues long after enough toxicant has been absorbed completely to prevent spore germination.

Against an adsorption hypothesis, it may be urged that the uptake of some materials is so large that the classical monomolecular film could not accommodate the observed toxicant (290).

To test these two hypotheses, the most direct approach is provided by model experiments on the uptake of methylene blue by bacteria (238, 239) and by ascospores of *Neurospora tetrasperma* (407). The uptake reaction is independent of temperature; a metabolically powered accumulation would have a high temperature coefficient. Dead cells adsorb dye as rapidly and completely as living cells. Different cations compete with each other for a limited number of sites; as in yeast (356, 357), it appears that the cell surface has a countable number of more or less strongly negative binding sites. Exploration of the uptake-concentration relation does not appear so profitable; any type of accumulation would show saturation effects as the external concentration is raised.

If it proves possible to regard the initial rapid uptake of metals as a surface adsorption, then the toxic action of heavy metals can be visualized, as already mentioned, as composed of a rapid stage of uptake at the surface followed by a slower penetration, perhaps through a damaged membrane, into the interior of the cell. Alternatively, the metal may enter as a coordination complex.

Effects of sorbed metals upon the cell surface must be considered as a possibility, although it seems doubtful that the major site of toxic action is outside the permeability barrier. Copper reduces the permeability of the erythrocyte to glycerol (84), and heavy metals, especially mercury, depress phosphate uptake by bacteria (294). Silver increases the loss of phosphorus from fungus spores, although mercury does not (288). Interference with catabolic, anabolic, or carrier mechanisms outside of or on the plasma membrane is also a possibility, as in the action of uranyl ion on yeast (p. 454). Increases in respiratory rate are induced by sublethal concentrations of metals (247); the explanation may lie in an increased permeability to exogenous substrate or, less likely, in inactivation of regulatory enzyme systems (20).

Present theories of the ultimate action of heavy metals visualize them as enzyme poisons and admit only the question of whether they are primarily effective against sulfhydryl enzymes or generally inhibitory to enzymes of all types.

The reaction of a divalent metal with a sulfhydryl enzyme is depicted conventionally as mercaptide formation:

$$\text{En} \begin{array}{c} \diagup \text{SH} \\ \diagdown \text{SH} \end{array} + \text{HgCl}_2 \rightarrow \text{En} \begin{array}{c} \diagup \text{S} \\ \diagdown \text{S} \end{array} \begin{array}{c} \diagdown \\ \diagup \end{array} \text{Hg} + 2\text{HCl} \tag{3}$$

The resemblance to a five-membered chelate complex—there are two points of attachment on the enzyme—is obvious. A monovalent metal or an organic mercurial like p-chloromercuribenzoic acid reacting as such presumably forms a mercaptide with only a single sulfhydryl group. The argument for the importance of this reaction is based primarily on the observation that heavy-metal poisoning of both bacteria and fungi can be prevented or, within certain time limits, reversed by such thiol compounds as cysteine, glutathione, and 2,3-dimercaptopropanol (107, 185). In addition, it can be shown that mercaptide-forming reagents react stoichiometrically with free sulfhydryl groups of proteins (13, 316).

Shaw (373) proposes a model for the inhibition of vital processes that is based on these considerations and the added assumption that the sulfhydryl groups with which cations combine are part of the catalytically active site of the inhibited enzyme. The driving force of Equation 3 is regarded as proportional to the free energy of the simple reaction:

$$\text{Me}^{++} + \text{S}^{--} \leftrightarrows \text{MeS} \tag{4}$$

That is, toxicity should be correlated with the insolubility of the metal sulfides (MeS). The order of insolubility is in fact very much like the order of toxicity: $\text{Hg} \cong \text{Ag} > \text{Cu} > \text{Pb} > \text{Cd} > \text{Zn}$. This is also the order of affinity of metals for the sulfhydryl group of purified serum albumin (204).

Emphasis on reaction with sulfhydryl groups may, however, divert attention from other possibilities. In particular, the simple demonstration that thiol compounds antagonize the toxicity of metals to intact cells cannot by itself prove that the primary effect of metals *in vivo* is on sulfhydryl enzymes. Thiols form stable covalent compounds with metals and would be expected, therefore, to compete successfully with almost any bond formed between enzyme and metal.

That the sulfhydryl hypothesis may be too limited is indicated above all by the observation that many enzymes which are not apparently dependent upon sulfhydryl groups for their activity are inhibited *in vitro* by one or more of the heavy metals. These include sucrase, β-glucosidase, arginase, asparaginase, carbonic anhydrase, catalase, and cytochrome oxidase (319, 388, 405). As already mentioned, inhibition of respiration and spore germination at approximately the same concentration by heavy metals is also suggestive of a general poisoning of many different enzymes.

If we grant that heavy metals are general enzyme poisons, we may inquire about the sites at which they might act on an enzyme. Obviously, as Horsfall (174) emphasizes, the order of toxicity closely resembles the order of stability of metal chelate complexes. From this, it is apparent that the heavy metals might act by displacing from an enzyme a metal like magnesium which is essential to its activity and which is bound normally in a coordination complex. However, the order of stability of chelate complexes is, for obvious reasons, much the same as the order of insolubility of metal sulfides just described, and either series may with equal probability be considered the more important.

Several potential binding sites are available on proteins to react with transition metals like mercury, silver, and copper. These include carboxyl, phosphoric, imidazolium, ammonium, and phenolic hydroxyl groups (204). The primary carboxyls and the α-amino groups of the amino acids are, of course, tied up in peptide bonds, and such side chains as the guanidine and amide groups cannot be expected to bind metals at biological pH values.

In principle at least, inactivation of enzymes by metals is not limited as to location; the enzyme or enzymes may just as well be at the surface of the cell as in the interior. However, it seems more probable that the metals reach the interior of the cell and are not confined in their action at fungistatic concentrations to the surface.

This discussion of toxicity of the heavy metals makes it clear that there are numerous unsolved problems, especially with regard to the penetration of heavy-metal ions into the cell. Some of the more important points may be listed in conclusion:

1. Differences in toxicity between various compounds of a given metal are ascribed to differences in the rate at which the toxic metal

reaches the site of action. The contrast between ionized salts and unionized lipid-soluble organic compounds is especially marked.

2. Toxicity of the metals is affected by hydrogen ion and divalent cations and by the presence of natural substances—proteins, amino acids, hydroxy acids, etc.—which bind metal ions.

3. Metals are accumulated by spores in large amounts from dilute solutions.

4. If metal ions cross a permeability barrier slowly, it is possible that accumulation occurs by an adsorption process and is followed by a slower entrance of the ion or a complex of it into the protoplast. Ion antagonism, according to this hypothesis, is exerted in the adsorption phase. For the present, however, it must be admitted that this mechanism is speculative.

5. Although the primary effect of metals is probably on enzymes in the interior of the cell, effects on the permeability barrier itself cannot be excluded entirely.

6. Heavy metals inactivate enzymes. Combination with essential sulfhydryl groups is the favored explanation, but it is likely that other inactivation reactions, involving the formation of electrostatic or coordinate bonds, also contribute to enzyme inhibition.

8. THE ACTION OF SULFUR

The most important organic sulfur fungicides are the dithiocarbamates, considered later as chelating agents. Many other organic sulfur compounds—dithiazolidines (12), thiourea (80, 112), mercaptobenzothiazole (100), xanthates (82), arylthioalkanecarboxylic acids (102), phenothiazone (131), 3-pyridinethiol (394), benzothiazoles (142), compounds with the N-trichloromethylthio grouping (201), substituted thiocyanates (215, 444), thiobisphenols (328), and such antibiotics as actithiazic acid and gliotoxin—are more or less fungitoxic. However, there is no reason to suppose that sulfur is necessarily directly involved in the reaction of all these diverse compounds with cellular constituents. In some organic molecules, the presence or absence of sulfur has no influence on toxicity (37, 82); in others it has (102). Some of the sulfur compounds probably act primarily as chelating agents (11, 174). In others sulfur may exert an effect by modifying the reactivity of nearby functional groups or by affecting solubility.

Inorganic sulfur, like copper, has been in use as a fungicide since the beginning of serious efforts to control plant disease. The various forms used, including liquid lime sulfur, all act ultimately as elemental sulfur. Sulfur is, of course, virtually water-insoluble, and a great deal of effort was earlier devoted to proving that some more soluble derivative is the active agent; the history of these investigations has been reviewed elsewhere (174, 244). It is now agreed that the form in which sulfur reaches the fungus spore is the vapor phase of elemental sulfur (246). Fungitoxicity in any particular situation of use is dependent upon temperature (459), the particle size of the sulfur deposit (370, 442), and, to some degree, the allotropic form of the sulfur (103).

For some time following a series of critical studies, the details of which are reviewed by McCallan (244, 246) and Horsfall (174), elemental sulfur was considered to be reduced by the fungus spore and the effective toxic agent was taken to be the hydrogen sulfide formed by the biological reduction. Hydrogen sulfide is fungistatic (442, 443) and somewhat fungicidal (248, 249). It appears now, however, that the toxicity of elemental sulfur on a weight basis is greater than that of an equivalent amount of hydrogen sulfide, as shown in Table 2. Conse-

Table 2. The Relative Toxicities of Sulfur and Hydrogen Sulfide* †

Species	Wettable Sulfur	Colloidal Sulfur	Hydrogen Sulfide
Monilinia fructicola	54	0.5	2.8‡
Cephalosporium acremonium	>1000	0.3	12‡
Aspergillus niger	>1000	0.3	15‡
Glomerella cingulata	>1000	0.4	20‡
Neurospora sitophila	>1000	1.0	38‡
Rhizopus nigricans	>1000	2.7	5.9
Alternaria oleracea	>1000	18	15
Stemphylium sarcinaeforme	>1000	31	8.8

* From Miller, McCallan, and Weed (289), by permission of the Boyce Thompson Institute for Plant Research, Inc.

† Toxicity is expressed as the dose, in parts per million, required to kill 50 per cent of spores in an exposure of 24 hours; concentrations are of the external solution or suspension.

‡ Highly significant difference between colloidal sulfur and hydrogen sulfide.

quently the second part of the older theory—that hydrogen sulfide is the ultimate toxicant—is untenable.

Attention has therefore been drawn to the process of sulfur reduction itself as a possible primary event in toxicity. The reduction of sulfur to hydrogen sulfide by fungus spores is a general phenomenon and has been shown to be brought about by spores of many different fungi, under both anaerobic and partially aerobic conditions (253, 289). The activity of species varies widely: *Cephalosporium acremonium* under anaerobic conditions forms 6.39 mg hydrogen sulfide per gram of spores per hour, almost 300 times the rate of the same process in *Rhizopus nigricans*. In these experiments there was no external hydrogen donor, so that cell constituents must have been oxidized; it is found, as would be expected, that under such circumstances high rates of hydrogen sulfide evolution are not maintained for long. Anaerobically, the formation of hydrogen sulfide from sulfur is accompanied by an equivalent release of carbon dioxide; aerobically, sulfur increases oxygen uptake (246b).

Mycelium of *Fusarium lini* is similarly capable of reducing elementary sulfur in the presence of isopropyl alcohol as hydrogen donor (369).

Fungi of different species differ very markedly in their sensitivity to sulfur under field or laboratory conditions; of the common test fungi for example, *Stemphylium sarcinaeforme* is about 60 times as resistant as *Monilinia fructicola* (Table 2). However, it has not yet been possible to correlate the enzymatic reduction of sulfur with its fungitoxicity —fungi which are relatively tolerant of sulfur are numbered among both those most active and those least active in reducing sulfur, whereas the more sulfur-sensitive species tend to be intermediate in reducing capacity (289). However, this type of study has only begun, and it is not yet possible to exclude any hypothesis with finality.

The production of large amounts of hydrogen sulfide from elemental sulfur in the absence of external hydrogen donors suggests that some relation may in the future be established between the derangement of metabolism associated with this process and the toxicity of sulfur (289). It is clear that sulfur is competing with normal hydrogen acceptors, and two speculative hypotheses are suggested by this conclusion. The first may be expressed, rather crudely, by the proposition that in the presence of very large amounts of a suitable hydrogen acceptor, sulfur, dehydrogenation reactions escape from the normal control imposed upon them under anaerobic conditions. This normal control may be either the limited supply of acceptors for "high-energy" phosphate or a poisoning of metabolism by the accumulation of such fermentation products as ethanol; the first of these is the more likely. The physiological effect of such an escape from regulation would be the disappearance of the cell's reserves. According to this hypothesis, sensitivity would be a function of the amount of utilizable reserve materials available to the spore and should be reduced by provision of an external hydrogen donor.

A related hypothesis to explain a deleterious effect of the reduction process itself is that utilization of reserves per se is less important than the fact that provision of sulfur results in a series of oxidations which are not coupled to the energy storage and energy utilization mechanisms of the cell. That is, sulfur diverts metabolism into non-productive or inefficient pathways.

Anaerobically, methylene blue prevents the reduction of sulfur by spores of *Neurospora sitophila* (289). It is known that methylene blue does not accept hydrogen directly from substrates or the pyridine nucleotide coenzymes but from hydrogen (electron) carriers, such as the flavoproteins and, possibly, cytochrome b (116). If the sulfur reduction process is in itself damaging to the cell, it is at this level that we should look first. It may be noted that sulfur reduction is also inhibited by 2,3-dichloro-1,4-naphthoquinone, the oxidation-reduction potential of which is presumably close to that of methylene blue.

Selenium and tellurium are much less toxic than sulfur, and their reduction to hydrides by yeast cells is correspondingly much less rapid (443). Selenium is accumulated in organic form by the mycelium of *Aspergillus niger* in competition with sulfur, and selenate inhibition is partially or wholly counteracted by reduced sulfur compounds (435). These and similar data on *Chlorella vulgaris* (378) can be interpreted in terms of competitive inhibition by a metabolite analogue.

9. QUINONES AND OTHER UNSATURATED COMPOUNDS

A number of actively fungistatic materials are characterized chemically by a system of conjugated double bonds. Of these, the most important are the quinonoid compounds, but the α,β-unsaturated ketones are also of interest.

The most generally active quinonoid compounds are the halogenated p-benzoquinones (266, 411) and 1,4-naphthoquinone and various derivatives of it (228, 229, 280, 364, 413), including synthetic vitamin K (2-methyl-1,4-naphthoquinone) (15, 70, 133). The triphenylmethane dyes, e.g., malachite green and crystal violet, are fungistatic and, significantly, the leuco form (benzenoid) is not active against either fungi (93) or bacteria (111).

The chromophoric group of the actinomycins is quinonoid (Chapter 8), and the antibacterial javanicin is a naphthoquinone (Chapter 6). The tropolones, some of which are produced by fungi (Chapter 6), have a modified quinonoid structure (325); some of the thujaplicins present in the decay-resistant heartwood of *Thuja plicata* show moderate fungistatic activity (19, 344, 345).

A few examples of quinonoid fungicides are shown in Figure 10.

It will be recalled that many fungi possess part or all of an enzymatic system which oxidizes phenols to quinones and further metabolizes the quinones to black melanin pigments (Chapter 6). It follows therefore

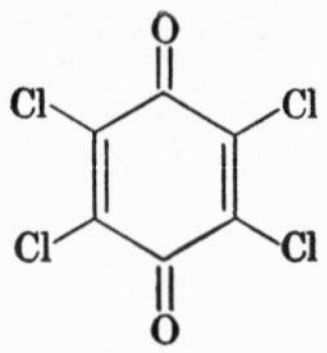

Tetrachloro-*p*-
benzoquinone
(Chloranil)

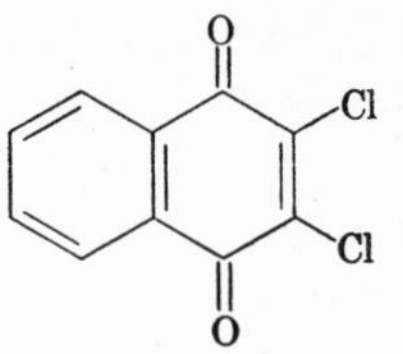

2,3-Dichloro-1,4-
naphthoquinone
(Dichlone)

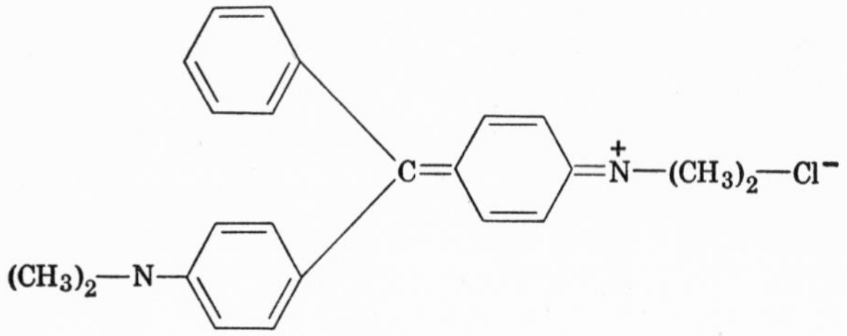

Malachite green

Figure 10. Fungistatic quinonoid compounds.

that appropriate hydroquinones, themselves non-toxic, may be converted to toxic quinones. Thus, 2,3-dichloro-1,4-naphthohydroquinone inhibits *Monilia laxa,* presumably because it is oxidized by the fungus to the corresponding naphthoquinone; esters of the hydroquinone are first hydrolyzed, then oxidized (56).

Detoxification of quinones would be expected of a fungus which forms melanin pigments; *Stemphylium sarcinaeforme,* which is normally black-pigmented, appears to convert many quinones to non-toxic products (347).

The reactivity of quinones is so great that more than one mode of action may easily be envisaged. Although any quinone affects the oxidation-reduction potential, it does not seem possible to correlate either bacteriostatic or fungistatic effects with this property (266, 321, 434). As α,β-unsaturated ketones, quinones can react with both sulfhydryl and amino groups (372), and these possibilities have enlisted considerable interest.

Quinones react, by addition, with simple thiols (212, 292). Correspondingly, the antimicrobial activity of quinones is often reversible by sulfhydryl compounds (70, 121). However, we have already noted that thiol reversal is not by itself sufficient proof of the nature of the *in vivo* reaction. Many of the enzymes known to depend upon sulfhydryl groups for their activity or known to be inhibited by sulfhydryl reagents are, it is true, inhibited *in vitro* by quinones and naphthoquinones (113, 159, 211, 213, 228, 319, 320, 364) and protected from this inhibition by thiols (319). However, a series of investigations shows, first, that quinones inhibit enzymes other than sulfhydryl-dependent types and, second, that the order of effectiveness of different quinones as enzyme inhibitors is not correlated with their antimicrobial activity (163–171). It is also to be noted that quinone toxicity to Gram-positive bacteria is not antagonized by thiols (121).

These considerations indicate that some other reaction with essential proteins should be considered, possibly an inactivation of amino groups. For the present, it is not possible to specify any particular ultimate site of action for the quinones, and the evidence suggests that they may be general rather than specific enzyme inhibitors comparable to the heavy metals.

The relation of structure to fungistatic activity in the quinones is reviewed by McNew and Burchfield (266). Toxicity generally decreases in the series naphthoquinone > phenanthraquinone > benzoquinone > anthraquinone. Halogenation improves effectiveness; the effect of other substituents depends upon specific type and position. Comparison of the effect of structure on inhibition of amylases reveals several instances in which a given structural feature affects fungitoxicity in one way, enzyme inhibition in another (320). Among the naphthoquinone antimalarials, activity is generally correlated with low water solubility; that is, not only a reactive grouping but also some non-polar properties are essential (105).

Although some quinones are natural products of fungi and could in principle participate in terminal respiration (Chapter 6), there is as yet no firm evidence that fungitoxic quinones act as metabolite analogues, although, as mentioned earlier, their action may be reversed by natural quinones.

Non-quinonoid α,β-unsaturated ketones are not so active as the quinones against fungi; many, however, are antibacterial. Several, e.g., patulin and penicillic acid, appeared first as antibiotics produced by fungi. These compounds inhibit sulfhydryl enzymes, and their inhibition of both isolated enzymes and intact cells is reversed by thiols. Consequently, it is believed that antibacterial action depends upon some reaction, perhaps addition across the reactive double bond, with sulfhydryl groups (122, 123, 351). Patulin, however, does not inhibit urease, a sulfhydryl enzyme (168), and the action of dehydroacetic acid is not reversed by thioglycolate (451).

Studies of the action of unsaturated compounds on *Botrytis allii* and other fungi have a direct bearing on the toxicity of quinones and other α,β-unsaturated ketones. It is proposed that any substituent which tends to withdraw electrons from a double bond increases toxicity (262, 301). Thus, derivatives of ω-nitrostyrene, $C_6H_5-CH=CH-NO_2$, are much more active than styrene, $C_6H_5-CH=CH_2$. The similarity to the α,β-unsaturated ketone structure,

is obvious. The same relation holds among the lachrymators: keto, aldehyde, ester (but not carboxyl), and nitro groups all confer ability on the double bond to attack sulfhydryl compounds; i.e., all increase activity toward nucleophilic reagents (94, 95).

10. CHELATION AND FUNGISTATIC ACTIVITY

A number of chemicals which are known to be strong chelating agents for metals are also found to be toxic to cells of fungi and other organisms. Since the most effort has gone into the problem of the mode of action of the dithiocarbamates and of 8-hydroxyquinoline (oxine), we shall limit this section largely to these compounds, after preliminary consideration of general topics.

Chelate compounds are compounds in which a metal ion combines with two or more electron-donating groups of a ligand in such a way that one or more rings are formed (276). As an example, the stepwise reaction of oxine with copper may be written:

(5)

In this example, the final product, the 1:2 chelate, has no exposed polar groups and hence extracts easily into a non-polar solvent. The 1:1 chelate is polar. A polar group not involved in the union with the metal would, of course, remain unchanged and reduce lipid solubility. The number of different complexes formed by a given metal with a ligand is a function of its coordination number.

Biological systems necessarily contain many different ions able to participate in chelate complexes, and the nature of competition must be considered. In general, most chelating agents form complexes of varying stability with metal ions in the order (from most to least stable): Cu++, Ni++, Co++, Zn++, Cd++, Fe++, Mn++, Mg++ (276). Thus copper will displace any of the other listed ions, magnesium none. However, some biologically important chelating substances do not follow this rough rule; α,α'-dipyridyl and o-phenanthroline, for example, have a specific affinity for iron.

Stability of metal chelates is usually expressed by the constant K, the formation (or dissociation) constant, a measure of the equilibrium:

$$M + xA \rightleftharpoons MA_x \qquad (6)$$

in which M = metal, A = ligand, and x = the number of ligand molecules per metal atom in the complex. Ideally, K is expressed by:

$$K = \frac{(MA_x)}{(M)(A)^x} \qquad (7)$$

in which brackets indicate activities (276). Values of log K may be very high, e.g., 23 for the copper-oxine complex; it is obvious that negligible amounts of free copper can exist in the presence of excess oxine.

Factors which fundamentally determine K are discussed by Calvin (59); Chabarek et al. (63) decribe the use, under biological conditions, of a plot of the negative logarithm of metal concentration against pH for prediction of the behavior of chelate systems. The ligand may be considered as a Lewis base; at low pH more of it is bound by protons and, consequently, the metal chelates are less stable under acid conditions.

Many normal cell metabolites are chelating agents; examples of such metabolites include amino and hydroxy acids, porphyrins, peptides, and polyphosphates. Some of these may owe their biological function to their chelating properties. Chelation is almost certainly necessary to the function of the manganese-requiring peptidases (289), and quite likely it is essential to the action of other metalloenzymes and electron or oxygen transport systems (59, 97).

We may approach the question of fungistatic action by first noting that chelating agents are often powerful inhibitors of metalloenzymes in cell-free preparations. The poisoning of certain iron enzymes, e.g., cytochrome oxidase, by cyanide or azide presumably involves chelate bonds with the iron atom. Enzymes known to depend on metals for their activity are inhibited by chelating agents: polyphenoloxidases by diethyldithiocarbamate, azide, and other compounds able to complex with copper (184, 319, 405), zinc metalloenzymes by oxine, α,α'-dipyridyl, and o-phenanthroline (420). The specificity of chelating agents is, however, so low at biological pH levels that inhibition by them does not as a rule suffice to identify the metal active for a given enzyme or enzymatic system.

In the systems just mentioned, it is not known whether the chelating agent combines with the metal *in situ* on an enzyme or coenzyme or competes with the catalyst for the limited amount of metal present. Inhibition of dialkylfluorophosphatase by 8-hydroxyquinoline and ethylenediaminetetraacetic acid (EDTA) appears to arise from removal of calcium from the enzyme (299); other enzymes dependent upon calcium for activity or stability are also inhibited by EDTA (86, 139).

Finally, a few examples of *in vivo* effects of chelating agents may be mentioned: inhibition of synthesis of phenolic compounds by *Phycomyces blakesleeanus* (48), prevention of the transformation of *Brucella abortus* from the smooth to the non-smooth form (68), and inhibition of glutamic acid assimilation by *Staphylococcus aureus* (117). In the two last-mentioned instances, it is believed that the biologically active metal is manganese, but the locus of the manganese chelate—within the cell or outside it—cannot be determined. Several metal complexing agents, including cyanide, sodium dimethyldithiocarbamate, and ethylenediaminetetraacetic acid, cause the release of subcellular particulates from cells of *Candida albicans* (284).

Although it is usually found that in any series of chelating agents many compounds are toxic (174, 180), and many empirically discovered toxicants turn out to be chelating agents (7, 60, 433), the association is not uniform, presumably because both the stability of the complex and its molecular architecture are factors in toxicity or in the ability of the molecule to reach the site of toxicity. Chelation alone, in other words, does not necessarily confer toxicity (8, 264). The best example of a close association between toxicity and chelation is in the series of compounds related to oxine: only those that complex metals are bacteriostatic (10, 11).

The association of toxicity and ability to chelate was at first thought to signify only that the chelating agent deprives the cell of essential metals (461, 462). Several subsequent developments, however, make it seem unlikely that metal starvation per se is the primary mechanism of toxicity at minimally fungistatic doses. First, copper oxine is as toxic as, or even more toxic than, oxine itself (281, 313, 424). The same relation holds for the metal complexes of other chelating agents (272, 372, 395, 433). Second, there is some evidence that toxicity to bacteria and fungi is less in a medium low in metals than in the usual medium (5, 9, 14, 358). Finally, successful use of chelating agents to supply metals both to fungi (Chapter 9) and to higher plants (143, 401) suggests that cells in general can compete successfully for metals, with even quite stable complexes.

Metal starvation cannot, however, be dismissed completely as a factor in toxicity. Chelating agents reduce the metal-dependent spore pigment of *Aspergillus niger* (338); EDTA prevents spore germination of *Neurospora tetrasperma* without apparently entering the cell (406), and citrate effects on enzymatic adaptation in *Azobacter* spp. can at least be interpreted as a depletion phenomenon (368). Inhibition of sporulation by chelating agents (179, 428) suggests that a higher metal requirement makes sporulation especially sensitive to metal deprivation.

A number of observations, covered in detail in the original literature (9, 31, 32), support a plausible working hypothesis for the action of oxine and its metal complexes. The hypothesis starts with the equilibria already described (Equation 5) of oxine, its charged 1:1 chelate and the neutral 1:2 chelate. It is believed that the 1:2 chelate, perhaps because of its higher lipid solubility, enters the cell more rapidly than the 1:1 chelate and in that sense is the active species. However, within the cell it seems likely that the 1:1 chelate is the more toxic, perhaps by reacting directly with essential metal-binding sites or with sulfhydryl groups essential to the cell. This hypothesis has the advantage of explaining the bimodal dose-response curve of oxine (6, 31, 281), which is similar in principle to that of the dithiocarbamates (Figure 11), and the complex interactions of metal and oxine concentrations (32). Still to be demonstrated, however, are the roles of free metal ions and free oxine, the site of the proposed toxic reaction, and the role of natural chelating substances within and on the cell. Also, as with all permeability hypotheses, the lack of direct evidence is distressing.

8-Hydroxyquinoline-5-sulfonic acid is a chelating agent but is not antibacterial (6). It fails to inhibit *Monilinia fructicola* but is active against *Macrosporium sarcinaeforme* (177). It seems possible that the anionic group acts by preventing access of the molecule to the site of action (6); on this hypothesis, *M. sarcinaeforme* must be more permeable to the compound than are bacteria and *M. fructicola*.

The action of the dithiocarbamates and their derivatives may be ex-

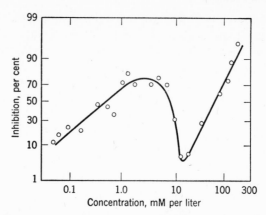

plained in a similar way. Figure 11 illustrates the well-known bimodal dose-response curve characteristic of this family of toxicants; the general form of the curve shown has been confirmed in studies on spore germination of *Venturia inaequalis* (298) and on growth of *Aspergillus niger* (196, 198).

The structures of interest are shown in Figure 12, with code abbreviations. Other complexes can, of course, be prepared and have been

Tetramethylthiuram disulfide (TMTD)

Sodium dimethyldithiocarbamate (Na DMDT)

Ferric dimethyldithiocarbamate (Fe DMDT)

Figure 12. The structure of some dithiocarbamate fungicides.

tested as fungitoxicants (174), but it is presumed that the active grouping is the same in all.

The important reactions of the dithiocarbamates from the standpoint
of mode of action may be summarized (127):

$$\text{TMTD}$$

$$\text{CS}_2 + (\text{CH}_3)_2\text{NH} \xleftarrow{\text{H}^+} \text{DMDT}^- \xrightleftharpoons{\text{metals}} \text{Metal complexes} \qquad (8)$$

Oxidation ↑↓ Reduction

Hydrolysis

$$\text{TMTM}$$

(Symbols are taken from Figure 11; TMTM = tetramethylthiuram
monosulfide.)

The primary problems of mode of action in this series are set for us
by (1) the bimodal response curve and (2) the effect of metals on toxicity. Although it has been considered possible that carbon disulfide,
formed under acid conditions (234) or enzymatically (191, 192, 384)
from DMDT, is the active toxicant, both this and other decomposition
products are of too low inherent toxicity to account for DMDT action
(322, 432).

The best available working hypothesis for the action of DMDT is
rather similar to that just discussed for oxine. It is proposed (127, 196)
that the first peak in the dose-response curve mirrors the formation of
a toxic 1:1 complex of DMDT with copper present in the medium. It
is suggested on the basis of work with yeast that this water-soluble
charged 1:1 complex exerts its effect at or just beneath the cell membrane (127); this suggestion, supported by indirect evidence, avoids the
problem of explaining penetration of a charged complex. At higher
DMDT concentrations the insoluble and non-toxic 1:2 copper complex
(2 moles DMDT per copper atom) forms and accounts for the trough
in the dose-response curve. At still higher concentrations of DMDT,
either the free anion becomes toxic (196) or some other toxic complex,
e.g., with zinc, is formed (127). The first of these possibilities seems
more probable; free dithiocarbamate inhibits enzymes *in vitro* (319).

It is to be noted that this hypothesis explains the first peak of the
bimodal response curve as a function of copper in the system; in a medium low in copper and other metals there should be only a single peak
in the curve. This is borne out by visual estimates of mycelial growth
(196) but has not yet been shown by the more precise spore germination
technique.

Liebermeister (225) has proposed that several drugs effective against *Mycobacterium tuberculosis* are also active by virtue of their formation of a toxic complex.

Some of the detailed data on the action of the dithiocarbamates is inconsistent with, or at least not explained by, the theory of action just outlined. These data are thoroughly reviewed by Horsfall (174), and it should be clear that many problems remain. No other hypothesis, however, explains the bimodal dose-response curve.

Imidazoles, which are themselves complexing agents, antagonize the action of DMDT in the concentration range of the first peak of toxicity (198). This suggests that the locus of toxicity of the 1:1 copper chelate is an enzyme which is normally coordinated to some metal, and that the available coordination positions of the copper in the 1:1 complex replace the metal on the enzyme.

Dithiocarbamates at minimally fungistatic concentrations have very slight activity against endogenous or glucose respiration in fungi (81, 127, 203, 314). Acetate oxidation in yeast is considerably more sensitive (127). The respiratory enzyme triose phosphate dehydrogenase is inhibited in yeast and in *Fusarium roseum* by TMTD (384, 385). This may be explained on the basis that the dithiocarbamates react with glutathione (432) and that the reduction of TMTD to DMDT (Equation 8) is likely to be coupled to an oxidation of such labile cell materials as glutathione. Since glutathione is the prosthetic group of triosephosphate dehydrogenase (210), it follows that this enzyme will be especially sensitive. It must be concluded that we are at present unable to point to any specific system, the inhibition of which is the primary effect of either free dithiocarbamates or their active complexes.

The present picture of the action of fungistatic chelating molecules is thus one of great complexity. A given compound exists as an anion or as an uncharged molecule and as complexes of various metal:ligand ratios with one or more metals. One or more of these molecular species reaches the sensitive region of the cell, at which point a new set of equilibrium conditions, complicated by the presence of cellular chelating agents, must be envisioned. Still other complications can be introduced by structural alteration of the chelating agent; such structural changes influence ionization, water and lipoid solubility, and the stability of metal complexes.

Although the bisdithiocarbamates are superficially similar to the dithiocarbamates and are also chelating agents, the evidence to date suggests that the mode of action is not the same. In particular, fungi show different sensitivities to the two classes of toxicant, for a given fungus the slopes of the dose-response curves are different, and the bimodal dose-response curve does not prevail in the bisdithiocarbamates (174, 246). Bisdithiocarbamates are unstable (234), and several breakdown products have been suggested as the active toxicant. Disodium ethylenebis[dithiocarbamate] itself is completely without fungicidal action (247, 432). Carbon disulfide, one of the breakdown products, is unlikely to be of primary importance (432). It appears that three derived compounds, which arise by breakdown of the parent substance, all contribute to toxicity: ethylene di*iso*thiocyanate, ethylene thiuram monosulfide, and polymers of the thiuram monosulfide (197, 236, 237, 414). Reactivity with thiol groups has suggested that the primary toxic action is on a sulfhydryl enzyme (197).

11. CONCLUDING REMARKS

In his treatise on the principles of fungicidal action, Horsfall (174) emphasizes the two requirements of a toxicant, that it be able in some way to react with an essential cell constituent, and that it be able to reach the site of this reaction. It seems fair to say that for no fungicidal or fungistatic material can both these requirements be specified in terms of structure. Nor does it seem likely to me that further empirical testing of ever-different organic compounds will by itself allow us to draw up accurate specifications as guides to both theory and practice. Instead, we need to know more about the toxicants we have, especially in terms of the theory of chemical reactions. On the biological side of the problem, a frontal attack on the problems of the cell surface is surely an urgent necessity. It must be realized that, at the present time, all explanations based on an assumed permeability or impermeability are no more than guesses, in the absence of independent evidence; i.e., evidence not based upon the toxic reaction itself.

Although no line of investigation can, of course, be ruled out, it does seem that the search in the fungi for specific enzymatic loci of toxicity is less promising. Many of the most active materials may be general rather than specific poisons; if this is true, they will inhibit almost any enzyme the investigator happens to test, but none of these will be "the" site of activity.

BIBLIOGRAPHY

1. Abelson, P. H. and E. Aldous. 1950. *J. Bacteriol.* 60: 401–413.
2. Agerberg, L. S., R. Schick, M. Schmidt, and R. von Sengbusch. 1933. *Zuchter* 5: 272–280.
3. Akai, S. and S. Itoi. 1954. *Botan. Mag.* (*Tokyo*) 67: 1–5.

4. Albert, A. 1947. *Proc. Intern. Congr. Pure and Appl. Chem., 11 Congr. London*, 4: 1–5.
5. Albert, A. 1950. *Proc. Roy. Soc. (London) B*, 136: 177–178.
6. Albert, A. 1951. *Selective Toxicity.* London: Methuen and Co., Ltd., pp. 228.
7. Albert, A. 1953. *Nature (London)* 172: 201.
8. Albert, A. 1956. *Nature (London)* 177: 525–526.
9. Albert, A., M. I. Gibson, and S. D. Rubbo. 1953. *Brit. J. Exp. Pathol.* 34: 119–130.
10. Albert, A. and D. Magrath. 1947. *Biochem. J. (London)* 41: 534–545.
11. Albert, A., S. D. Rubbo, R. J. Goldacre, and B. G. Balfour. 1947. *Brit. J. Exp. Pathol.* 28: 69–87.
12. Allen, R. E., R. S. Shelton, and M. G. Van Campen, Jr. 1954. *J. Am. Chem. Soc.* 76: 1158–1159.
13. Ambrose, J. F., G. B. Kistiakowsky, and A. G. Kridl. 1951. *J. Am. Chem. Soc.* 73: 1232–1236.
14. Anderson, B. I. and R. J. Swaby. 1951. *Australian J. Sci. Research Ser. B*, 4: 275–282.
15. Arêa Leão, A. E. de and A. da R. Furtado. 1950. *Mycopathol. Mycol. Appl.* 5: 121–124.
16. Arima, K. and S. Abe. 1951. *J. Antibiotics (Japan)* 4: 342–346.
17. Arny, D. C. and C. Leben. 1954. *Phytopathol.* 44: 380–383.
18. Badger, G. M. 1946. *Nature (London)* 158: 585.
19. Baillie, A. J., G. G. Freeman, J. W. Cook, and A. R. Somerville. 1950. *Nature (London)* 166: 65.
20. Barron, E. S. G., L. Nelson, and M. I. Ardao. 1948. *J. Gen. Physiol.* 32: 179–190.
21. Barron, E. S. G. and T. P. Singer. 1945. *J. Biol. Chem.* 157: 218–240.
22. Bateman, E. 1933. *U. S. Dept. Agr. Tech. Bull.* 346: 1–53.
23. Bedford, C. L. 1936. *Zentr. Bakteriol. Parasitenk. Abt. II*, 94: 102–112.
24. Beevers, H., E. F. Goldschmidt, and H. Koffler. 1952. *Arch. Biochem. Biophys.* 39: 236–238.
25. Beran, F., A. Janke, and G. Schmidt. 1954. *Phytiat.-Phytopharm. 1954* (Special Issue): 543–547. (*Chem. Abstr.* 50: 13353. 1956.)
26. Bergman, S. 1955. *Acta Pathol. Microbiol. Scand., Suppl. No. 104*: 1–130.
27. Berliner, M. D. 1954. *Am. J. Botany* 41: 93–104.
28. Biedermann, W. and E. Müller. 1951. *Phytopathol. Z.* 18: 307–338.
29. Blackman, G. E., M. H. Parke, and G. Garton. 1955. *Arch. Biochem. Biophys.* 54: 45–54, 55–71.
30. Bliss, C. I. 1935. *Ann. Appl. Biol.* 22: 134–167.
31. Block, S. S. 1955. *J. Agr. Food Chem.* 3: 229–234.
32. Block, S. S. 1956. *J. Agr. Food Chem.* 4: 1042–1046.
33. Blumer, S. and J. Kundert. 1950. *Phytopathol. Z.* 17: 161–199.
34. Bodnár, J. and A. Terényi. 1930. *Z. Physiol. Chem. Hoppe-Seyler's* 186: 157–182.
35. Bodnár, J. and T. Terényi. 1932. *Z. Physiol. Chem. Hoppe-Seyler's* 207: 78–92.
36. Bodnár, J., I. Villányi, and A. Terényi. 1927. *Z. Physiol. Chem. Hoppe-Seyler's* 163: 73–93.
37. Bradsher, C. K., F. C. Brown, and R. J. Grantham. 1954. *J. Am. Chem. Soc.* 76: 114–115.
38. von Brand, T., E. J. Tobie, B. Mehlman, and E. C. Weinbach. 1953. *J. Cellular Comp. Physiol.* 41: 1–22.
39. Brewer, J. H. 1954. In G. F. Reddish (ed.), *Antiseptics, Disinfectants, Fungicides, and Chemical and Physical Sterilization*, p. 212–240. Philadelphia: Lea and Febiger.

40. Brian, P. W. 1944. *Nature (London)* 153: 83–84.
41. Brian, P. W. 1945. *J. Soc. Chem. Ind., Trans. (London)* 64: 315–316.
42. Brian, P. W. 1949. *Ann. Botany* 13: 59–77.
43. Brian, P. W., P. J. Curtis, and H. G. Hemming. 1946. *Trans. Brit. Mycol. Soc.* 29: 173–187.
44. Brian, P. W., J. M. Wright, J. Stubbs, and A. M. Way. 1951. *Nature (London)* 165: 347–349.
45. Briggs, G. E. 1954. *J. Exp. Botany* 5: 263–268.
46. Brink, F. and J. M. Posternak. 1948. *J. Cellular Comp. Physiol.* 32: 211–234.
47. Brook, M. 1952. *Nature (London)* 170: 1022.
48. Brucker, W. 1957. *Arch. Mikrobiol.* 26: 302–306.
49. Burchfield, H. P. and G. L. McNew. 1950. *Contribs. Boyce Thompson Inst.* 16: 131–161.
50. Burchfield, H. P. and E. E. Storrs. 1956. *Contribs. Boyce Thompson Inst.* 18: 395–418.
51. Burchfield, H. P. and E. E. Storrs. 1957. *Contribs. Boyce Thompson Inst.* 18: 429–452.
52. Burris, R. H. and P. W. Wilson. 1942. *J. Cellular Comp. Physiol.* 19: 361–371.
53. Burtt, E. T. 1945. *Ann. Appl. Biol.* 32: 247–260.
54. Byrde, R. J. W., J. F. Harris, and D. Woodcock. 1956. *Biochem. J. (London)* 64: 154–160.
55. Byrde, R. J. W., J. T. Martin, and D. J. D. Nicholas. 1956. *Nature (London)* 178: 638–639.
56. Byrde, R. J. W. and D. Woodcock. 1953. *Ann. Appl. Biol.* 40: 675–687.
57. Byrde, R. J. W. and D. Woodcock. 1957. *Biochem. J. (London)* 65: 682–686.
58. Cade, A. R. and W. S. Gump. 1954. In G. F. Reddish (ed.), *Antiseptics, Disinfectants, Fungicides, and Chemical and Physical Sterilization*, p. 250–278. Philadelphia: Lea and Febiger.
59. Calvin, M. 1954. In W. D. McElroy and B. Glass (eds.), *A Symposium on the Mechanism of Enzyme Action*, p. 221–245. Baltimore: The Johns Hopkins Press.
60. Carl, E. and P. Marquardt. 1949. *Z. Naturforsch.* 4b: 280–283.
61. Cartwright, K. St. G. and W. P. K. Findlay. 1946. *Decay of Timber and Its Prevention.* London: H. M. Stationery Office, pp. 294.
62. Cavill, G. W. K. and J. M. Vincent. 1945. *Nature (London)* 155: 301.
63. Chaberek, S., F. C. Bersworth, and A. E. Martell. 1955. *Arch. Biochem. Biophys.* 55: 321–337.
64. Chance, B. 1952. *Nature (London)* 169: 215–221.
65. Christensen, C. H., F. H. Kaufert, H. Schmitz, and J. L. Allison. 1942. *Am. J. Botany* 29: 552–558.
66. Clark, N. G. and A. F. Hams. 1953. *Biochem. J. (London)* 55: 839–851.
67. Clifton, C. E. and W. A. Logan. 1939. *J. Bacteriol.* 37: 523–540.
68. Cole, L. J. 1952. *J. Bacteriol.* 64: 847–853.
69. Colhoun, J. 1954. *Ann. Appl. Biol.* 41: 290–304.
70. Colwell, C. A. and M. McCall. 1946. *J. Bacteriol.* 51: 659–670.
71. Committee on Standardization of Fungicidal Tests. 1943. *Phytopathol.* 33: 627–632.
72. Committee on Standardization of Fungicidal Tests. 1947. *Phytopathol.* 37: 354–356.
73. Corey, R. R. and H. G. Shirk. 1955. *Arch. Biochem. Biophys.* 56: 196–203.
74. Crowdy, S. H., J. F. Grove, H. G. Hemming, and K. C. Robinson. 1956. *J. Exp. Botany* 7: 42–64.
75. Cruess, W. V. and P. H. Richert. 1929. *J. Bacteriol.* 17: 363–371.
76. Cruess, W. V., P. H. Richert, and J. H. Irish. 1931. *Hilgardia* 6: 295–314.
77. Cushing, J. E., M. Schwartz, and R. Bennett. 1949. *J. Bacteriol.* 58: 433–442.
78. Dagys, J. and O. Kaikaryte. 1943. *Protoplasma* 38: 127–154.

79. Danielli, J. F. 1950. *Cell Physiology and Pharmacology.* New York: Elsevier Publishing Co., pp. 156.
80. Danowski, T. S. and M. Tager. 1948. *J. Infectious Diseases* 82: 119–125.
81. Darby, R. T. and D. R. Goddard. 1950. *Physiol. Plantarum* 3: 435–446.
82. Davies, W. H. and W. A. Sexton. 1946. *Biochem. J.* (*London*) 40: 331–334.
83. Davis, D. and A. E. Dimond. 1952. *Phytopathology* 42: 563–567.
84. Davson, H. and J. F. Danielli. 1943. *The Permeability of Natural Membranes.* New York: The Macmillan Co., pp. 361.
85. Demerec, M. 1948. *J. Bacteriol.* 56: 63–74.
86. DiCarlo, F. J. and S. Redfern. 1947. *Arch. Biochem.* 15: 343–350.
87. Dickey, F. H., G. H. Cleland, and C. Lotz. 1949. *Proc. Natl. Acad. Sci. U. S.* 35: 581–586.
88. Dillon Weston, W. A. R. and J. R. Booer. 1935. *J. Agr. Sci.* 25: 628–649.
89. Dimock, A. W. 1936. *Zentr. Bakteriol. Parasitenk. Abt. II,* 95: 341–347.
90. Dimond, A. E., D. Davis, R. A. Chapman, and E. M. Stoddard. 1952. *Conn.* (*New Haven*) *Agr. Exp. Sta. Bull.* 557: 1–82.
91. Dimond, A. E., J. G. Horsfall, J. W. Heuberger, and E. M. Stoddard. 1941. *Conn.* (*New Haven*) *Agr. Exp. Sta. Bull.* 451: 635–667.
92. Dimond, N. S. 1941. *Science* 94: 420–421.
93. Dion, W. M. and K. A. Lord. 1944. *Ann. Appl. Biol.* 31: 221–231.
94. Dixon, M. 1948. *Biochem. Soc. Symposia* (*Cambridge, Engl.*) *No. 2:* 39–49.
95. Dixon, M. and D. M. Needham. 1946. *Nature* (*London*) 158: 432–438.
96. Dunshee, B. R., C. Leben, G. W. Keitt, and F. M. Strong. 1949. *J. Am. Chem. Soc.* 71: 2436–2437.
97. Eichhorn, G. L. 1956. In J. C. Bailar, Jr. (ed.), *The Chemistry of the Coordination Compounds,* p. 698–742. New York: Reinhold Publishing Corp.
98. Emerson, S. 1947. *J. Bacteriol.* 54: 195–207.
99. Engelhard, H., O. Müller, and K. Bertl. 1949. *Zentr. Bakteriol. Parasitenk. Abt. I Orig.,* 153: 326–335.
100. Everitt, E. L. and M. X. Sullivan. 1940. *J. Wash. Acad. Sci.* 30: 125–131.
101. Ezekiel, W. N. 1938. *J. Agr. Research* 56: 553–578.
102. Fawcett, C. H., D. M. Spencer, and R. L. Wain. 1957. *Ann. Appl. Biol.* 45: 158–176.
103. Feichtmeir, E. F. 1949. *Phytopathology* 39: 605–615.
104. Ferguson, J. 1939. *Proc. Roy. Soc.* (*London*) *B,* 127: 387–404.
105. Fieser, L. F., M. G. Ettlinger, and G. Fawaz. 1948. *J. Am. Chem. Soc.* 70: 3228–3232.
106. Fieser, L. F. and H. Heymann. 1948. *J. Biol. Chem.* 176: 1363–1370.
107. Fildes, P. 1940. *Brit. J. Exp. Pathol.* 21: 67–73.
108. Findlay, W. P. K. and J. W. Vernon. 1951. *Ann. Appl. Biol.* 38: 876–880.
109. Finholt, R. W. 1951. *Anal. Chem.* 23: 1038–1039.
110. Finholt, R. W., M. Weeks, and C. Hathaway. 1952. *Ind. Eng. Chem.* 44: 101–105.
111. Fischer, E., O. Hoffmann, E. Prado, and R. Boné. 1944. *J. Bacteriol.* 48: 439–445.
112. Fleury, C. 1948. *Ber. schweiz. botan. Ges.* 58: 462–477.
113. Foote, M. W., J. E. Little, and T. J. Sproston. 1949. *J. Biol. Chem.* 181: 481–487.
114. Forsberg, J. L. 1949. *Phytopathology* 39: 172–174.
115. Fries, N. 1950. *Hereditas* 36: 134–150.
116. Fruton, J. S. and S. Simmonds. 1953. *General Biochemistry.* New York: John Wiley and Sons, pp. 940.
117. Gale, E. F. 1949. *J. Gen. Microbiol.* 3: 369–384.
118. Gale, E. F. and E. S. Taylor. 1947. *J. Gen. Microbiol.* 1: 77–85.
119. Gale, G. R. 1953. *J. Bacteriol.* 65: 505–508.

120. Gattani, M. L. 1954. *Phytopathology* 44: 113–115.
121. Geiger, W. B. 1946. *Arch. Biochem.* 11: 23–32.
122. Geiger, W. B. 1948. *Arch. Biochem.* 16: 423–435.
123. Geiger, W. B. and J. E. Conn. 1945. *J. Am. Chem. Soc.* 67: 112–116.
124. Gibson, I. A. S. 1953. *Trans. Brit. Mycol. Soc.* 36: 324–334.
125. Giese, A. C. and E. L. Tatum. 1946. *Arch. Biochem.* 9: 15–23.
126. Göhre, K. 1955. *Arch. Forstw.* 4: 293–301. (*Rev. Appl. Mycol.* 36: 76. 1957.)
127. Goksøyr, J. 1955. *Physiol. Plantarum* 8: 719–835.
128. Golden, M. J. and K. A. Oster. 1947. *J. Am. Pharm. Assoc., Sci. Ed.*, 36: 359–362.
129. Goldsworthy, M. C. and E. L. Green. 1936. *J. Agr. Research* 52: 517–533.
130. Goldsworthy, M. C. and E. L. Green. 1938. *J. Agr. Research* 56: 489–506.
131. Goldsworthy, M. C. and E. L. Green. 1939. *Phytopathology* 29: 700–716.
132. Gonzalez, E. L. and E. S. G. Barron. 1956. *Biochim. et Biophys. Acta* 19: 425–432.
133. Gonzalez, F. 1945. *Science* 101: 494.
134. Gottlieb, D. 1957. *Phytopathology* 47: 59–67.
135. Gould, B. S., M. A. Bosniak, S. Neidleman, and S. Gatt. 1953. *Arch. Biochem. Biophys.* 44: 284–297.
136. Gould, B. S., N. A. Frigerio, and W. B. Lebowitz. 1955. *Arch. Biochem. Biophys.* 56: 476–486.
137. Graveri, R. and U. Veronesi. 1956. *Exp. Cell Research* 11: 560–567.
138. Greig, M. E. 1946. *J. Pharmacol. Exp. Therap.* 87: 185–192.
139. Gross, M. 1953. *Science* 118: 218–219.
140. Grove, J. F. 1948. *Ann. Appl. Biol.* 35: 37–44.
141. Gruenhagen, R. H., P. A. Wolf, and E. E. Dunn. 1951. *Contribs. Boyce Thompson Inst.* 16: 349–356.
142. Grunberg, E. et al. 1950. *Trans. N. Y. Acad. Sci.* II, 13: 22–27.
143. Haertl, E. J. and A. E. Martell. 1956. *J. Agr. Food Chem.* 4: 26–32.
144. Hamilton, J. M., D. H. Palmiter, and G. L. Mack. 1943. *Phytopathology* 33: 533–550.
145. Harley, J. L., C. C. McCready, J. K. Brierley, and D. H. Jennings. 1956. *New Phytologist* 55: 1–28.
146. Harry, J. B. et al. 1948. *Contribs. Boyce Thompson Inst.* 15: 195–210.
147. Hartelius, V. 1946. *Compt. rend. trav. lab. Carlsberg, Sér. physiol.* 24: 178–184.
148. Hartelius, V. and K. Roholt. 1946. *Compt. rend. trav. lab. Carlsberg, Sér. physiol.* 24: 163–171.
149. Hassebrauk, K. 1952. *Phytopathol. Z.* 19: 56–78.
150. Hawkins, L. A. 1913. *Physiol. Research* 1: 57–92.
151. Herrick, J. A. and J. E. Kempf. 1944. *J. Bacteriol.* 48: 331–336.
152. Hessayon, G. 1953. *Soil Sci.* 75: 317–327.
153. Heuberger, J. W. and J. G. Horsfall. 1942. *Phytopathology* 32: 370–378.
154. Hickey, R. J. 1953. *Arch. Biochem. Biophys.* 46: 331–336.
155. Hill, C. H. 1952. *J. Biol. Chem.* 199: 329–332.
156. Hill, C. H. 1953. *J. Bacteriol.* 65: 578–80.
157. Hirschorn, E. and D. E. Munnecke. 1950. *Phytopathology* 40: 524–526.
158. Hirt, R. R. 1949. *Phytopathology* 39: 31–36.
159. Hochstein, P. E. and C. E. Cox. 1952. *Phytopathology* 42: 13.
160. Hochstein, P. E. and C. E. Cox. 1956. *Am. J. Botany* 43: 437–441.
161. Hoffman, C., T. R. Schweitzer, and G. Dalby. 1940. *J. Am. Chem. Soc.* 62: 988–989.
162. Hoffman, C., T. R. Schweitzer, and G. Dalby. 1941. *Ind. Eng. Chem.* 33: 749–751.
163. Hoffmann-Ostenhof, O. and E. Biach. 1947. *Monatsh. Chem.* 76: 319–324.
164. Hoffmann-Ostenhof, O. and E. Biach. 1948a. *Monatsh. Chem.* 78: 53–57.

165. Hoffmann-Ostenhof, O. and E. Biach. 1948b. *Monatsh. Chem.* 79: 248–252.
166. Hoffmann-Ostenhof, O., E. Biach, S. Gierer, and O. Kraupp. 1948. *Monatsh. Chem.* 79: 576–580.
167. Hoffmann-Ostenhof, O. and E. Kriz. 1950. *Monatsh. Chem.* 81: 90–100.
168. Hoffmann-Ostenhof, O. and W. H. Lee. 1946. *Monatsh. Chem.* 76: 180–184.
169. Hoffmann-Ostenhof, O. and H. Moser. 1948. *Monatsh. Chem.* 79: 570–575.
170. Hoffmann-Ostenhof, O. and E. Putz. 1948. *Monatsh. Chem.* 79: 421–425.
171. Hoffmann-Ostenhof, O. and E. Putz. 1950. *Monatsh. Chem.* 81: 703–707.
172. Horsfall, J. G. 1945a. *Fungicides and Their Action.* Waltham, Mass.: Chronica Botanica Co., pp. 239.
173. Horsfall, J. G. 1945b. *Botan. Rev.* 11: 357–398.
174. Horsfall, J. G. 1956. *Principles of Fungicidal Action.* Waltham, Mass.: Chronica Botanica Co., pp. 279.
175. Horsfall, J. G. and A. E. Dimond. 1951a. *Ann. Rev. Microbiol.* 5: 209–222.
176. Horsfall, J. G. and A. E. Dimond. 1951b. *Trans. N. Y. Acad. Sci.* II, 13: 338–341.
177. Horsfall, J. G. and S. Rich. 1951. *Contribs. Boyce Thompson Inst.* 16: 313–347.
178. Horsfall, J. G. and S. Rich. 1953. *Indian Phytopathol.* 6: 1–14.
179. Horsfall, J. G. and S. Rich. 1955. *Trans. N. Y. Acad. Sci.* II, 18: 69–80.
180. Horsfall, J. G. and G. A. Zentmyer. 1944. *Phytopathology* 34: 1004.
181. Hotchkiss, R. D. 1946. *Ann. N. Y. Acad. Sci.* 46: 479–493.
182. Hugo, W. B. 1956. *J. Gen. Microbiol.* 15: 315–323.
183. Hwang, L. and L. J. Klotz. 1938. *Hilgardia* 12: 1–38.
184. James, W. O. and N. Garton. 1952. *J. Exp. Botany* 3: 310–318.
185. Janke, A., F. Beran, and G. Schmidt. 1953. *Pflanzenschutz Ber.* 10: 65–87.
186. Jarvis, F. G. and M. J. Johnson. 1950. *J. Bacteriol.* 59: 51–60.
187. Jensen, H. L. 1947. *Proc. Linn. Soc. N. S. Wales* 71: 119–129.
188. Jensen, K. A., I. Kirk, G. Kølmark, and M. Westergaard. 1951. *Cold Spring Harbor Symposia Quant. Biol.* 16: 245–261.
189. Jensen, K. A., G. Kølmark, and M. Westergaard. 1949. *Hereditas* 35: 521–524.
190. Johnson, F. H., H. Eyring, and M. J. Polissar. 1954. *The Kinetic Basis of Molecular Biology.* New York: John Wiley and Sons, pp. 874.
191. Johnston, C. D. 1953. *Arch. Biochem. Biophys.* 44: 249–251.
192. Johnston, C. D. and C. S. Prickett. 1952. *Biochim. et Biophys. Acta* 9: 219–220.
193. Jowett, M. 1938. *J. Physiol.* 92: 322–335.
194. Jowett, M. and J. H. Quastel. 1937. *Biochem. J. (London)* 31: 1101–1112.
195. Jurkowska, H. 1951. *Bull. intern. acad. polon. sci., Classe sci. math. nat., Sér. B,* I, 1951: 167–203.
196. Kaars Sijpesteyn, A., M. J. Janssen, and G. J. M. van der Kerk. 1957. *Biochim. et Biophys. Acta* 23: 550–557.
197. Kaars Sijpesteyn, A. and G. J. M. van der Kerk. 1954a. *Biochim. et Biophys. Acta* 13: 545–552.
198. Kaars Sijpesteyn, A. and G. J. M. van der Kerk. 1954b. *Biochim. et Biophys. Acta* 15: 69–77.
199. van der Kerk, G. J. M. and J. G. A. Luitjen. 1954. *J. Appl. Chem.* 4: 314–319.
200. Kirkham, D. S. 1954. *Nature (London)* 173: 690–691.
201. Kittleson, A. R. 1953. *J. Agr. Food Chem.* 1: 677–679.
202. Klarmann, E. G. and E. S. Wright. 1954. In G. F. Reddish (ed.), *Antiseptics, Disinfectants, Fungicides, and Chemical and Physical Sterilization,* p. 429–464. Philadelphia: Lea and Febiger.
203. Klöpping, H. L. 1951. *Chemical Constitution and Antifungal Action of Sulfur Compounds.* Utrecht: Schotanus and Jens, pp. 142.
204. Klotz, I. M. 1954. In W. D. McElroy and B. Glass (eds.), *A Symposium on the Mechanism of Enzyme Action,* p. 257–284. Baltimore: The Johns Hopkins Press.
205. Knight, S. G. and W. C. Frazier. 1945. *J. Bacteriol.* 50: 505–516.

206. Kobs, E. and W. J. Robbins. 1935. *Am. J. Botany* 23: 133–139.
207. Koffler, H., F. H. Johnson, and P. W. Wilson. 1947. *J. Am. Chem. Soc.* 69: 1113–1117.
208. Kølmark, G. and N. H. Giles. 1955. *Genetics* 40: 890–902.
209. Krebs, H. A., R. Whittam, and R. Hems. 1957. *Biochem. J. (London)* 66: 53–60.
210. Krimsky, I. and E. Racker. 1952. *J. Biol. Chem.* 198: 721–729.
211. Kuhn, R. and H. Beinert. 1943. *Ber. deut. chem. Ges.* 76 B: 904–909.
212. Kuhn, R. and H. Beinert. 1944. *Ber. deut. chem. Ges.* 77 B: 606–608.
213. Kuhn, R. and H. Beinert. 1947. *Chem. Ber.* 80: 101–109.
214. Kunkel, L. O. 1914. *Bull. Torrey Botan. Club* 41: 265–293.
215. Landis, L., D. Kley, and N. Ercoli. 1951. *J. Am. Pharm. Assoc., Sci. Ed.* 40: 321–325.
216. Laskowski, W. 1955. *Science* 121: 299–300.
217. Leben, C., D. M. Boone, and G. W. Keitt. 1955. *Phytopathology* 45: 467–472.
218. Leben, C. and G. W. Keitt. 1950. *Phytopathology* 40: 950–954.
219. Leben, C. and G. W. Keitt. 1954. *J. Agr. Food Chem.* 2: 234–239.
220. Lehman, S. G. 1943. *Phytopathology* 33: 431–448.
221. Leonard, J. M. and V. L. Blackford. 1949. *J. Bacteriol.* 57: 339–347.
222. Leopold, H. and H. G. German. 1940. *Zentr. Bakteriol. Parasitenk. Abt. II,* 102: 65–99.
223. Leutritz, J., Jr. 1951. *Trans. N. Y. Acad. Sci.* II, 13: 177–181.
224. Levine, S. and M. Novak. 1949. *J. Bacteriol.* 57: 93–94.
225. Liebermeister, K. 1950. *Z. Naturforsch.* 5b: 79–86.
226. Lin, C.-K. 1940. *Cornell Univ. Agr. Exp. Sta. Mem.* 233: 1–33.
227. Lindgren, R. M. and M. H. Harvey. 1952. *J. Forest Products Research Soc.* 2: 1–7.
228. Little, J. E., T. J. Sproston, and M. W. Foote. 1948. *J. Biol. Chem.* 174: 335–342.
229. Little, J. E., T. J. Sproston, and M. W. Foote. 1949. *J. Am. Chem. Soc.* 71: 1124.
230. LoCicero, J. C., D. E. H. Frear, and H. J. Miller. 1948. *J. Biol. Chem.* 172: 689–693.
231. Lockwood, J. L., C. Leben, and G. W. Keitt. 1954. *Phytopathology* 44: 438–446.
232. Lohrmann, W. 1940. *Arch. Mikrobiol.* 11: 329–367.
233. Loomis, W. F. and F. Lipmann. 1948. *J. Biol. Chem.* 173: 807–808.
234. Lopatecki, L. E. and W. Newton. 1952. *Can. J. Botany* 30: 131–138.
235. Lowry, R. J., A. S. Sussman, and B. Heidenhain. 1956. *Mycologia* 48: 241–252.
236. Ludwig, R. A., G. D. Thorn, and D. M. Miller. 1954. *Can. J. Botany* 32: 48–54.
237. Ludwig, R. A., G. D. Thorn, and C. H. Unwin. 1955. *Can. J. Botany* 33: 42–59.
238. McCalla, T. M. 1940. *J. Bacteriol.* 40: 23–32.
239. McCalla, T. M. 1941. *J. Bacteriol.* 41: 775–784.
240. McCallan, S. E. A. 1944. *Contribs. Boyce Thompson Inst.* 13: 367–383.
241. McCallan, S. E. A. 1947. *Proc. Intern. Congr. Pure and Appl. Chem., 11th Congr. London,* 3: 149–156.
242. McCallan, S. E. A. 1948a. *Contribs. Boyce Thompson Inst.* 15: 77–90.
243. McCallan, S. E. A. 1948b. *Contribs. Boyce Thompson Inst.* 15: 91–117.
244. McCallan, S. E. A. 1949. *Botan. Rev.* 15: 629–643.
245. McCallan, S. E. A. 1951. *Contribs. Boyce Thompson Inst.* 16: 299–302.
246. McCallan, S. E. A. 1956. *Proc. Intern. Conf. Plant Protection, 2nd Conf.* p. 77–95.
246a. McCallan, S. E. A. and L. P. Miller. 1957a. *Contribs. Boyce Thompson Inst.* 18: 483–495.
246b. McCallan, S. E. A. and L. P. Miller. 1957b. *Contribs. Boyce Thompson Inst.* 18: 497–506.

247. McCallan, S. E. A., L. P. Miller, and R. M. Weed. 1954. *Contribs. Boyce Thompson Inst.* 18: 39–68.
248. McCallan, S. E. A. and C. Setterstrom. 1940. *Contribs. Boyce Thompson Inst.* 11: 325–330.
249. McCallan, S. E. A. and F. R. Weedon. 1940. *Contribs. Boyce Thompson Inst.* 11: 331–342.
250. McCallan, S. E. A. and R. H. Wellman. 1942. *Contribs. Boyce Thompson Inst.* 12: 451–464.
251. McCallan, S. E. A. and R. H. Wellman. 1943. *Contribs. Boyce Thompson Inst.* 13: 93–134.
252. McCallan, S. E. A., R. H. Wellman, and F. Wilcoxon. 1941. *Contribs. Boyce Thompson Inst.* 12: 49–78.
253. McCallan, S. E. A. and F. Wilcoxon. 1931. *Contribs. Boyce Thompson Inst.* 3: 13–38.
254. McCallan, S. E. A. and F. Wilcoxon. 1932. *Contribs. Boyce Thompson Inst.* 4: 233–243.
255. McCallan, S. E. A. and F. Wilcoxon. 1933. *Contribs. Boyce Thompson Inst.* 5: 173-180.
256. McCallan, S. E. A. and F. Wilcoxon. 1934. *Contribs. Boyce Thompson Inst.* 6: 479–500.
257. McCallan, S. E. A. and F. Wilcoxon. 1936. *Contribs. Boyce Thompson Inst.* 8: 151–165.
258. McCallan, S. E. A. and F. Wilcoxon. 1939. *Contribs. Boyce Thompson Inst.* 11: 5–20.
259. McCallan, S. E. A. and F. Wilcoxon. 1940. *Contribs. Boyce Thompson Inst.* 11: 309–324.
260. McClellan, W. D. 1942. *Phytopathology* 32: 394–398.
261. McElroy, W. D. 1947. *Quart. Rev. Biol.* 22: 25–58.
262. McGowan, J. C., P. W. Brian, and H. G. Hemming, 1948. *Ann. Appl. Biol.* 35: 25–36.
263. McKee, R. K. 1951. *Nature (London)* 167: 611.
264. MacLeod, R. A. 1952. *J. Biol. Chem.* 197: 751–761.
265. McNew, G. L. and H. P. Burchfield. 1950. *Contribs. Boyce Thompson Inst.* 16: 163–176.
266. McNew, G. L. and H. P. Burchfield. 1951. *Contribs. Boyce Thompson Inst.* 16: 357–374.
267. McNew, G. L. and N. K. Sundholm. 1949. *Phytopathology* 39: 721–751.
268. Mandels, G. R. and R. T. Darby. 1953. *J. Bacteriol.* 65: 16–26.
269. Mandels, G. R. and R. G. H. Siu. 1950. *J. Bacteriol.* 60: 249–262.
270. Manten, A., H. L. Klöpping, and G. J. M. van der Kerk. 1950a. *Antonie van Leeuwenhoek J. Microbiol. Serol.* 16: 45–55.
271. Manten, A., H. L. Klöpping, and G. J. M. van der Kerk. 1950b. *Antonie van Leeuwenhoek J. Microbiol. Serol.* 16: 282–294.
272. Manten, A., H. L. Klöpping, and G. J. M. van der Kerk. 1951. *Antonie van Leeuwenhoek J. Microbiol. Serol.* 17: 58–68.
273. Marsh, P. B. 1945. *Phytopathology* 35: 54–61.
274. Marsh, P. B. and M. L. Butler. 1946. *Ind. Eng. Chem.* 38: 701–705.
275. Marsh, P. B., M. L. Butler, and B. S. Clark. 1949. *Ind. Eng. Chem.* 41: 2176–2184.
276. Martell, A. E. and M. Calvin. 1952. *Chemistry of the Metal Chelate Compounds.* New York: Prentice-Hall, pp. 613.
277. Martin, G. J. 1951. *Biological Antagonism.* New York: The Blakiston Co., pp. 516.
278. Martin, H. 1940. *The Scientific Principles of Plant Protection,* 3rd ed. London: Edward Arnold, pp. 385.

279. Martin, H., R. L. Wain, and E. H. Wilkinson. 1942. *Ann. Appl. Biol.* 29: 412–438.
280. Maselli, J. A. and F. F. Nord. 1952. *Arch. Biochem. Biophys.* 39: 406–418.
281. Mason, C. L. 1948. *Phytopathology* 38: 740–751.
282. Mason, C. L., R. W. Brown, and A. E. Minga. 1951. *Phytopathology* 41: 164–171.
283. Mason, C. L. and D. Powell. 1947. *Phytopathology* 37: 527–528.
284. Merkel, J. R. and W. J. Nickerson. 1953. *Proc. Natl. Acad. Sci. U. S.* 39: 1008–1013.
285. Michaelis, L. M. and J. H. Quastel. 1941. *Biochem. J. (London)* 35: 518–533.
286. Miles, P. G. and J. R. Raper. 1956. *Mycologia* 48: 484–494.
286a. Miller, H. and W. D. McElroy. 1948. *Science* 107: 193–194.
287. Miller, H. J. 1950. *Phytopathology* 40: 326–332.
288. Miller, L. P. and S. E. A. McCallan. 1957. *J. Agr. Food Chem.* 5: 116–122.
289. Miller, L. P., S. E. A. McCallan, and R. M. Weed. 1953a. *Contribs. Boyce Thompson Inst.* 17: 151–171.
290. Miller, L. P., S. E. A. McCallan, and R. M. Weed. 1953b. *Contribs. Boyce Thompson Inst.* 17: 173–195.
291. Miller, L. P., S. E. A. McCallan, and R. M. Weed. 1953c. *Contribs. Boyce Thompson Inst.* 17: 282–298.
292. Miller, L. P., S. E. A. McCallan, and R. M. Weed. 1954. *Radioisotope Conf. Oxford, Engl.* 1: 381–389.
293. Minegawa, T. 1955. *Biochim. et Biophys. Acta* 16: 539–552.
294. Mitchell, P. 1954. *Symposia Soc. Exp. Biol.* 8: 254–261.
295. Miyahara, Y. 1953. *Ann. Phytopathol. Soc. Japan* 28: 37–40.
296. Molho, D. and L. Lacroix. 1949a. *Bull. soc. chim. biol.* 31: 1348–1356.
297. Molho, D. and L. Lacroix. 1949b. *Bull. soc. chim. biol.* 31: 1357–1361.
298. Montgomery, H. B. S. and H. Shaw. 1943. *Nature (London)* 151: 333.
299. Mounter, L. A. and A. J. Chanutin. 1953. *J. Biol. Chem.* 204: 837–846.
300. Mücke, D. 1954. *Flora (N.F.)* 41: 30–50.
301. Muirhead, I. 1949. *Ann. Appl. Biol.* 36: 250–256.
302. Müller, E. and W. Biedermann. 1952. *Phytopathol. Z.* 19: 343–350.
303. Müller-Stoll, W. R. 1950. *Phytopathol. Z.* 17: 265–286.
304. Napier, E. J., D. I. Turner, and A. Rhodes. 1956. *Ann. Botany* 20: 461–466.
305. Nason, A. and A. R. Lehman. 1955. *Science* 122: 19–22.
306. Neilands, J. B. and P. K. Stumpf. 1955. *Outlines of Enzyme Chemistry.* New York: John Wiley and Sons, pp. 315.
307. Newton, B. A. 1956. *Bacteriol. Revs.* 20: 14–27.
308. Neyland, M., P. Dunkel, and A. L. Schade. 1952. *J. Gen. Microbiol.* 7: 409–416.
309. Nickerson, W. J. 1946. *Science* 103: 484–486.
310. Nickerson, W. J. and N. J. W. Van Rij. 1949. *Biochim. et Biophys. Acta* 3: 461–475.
311. Nielsen, L. W. 1942. *Cornell Univ. Agr. Exp. Sta. Mem.* 248: 1–44.
312. Nielsen, L. W. and C. E. Williamson. 1942. *Phytopathology* 32: 1026–1030.
313. Nordbring-Herz, B. 1955. *Physiol. Plantarum* 8: 691–717.
314. Ohta, Y. 1944. *Acta Phytochim. (Japan)* 14: 159–166.
315. Okazaki, R. 1956. *Exp. Cell Research* 10: 489–504.
316. Olcott, H. S. and H. Fraenkel-Conrat. 1947. *Chem. Revs.* 41: 151–197.
317. Oster, K. A. and M. J. Golden. 1947. *J. Am. Pharm. Assoc., Sci. Ed.* 36: 283–288.
318. Oster, K. A. and M. J. Golden. 1954. In G. F. Reddish (ed.), *Antiseptics, Disinfectants, Fungicides, and Chemical and Physical Sterilization*, p. 132–141. Philadelphia: Lea and Febiger.
319. Owens, R. G. 1953a. *Contribs. Boyce Thompson Inst.* 17: 221–242.

320. Owens, R. G. 1953b. *Contribs. Boyce Thompson Inst.* 17: 273–282.
321. Page, J. E. and F. A. Robinson. 1943. *J. Chem. Soc. (London)* 1943: 133–135.
322. Palmer, H. C., R. W. Greenlee, and M. M. Baldwin. 1952. *Phytopathology* 42: 472.
323. Parker-Rhodes, A. F. 1942a. *Ann. Appl. Biol.* 29: 126–135.
324. Parker-Rhodes, A. F. 1942b. *Ann. Appl. Biol.* 29: 404–411.
325. Pauson, P. 1955. *Chem. Revs.* 55: 9–136.
326. Pennington, R. J. 1957. *Biochem. J. (London)* 65: 534–540.
327. Petit, A. 1930. *Ann. service botan. et agron. Tunisie* 6: 57–70.
328. Pfleger, R., E. Schraufstätter, F. Gehringer, and J. Sciuk. 1949. *Z. Naturforsch.* 4b: 344–350.
329. Phillips, C. R. 1949. *Am. J. Hyg.* 50: 280–288.
330. Phillips, J. N. and J. M. Vincent. 1948. *Nature (London)* 161: 210–211.
331. Pickett, M. J. and C. E. Clifton. 1943. *J. Cellular Comp. Physiol.* 22: 147–165.
332. Pinckard, J. A. et al. 1939. *Phytopathology* 29: 177–187.
333. Plakidas, A. G. 1938. *Phytopathology* 28: 307–329.
334. Pope, H. and I. Christison. 1953. *J. Bacteriol.* 66: 639–641.
335. Potter, V. R. and A. E. Reif. 1952. *J. Biol. Chem.* 194: 287–297.
336. Pramer, D. 1956. *Arch. Biochem. Biophys.* 62: 265–273.
337. Pridham, T. G. et al. 1956. *Phytopathology* 46: 568–575.
338. van Raalte, M. H. 1952. *Mededel. Landbouwhogeschool en Opzoekingsstas. Staat Gent* 17: 163–173. (*Chem. Abstr.* 46: 11543. 1952.)
339. Rahn, O. and J. E. Conn. 1944. *Ind. Eng. Chem.* 36: 185–187.
340. Ramsey, G. B., M. A. Smith, and B. C. Heiberg. 1944. *Botan. Gaz.* 106: 74–83.
341. Rangaswami, G. 1956. *Mycologia* 48: 800–804.
342. Reavill, M. J. 1954. *Ann. Appl. Biol.* 41: 448–460.
343. Reif, A. and V. R. Potter. 1954. *Arch. Biochim. Biophys.* 48: 1–6.
344. Rennerfelt, E. 1948. *Physiol. Plantarum* 1: 245–254.
345. Rennerfelt, E. and G. Nacht. 1955. *Svensk Botan. Tidskr.* 49: 419–432.
346. Rich, S. and J. G. Horsfall. 1952. *Phytopathology* 42: 457–460.
347. Rich, S. and J. G. Horsfall. 1954. *Proc. Natl. Acad. Sci. U. S.* 40: 139–145.
348. Richards, C. A. and R. M. Addoms. 1947. *Proc. Am. Wood-Preservers' Assoc.* 1947: 41–58. (*Chem. Abstr.* 42: 4702–4703. 1948.)
349. Richardson, L. T. 1954. *Can. J. Botany* 32: 335–346.
350. Rigler, N. E. and G. A. Greathouse. 1940. *Am. J. Botany* 27: 701–704.
351. Rinderknecht, H., J. L. Ward, F. Bergel, and A. L. Morrison. 1947. *Biochem. J. (London)* 41: 463–469.
352. Ringel, S. M. and E. S. Beneke. 1956. *Mycologia* 48: 329–336.
353. Roblin, R. O., Jr. 1946. *Chem. Revs.* 38: 255–377.
354. Rolinson, G. N. 1954. *J. Appl. Bact.* 17: 190–195.
355. Roper, J. A. and E. Käfer. 1957. *J. Gen. Microbiol.* 16: 660–667.
356. Rothstein, A. 1954. *Symposia Soc. Exp. Biol.* 8: 164–201.
357. Rothstein, A. and A. D. Hayes. 1956. *Arch. Biochem. Biophys.* 63: 87–99.
358. Rubbo, S. D., A. Albert, and M. I. Gibson. 1950. *Brit. J. Exp. Pathol.* 31: 425–441.
359. Sampson, R. E. and R. A. Ludwig. 1953. *Can. J. Botany* 31: 531–536.
360. Sampson, R. E. and R. A. Ludwig. 1956. *Can. J. Botany* 34: 37–43.
361. Sansome, E. R. 1949. *Trans. Brit. Mycol. Soc.* 32: 305–314.
362. Sansome, E. R. 1956. *Trans. Brit. Mycol. Soc.* 39: 67–78.
363. Schmidt, E. W. 1924. *Centr. Bakteriol. Parasitenk. Abt. II,* 60: 329–338.
364. Schopfer, W. H. and E. C. Grob. 1949. *Helv. Chim. Acta* 32: 829–838.
365. Schopfer, W. H. and M. Guilloud. 1946. *Helv. Physiol. Pharmacol. Acta (Compt. rend.)* 4: 24–25.
366. Schueler, F. W. 1947. *J. Infectious Diseases* 81: 139–146.
367. Schuldt, P. H. and C. N. Wolf. 1956. *Contribs. Boyce Thompson Inst.* 18: 377–393.

368. Schutter, J. and P. W. Wilson. 1955. *J. Gen. Microbiol.* 12: 446–454.
369. Sciarini, L. J. and F. F. Nord. 1943. *Arch. Biochem.* 3: 261–267.
370. Sempio, C. and M. Castori. 1949. *Riv. biol. (Perugia)* 41: 163–172.
371. Severens, J. M. and F. W. Tanner. 1945. *J. Bacteriol.* 49: 383–393.
372. Sexton, W. A. 1953. *Chemical Constitution and Biological Activity*, 2nd ed. New York: D. Van Nostrand Co., Inc. pp. 424.
373. Shaw, W. H. R. 1954. *Science* 120: 361–363.
374. Shirk, H. G. and H. E. Byrne. 1951. *J. Biol. Chem.* 191: 783–786.
375. Shirk, H. G. and R. R. Corey, Jr. 1952. *Arch. Biochem. Biophys.* 38: 417–423.
376. Shirk, H. G., R. R. Corey, Jr., and P. L. Poelma. 1951. *Arch. Biochem. Biophys.* 32: 392–395.
377. Shirk, H. G., P. L. Poelma, and R. R. Corey, Jr. 1951. *Arch. Biochem. Biophys.* 32: 386–391.
378. Shrift, A. 1954. *Am. J. Botany* 41: 223–230, 345–352.
379. Simon, E. W. 1953a. *J. Exp. Botany* 4: 377–392, 393–402.
380. Simon, E. W. 1953b. *Biol. Revs. Cambridge Phil. Soc.* 28: 453–479.
381. Simon, E. W. and H. Beevers. 1951. *Science* 114: 124–126.
382. Simon, E. W. and H. Beevers. 1952. *New Phytologist* 51: 163–190, 191–197.
383. Simon, E. W. and G. E. Blackman. 1949. *Symposia Soc. Exp. Biol.* 3: 253–265.
384. Sisler, H. D. and C. E. Cox. 1954. *Am. J. Botany* 41: 338–345.
385. Sisler, H. D. and C. E. Cox. 1955. *Am. J. Botany* 42: 351–356.
386. Siu, R. G. H. 1951. *Microbial Decomposition of Cellulose.* New York: Reinhold Publ. Corp., pp. 531.
387. Sletten, O. and C. E. Skinner. 1948. *J. Bacteriol.* 56: 679–681.
388. Smalt, Sister M. A., C. W. Kreke, and E. S. Cook. 1957. *J. Biol. Chem.* 224: 999–1004.
389. Smith, E. L., N. C. Davis, E. Adams, and D. H. Spackman. 1954. In W. D. McElroy and B. Glass (eds.), *A Symposium on the Mechanism of Enzyme Action*, p. 291–312. Baltimore: The Johns Hopkins Press.
390. Smith, F. G., J. C. Walker, and W. J. Hooker. 1946. *Am. J. Botany* 33: 351–356.
391. Smith, J. H. 1921. *Ann. Appl. Biol.* 8: 27–50.
392. Snell, J. M. and A. Weissberger. 1939. *J. Am. Chem. Soc.* 61: 450–453.
393. Snow, D. and P. S. Watts. 1945. *Ann. Appl. Biol.* 32: 102–112.
394. Soo-Hoo, G. and E. Grunberg. 1950. *J. Invest. Dermatol.* 14: 169–172.
395. Sorkin, E., W. Roth, and H. Erlenmeyer. 1952. *Helv. Chim. Acta* 35: 1736–1741.
396. Stallings, J. H. 1954. *Bacteriol. Revs.* 18: 131–146.
397. Starkey, R. L. and S. A. Waksman. 1943. *J. Bacteriol.* 45: 509–519.
398. Stedtman, R. L., E. Kravitz, and J. D. King. 1957. *J. Bacteriol.* 73: 655–660.
399. Steinberg, R. A. 1940. *J. Agr. Research* 60: 765–773.
400. Stevens, C. M. and A. Mylroie. 1953. *Am. J. Botany* 40: 424–429.
401. Stewart, I. and C. D. Leonard. 1952. *Science* 116: 564–566.
402. Stoddard, E. M. and A. E. Dimond. 1949. *Botan. Rev.* 15: 345–376.
403. Stokes, A. 1954. *Plant and Soil* 5: 132–141.
404. Strecker, B. 1957. *Z. Pflanzenkr.* 64: 9–35.
405. Sumner, J. B. and G. F. Somers. 1953. *Chemistry and Methods of Enzymes*, 3rd ed. New York: Academic Press, pp. 462.
406. Sussman, A. S. 1954. *J. Gen. Physiol.* 38: 59–77.
407. Sussman, A. S. and R. J. Lowry. 1955. *J. Bacteriol.* 70: 675–685.
408. Suter, C. M. 1941. *Chem. Revs.* 28: 269–299.
409. Tatum, E. L. 1950. *J. Cellular Comp. Physiol.* 35, Suppl. 1: 119–131.
410. Tatum, E. L. and G. W. Beadle. 1942. *Proc. Natl. Acad. Sci. U. S.* 28: 234–243.
411. Tehon, L. R. 1951. *Science* 114: 663–664.
412. Teply, L. J. 1949. *Arch. Biochem.* 24: 383–388.
413. Ter Horst, W. P. and E. L. Felix. 1943. *Ind. Eng. Chem.* 35: 1255–1259.

414. Thorn, G. D. and R. A. Ludwig. 1954. *Can. J. Chem.* 32: 872–879.
415. Thornberry, H. H. 1950. *Phytopathology* 40: 419–429.
416. Treffers, H. P. 1956. *J. Bacteriol.* 72: 108–114.
417. Trim, A. R. and A. E. Alexander. 1949. *Symposia Soc. Exp. Biol.* 3: 111–142.
418. Tröger, R. 1956. *Arch. Mikrobiol.* 25: 166–192.
419. Valko, E. I. 1946. *Ann. N. Y. Acad. Sci.* 46: 451–478.
420. Vallee, B. L. and F. L. Hoch. 1955. *Proc. Natl. Acad. Sci. U. S.* 41:327–338.
421. Velick, S. F. 1956. *Ann. Rev. Biochem.* 25: 257–290.
422. Verdcourt, B. 1952. *Mycologia* 44: 377–386.
423. Verrall, A. F. 1949. *J. Agr. Research* 78: 695–703.
424. Vicklund, R. E., M. Manowitz, and V. J. Bagdon. 1954. *Mycologia* 46: 133–142.
425. Villemin, P. F., H. A. Lechevalier, and S. A. Waksman. 1953. *Intern. Congr. Microbiol., 6th Congr. Rome*, 5: 146–173.
426. Vincent, J. M. 1947. *J. Soc. Chem. Ind.* 66: 149–155.
427. Volk, W. A. 1954. *J. Biol. Chem.* 208: 777–784.
428. Volkmann, C. M. and E. Beerstecher, Jr. 1955. *J. Bacteriol.* 70: 476–480.
429. Wain, R. L. and E. H. Wilkinson. 1945. *Ann. Appl. Biol.* 32: 240–243.
430. Waksman, S. A., A. H. Romano, H. Lechevalier, and F. Raubitschek. 1952. *Bull. World Health Organization* 6: 163–173.
430a. Walker, A. T. 1955. *Iowa State Coll. J. Sci.* 30: 229–241.
431. Walker, A. T. and F. G. Smith. 1952. *Proc. Soc. Exp. Biol. Med.* 81: 556–559.
432. Weed, R. M., S. E. A. McCallan, and L. P. Miller. 1953. *Contribs. Boyce Thompson Inst.* 17: 299–315.
433. Weinberg, E. D. 1957. *Bacteriol. Revs.* 21: 46–68.
434. Weiss, S., J. V. Fiore, and F. F. Nord. 1949. *Arch. Biochem.* 22: 314–322.
435. Weissman, G. S. and S. F. Trelease. 1955. *Am. J. Botany* 42: 489–495.
436. Wellman, R. H. and S. E. A. McCallan. 1942. *Contribs. Boyce Thompson Inst.* 12: 431–450.
437. Wellman, R. H. and S. E. A. McCallan. 1946. *Contribs. Boyce Thompson Inst.* 14: 151–160.
438. West, B. and F. T. Wolf. 1955. *J. Gen. Microbiol.* 12: 396–401.
439. Whaley, F. R. and J. B. Harry. 1951. *Contribs. Boyce Thompson Inst.* 16: 375–386.
440. Whiffen, A. J. 1950. *Mycologia* 44: 253–258.
441. Wilcoxon, F. and S. E. A. McCallan. 1930. *Phytopathology* 20: 391–417.
442. Wilcoxon, F. and S. E. A. McCallan. 1931. *Contribs. Boyce Thompson Inst.* 3: 509–528.
443. Wilcoxon, F. and S. E. A. McCallan. 1932. *Contribs. Boyce Thompson Inst.* 4: 415–424.
444. Wilcoxon, F. and S. E. A. McCallan. 1935. *Contribs. Boyce Thompson Inst.* 7: 333–339.
445. Wilcoxon, F. and S. E. A. McCallan. 1939. *Contribs. Boyce Thompson Inst.* 10: 329–338.
446. Winzler, R. J. 1940. *J. Cellular Comp. Physiol.* 15: 343–354.
447. Wolf, C. N., P. H. Schuldt, and M. M. Baldwin. 1955. *Science* 121: 61–62.
448. Wolf, F. A. et al. 1940. *Phytopathology* 30: 213–227.
449. Wolf, F. T. 1947. In W. J. Nickerson (ed.), *Biology of the Pathogenic Fungi*, p. 91–114. Waltham, Mass.: Chronica Botanica Co.
450. Wolf, F. T. and F. A. Wolf. 1950. *Bull. Torrey Botan. Club* 77: 77–82.
451. Wolf, P. A. and W. M. Westveer. 1950. *Arch. Biochem.* 28: 201–206.
452. Woods, D. D. 1940. *Brit. J. Exp. Pathol.* 21: 74–89.
453. Woolley, D. W. 1945. *Proc. Soc. Exp. Biol. Med.* 60: 225–228.
454. Woolley, D. W. 1952. *A Study of Antimetabolites.* New York: John Wiley and Sons, pp. 269.

455. Work, T. S. and E. Work. 1948. *The Basis of Chemotherapy.* New York: Interscience Publishers, pp. 435.
456. Wyss, O., B. J. Ludwig, and R. R. Joiner. 1945. *Arch. Biochem.* 7: 415–425.
457. Yarwood, C. E. 1937. *Phytopathology* 27: 931–941.
458. Yarwood, C. E. 1943. *Hilgardia* 14: 595–691.
459. Yarwood, C. E. 1950. *Phytopathology* 40: 173–179.
460. Yarwood, C. E. 1955. In T. H. Sternberg and V. D. Newcomer (eds.), *Therapy of Fungus Diseases,* p. 130–135. Boston: Little, Brown, and Co.
461. Zentmyer, G. A. 1943. *Phytopathology* 33: 1121.
462. Zentmyer, G. A. 1944. *Science* 100: 294–295.
463. Zentmyer, G. A. 1955. *Phytopathology* 45: 398–404.

Organism
Index

(Binomial names only)

Subject
Index